Prentice Hall Brief Review

Earth Science:
The Physical Setting

Jeffrey C. Callister

LEARNING COMPANY

About the Author

Jeffrey C. Callister received his B.S. in Secondary Education from SUNY New Paltz and his M.S. in Earth Science from Union College, Schenectady. He taught both earth science and geology at Newburgh Free Academy in Newburgh, N.Y., for over 30 years in addition to being a part-time instructor of geology at various SUNY colleges. Mr. Callister has authored five publications for the National Science Teachers Association (NSTA) and part of the second edition of the Earth Science Curriculum Project. He is a current member of American Association for the Advancement of Science, NSTA, National Association of Geoscience Teachers, National Earth Science Teachers Association, New York State Science Teachers Association, and New York State Earth Science Teachers Association.

Teacher Reviewers and Contributors

Timothy Denman
Planetarium Director, Retired
Newburgh Free Academy
Newburgh, New York

Tom Elkins
John L. Miller Great Neck North High School
Great Neck, New York

David Keith
Science Chair
John L. Miller Great Neck North High School
Great Neck, New York

Peter Le Rose
Mount Saint Mary College
Newburgh, New York

Elise Russo, Ed.D.
Administrator for Secondary Curriculum
Amityville Union Free School District
Amityville, New York

Peter Suchmann
Science Chair, retired
Great Neck South Middle School
Great Neck, New York

Harold P. Coyle
Science Education Department
Harvard-Smithsonian Center for Astrophysics
Cambridge, MA

ISBN-13: 978-1-4183-1195-7
ISBN-10: 1-4183-1195-2

3 20

Brief Review in
Earth Science: The Physical Setting

New York Standards

Standard | Key Idea

KEY

4.2.1

Major Understanding

1.M1	4.3.1a	6.6
1.S3	4.3.1c	7.1
2.3	6.3	7.2
4.1.2c	6.4	
4.2.1b	6.5	

1.E1	4.1.1i	4.2.1q
1.M1	4.1.2c	6.2
1.S3	4.2.1b	6.3
4.1.1c	4.2.1g	7.2
4.1.1d	4.2.1j	
4.1.1f	4.2.1l	

1.M2	4.1.2a	4.1.2d
4.1.1a	4.1.2b	6.3
4.1.1b	4.1.2c	6.4

1.M2	4.1.1d	4.1.1h
1.S1	4.1.1e	4.2.2a
4.1.1a	4.1.1f	6.3
4.1.1b	4.1.1g	

1.E1	4.2.1a	4.2.2a
4.1.2b	4.2.1b	4.2.2b
4.1.2g	4.2.1i	6.4

New York Standards

1.S3	4.1.1h	4.2.2d
4.1.1	4.2.1a	6.5
4.1.1a	4.2.1b	6.6
4.1.1b	4.2.2a	
4.1.1f	4.2.2b	

2.1	4.2.1d	4.2.2b
2.3	4.2.1e	4.2.2c
4.1.1f	4.2.1f	4.2.2d
4.1.2g	4.2.1g	6.4
4.2.1	4.2.1h	6.5
4.2.1b	4.2.1i	7.2
4.2.1c	4.2.2a	

1.E1	4.2.1f	4.2.2c
2.3	4.2.1i	4.2.2d
4.1.2g	4.2.2a	7.2

1.M1	4.2.1p	4.2.1u
1.M2	4.2.1s	6.1
2.3	4.2.1t	7.2

1.M2	4.2.1t	4.2.1w
1.S2	4.2.1u	4.3.1b
4.2.1p	4.2.1v	6.1

4.1.2f	4.3.1a	6.6
4.1.2j	4.3.1b	7.1
4.2.1m	4.3.1c	
4.2.1w	6.2	

2.3	4.2.1k	4.2.1o
4.1.2j	4.2.1l	4.2.1p
4.2.1b	4.2.1m	6.5
4.2.1j	4.2.1n	7.2

New York Standards

2.3	4.1.2g	6.3
4.1.2c	4.1.2h	7.1
4.1.2d	4.1.2i	7.2
4.1.2e	4.1.2j	
4.1.2f	4.3.1c	

1.E1	4.2.1o	4.2.2c
4.1.2d	4.2.1p	4.2.2d
4.2.1a	4.2.1q	6.2
4.2.1b	4.2.1r	6.4
4.2.1k	4.2.1t	6.6
4.2.1l	4.2.1u	
4.2.1n	4.2.2a	

Separate Answer Key Contents:

Answers for Review and Practice Questions

Answers for Regents Examinations

Diagnostic Tests and Answers

Topic Quizzes and Answers

About This Book

This book is designed to enhance review of the concepts, skills, and application of the Physical Setting/Earth Science Core Curriculum that may be tested on the Regents Examination for The Physical Setting: Earth Science. Students can use the book in any order as each topic is independent except for the introduction of vocabulary words.

Features

Content Review

The presentation features aids for accessing the basic content that will be tested on the Regents Examination as well as practice for interpreting and answering Regents Examination questions.

Illustrations Graphics are designed to visualize the concepts and vocabulary of earth science as well as familiarize students with the types of drawings they will be required to interpret on the Regents Examination.

Vocabulary An understanding of the language of earth science is needed to answer many Regents Examination questions.

Bold Words The vocabulary listed at the beginning of a topic are terms defined within that topic and are shown in bold type.

Underlined Words Terms that are underlined are either words that appear as bold in other topics or are terms describing basic earth science concepts. These may be used in Regents Examination questions.

Sidebars

Memory Jogger This sidebar helps you recall relevant information covered elsewhere in this book or previous science courses.

Digging Deeper This sidebar provides specific examples of some concepts or expands core content.

Review Questions Questions similar to those on Regents Examinations, totaling more than 680, appear throughout each topic to clarify and reinforce understanding.

Practice Questions for the New York Regents Exam

A total of more than 580 practice questions are written and organized for each topic in the format of the Regents Examination.

Part A These multiple-choice questions test your knowledge of concepts from the core curriculum.

Part B Both multiple-choice and constructed response questions test understandings and skills outlined in the core curriculum.

Part C These questions often require an extended constructed response. The number in brackets tells how many points the question is worth on a Regents Examination.

Reference and Support

Strategies for Answering Test Questions Support to help you interpret and answer the range of Regents Examination questions.

Appendix 1 *Earth Science Reference Tables* The Reference Tables are integral to this content review and are indicated by an Ⓡ. Review and Practice Questions also refer you to them.

Appendix 2 *Earth Science Performance Test* Part D of the Regents Examination on laboratory and classroom procedures is partly described.

Appendix 3 *Landscape Regions of New York State* This map and descriptions support review.

Appendix 4 *Paths of the Sun at Different Times and Latitudes* shows 24 different paths of the sun based on an observer's view. For easy reference while reading, look for the Ⓐ④ icon, which will direct you from relevant topics in the text back to the Appendix.

Glossary Defines all bold vocabulary words and underlined words in the topics.

Index Cross-references concepts in the topics.

Regents Examinations

Several of the most recent Regents Examinations are reproduced at the end of this book to provide practice in taking actual Regents Examinations.

Strategies for
Answering Test Questions

This section provides strategies to help you answer various types of questions on the Regents Examination for Physical Setting: Earth Science. Strategies are provided for answering multiple-choice and constructed-response questions as well as for questions based on diagrams, data tables, and graphs and questions that use the *Earth Science Reference Tables*, which are reproduced in the Appendix.

Strategies for Multiple-Choice Questions

Multiple-choice questions will likely account for more than 50 percent of the Regents Examination for Physical Setting: Earth Science. Part A is comprised totally of multiple-choice questions, and Part B includes some. Therefore, it is important to be good at deciphering multiple-choice questions. Here are a few helpful strategies. For any one question, not all strategies will need to be used. The numbers are provided for reference, not to specify an order (except for Strategies 1 and 2).

1. Always read the entire question, but wait to read the choices. (See Strategy 4.)

2. Carefully examine any data tables, diagrams, photographs, or relevant part(s) of the *Earth Science Reference Tables* associated with the question.

3. Underline key words and phrases in the question that signal what you should be looking for in the answer. This will make you read the question more carefully. This strategy applies mostly to questions with a long introduction.

4. Try to think of an answer to the question before looking at the choices given. If you think you know the answer, write it on a separate piece of paper before reading the choices. Next, read all of the choices and compare them to your answer before making a decision. Do not select the first answer that seems correct. If your answer matches one of the choices, and you are quite sure of your response, you are probably correct. Even if your answer matches one of the choices, carefully consider all of the answers because the obvious choice is not always the correct one. If there are no exact matches, re-read the question and look for the choice that is most similar to your answer.

5. Eliminate any choices that you know are incorrect. Lightly cross out the numbers for those choices on the exam paper. Each choice you can eliminate increases your chances of selecting the correct answer.

6. If the question makes no sense after reading through it several times, leave it for later. After completing the rest of the exam, return to the question. Something you read on the other parts of the exam may give you some ideas about how to answer this question. If you are still unsure, go with your best guess. There is no penalty for guessing, but answers left blank will be counted as wrong. If you employ your best test-taking strategies, you just may select the correct answer.

Answer Key with Diagnostics and Quizzes A separate Answer Key includes all answers to the Review and Practice Questions plus topic-by-topic Diagnostic Tests to help determine which concepts require more intensive review and Topic Quizzes for quick assessment with different questions.

Strategies for Constructed-Response Questions

Some questions in Part B and all questions in Part C of the Regents Examination for Physical Setting: Earth Science require a constructed response. No matter which type of answer is requested, the following strategies will help you write constructed responses.

1. Always read through the entire question.
2. Underline key words and phrases in the question that signal what you should be looking for in the answer. This will make you read the question more carefully.
3. Look over the *Earth Science Reference Tables* for any helpful information related to the question.
4. Write a brief outline, or at least a few notes to yourself, about what should be included in the answer.
5. Pay attention to key words that indicate how to answer the question and what you need to say in your answer. Several of these words are very common. For example, you might be asked to discuss, describe, explain, define, compare, contrast, or design. The table below lists key words and directions for your answers.

Using Key Words to Direct Your Answers	
Key Word	**What Direction Your Answers Should Take**
Analyze	• Break the idea, concept, or situation into parts, and explain how they relate. • Carefully explain relationships, such as cause and effect.
Discuss	• Make observations about the topic or situation using facts. • Thoroughly write about various aspects of the topic or situation.
Describe	• Illustrate the subject using words. • Provide a thorough account of the topic. • Give complete answers.
Explain	• Clarify the topic of the question by spelling it out completely. • Make the topic understandable. • Provide reasons for the outcome.
Define	• State the exact meaning of the topic or word. • Explain what something is or what it means.
Compare	• Relate two or more topics with an emphasis on how they are alike. • State the similarities between two or more examples.
Contrast	• Relate two or more topics with an emphasis on how they are different. • State the differences between two or more examples.
Design	• Plan an experiment or component of an experiment. Map out your proposal, being sure to provide information about all of the required parts.
State	• Express in words. • Explain or describe using at least one fact, term, or relationship.

6. When you write your answer, don't be so general that you are not really saying anything. Be very specific. You should use the correct terms and clearly explain the processes and relationships. Be sure to provide details, such as the names of processes, names of structures, and, if it is appropriate, how they are related. If only one example or term is required, do not give two or more. If one is correct and the other is wrong, your answer may be marked wrong.

7. If a question has two or three parts, answer each part separately. This will make it easy for the person scoring your paper to find all of the information. When writing your answer, don't shortchange one part of the question by spending too much time on another part.

8. Note that you will not lose points for incorrect grammar, spelling, punctuation, or poor penmanship. However, such errors and poor penmanship could impair your ability to make your answer clear to the person scoring your paper. If that person cannot understand what you are trying to say, you will not receive the maximum number of points.

Strategies for Questions Based on Diagrams

Both multiple-choice and extended-response questions frequently include diagrams or pictures. Usually the diagrams provide information needed to answer the question. The diagrams may be realistic, or they may be schematic. Schematic drawings show the relationships among parts and sometimes the sequence in a system. Follow these steps:

1. First study the diagram and think about what the diagram shows you. Be sure to read any information, such as titles or labels, that goes with the diagram.

2. Read the question. Follow the strategies for either multiple-choice or constructed-response questions listed previously.

Strategies for Questions Based on Data Tables

Most data tables contain information that summarizes a topic. A table uses rows and columns to condense information and to present it in an organized way. Rows are the horizontal divisions going from left to right across the table, while columns are vertical divisions going from top to bottom. Column headings name the type of information included in a table. Sometimes different categories of information are listed down the left-hand column of the table. See the sample data table, and identify the kind of information in the columns and rows. When answering a question with a data table, use the following strategies.

1. Find the title of the table. It is usually located across the top.

2. Determine the number of columns in the table and their purpose.

3. Determine the number of rows and their purpose.

4. Read across the rows and down the columns to determine what the relationships are.

5. Now you are ready to read the question with the data table. Answer the question by using the suggested strategies for multiple-choice or constructed-response questions listed previously.

Table 1. Planet Data		
Planet	Average Distance From the Sun (AU)	Average Orbital Speed (km/s)
Mercury	0.4	48.0
Venus	0.7	35.0
Earth	1.0	30.0
Mars	1.5	24.0
Jupiter	5.2	13.0
Saturn	9.6	10.0
Uranus	19.0	7.0
Neptune	30.0	5.1

Strategies for Questions Based on Graphs

Graphs represent relationships in a visual form that is easy to read. Three different types of graphs commonly used on science Regents Examinations are line graphs, bar graphs, and circle graphs. Line graphs are the most common, and they show the relationship between two changing quantities, or variables. When a question is based on any of the three types of graphs, the information you need to correctly answer the question can usually be found on the graph.

When answering a question that includes a graph, first ask yourself these questions:

- What information does the graph provide?
- What are the variables?
- What seems to happen to one variable as the other changes?

After a careful analysis of the graph, use the appropriate strategies for multiple-choice or constructed-response questions.

Use of the Earth Science Reference Tables to Help Answer Questions

In recent Regents Examinations between 35% to 45% of the questions have involved the use of the *Earth Science Reference Tables*. You should become thoroughly familiar with all details of these tables. Sometimes the questions will specifically refer you to the reference tables, but most often you will be expected to know what information is included within the reference tables. The text helps you become familiar with the content of the reference tables by referring to the tables within the text presentation. These references are indicated by an ® on the pages in each topic. Listed below are some of the ways the reference tables are used in Regents Examination questions.

- to find a specific fact, such as the composition of Earth's inner core
- to find the relationship between two facts on different parts of the reference tables, such as the latitude and longitude of the center of the Tug Hill Plateau
- using an equation on the reference tables to solve a problem, such as a rate of change of an event
- graphing or recognizing the correct graph of data on the reference tables, such as the percent by mass of the elements in Earth's crust
- decoding a graphic symbol in a question, such as present weather or air mass type on a weather map
- performing a procedure using part of the reference tables, such as determining the distance of a location to an epicenter using the Earthquake P-wave and S-wave Travel Time graph
- interpretation of data on the reference tables, such as the temperature of white dwarf stars

Introduction to Earth's Changing Environment

How **Scientists Study** Earth's Changing Environment

? *Would a piece of wax float in melted wax?* **?**

Every day you probably observe the property of density just by getting a cold drink. You know ice floats in water because ice, or solid water, is less dense than liquid water. But how does the density of other solid and liquid phases of the same substance compare? If you dropped a chunk of solid candle wax into a container of liquid wax, would it sink or float? What do you think would happen to a chunk of iron in a tub of melted iron?

If you lived 200 years ago, you likely wouldn't have to think about the answer because you would have observed what happened while candles or iron horseshoes were being made. Now, you probably think about the ice in your drink first. The truth is, for almost all substances, when the solid, liquid, and gas of the same substance are in the same environment, they will naturally arrange themselves in order by density with the denser solid at the bottom, the least-dense gas at the top, and the liquid in between. Thus for almost all substances, the solid would sink into the liquid of the same material. The major exception to this principle is the substance water, since liquid water is denser than solid water (ice).

Introduction to Earth's Changing Environment

Vocabulary

classification	interface	percent deviation
cyclic change	mass	pollution
density	measurement	prediction
dynamic equilibrium	natural hazard	rate of change
inference	natural resources	universe
instrument	observation	volume

Topic Overview

Earth science is the study of Earth and its position in the universe. Often Earth science is considered a combination of four science disciplines:

- Geology is the study of the history, structure, processes, and composition of Earth's solid surface down to Earth's center.
- Oceanography is the study of all aspects of Earth's oceans.
- Meteorology is the study of Earth's atmosphere, including weather and climate.
- Astronomy is the study of the **universe**—that is all matter, time, energy, and space.

Note to student: *Much of the information presented in this topic explains process skills that you will use as you study earth science. You have probably already used some of these process skills. Most of the information in this topic will be discussed in more detail elsewhere. While you will not be tested on concepts in this topic independently, many of these concepts will be tested in conjunction with specific concepts. For example, you will be expected to use equations found in this topic to solve problems in percent deviation, density, and rate of change.*

Observations

An **observation** is the perception of some aspect of the environment by one or more human senses—sight, hearing, touch, taste, or smell.

Observing with Senses and Instruments

The senses are limited in range and precision. An **instrument** is a human-made device that extends the senses beyond their normal limits, thus enabling them to make observations that would otherwise be impossible or highly inaccurate. For example, a microscope makes it possible to see objects and details too small for the unaided eye to detect, and a magnet allows one to observe something the senses do not perceive at all. We would not even know about many forms of energy—such as X-rays, radio, microwave, and ultraviolet—without certain instruments.

Inferences and Misconceptions

An **inference** is an interpretation of an observation. It is a mental process that proposes causes, conclusions, or explanations for what has been observed. For example, the observation of an impression shaped like a dog's foot leads to the inference that a dog has been present. This inference may or may not be correct. Additional observations may make the inference more likely to be true.

A prediction of a future event, such as a hurricane or snowstorm, is a type of inference. Misconceptions about environmental characteristics often result from incorrect inferences that become commonly believed. A misconception is a mistaken belief or a misunderstanding. For thousands of years, humans believed the inference that Earth was the center of the universe and didn't spin or move around the sun.

Classification

Scientists group together similar observations and inferences to make the study of objects and events in the environment more meaningful or easier to understand. This grouping is called **classification**. In later topics, you will study classifications of objects and events such as planets, stars, minerals, storms, types of energy, and natural disasters.

Measurement

A **measurement** is a means of expressing an observation with greater accuracy or precision. It provides a numerical value for an aspect of the object or event being observed. Every measurement includes at least one of the three basic dimensional quantities—length, mass, and time—which are defined as follows:

- Length may be described as the distance between two points.
- The amount of matter in an object is its **mass**. It is often determined by using a balance. Mass should not be confused with weight, which is the pull (force) of Earth's gravitation on an object. The weight of an object may vary with its location, but its mass remains the same.
- Time is often described as our sense of things happening one after another or as the duration of an event.

Some types of measurements require the mathematical combination of basic dimensional quantities. For example, a unit of volume is actually a unit of length cubed, as in 25 cm^3 (25 cubic centimeters). **Volume** is the amount of space that an object occupies. The volume of solid objects is often determined by finding the volume of water an object displaces when it is placed in water in an instrument such as a graduated cylinder. (See Figure 1-1.) Other examples of such types of measurement are density (mass per unit volume, as in 4 g/cm^3) and speed (distance per unit time, as in 9.8 km/sec).

All measurements of the basic quantities (length, mass, and time) are made by a direct comparison to certain accepted standard units of measurement. For example, length is measured by comparing it to a standard unit such as the centimeter, mass to a unit such as the gram, and time to a unit such as the second. Imagine you asked some friends how much time an experiment took to perform, and they answered 60. Wouldn't you

Figure 1-1. Measuring volume of irregular objects: (A) To measure the volume of an irregular object that will fit in a graduated cylinder, pour water to a known level in a graduate around halfway up and carefully record the volume shown by the meniscus. Then tip the graduated cylinder and carefully slide the unknown solid into the graduate. Observe the new level of the meniscus. The difference in the two values is the volume of the unknown solid object. (B) For larger irregular objects, use an overflow can. Fill the overflow can so that water easily pours out the spout until the flow stops. Discard this water. Carefully drop the irregular object into the overflow can (without splashing). Collect and measure the water from the spout in a graduated cylinder or graduated beaker. The volume of the water in the beaker equals the volume of the unknown solid.

have to ask 60 of what? A measurement must always state the units used, for example, 27.9 grams or 26 kilometers.

Percent Deviation or Percent Error No measurement is perfect because of the imperfection of the senses and of instruments. People may also introduce errors by carelessness or the improper use of an instrument. Any measurement is therefore an approximation of a true value and must be considered to contain some error.

Science has accepted values for some given qualities (for example, 1 g/cm^3 for the density of liquid water at 4°C). It is therefore possible to determine the accuracy, or amount of error, of a given measurement by comparing it with the accepted value.

$$\text{percent deviation} = \frac{\text{difference from accepted value}}{\text{accepted value}} \times 100\%$$

For example, suppose a student measures the mass of an object as 127.5 grams and the accepted value is 125.0 grams. Then,

$$\begin{aligned}\text{amount of deviation} &= \text{difference from accepted value}\\ &= 127.5 \text{ grams} - 125.0 \text{ grams}\\ &= 2.5 \text{ grams}\end{aligned}$$

$$\begin{aligned}\text{percent deviation} &= \frac{\text{amount of deviation}}{\text{accepted value}} \times 100\%\\ &= \frac{2.5 \text{ grams}}{125.0 \text{ grams}} \times 100\%\\ &= 2.0\%\end{aligned}$$

When the amount of error is expressed as a percentage, it is called **percent deviation**, or percent error. The percent deviation is obtained by dividing the difference between the measured and accepted values by the accepted value and multiplying the result by 100 percent.

Review Questions

1. In the classroom during a visual inspection of a rock, a student recorded four statements about the rock. Which statement about the rock is an observation?

   (1) The rock formed deep in Earth's interior.
   (2) The rock cooled very rapidly.
   (3) The rock dates from the Cambrian Period.
   (4) The rock is black and shiny.

2. To make observations, an observer must always use

   (1) experiments
   (2) the senses
   (3) proportions
   (4) mathematical calculations

3. Which statement made by a student after examining a rock specimen is an inference?

   (1) The rock is of igneous origin.
   (2) The rock has rounded edges.
   (3) The rock is light-colored.
   (4) The rock contains large fragments.

4. A measurement is best defined as

   (1) an inference made by using the human senses
   (2) direct comparison to a known standard
   (3) an interpretation based on theory
   (4) a group of inferred properties

5. A student measures the velocity of the water in a stream as 2.5 meters per second. The actual velocity of the water is 3.0 meters per second. What is the approximate percent deviation of the student's measurements?

   (1) 0.50% (2) 17%   (3) 20%   (4) 50%

6. Which statement best illustrates a classification system?

   (1) A glacier melts at the rate of one meter per year.
   (2) Ocean depths are measured using sound waves.
   (3) Snowfall predictions for winter storms vary.
   (4) Stars are grouped according to color.

7. A classification system is based on the use of

   (1) the human senses to infer properties of objects
   (2) instruments to infer properties of objects
   (3) observed properties to group objects with similar characteristics
   (4) inferences to make observations

8. Organizing information in a meaningful way is an example of

   (1) prediction   (3) observation
   (2) measurement   (4) classification

9. A sphere was dropped into water in a graduated cylinder as shown in the following diagram. The water level rose to the new level shown.

Before   After

   What is the volume of the sphere?

   (1) 15 mL   (2) 25 mL   (3) 40 mL   (4) 65 mL

Density

The concentration of matter in an object is known as its **density**. If we model matter with students, then a full classroom with 35 students has a high density, and a classroom with only 2 students has a low density. The density of an object is the ratio of its mass to its volume; that is, density is the mass per each unit of volume. Density is important in the study of earth science. This is because density is a property of materials that affects the way in which materials interact in the environment.

Computing Density

To determine the density of an object, divide its mass by its volume. This formula for density is found in the *Earth Science Reference Tables:* **R**

$$\text{density} = \frac{\text{mass}}{\text{volume}}$$

The density of a material does not depend on the size or shape of the sample as long as the temperature and pressure remain the same. For example, a cube of the mineral graphite with a volume of 20 cm^3 has a mass of 44 g. Its density is 44 grams divided by 20 cm^3 = 2.2 g/cm^3. A graphite ball with a volume of 40 cm^3 (twice the volume of the cube) will have a mass of 88 g (twice the mass of the cube), but its density will be the same: 88 g/40 cm^3 = 2.2 g/cm^3.

Determining Relative Density

An object immersed in a liquid is buoyed by a force equal to the weight of liquid it displaces (Archimedes' principle). If the density of the object is less than the density of the liquid, the weight of displaced liquid will be greater than the weight of the object. Therefore, the upward force will be enough to support the object, and it will float in the liquid.

Flotation of objects in liquids (and in gases) is one method of determining their relative, or comparative, densities. The lower the density of a floating object, the higher it floats in the liquid. This means that a greater percentage of the object's volume is above the surface of the liquid. As the density of a floating object increases, it sinks relatively deeper into the liquid. If its density is greater than that of the liquid, it will sink to the bottom. If an object and a liquid have exactly the same density (for example, a fish in water), the object can remain stationary anywhere in the liquid. (See Figure 1-2.)

Physical Changes That Affect Density

Changes in temperature and pressure affect the densities of substances, especially those of gases. If the temperature of a gas increases and its pressure remains the same, its molecules move farther apart (the gas expands). The temperature rise thus results in less mass per unit volume, so that the density of the gas decreases. This explains why hot air rises when surrounded by cooler air. This rising of less-dense objects and falling of more-dense objects results in the convection currents, which affect movements in many portions of Earth and help to distribute heat energy.

If the pressure on a gas increases, the molecules come closer together (the gas contracts). The pressure rise thus results in more mass per unit volume, and the density increases. The effects of pressure on liquids and solids can be significant. This is illustrated by the increasing densities of the zones of Earth's interior illustrated in the Inferred Properties of Earth's Interior in the *Earth Science Reference Tables*.

Phases of Matter and Density

Matter on Earth usually exists in three forms: solid, liquid, and gas. Each form is known as a phase, or state, of matter. The density of a substance changes with changes in its phase. The layering of the outer spheres of Earth is the result of the effects of gravity pulling differently on solids, liquids, and gases due to their density differences. Almost all substances increase in density as they change from gas to liquid and from liquid to solid. They have their highest density as a solid because the atoms are closest together in that phase.

Water is an exception; its highest density is in the liquid state at a temperature of 3.98°C. Therefore, solid water (ice) floats on liquid water, while in most substances the solid sinks in the liquid. Water at 4°C will also lie below layers of water at any other temperature.

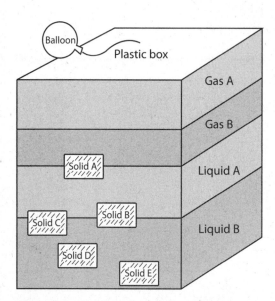

Figure 1-2. Density and height of flotation: The various substances in the plastic box are arranged by the height at which they float. Make inferences about the relative density of the substances before you continue to read. From highest to lowest, the relative densities of the substances are solid E, solid D and liquid B (about equal), solid C, solid B, liquid A, solid A, gas B, gas A, and the balloon.

10. A student finds the density of an ice cube to be 0.80 g/cm³; it is actually 0.90 g/cm³. What is the percent deviation (percent error) in this calculation?

(1) 6 percent (3) 13 percent
(2) 11 percent (4) 88 percent

11. The amount of space a substance occupies is its

(1) mass (2) volume (3) density (4) weight

12. Under the same conditions of temperature and pressure, three different samples of the same uniform substance will have the same

(1) shape (2) density (3) mass (4) volume

13. As shown in the following diagram, an empty 1000 mL container has a mass of 250 g. When filled with a liquid, the container and the liquid have a combined mass of 1300 g.

Empty
Mass = 250.0 g

Filled
Mass = 1300 g

What is the density of the liquid?
(1) 1.00 g/mL (3) 1.30 g/mL
(2) 1.05 g/mL (4) 0.95 g/mL

14. An empty 250 mL beaker has a mass of 60 g. When 100 mL of oil is added to the beaker, the total mass is 140 g. The density of the oil is approximately

(1) 1.7 g/mL (3) 0.8 g/mL
(2) 1.4 g/mL (4) 0.6 g/mL

15. The diagram at the right represents a cylinder containing four liquids—W, X, Y and Z—each with a different density (D), as indicated. A piece of solid quartz having a density of 2.7 g/cm³ is placed on the surface of liquid W. When the quartz is released, it will pass through

(1) W, but not X, Y, or Z
(2) W and X, but not Y or Z
(3) W, X, and Y, but not Z
(4) W, X, Y, and Z

16. A student mixed several different 12 mm plastic beads together by mistake. Luckily the beads had different densities. One group of beads had a density of 0.6 g/cm³; the other beads had a density of 1.2 g/ cm³. Describe a method the student can use to sort the beads.

17. A student has a sample of a mineral that is too big to fit in a graduated cylinder. The density of the sample is known. How can the student determine the volume of the sample?

18. Which is the best definition for the mass of an object?

(1) the amount of space the object occupies
(2) its ratio of weight to volume
(3) the quantity of matter the object contains
(4) the force of gravity acting on the object

The Changing Environment

Human observations indicate that most, if not all, environments of Earth and the rest of the universe are undergoing changes. Much of the study of earth science involves analysis of these environmental changes.

What Change Is

A <u>change</u> occurs when the properties or characteristics of a part of the environment have been altered. As a result, descriptions of an environment at two different times are never exactly the same in all details. The occurrence of a change in the properties of an object or a system is called an event. Events may be almost instantaneous, as in the case of lightning and meteors, or they may occur over long periods of time, as in changes in sea level or elevation of mountains.

Change can be described with respect to time and space (location). Time and space are called the frames of reference for studying change. As an example, you might say that Earth's moon changes because we observe it in different locations in the sky and in different phases at different times during a month.

Rate of Change

How much a measurable aspect of the environment, called a <u>field</u>, is altered over a given time—years, hours, or seconds—is the **rate of change.**

Consider the information in the data table and graph in Figure 1-3. The rate of change in temperature—the field—can be estimated by comparing the steepness (how close the plotted line is to a vertical) of the plotted line. In part A of the graph, the rate of temperature change is greater than that of part B. In part C, there is a zero rate of change, as shown by a horizontal line. More precision about rate of change can be obtained by using the following equation, which is similar to one found in the *Earth Science Reference Tables.* Ⓡ

Time (P.M.)	Rock Temperature (°C)
2:10	30
2:11	33
2:12	38
2:13	40
2:14	41
2:15	42
2:16	43
2:17	43
2:18	43

$$\text{rate of change} = \frac{\text{change in field value}}{\text{change in time}}$$

Based on the data table in Figure 1-3, what is the rate of change in rock temperature from 2:10 to 2:13 P.M.? The amount of change in the temperature (the field value) is 40°C – 30°C, or 10°C. The amount of change in time is 2:13 P.M. – 2:10 P.M., or 3 minutes.

$$\text{rate of change} = \frac{10°C}{3 \text{ min}} = 3.3°C/\text{min}$$

Cyclic Change

Many changes in the environment occur in some orderly fashion in which the events constantly repeat. Such an orderly change is called a **cyclic change.** Some cyclic changes are the movement of celestial objects (sun, moon, stars, planets), the numbers of sunspots, tides, seasonal events, and the water and rock cycles.

Prediction of Change

A **prediction** is a type of inference about the conditions and behavior of the environment in the future. Predictions can be made if the amount, type, and direction of change can be determined. For example, because eclipses are cyclic, astronomers can predict the occurrence of solar and lunar eclipses many hundreds of years into the future.

It is important in protecting against loss of life, personal injury, and loss of property that we have

Figure 1-3. Data to be used to compute sample rate of change problems: The data represents the temperature of an area of rock that is exposed to nearby lava (liquid rock at Earth's surface) that just erupted from a volcano in Hawaii.

accurate predictions of natural hazards. A **natural hazard** is a non-human-related object, process, or situation that has the possibility of causing loss of life, personal injury, or loss of property. Natural hazards include asteroid impacts, blizzards, earthquakes, floods, hurricanes, thunderstorms, tornadoes, heat waves, tsunamis, and volcanic eruptions.

In the United States from 1975 to 1994, approximately 24,000 people died from natural disasters, and there were approximately 120,000 injuries. The loss of property in these same years was approximately $500 billion. Weather-related events accounted for approximately 80 percent of the deaths, injuries, and loss of property in this time period. Worldwide, about one in 100,000 people die each year in natural disasters. Each of these types of natural hazards will be discussed in later topics. With accurate predictions of these hazards, people can use predetermined escape routes and follow emergency action plans.

Energy, Interfaces, and Change

All change involves a flow of energy from one part of the environment (that loses energy) to another part (that gains it). For example, during an earthquake, internal Earth energy stored in rocks is released, or lost, from the rocks and converted into sound, heat, and the mechanical energy of the Earth's shaking surface. Energy is usually exchanged across an **interface**, which is the boundary between regions with different properties. In the case of an earthquake, there is an interface between the place where the rocks break and start moving and Earth's surface where the shaking occurs. Other interfaces are where Earth's atmosphere blends into outer space or at the shoreline where Long Island, New York, borders the Atlantic Ocean.

Environmental Equilibrium

Although change occurs continuously throughout the environment, certain general characteristics tend to remain constant. For example, the wooded shore of a lake tends to look the same from one day to the next. Although it may go through a cycle of seasonal changes, it tends to look the same each year at the same season. This is the result of a natural balance among all the changes taking place, called environmental equilibrium. This equilibrium is easily upset on a small scale, for example by the burrowing of a worm in the soil, but it is normally not upset on a large scale. Human activities, however, often severely disrupt the environmental equilibrium. For example, construction equipment can rapidly change a rain forest into an urban area, thus introducing change on a large scale.

Environmental equilibrium resulting from opposing forces or actions balancing out is called a **dynamic equilibrium.** An example would be the level of a lake remaining the same even though thousands of liters of water move in and out of the lake per day. Another example would be the stable amount of oxygen in the atmosphere. Billions of molecules of oxygen are moving into and out of the atmosphere each day, but the total amount stays the same. In your lifetime, the elevation of a local mountain, the amount of gravity pulling on your body in your house, or the average distance to a star in the night sky will stay about the same. When environmental equilibrium results from little noticeable change it is static equilibrium.

19. Which graph represents the greatest rate of temperature change?

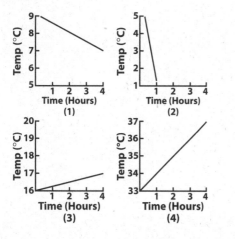

20. Refer to the following data table. At approximately what rate did the temperature rise inside the greenhouse between 8:00 A.M. and 10:00 A.M.?

Time Average	Greenhouse Temperature
6:00 A.M.	13°C
8:00 A.M.	14°C
10:00 A.M.	16°C
12:00 noon	20°C

(1) 1.0°C/hr
(2) 2.0°C/hr
(3) 0.5°C/hr
(4) 12.0°C/hr

21. The following graph shows temperature readings for a day in April.

The average rate of temperature change, in Fahrenheit degrees per hour, between 6 A.M. and noon was

(1) 6°/hr   (2) 8°/hr   (3) 3°/hr   (4) 18°/hr

22. Some changes that occur on Earth are cyclic—they occur over and over again at regular intervals. List two changes that occur on a regular basis and can be considered cyclic and two changes that are not cyclic.

23. Which of the following is NOT a natural hazard?

(1) blizzard
(2) flood
(3) dynamite blasting
(4) asteroid impact

24. The following graph shows the relative amount of air pollution over a city for several years.

Which statement about air pollution over this city is best supported by the graph?

(1) It is decreasing at a constant rate.
(2) It is increasing at a constant rate.
(3) It is a cyclic event.
(4) It has no pattern.

25. A student measures the distance from a bridge to a rock every day for a week.

What is indicated by the graph of the student's data?

(1) No change in time or distance took place.
(2) As distance decreased, time increased.
(3) As distance increased, time decreased.
(4) As time increased, distance remained the same.

26. What always happens when a change occurs?

   (1) Pollution is produced.
   (2) The temperature of a system increases.
   (3) The properties of a system are altered.
   (4) Dynamic equilibrium is reached.

27. Which statement is true about the environment of most of Earth?

   (1) It is usually greatly unbalanced.
   (2) It is usually in equilibrium and hard to change.
   (3) It is usually in equilibrium but easy to change on a small scale.
   (4) It is normally heavily polluted by natural occurrences.

28. Humans can cause rapid changes in the environment that may result in catastrophic events. Which statement below is the best example of this?

   (1) Concrete and brick buildings cause a city to absorb more heat than surrounding areas do.
   (2) A project to straighten out a river causes flooding at a city downstream.
   (3) A new housing development uses well water, causing the water table level to drop.
   (4) Streetlights make it more difficult to observe stars and planets at night near a city.

Human Interaction with the Environment

Natural Resources

The materials and energy sources found in the environment that humans use in their daily lives are **natural resources**. Natural resources include the air you breathe, the water you drink, the plants and animals you use for food and clothing, and the energy from the sun. Natural resources also include fossil fuels and rock and mineral resources.

Individuals and societies are always in conflict over the ownership, supply, and use versus preservation of often-limited natural resources. There have to be trade-offs between the use of a natural resource and other uses of the land, water, or air. Often, through the use of human technology, natural resource shortages can be solved by substituting one material for another or by recycling limited resources so that "new" resources don't have to be harvested, mined, or otherwise acquired.

Pollution of the Environment

Pollution of the environment occurs when the concentration of any substance or form of energy reaches a proportion that adversely affects people or their property, or other life forms. The key word in defining a polluted situation is concentration. Think of sodium chloride (NaCl), rock salt, which is essential to life. If the concentration of salt in an organism's body is too high, it can cause injury or death.

Causes of Pollution Many forms of pollution are the result of technology, which often produces and distributes harmful concentrations of substances and forms of energy. Other forms of pollution are the result of natural events or processes and would occur without the presence of people.
High concentrations of pollen in the air, volcanic ash and gases from volcanic eruptions, and X-rays from uranium and radon in rocks and soil are examples of natural pollution. Substances and forms of energy that pollute—pollutants—include solids, liquids, gases, biologic organisms, and forms of energy such as

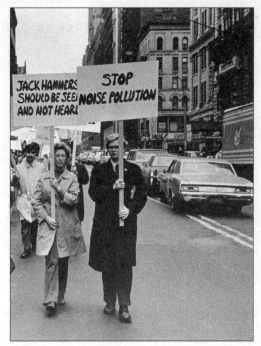

Figure 1-4. Protesting noise pollution: Not all pollution is caused by substances, some pollutants are types of energy such as sound (noise). Think of the times when loud or intrusive sounds have interfered with your life.

heat, sound, visible light, and nuclear radiation. Generally, the more urban an environment and the more industrial the processes, the higher the pollutant levels.

Review Questions

29. Which of the following statements is an example of a way of conserving our natural resources?
    (1) opening new mines for valuable metals that are running out
    (2) using well water in desert areas for growing crops and building golf courses
    (3) finding alternate sources and materials to replace natural petroleum products
    (4) building industrial plants in national parks where they are away from populated areas

30. When organisms, sound, and radiation added to the environment reach a level that harms people, these factors are referred to as environmental
    (1) interfaces
    (2) pollutants
    (3) phase changes
    (4) equilibrium exchanges

31. List three substances or forms of energy that are common natural (NOT caused by humans) pollutants.

32. Which energy source is LEAST likely to pollute the environment?
    (1) solar   (3) coal
    (2) petroleum   (4) wood

33. Which type of human environment usually has the highest pollution levels?

34. A major argument against the construction of nuclear-powered electric generation stations is the claim that they pollute bodies of water by discharging large quantities of
    (1) noise   (3) heat
    (2) carbon dioxide (4) ozone

Base your answers to questions 35 through 39 on the diagram below, which shows, air, water, and noise pollution in a densely populated industrial area.

35. Air pollution would probably be greatest at which location?
    (1) A   (2) B   (3) C   (4) D

36. Water pollution would probably be greatest at which location?
    (1) A   (2) B   (3) C   (4) D

37. Noise pollution would be greatest at which location?
    (1) B   (2) C   (3) D   (4) E

38. Which location is subjected to the greatest number of pollution factors?
    (1) A   (2) B   (3) D   (4) E

39. If the water intakes supplied drinking water to the area, which intake would most likely require the most extensive purification procedures?
    (1) 1   (2) 2   (3) 3   (4) 4

Directions
Review the Test-Taking Strategies section of this book. Then answer the following questions. Read each question carefully and answer with a correct choice or response.

Part A

Base your answers to questions 1 through 4 on the graph below, which shows the masses and volumes of four Earth materials.

1 Which material has the greatest density?
(1) A   (2) B   (3) C   (4) D

2 If the density of water is 1 g/cm^3, which material will float in water?
(1) A   (2) B   (3) C   (4) D

3 If the volume of sample C is 3.0 cm^3, what is its mass?
(1) 7.5 g   (2) 2.1 g   (3) 3.0 g   (4) 21 g

4 Which material has a density of about 4.0 g/cm^3?
(1) A   (2) B   (3) C   (4) D

Masses and Volumes of Earth Materials

5 Substances A, B, C, and D are at rest in a container of liquid as shown by the following diagram. Which choice lists the substances in order of lowest to highest density?
(1) A, B, C, D
(2) A, D, C, B
(3) D, C, B, A
(4) C, B, A, D

6 Substances A, B, C, and D are at rest in a container of liquid as shown in the following diagram. Which substance probably has a density closest to that of the liquid?
(1) A
(2) B
(3) C
(4) D

Base your answers to questions 7 through 11 on the following diagrams. Objects A and B are solid and made of the same uniform material.

7 If object B has a mass of 173 g, what is its density?
(1) 0.37 g/cm^3
(2) 2.7 g/cm^3
(3) 3.7 g/cm^3
(4) 5.7 g/cm^3

8 Object A expands when it is heated. Which graph best represents the relationship between the temperature and the density of object A?

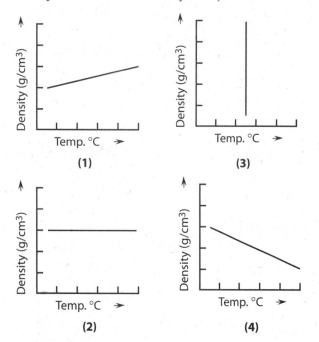

(1) **(3)** **(2)** **(4)**

9 A student measures the mass of object B as 156 g, but the actual mass is 173 g. What is the student's approximate percent deviation (percentage of error)?
   (1) 1 percent   (3) 10 percent
   (2) 5 percent   (4) 20 percent

10 A third object is made of the same uniform material as object B, but it has twice the volume of object B. How does the density of this third object compare to the density of object B?
   (1) It is one-half as dense as B.
   (2) It has approximately the same density as B.
   (3) It is twice as dense as B.
   (4) It is four times as dense as B.

11 How does the mass of object B compare to the mass of object A?
   (1) The mass of B is less than the mass of A.
   (2) The mass of B is greater than the mass of A.
   (3) The mass of B is the same as the mass of A.

12 If pressure is applied to a rock until its volume is reduced by one half, how does its new density compare to its original density?
   (1) It is half its original density.
   (2) It is twice its original density.
   (3) It is the same as its original density.
   (4) It is one-third its original density.

13 The following diagrams show physical changes in four materials over time. The chemical composition of each material remains the same. Which material most likely changed in density?

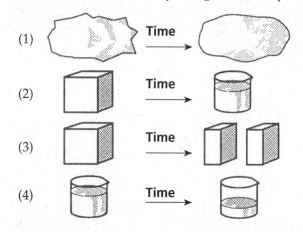

14 Which graph best represents for most Earth materials, excluding water, the relationship between the density of a substance and its state of matter (phase)?
   [Key: S = solid, L = liquid, G = gas]

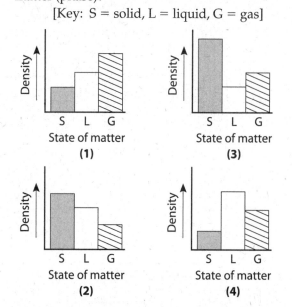

15 After the mass of a mineral was measured, the mineral sample was dropped and a piece chipped off the sample before the volume of the sample was measured. How would the calculated value of the sample's density compare to the value of the density of the sample if it had not been chipped?
   (1) The calculated density value would be greater (without the chipping).
   (2) The calculated density value would be less (without the chipping).
   (3) The calculated density value would be the same (without the chipping).

16 A prediction of next winter's weather is an example of
(1) a measurement   (3) an observation
(2) a classification   (4) an inference

17 The rising and setting of the sun are examples of
(1) noncyclic events   (3) predictable changes
(2) unrelated events   (4) random motion

18 Future changes in the environment can best be predicted from data that are
(1) highly variable and collected over short periods of time
(2) highly variable and collected over long periods of time
(3) cyclic and collected over short periods of time
(4) cyclic and collected over long periods of time

19 An interface can best be described as
(1) a zone of contact between different substances across which energy is exchanged
(2) a region in the environment with unchanging properties
(3) a process that results in changes in the environment
(4) a region beneath the surface of Earth where change is not occurring

20 Which condition exists when the rates of water flowing into and out of a lake are balanced so that the lake's depth appears to be constant?
(1) dynamic equilibrium   (3) precipitation
(2) transpiration   (4) saturation

Part B

21 Three students tried to guess Joe's weight. They guessed 140 lb, 150 lb, and 160 lb. If Joe really weighed 146 lb, calculate each person's percent deviation. [5]

22 The springs and geysers in Yellowstone National Park contain enough heat energy to provide for the annual electric needs of New York City. Why is this energy not being used?
(1) Energy from hot water is not easy to convert to electricity.
(2) No electric transmission lines connect Yellowstone National Park with the rest of the United States.
(3) It has been decided to protect the natural environment of Yellowstone National Park.
(4) Using the geyser and spring water would cause a drought in the Yellowstone National Park region.

23 A student placed a 20-cm plastic foam ball and a 5-cm piece of sandstone in a container of water. The sandstone sank and the ball floated. Propose a reason why the larger object floated and the smaller object sank. [1]

Base your answers to questions 24 through 28 on the following data table. The table shows the mass of three liquids—A, B, and C—each of which has a volume of 500 mL.

Liquid	Volume (mL)	Mass (g)
A	500	400
B	500	500
C	500	600

24 What is the density of liquid A? [1]

25 If half of liquid B is removed from its container, what will the density of the remaining liquid be in relationship to the original density? [1]

26 The accepted mass for liquid C is 600 g, but a student measures the mass as 612 g. What is the percent deviation (percent of error) of the student's measurement? [1]

27 The following graph shows the volume of liquid B as the temperature changes from 0°C to 10°C. According to the graph, at what temperature is the density of liquid B the greatest? [1]

28 Liquid A is NOT water. Some of liquid A is frozen into a solid block and placed in a container of liquid A. What will probably happen to the location of the solid block in relationship to the liquid? [1]

29 Mount St. Helens erupted in 1980, depositing volcanic ash over much of the countryside. Why is it important for scientists to try to predict volcanic eruptions? [1]

Base your answers to questions 30 and 31 on the data table below, which shows the volume and mass of three different samples, A, B, and C, of the mineral pyrite.

Pyrite		
Sample	Volume (cm³)	Mass (g)
A	2.5	12.5
B	6.0	30.0
C	20.0	100.0

30 On the grid provided above, plot the data (volume and mass) for the three samples of pyrite and connect the points with a line. [2]

31 State the mass of a 10.0-cm³ sample of pyrite. [1]

Part C

The following fictional article describes an oil spill that resulted from an earthquake in Saudi Arabia. Use your knowledge of earth science and the information in the article to answer questions 32 through 36.

An earthquake in Saudi Arabia caused a break in an oil pipeline that connected oil wells to shipping facilities in the Persian Gulf. A total of 120,000 gallons of crude oil (density 0.86 g/cm³) spilled onto the desert soil. At first it was thought that 50,000 gallons eventually flowed into a reservoir that supplies drinking water to several communities. Later it was learned that only 35,000 gallons had flowed into the reservoir.

The cleanup crews removed the crude oil from the reservoir in a little over a week. It took much longer to remove the crude oil from the sandy desert soil. After two weeks of continuous effort, only 5000 gallons of oil had been removed. This area of the desert is irrigated and used for growing crops, most of which were killed by the crude oil. It is not yet known if all the oil can be removed from the soil and if crops will grow in the region again.

32 Which physical property of the crude oil allowed it to be easily cleaned up from the water reservoir? [1]

33 Why is the earthquake in the article considered to be a natural disaster? [1]

34 Calculate the percent deviation of the first estimate of the amount of crude oil in the reservoir compared to the actual amount. Be sure to show ALL work including writing the equation, substituting values, and indicating the answer. [2]

35 What was the rate of crude oil recovery from the soil in gallons per day for the two-week period described in the article? Be sure to show ALL work including writing the equation, substituting values, and indicating the answer. [2]

36 Explain why the crude oil in the soil would be considered pollution. Be sure to use the term *concentration* in your answer. [1]

37 A hurricane traveled 2,600 kilometers during a 4-day period. Calculate the average rate of daily movement of a hurricane following the directions below.
   (a) Write the equation used to determine the rate of change.
   (b) Substitute data into the equation. [1]
   (c) Calculate the rate and label it with the proper units. [1]

38 The students decided to measure the speed of the stream by floating apples down a straight section of the stream. Describe the steps the students must take to determine the stream's surface rate of movement (speed) by using a stopwatch, a 10-foot rope, and several apples. Include the equation for calculating rate. [3]

Measuring Earth

How Scientists Study Measuring Earth

? *Would you consider the crust of your toast part of your plate?* **?**

You wouldn't think that the crust of toast you left on your plate at breakfast is part of the plate you eat from. If you use the same concept for Earth's crust, you would jump to the conclusion that the crust is separate from any other section. Using this erroneous belief, some science periodicals have used the term "crustal plates." Do you think this is a scientifically accurate term?

Actually, there is no such thing as a "crustal plate" in Earth Science. Earth's plates are much thicker than average crust, and incorporate the crust and the uppermost mantle, often called the rigid mantle. The crust of Earth is mineralogically different than the mantle below it, but the physical properties of rigidity and solidity of the crust and the uppermost mantle are very similar. Thus, the crust and the uppermost mantle are grouped together as Earth's lithosphere. Therefore, there are *lithospheric plates*, or tectonic plates, and not "crustal plates."

Measuring Earth

Vocabulary

atmosphere	field	meridian of longitude
contour line	gradient	model
coordinate system	hydrosphere	pauses (of atmosphere)
crust	isoline	prime meridian
Earth's interior	latitude	profile
elevation	lithosphere	topographic map
equator	longitude	

Topic Overview

People have always wanted to know about where they live, be it Earth in general, or their part of their country. In this topic you will learn about the basic dimensions of Earth and its layered structure and composition. You will also learn about its spheres, and how to locate and model Earth positions and landscape features. People have struggled for thousands of years to find accurate and reproducible methods of locating specific positions on Earth's surface to find natural resources, decide who owns what land, and determine where crops can be grown well. The problem of how to find positions on Earth's surface has largely been solved by the latitude and longitude system—studied in this topic—coupled with the Global Positioning System (GPS), which uses measurements from Earth-orbiting satellites.

Size and Shape of Earth

Earth's shape is very close to being a perfect sphere. The actual shape is of a sphere that has a slight flattening at the polar regions and a 0.3 percentage bulging at the equatorial region. The human eye cannot detect this distortion from a perfect sphere, even in the most accurate globe models of Earth. A **model** is a way of representing the properties of an object or system. A model may be an object, such as a globe representing Earth, or a drawing, diagram, graph, chart, table, or mathematical formula or equation.

Evidence of Earth's spherical shape includes photographs taken from space and the way ships appear to sink as they travel past the horizon. Other evidence is the similarity of the strength of gravity at sea level all over Earth's surface. Besides being very close to a perfect sphere, Earth's surface is very smooth (has very little relief) compared to its diameter. This smoothness is evident in any photographs of Earth taken from space.

Figure 2-1 illustrates some of the basic dimensions of Earth's surface below the atmosphere. Earth's surface is the top of the liquid portion or the solid portions of Earth—described later in this topic.

Spheres of Earth

Earth is composed of a series of spheres held together by gravity and thus arranged from lowest to highest density moving towards Earth's center. Table 2-1 compares the spheres and Figure 2-2 is a model of this arrangement of spheres. There is no agreement as to the exact thickness of the atmosphere. The line in the model indicating Earth's surface is actually too thick to represent the hydrosphere/ocean average depth. The divisions of the atmosphere and their interfaces—the pauses—are also found with some of their properties in Selected Properties of Earth's Atmosphere (R) in the *Earth Science Reference Tables*. The average chemical compositions of some of these spheres is shown in Average Chemical Composition of Earth's Crust, Hydrosphere, (R) and Troposphere in the *Earth Science Reference Tables*.

Outer Spheres of Earth

The region that extends from the outer portion of Earth's interior to where the atmosphere blends into outer space can be considered the outer part of Earth. This portion of Earth is divided into three spheres—atmosphere, hydrosphere, and lithosphere.

Atmosphere The layer of gases that surrounds Earth above the surface of liquid water and rocky material is the **atmosphere.** It is, by volume, composed mostly of the gases nitrogen (78%) and oxygen (21%), but also includes some aerosols—suspended liquids and solids. The atmosphere is the sphere farthest from Earth's center because it is the least dense, and Earth's gravity pulls on it less than on the other spheres. It extends out several hundred kilometers into space, but nearly all of its mass is confined to the few kilometers nearest Earth's surface. The atmosphere is stratified, or layered, into zones—troposphere, stratosphere, mesosphere, and thermosphere—each with its own distinct characteristics such as temperature and composition. The interfaces, or boundaries, of the layers of Earth's atmosphere are called **pauses.** The tropopause, for example, is between the troposphere and stratosphere. (See Selected Properties of Earth's Atmosphere (R) in the *Earth Science Reference Tables*.)

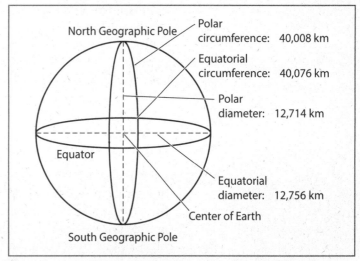

Figure 2-1. Some basic Earth dimensions: The similarities of the polar and equatorial diameters and circumferences indicate that Earth is close to being a perfect sphere. The average diameter of Earth is 12,735 kilometers.

Table 2–1 Comparison of the Spheres of Earth			
Sphere Name	**Density (in g/cm)**	**Phase(s) of Matter**	**Thickness (in km)**
Atmosphere	0.0–0.0001	Gas	600 (approximately)
Hydrosphere	1.0	Liquid	3.8 (average for oceans)
Lithosphere	2.7–3.3	Solid	100
Earth's interior (Geosphere)	2.7–13.1	Mostly solid, some liquid	6378

Figure 2-2. A wedge of Earth: The wedge shows the spheres of Earth drawn very close to scale.

Hydrosphere The **hydrosphere** is the layer of liquid water that lies between the atmosphere and much of the upper layer of Earth's interior. The hydrosphere consists of the oceans, which cover about 70 percent of Earth's surface, and other bodies of water such as lakes, streams, and rivers. The hydrosphere is relatively thin, with the oceans averaging only 3.8 kilometers in thickness. The chemical composition of the hydrosphere is mostly liquid H_2O, thus mostly hydrogen and oxygen. Earth's surface waters also contain varying amounts of dissolved gases and dissolved and suspended solids, including life forms.

Lithosphere The layer of rock that forms the solid outer shell at the top of Earth's interior is the **lithosphere.** (See Figure 2-2.) The lithosphere lies directly beneath the atmosphere or the hydrosphere. The lithosphere is approximately 100 kilometers thick and is divided into sections called lithospheric plates. The upper portion of the lithosphere is called the **crust.** Where the crust is not covered by the liquid water (hydrosphere), it is usually covered by a very thin layer of broken-up rocky material. When this material contains abundant organic matter, it is called soil.

Earth's Interior

The region extending from the rocky part of Earth's surface to Earth's center is called **Earth's interior** (geosphere). Many of the features of Earth's interior are shown in the Inferred Properties of Earth's Interior in the *Earth Science Reference Tables.*

Review Questions

1. Which object best represents a true scale model of the shape of Earth?

   (1) a table tennis ball   (3) an egg
   (2) a football   (4) a pear

2. Which of the following is NOT evidence that supports Earth's spherical shape?

   (1) photographs taken from outer space
   (2) ships appearing to sink as they sail past the horizon
   (3) the changing seasons
   (4) the similarities in gravity at sea level all over Earth

3. In which group are the spheres of Earth listed in order of increasing density?

   (1) atmosphere, hydrosphere, lithosphere
   (2) hydrosphere, lithosphere, atmosphere
   (3) lithosphere, hydrosphere, atmosphere
   (4) lithosphere, atmosphere, hydrosphere

4. Which makes up most of Earth's surface?

   (1) the atmosphere
   (2) the lithosphere
   (3) the hydrosphere

5. The lower atmosphere and hydrosphere are bound to Earth by

   (1) magnetic fields
   (2) atmospheric pressure
   (3) the force of gravity
   (4) a molecular bonding at the interface

6. What do the tropopause, stratopause, and mesopause all have in common?

   (1) Each is a point of maximum temperature in its layer of the atmosphere.
   (2) Each is an interface of two layers of the atmosphere.
   (3) Each is a region of increasing pressure within the atmosphere.
   (4) Each is a zone of decreasing water vapor content within the atmosphere.

7. As depth within Earth's interior increases, the

   (1) density, temperature, and pressure decrease
   (2) density, temperature, and pressure increase
   (3) density and temperature decrease, but pressure increases
   (4) density decreases, but temperature and pressure increase

8. The following diagram shows Earth's spheres. Which spheres are zones of Earth's atmosphere?

Mantle

Asthenosphere
Lithosphere
Hydrosphere
Troposphere
Stratosphere
Mesosphere
Thermosphere

(Not drawn to scale.)

(1) lithosphere, hydrosphere, and troposphere
(2) stratosphere, mesosphere, and thermosphere
(3) asthenosphere, lithosphere, and hydrosphere
(4) hydrosphere, troposphere, and stratosphere

9. The layer of bedrock near Earth's surface that forms a continuous shell around Earth is called the

(1) troposphere   (3) lithosphere
(2) stratosphere   (4) hydrosphere

10. Oxygen is the most abundant element by volume in Earth's

(1) inner core   (3) hydrosphere
(2) crust   (4) troposphere

11. What is the approximate altitude of the mesopause in the atmosphere?

(1) 50 km   (2) 66 km   (3) 82 km   (4) 90 km

12. Which statement most accurately describes Earth's atmosphere?

(1) The atmosphere is layered, with each layer possessing distinct characteristics.
(2) The atmosphere is a mass of gases surrounding most of Earth.
(3) The atmosphere's altitude is less than the depth of the ocean.
(4) The atmosphere is more dense than the hydrosphere, but less dense than the lithosphere.

13. Which layer of Earth's atmosphere contains no water vapor, has an atmospheric pressure less than 0.1 atmosphere, and has an air temperature that increases with altitude?

(1) troposphere   (3) mesosphere
(2) stratosphere   (4) thermosphere

14. The water sphere of Earth is known as the

(1) atmosphere   (3) lithosphere
(2) troposphere   (4) hydrosphere

15. In the following diagrams, the dark zone at the surface of each wedge-shaped segment of Earth represents average ocean depth. Which segment is drawn most nearly to scale?

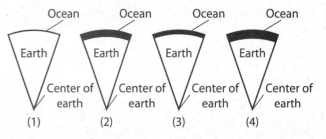

Ocean   Ocean   Ocean   Ocean

Earth   Earth   Earth   Earth

Center of earth   Center of earth   Center of earth   Center of earth

(1)   (2)   (3)   (4)

16. The following maps show Earth as viewed from above the North Pole and from above the South Pole. Which statement is best supported by these maps?

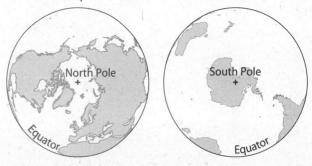

North Pole   South Pole

Equator   Equator

(1) Most of Earth's surface is land.
(2) Most of Earth's landmass is in the Southern Hemisphere.
(3) The geographic North Pole is the south magnetic pole.
(4) Most of Earth's surface is hydrosphere.

17. Which graph best represents the percentage by volume of the elements making up Earth's hydrosphere?

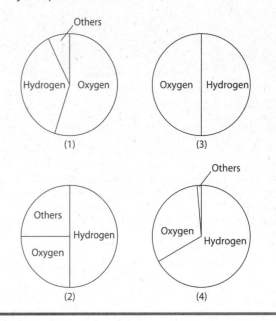

Others

Hydrogen   Oxygen

(1)

Oxygen   Hydrogen

(3)

Others

Hydrogen

Oxygen

(2)

Others

Oxygen

Hydrogen

(4)

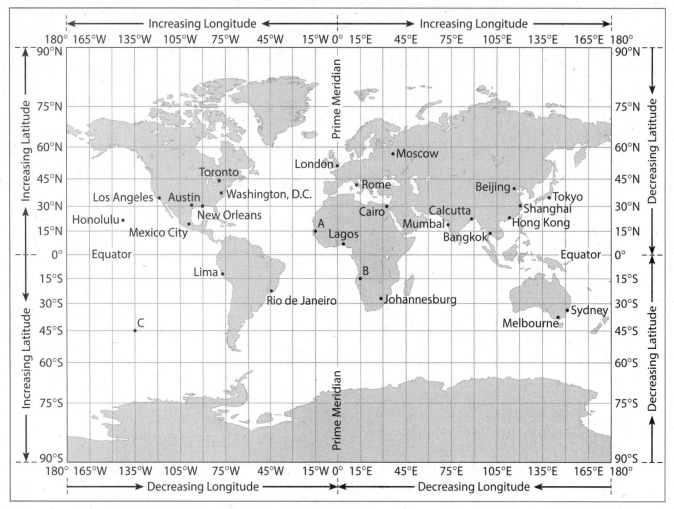

Figure 2-3. **World map with latitude-longitude coordinate system**

Figure 2-4. **The meaning of latitude:** Latitude is the angular distance north or south of the equator. On the left, Earth is shown as a sphere with the parallel for 60° N latitude shown as a circle parallel to the equator. On the right, Earth is shown with the north-south axis vertical; the equator and the parallels of latitude then become horizontal lines.

Locating Positions on Earth

To fix the location of a point on any two-dimensional surface such as the surface of Earth, two numbers, called coordinates, are needed. The system for determining the coordinates of a point is called a **coordinate system.** (See Figure 2-3.) The latitude-longitude coordinate system is the one most commonly used to locate points on Earth's surface. Latitude and longitude are measured in angular units: degrees (°) and minutes (′). There are 60 minutes in a degree.

Latitude

The angular distance north or south of the equator is **latitude.** The **equator** marks the middle location on Earth's surface, halfway between the geographic North and South Poles. If a line is drawn from any point on Earth's surface to the center of Earth, the latitude of that point is the number of degrees in the angle between that line and the plane of the equator. All points that have the same latitude lie on a circle that is parallel to the equator. These circles are called parallels <u>of</u> <u>latitude</u> or just <u>parallels.</u> The equator may be considered to be the parallel of latitude 0°. (See Figure 2-4.) As indicated in Figure 2-4, latitude increases north and south of the equator to a maximum of 90° at each pole.

Be sure you understand the meaning of increasing and decreasing latitudes. Increasing latitude means moving away from the equator or towards the geographic poles. Decreasing latitude means moving towards the equator or away from the geographic poles. Remember when writing a location's latitude you must include an "N" for north or an "S" for south, except for the equator, which is just 0° latitude.

Measuring Latitude

As shown in Figure 2-5 the altitude of Polaris—the North Star—equals the degree of latitude in the Northern Hemisphere. The altitude of an object in the sky is its angle above the horizon. The latitude of a point on Earth's surface is its angle north or south of the equator. The star Polaris is almost directly over the geographic North Pole of Earth. The altitude of Polaris at any point in the Northern Hemisphere should be the same as the latitude of that point. That is, the altitude of Polaris should change from 0° at the equator to 90° at the geographic North Pole. In the Southern Hemisphere, latitude can be determined by measuring the altitude of certain other stars. To determine the altitude of an object in the sky, an angle-measuring instrument such as a sextant is used.

Longitude

As shown in Figure 2-6, **longitude** is an angular distance east or west of the prime meridian. A **meridian of longitude,** or <u>meridian,</u> is any semi-circle on Earth's surface connecting the north and south geographic poles. The meridian that passes through Greenwich, England, has been designated the **prime meridian,** or the meridian of zero longitude. The longitude of any point on the prime meridian is 0°. The longitude of any other point on Earth's surface is the number of degrees between the meridian that passes through that point and the prime meridian. This angle can be measured along the equator or any parallel of latitude. Since a full circle is 360°, longitude increases east or west of the prime meridian from 0° at the prime meridian to 180°. The 180° meridian is the continuation of the prime meridian on the other side of Earth. This meridian somewhat follows the International Date Line.

In writing a location's longitude, be sure to include a west or east direction (80° W longitude; 70° E longitude) except for 0° longitude—the prime meridian—and the 180° meridian. Increasing longitude means going away from the prime meridian or towards the 180° meridian. Decreasing longitude means moving towards the prime meridian or away from the 180° meridian.

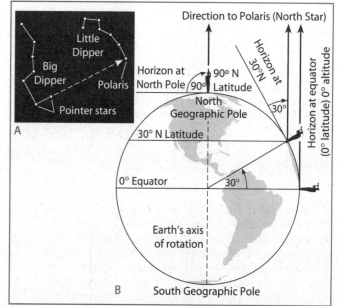

Figure 2-5. Altitude of Polaris equals latitude in the Northern Hemisphere: Diagram A shows the method used to find Polaris, or the North Star, in the night sky. Generally, face north and find the Big Dipper. The Big Dipper is a bright group of stars that is part of the constellation Ursa Major, or Big Bear. Following the pointer stars, move your eye five times the distance that separates the pointer stars. You should easily locate Polaris. The direction toward Polaris is true, or geographic north. The direction toward Polaris is the same for all locations on Earth because Polaris is trillions of miles away. Diagram B shows that the angular altitude of Polaris in the sky equals an observer's latitude in the Northern Hemisphere.

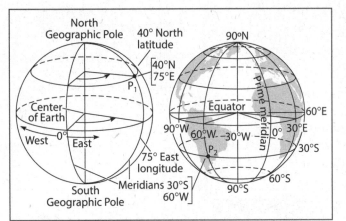

Figure 2-6. The meaning of longitude: Longitude is the angular distance east or west of the prime meridian, which is the meridian passing through Greenwich, England. Latitude and longitude together provide a system of coordinates for locating any point on Earth. The coordinates of point P₁ are 40° N latitude and 75° E longitude. Those for point P₂ are 30° S latitude and 60° W longitude.

Digging Deeper

Find point A on Figure 2-3, and write down the latitude and longitude as accurately as you can. Since this location is right at the intersection of a parallel and meridian, you can be quite accurate. The coordinates for point A are 15° N, 15° W, which is read as "latitude 15 degrees north and longitude 15 degrees west." Try location B. The coordinates are 15° S, 15° E. Location C is 45° S, 135° W. Rio de Janeiro is approximately 23° S, 43° W. Moscow is approximately 56° N, 37° E. Try determining the coordinates of some other locations on Figure 2-3, and check your answers in a world atlas. You can also practice placing locations on a map (such as Figure 2-3) when you know the coordinates. For example, plot 39° N, 77° W on a map. You should be at Washington, D.C. Plot 34° S, 151° E. You should be at Sydney, Australia.

Measuring Longitude

Local noon (12:00) at any point on Earth occurs when a line from the sun to the center of Earth cuts the meridian of that point. At that moment, the sun reaches its highest altitude of the day in the sky. Therefore, the instant of local noon can be determined by observing the sun. Since Earth rotates from west to east at the rate of one rotation per day—360° in 24 hours—it rotates 15° per hour. Therefore, the occurrence of local noon moves from east to west at the same rate of 15° per hour. Longitude can be calculated if, when local noon occurs, the observer knows what time it is at Greenwich, England—or any other location on the prime meridian. For example, if local noon occurs at 1:00 p.m. Greenwich Mean Time (GMT), one hour has passed since the sun crossed the prime meridian; the local longitude is therefore 15° W. Greenwich Mean Time is also called Universal Time. In general, longitude can be calculated by finding the time difference in hours between local sun time and Greenwich Mean Time, and multiplying by 15°. If local time is earlier than Greenwich Mean Time, the longitude is west; if later, it is east.

Using Latitude and Longitude

To read or plot a location on an Earth model such as a map or globe, you need to locate the coordinates for both latitude and longitude and to be able to locate and read the values of the parallels and meridians. Use Figure 2-3 as a typical map with north at the top. The parallels run east and west (right and left). The meridians run north and south (up and down). The values for latitude are at the ends of the parallels on the left and right sides of the map. The values for longitude are at the ends of meridians at the top and bottom of the map. The accuracy of a reading or a plotting of coordinates partly depends upon the size of the map and the spacing of the meridians and parallels.

Review Questions

18. Polaris is used as a celestial reference point for Earth's latitude system because Polaris

    (1) always rises at sunset and sets at sunrise
    (2) is located over Earth's axis of rotation
    (3) can be seen from any place on Earth
    (4) is a very bright star

19. An airplane takes off from a location at 17°S latitude and flies to a new location 55° due north of its starting point. What latitude has the airplane reached?

    (1) 28° N   (2) 38° N   (3) 55° N   (4) 72° N

20. What happens to the altitude of Polaris as you travel northward?

Refer to the following diagrams to answer questions 21 and 22. These diagrams illustrate systems that can be used to determine position on a sphere.

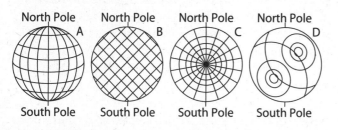

21. Systems of lines such as those illustrated above are called

(1) latitude systems
(2) coordinate systems
(3) great circle systems
(4) axis systems

22. Which of the illustrated systems is most like the latitude-longitude system used on Earth?

(1) A   (2) B   (3) C   (4) D

23. How are latitude and longitude lines drawn on a globe of Earth?

(1) Latitude lines are parallel and longitude lines meet at the poles.
(2) Latitude lines are parallel and longitude lines meet at the equator.
(3) Longitude lines are parallel and latitude lines meet at the poles.
(4) Longitude lines are parallel and latitude lines meet at the equator.

24. In the following diagram, what is the latitude of the observer?

(1) 30° N   (2) 60° N   (3) 90° N   (4) 120° N

25. What is the location of Binghamton, New York?

(1) 42°06′ N, 75°55′ W
(2) 42°06′ S, 76°05′ W
(3) 42°54′ N, 76°05′ W
(4) 42°54′ N, 75°55′ W

26. Which diagram best shows the altitude of Polaris observed near Buffalo, New York?

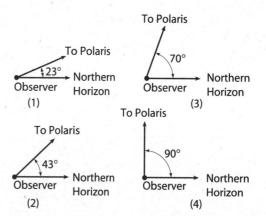

27. Which reference line passes through both the geographic North Pole and the geographic South Pole?

(1) 0° latitude
(2) 0° longitude
(3) Tropic of Cancer (23 $\frac{1}{2}$° S)
(4) Tropic of Capricorn (23 $\frac{1}{2}$° N)

28. The following diagram represents a portion of Earth's latitude and longitude system. What are the approximate latitude and longitude of point A?

(1) 15° S 20° W   (3) 15° N 20° W
(2) 15° S 20° E   (4) 15° N 20° E

29. A person knows the sun time on the prime meridian and the local sun time. What determination can be made?

(1) the date
(2) the altitude of Polaris
(3) the longitude at which the person is located
(4) the latitude at which the person is located

30. Which New York landscape region includes the location 43°30′ N, 75°45′ W?

(1) Adirondack Mountains
(2) Erie-Ontario Lowlands
(3) St. Lawrence Lowlands
(4) Tug Hill Plateau

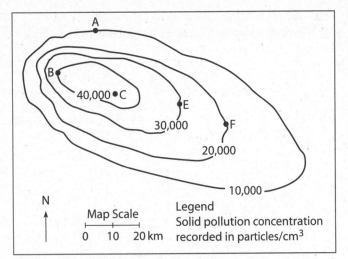

Figure 2-7. Sample field map of solid air pollutants: The data values were measured just above Earth's surface of an area around a coal-fired, electric-generating plant.

Fields

Any region of space or the environment that has some measurable value of a given quantity at every point is a **field**. Thus any aspect of matter or energy that can be measured is a type of field. Examples of field quantities are magnitudes of gravity or magnetism, temperature values, X-ray concentration, sound levels, elevation or depth, atmospheric pressure, wind speeds, acidity of the oceans, and relative humidity.

Isolines

The varying values of a field are often represented on maps by the use of lines that connect points of equal field values—**isolines**. Figure 2-7 is a sample isoline map that has isolines for equal values of the amount of solid pollutants (aerosols) in the air for a portion of Earth's surface. By reading these values of air pollutants, the source of the air pollution could be inferred to be located around area B-C on the map.

Some common examples of isolines are isotherms—which connect points of equal temperature, isobars—which connect points of equal air pressure, and **contour lines**—which connect points of equal elevation.

Gradients and Changes in Fields

Since the environment is constantly changing, field characteristics change with time. This means that any model of a field, such as a weather map, shows the field for only one particular time. The rate of change from place to place within the field is called the **gradient,** or slope.

The gradient can be calculated in two ways. Gradients can be estimated by observing the closeness of the isolines. The closer together the isolines are on a field map, the greater the gradient. On Figure 2-7, you can see that the gradient is large between A and B because the isolines are relatively close. On the other hand, the gradient is small between E and F because the isolines are not as close together for the same amount of horizontal distance as from A to B.

The second method of determining gradient is to calculate it using the following formula:

$$\text{gradient} = \frac{\text{change in (amount of) field value}}{\text{change in distance (horizontal distance)}}$$

A similar formula is found in the formula section of the *Earth Science* ®
Reference Tables. For example, if a weather map shows a change in temperature of 12°C between two locations that are 3 kilometers apart, the gradient between the two locations is 4°C per kilometer (12°C divided by 3 km).

31. The following isoline map shows the variations in the relative strength of Earth's magnetic field from 1 (strong) to 11 (weak).

Which of Earth's plates has the weakest magnetic field strength?

(1) South American plate
(2) African plate
(3) North American plate
(4) Pacific plate

32. As gradient increases, what happens to the distance between isolines?

33. The following four temperature field maps represent the same region on four different occasions. All maps have been drawn to the same scale. Which map shows the greatest temperature field gradient?

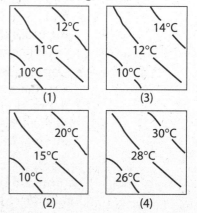

34. One thermometer that is held 2 meters above the floor shows a temperature of 30°C. A thermometer on the floor shows a temperature of 24°C. What is the temperature gradient between the two thermometers?

(1) 6°C/m   (2) 2°C/m   (3) 3°C/m   (4) 4°C/m

Mapping Earth's Surface

A map is a model that usually represents a portion or all of Earth's surface on a two-dimensional, or flat, surface. Maps can also model other objects or parts of Earth and the universe.

Topographic Maps

A **topographic map,** or contour map, is a commonly used model of the elevation field of the surface of Earth. The vertical distance or height above or below sea level is **elevation.** What distinguishes topographic maps from other maps is that they use contour lines to model the elevations and shapes of Earth's surface features or landforms. The contour lines are isolines that connect points of equal elevation above—and rarely, below— sea level.

There are many uses for topographic maps including: an aid in hiking or fishing, construction site selection, finding natural resources such as fresh water and trees, and planning highway locations. Topographic maps can also help you find escape routes when natural disasters are predicted.

Reading Contour Lines The difference in elevation between consecutive and different-in-value contour lines is the contour interval. The contour interval is usually listed in the key or legend. If the contour interval is not listed, subtract the difference in the value of two nearby contour lines and divide that number by the number of spaces between the known contour lines. In reading contour lines, pay attention to the following points.

- When contour lines cross a stream, they bend upward toward higher elevations. Contour lines "point" upstream. (See Figure 2-8.)
- When there is a series of consecutively smaller and smaller contour lines, it means that elevation is increasing toward the top of a hill or mountain. (See Paul Hill on Figure 2-8.)
- On most topographic maps, every fourth or fifth contour line—an index contour—is thicker and bolder, and the elevation is shown on that line.
- Often maps show the location of benchmarks with the symbols BM X and an elevation value. The X marks the spot where a metal marker is in the ground labeled with an exact elevation for a location. Figure 2-8 has two benchmarks.
- Depression contour lines are marked with small lines pointing toward the center of a depression. When going uphill on a map, the first depression contour line has the same value as the last regular contour line. Each smaller and smaller depression contour line is one contour interval less than the previous line.

Symbols on Topographic Maps Various types of symbols are used to identify natural and human-made features on topographic maps. There are hundreds of graphic symbols like those shown in the key for Figure 2-8. Most government maps use colors: brown for contour lines to show landform features; red and black for human constructions such as boundaries, roads, and structures; blue for water features; green for woods or areas with trees; and purple where the map has been revised using aerial photographs.

Horizontal Distance on Maps

Contour intervals and contour lines are used to show elevations and depressions. The map scale is used to show distances along Earth's surface. A map scale is a ratio of distance between two places on a map and the actual distance on Earth's surface. Map scales can be expressed in three ways:

- verbally, such as "one inch equals a mile"
- fractionally, such as 1/500,000 or 1:500,000—which means any one unit of distance on the map equals 500,000 of the same units on Earth's surface
- graphically, as shown just below the bottom of the map in Figure 2-8 (This scale is most common.)

To measure the horizontal distance between two places, use a piece of paper with a straight edge. Place this paper on the map, and make a mark on the paper extending it onto the map to mark the beginning location. If it is just a straight-line distance you are trying to measure, then place another mark to match the ending distance on the map. Match up the marks on the piece of paper with the map scale, and read the distance between the two marks. For example, on Figure 2-8, measure the part of Route 84 from the west (left) edge of the map to the eastern (right) edge of the Newburgh River. The answer is 3 miles.

If the horizontal distance to be measured is a curved line, start by putting the straight edge of a piece of paper at the beginning location. Then draw a line on the paper extending it onto the map to mark the beginning spot. Repeat this each time you come to a significant bend on the map. Keep twisting the piece of paper and drawing lines until you come to the end of

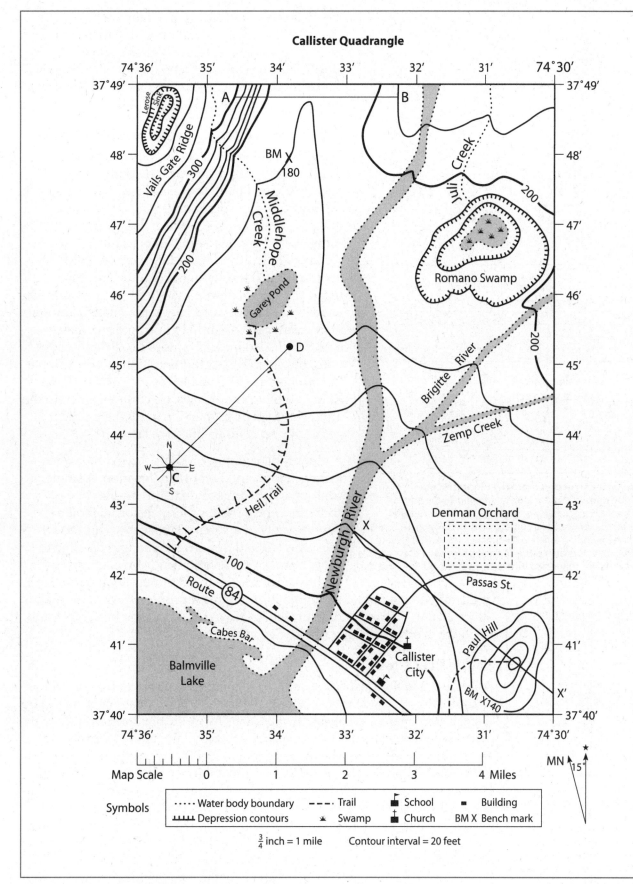

Figure 2-8. A sample topographic (contour) map

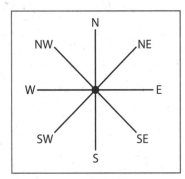

Figure 2-9. Constructing a profile along the line X-X' on the contour map of figure 2-8: In drawing A, the edge of a strip of paper is placed along the line, and a mark is made wherever the paper crosses a contour line. The marks are labeled with the corresponding altitude. The marks are then projected upward to locate dots on a piece of lined paper as in drawing B. Finally the dots are connected with a smooth curved line, and the profile is complete.

Figure 2-10. A sample compass rose: Compass roses are used to determine directions on maps and in many cases give geographic directions and not magnetic, or compass directions—which are usually different. Directions are often determined to the accuracy of the eight cardinal directions shown here.

the distance to be measured. Compare the total length of the marks on the piece of paper with the map scale and measure the distance. On Figure 2-8, Heil Trail from Route 84 to Garey Pond shows the marks made to measure its distance. The length of the Heil Trail is approximately 4 miles.

Topographic Map Gradient and Profile

Gradient, or slope, on topographic maps seems unusual because you are dealing with two distances. The field value is a vertical distance, or elevation, and the other value is the horizontal distance along Earth's surface. For practice, compute the gradient—in feet per mile—of the Newburgh River in Figure 2-8 from the 180-foot contour line to the 100-foot contour line. Your result should be approximately 21 feet per mile. On any map of the elevation field, the relative amount of gradient can be estimated using the distance between the isolines. The more closely spaced the lines, the steeper the gradient. In the map example, the gradient is steep just to the east of Vails Gate Ridge, so the contour lines are close together. In the area around the Denman Orchard, the gradient is gentle, so the contour lines are far apart.

A topographic map represents three dimensions— length, width, and height, or elevation. A single contour is two-dimensional, but a series of contours shows the third dimension. A **profile** is the side view of an area's landscape. This model uses upward and downward changes of a line to show changes in elevation and slope. Drawing a profile can show the three-dimensional nature and the gradient of a field. The method for making a profile of a contour map is illustrated in Figure 2-9. The profile is drawn for the region between X and X′ in the southeast corner of the map in Figure 2-8.

Map Direction

Maps are usually constructed so that the top of the map is north, the bottom is south, the right side is east, and the left side is west. Most maps, including topographic maps, usually show directions by indicating geographic north with some type of arrow. Geographic north is the direction to Earth's geographic North Pole. The map in Figure 2-8 indicates geographic north by ★. An MN on the map indicates the direction of magnetic north. Often, instead of a north arrow, a map will have a compass rose, such as the one in Figure 2-10. To find the direction from one location to another, draw a simple compass rose on the location from which you are determining the direction. Then draw a straight line to the other location. The straight line crosses the compass rose at the correct direction. This method is illustrated in Figure 2-8 from point C to point D where the compass direction of D from C is northeast. Compass directions are usually given to the nearest of the eight cardinal directions shown on the compass rose in Figure 2-10.

Base your answers to questions 35 through 44 on the map in Figure 2-8.

35. What is the maximum altitude of Denman Orchard?

(1) 140 feet   (3) 159 feet
(2) 150 feet   (4) 161 feet

36. What is the longitude of the middle of Romano Swamp?

(1) 37°47′ North   (3) 74°31′ North
(2) 37°47′ West   (4) 74°31′ West

37. What is the distance from Passas Street at the margin of the map to where it meets Route 84?

(1) $2\frac{1}{2}$ miles   (3) $3\frac{1}{2}$ miles
(2) 3 miles   (4) 4 miles

38. What is the gradient of the Brigitte River from the 200-foot contour line to the contour line before the Brigitte River meets the Newburgh River?

(1) 5 to 10 feet/mile   (3) 25 to 30 feet/mile
(2) 15 to 20 feet/mile   (4) 35 to 40 feet/mile

39. What is the latitude of the church?

(1) 74°32′ North   (3) 37°41′ West
(2) 74°32′ West   (4) 37°41′ North

40. Where is the steepest slope located on the map?

41. The biggest area of gentle slopes is found in the vicinity of

(1) Garey Pond   (3) Paul Hill
(2) Denman Orchard   (4) Zemp Creek

42. Which direction is Vails Gate Ridge from Callister City?

(1) north   (3) northeast
(2) northwest   (4) west

43. Toward what direction is the Brigitte River flowing?

(1) south   (3) north
(2) southwest   (4) northeast

44. Which of the following profiles represents the shape of the landscape between A and B on the map?

45. On the following topographic map, what is the most likely elevation of point A?

(1) 1250 m
(2) 1650 m
(3) 1750 m
(4) 1850 m

46. What is the approximate straight-line distance from Mt. Marcy in the Adirondacks to Slide Mountain in the Catskills?

(1) 120 km
(2) 150 km
(3) 205 km
(4) 235 km

Base your answers to questions 47 and 48 on the following diagram, which represents a topographic map of a hill.

Contour interval=10 meters

47. On which side of the hill does the land have the steepest slope?

(1) east
(2) south
(3) northeast
(4) northwest

48. What is the approximate gradient of the hill between points X and Y?

(1) 1 m/km
(2) 10 m/km
(3) 3 m/km
(4) m/km

Directions

Review the Test-Taking Strategies section of this book. Then answer the following questions. Read each question carefully and answer with a correct choice or response.

Part A

1 The latitude of an observer on Earth's surface can be determined by measuring the altitude of Polaris because Earth has a
(1) nearly spherical shape
(2) nearly circular orbit around the sun
(3) variable length of day
(4) fairly constant period of revolution

2 Which line best identifies the interface of the lithosphere and the troposphere?

(Not to scale.)

(1) A   (2) B   (3) C   (4) D

3 The following data table shows the altitude of Polaris as recorded by four observers at different locations on Earth.

Observer	Altitude of Polaris
A	90°
B	30°
C	30°
D	20°

Which statement is best supported by the information in the table?
(1) Observer A was at the equator.
(2) Observers A and B measured the altitude during daytime hours.
(3) Observers B and C measured the altitude at the same latitude.
(4) Observers B, C, and D were in the Southern Hemisphere.

4 Which latitude and longitude coordinates represent a location on the continent of Australia?
(1) 20° N, 135° E   (3) 20° S, 135° E
(2) 20° N, 135° W   (4) 20° S, 135° W

5 Which statement is true about an isoline on an air temperature field map?
(1) It represents an interface of high and low barometric pressures.
(2) It indicates the direction of maximum insolation.
(3) It increases in magnitude as it bends southward.
(4) It connects points of equal air temperature.

6 Which of the following items is a model?
(1) a globe   (3) a hand lens
(2) a ruler   (4) a mineral specimen

7 The following map represents an elevation field.

Which graph best represents the elevation profile along a straight line from point A to point B?

Base your answers to questions 8 through 12 on the following topographic map of an island. Points A through G represent locations on the island. Elevations are in meters.

Atlantic Ocean

0 1 2 3 4 5 km

8 Which point is located on the steepest slope?
(1) F   (2) B   (3) C   (4) D

9 In which direction does the Cinder River flow?
(1) southeast   (3) northeast
(2) southwest   (4) northwest

10 What is the contour interval for this map?
(1) 10 m   (2) 15 m   (3) 20 m   (4) 25 m

11 Which two points have the same elevation?
(1) G and F   (3) C and D
(2) B and D   (4) G and C

12 Which diagram best represents the topographic profile between location C and location B?

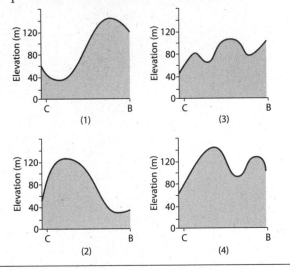

13 A movement of volcanic ash occurred at an altitude of 1.5 kilometers. In which layer of Earth's atmosphere did the ash cloud travel?
(1) troposphere   (3) mesosphere
(2) stratosphere   (4) thermosphere

14 What is the distance in degrees east or west of the prime meridian called?
(1) longitude   (3) equator
(2) latitude   (4) altitude

15 The following diagram represents contour lines on a topographic map with cross-section line AB.

Which diagram best represents the topographic profile along line AB?

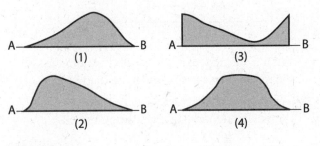

Part B

The following topographic map shows a portion of an area of inactive volcanoes in the United States. The contour interval is 20 feet. Base your answers to questions 16 through 20 on this diagram.
REMEMBER: State directions or units of measure when appropriate.

16 What is the latitude of point E to the nearest minute? [2]

17 What is the longitude of point E to the nearest minute? [2]

18 In which direction does Johnson River generally flow? [1]

19 What is the elevation of point H on the rim of the crater of Mt. Hall in feet? [1]

20 What is the distance along Lobeck River from point A to point B to the nearest quarter-mile? [1]

---

21 The following is a topographic map.

What is the approximate length in kilometers of the railroad tracks shown on the map? [1]

22 The following diagram shows a three-dimensional model of a landscape region.

Which map view best represents the topography of this region? [1]

Base your answers to questions 23 through 26 on the following topographic map of Cottonwood, Colorado. Points A, B, X, and Y are marked for reference.

Cottonwood, Colorado

Distance scale (km)
Contour interval 20 meters

23 State the general direction in which Cottonwood Creek flows. [1]

24 State the highest possible elevation, to the nearest meter, for point B on the topographic map. [1]

25 On the following grid, draw a profile of the topography along line AB shown on the map. [2]

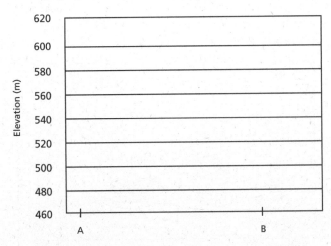

26 Use the following directions to calculate the gradient of the slope between points X and Y on the topographic map.
 (a) Write the equation for gradient. [1]
 (b) Substitute data from the map into the equation. [1]
 (c) Calculate the gradient and label it with the proper units. [1]

Base your answers to questions 27 and 28 on the topographic maps and block diagrams of two landscape regions shown below. The block diagrams show a three-dimensional view of the topographic maps directly above them. Elevations are measured in feet. Points A, B, C, and D are locations on Earth's surface.

Landscape 1   Landscape 2

27 Which contour interval is used on both topographic maps?
 (1) 10 ft
 (2) 20 ft
 (3) 30 ft
 (4) 40 ft

28 A stream begins to flow downhill from point D toward the depression. After a period of time, the depression fills with water. Overflowing water from the depression moves downhill toward point C. Which topographic map shows the most likely resulting change in the contour lines?

Base your answers to questions 29 through 32 on the weather map provided below which shows partial weather station data for several cities in eastern North America.

29 On the weather map provided, draw isotherms every 10°F, starting with 40°F and ending with 70°F. Isotherms must extend to the edges of the map. [2]

30 Calculate the temperature gradient between Richmond, Virginia, and Hatteras, North Carolina, by following the directions below.

(a) Write the equation for gradient.
(b) Substitute data from the map into the equation. [1]
(c) Calculate the average gradient and label your answer with the correct units. [1]

31 In which city is the temperature gradient the smallest?
(1) Cincinnati   (3) Richmond
(2) New Orleans   (4) Detroit

32 State the general relationship between air temperature and latitude for locations shown on the map. [1]

Part C

The planet in the following paragraph is fictional. Use the information in the paragraph and your knowledge of earth science to answer questions 33 through 38.

Glick is a planet in a solar system very similar to our own. Planet Glick is very similar to Earth except for the following differences. Glick's axis of rotation has no tilt. It rotates from east to west, approximately twice as fast as Earth. Zelda is a star that is visible directly over Glick's South Pole and Glotch is a star visible directly over Glick's North Pole. A latitude-longitude system such as that on Earth has been established for Glick.

33 Why would a plastic relief replica of a continent on Glick be considered a model? [1]

34 If planet Glick has a hydrosphere, what two chemical elements is it primarily composed of? [1]

35 In relationship to Glick's atmosphere and lithosphere, what would be the relative location of its hydrosphere? [1]

36 Where would a majority of Glick's most dense substances be located in the planet? [1]

37 At a certain location on Glick, the star Zelda is observed at 37° above the horizon. From this information, what conclusion can you draw about the latitude and longitude of this location? [2]

38 If you traveled due west in the northern hemisphere of Glick at night, what changes might you observe in the altitude of the star Glotch? [1]

Base your answers to questions 39 through 42 on the topographic map below. The map shows a location where a series of students went camping using mountain bicycles on July 1, 2003.

Key
▲ Campsite
---- Bike trail

0 1 2 3 miles
Contour interval: 20 feet
N

39 State the evidence shown on the map that indicates that the area directly north of Hidden Lake is relatively flat. [1]

40a State the general compass direction in which the stream is flowing. [1]

40b State how the contour lines provide the evidence for determining this direction. [1]

41 On July 2, 2003 the students decided to move their campsite 1 mile directly east of their original campsite that is located on the map above. On the map above place another campsite symbol to indicate the location of the July 2 campsite. [1]

42 The students decided to take a route home to avoid riding their bicycles up the steep hill. Plan a route that will take the campers back to point P from their July 2 campsite that will involve the least change in elevation. On the map above draw a line that shows this route. Place arrows on the route line to show the direction that the students will be traveling. [1]

Earth in the Universe

How Scientists Study Earth in the Universe

? *Do you think Earth's orbital shape and its variable distance from the sun is a major cause of Earth's seasons?*

If you said yes, you might be surprised! Consider this: The shape of Earth's orbit is much closer to a circle than an oval. Yet there are small changes in Earth's distance from the sun throughout the year. Earth is farthest from the sun around July 4 when it is summer in the northern hemisphere. This doesn't make sense if Earth's distance from the sun is the reason it is sweltering outside.

The whole sky is 180 degrees from one horizon to the sky top to the opposite horizon. Angular degrees (°) can be divided into 60 minutes (') and each minute divided into 60 seconds ("). Both the sun and the moon are about 0.5 degrees in apparent angular diameter, thus you could place about 360 suns or moons in the sky from horizon to horizon.

When the sun is closest to Earth around January 3, its apparent diameter is 0° 32' 35", and around July 4, the sun's apparent angular diameter is 0° 31' 31". The difference is 0° 01' 04", which is very small. Thus other factors must be the major cause of the seasons.

Earth in the Universe

Vocabulary

asteroid

Big Bang theory

celestial object

comet

Doppler effect

eccentricity

ellipse

focus (pl., foci)

galaxy

gravitation

impact crater

impact event

inertia

Jovian planet

luminosity (of a star)

meteor

Milky Way Galaxy

moon

nuclear fusion

red shift

revolution

rotation

solar system

star

terrestrial planet

universe

Topic Overview

Throughout the ages, humans have observed the celestial objects in the sky and wondered about them. From Earth, a **celestial object** is any object outside or above Earth's atmosphere. There are about 6000 celestial objects visible with the unaided eye from any location on Earth. Where do people fit? Are they alone? Are there other solar systems with an environment in which humans could live? This topic focuses on our solar system, our galaxy, and the universe. In recent years there has been much discussion of and evidence for dark matter and dark energy, which may compose a major portion of the universe and our home Milky Way Galaxy. Dark matter and dark energy are not presently a part of this course of study.

Origin and Age of the Universe

Over the thousands of years of human thinking, various cultures have produced a multitude of theories concerning the origin, evolution, and structure of the universe. **Universe** means everything that exists in any place—all the space, matter, and energy in existence. The majority of scientists today think that the universe is extremely vast, and that it is more than 10 billion years old—maybe as many as 13.7 billion years old.

Presently, the majority of scientists believe that the universe began with an event called the Big Bang and has been expanding in volume ever since. The **Big Bang theory** states that all matter and energy started out concentrated in a small area and, after a gigantic explosion, matter began to organize into subatomic particles and atoms. Most, if not all, of the earliest atoms were hydrogen and helium. Within a few hundred million to a billion years, atoms became organized into celestial bodies, and then most stars became part of gravitational groupings. As this organization of

Digging Deeper

To help you understand the Doppler effect, compare the Doppler effect of electromagnetic energy with that of sound waves. If you are standing on a street corner and a fire truck is coming towards you with the siren constantly blaring, the sound waves are bunched together as the truck gets closer to you. These shorter wavelengths are observed as a higher pitch or sound to your ears. After the truck passes, with the siren still blaring, the sound waves are stretched out (like the red shift). The sound has a lower pitch and sounds softer or muted.

matter was occurring, the universe kept expanding in all directions, and continues to expand at present.

Evidence for the Big Bang

Scientists have theorized that if a Big Bang did occur, the energy created by the explosion expanded along with the matter. Thus, there should be radiation from the Big Bang in all parts of the universe mixed with the energy given off by stars at later times. Recently, scientists have found evidence of long-wavelength microwave background radiation that appear to be coming from all directions in the universe. This cosmic background radiation is evidence supporting the Big Bang theory.

Other evidence of the Big Bang is found in the spectrum of the radiation emitted by stars. Look over the Electromagnetic Spectrum in the *Earth Science Reference Tables*. The various types of waves that transmit energy through space are called electromagnetic energy. Each element emits energy in specific portions—wavelengths—within the electromagnetic spectrum. Because the human eye observes different wavelengths of visible light as different colors, people can distinguish specific portions of the electromagnetic spectrum. When scientists study the spectrum of electromagnetic energy coming from stars and other celestial objects, they can infer which elements are in these objects. Scientists base these inferences on the comparison of the signature wavelengths produced by elements on Earth with those coming from the other celestial objects.

Scientists have found that the position of the characteristic wavelengths, or colored lines, are shifted to either the shorter (blue end) or longer (red end) wavelengths. This shifting of wavelengths is called the **Doppler effect**. The relative movement between Earth and the other celestial object causes the Doppler effect. If Earth and another celestial object are coming closer together, the electromagnetic waves are bunched together, resulting in a blue shift Doppler effect. If Earth and some other celestial object are moving apart, the electromagnetic waves are spread out causing a **red shift** Doppler effect.

The collective light from the stars in all galaxies, except for a few galaxies close to Earth, is shifted to the red end of the spectrum. The fact that almost all galaxies have a red shift indicates that the universe is expanding in all

Figure 3–1. Big Bang and expanding universe: (A) Approximately 13.7 billion years ago, all mass and energy was concentrated in a small area that started expanding with a big explosion called the Big Bang. **(B)** The expanding, cooling universe first formed subatomic particles and finally small atoms of hydrogen and helium. **(C)** After approximately a few hundred million to a billion years, matter clumped together forming stars and early galaxies, and the universe kept expanding.

Figure 3-2. Doppler effect blue and red shifts: Galaxy B is not moving towards or away from Earth. The spectral lines of one element are the same as they would be if they were produced on Earth. Galaxy A is moving towards Earth—bunching up the light rays and shifting the spectral lines of the element to the blue end of the spectrum. Galaxy C is moving away from Earth—as most galaxies are—spreading out the light waves and shifting the spectral lines of the element to the red end—red shift.

directions. This evidence further supports the Big Bang theory and the expansion from the initial explosion. In addition, the farther away a galaxy is from Earth, the greater the red shift. This fact indicates that the rate of expansion of the universe is increasing.

Review Questions

1. From your location, what is the best definition of a celestial object?
   (1) any object in the universe
   (2) any object in the universe above Earth's atmosphere
   (3) any object in the universe outside our solar system
   (4) any object in the universe outside our home galaxy

2. The age of the universe is measured in 10 to 20
   (1) thousands of years
   (2) millions of years
   (3) billions of years
   (4) trillions of years

3. Studies of the universe generally indicate that
   (1) almost all galaxies appear to be moving away from Earth at tremendous velocities
   (2) few galaxies other than our own exist
   (3) all galaxies are approximately the same size
   (4) all galaxies are spiral in shape

4. Background radiation detected in space is believed to be evidence that
   (1) the universe began with an explosion
   (2) the universe is contracting
   (3) all matter in the universe is stationary
   (4) galaxies are evenly spaced throughout the universe

5. Which statement best describes how most galaxies generally move?
   (1) Galaxies move toward one another.
   (2) Galaxies move away from one another.
   (3) Galaxies move randomly.
   (4) Galaxies do not move.

6. The following diagram represents a standard spectrum for an element.

Violet   Red

The spectral lines of this element are observed in light from a distant galaxy. Which diagram represents these spectral lines?

(1)
Violet   Red

(2)
Violet   Red

(3)
Violet   Red

(4)
Violet   Red

Structure of the Universe

In recent years instruments such as the Hubble space telescope have allowed scientists to infer some basic structure to the known universe.

Galaxies

The basic structural unit of matter in the universe appears to be the galaxy. A **galaxy** is a collection of billions of stars and various amounts of gas and dust held together by gravity. An average galaxy will have over 100 billion

Figure 3–3. The Milky Way Galaxy: This spiral-shaped galaxy of which Earth is a part measures approximately 100,000 light years at its greatest diameter. Each light year is about 6 trillion miles or 9.5 trillion kilometers. The halo region is made up of clusters of stars that are billions of years older than our sun. The sun indicates our solar system's location near a spiral arm.

stars, and there are over 100 billion galaxies. Galaxies have been classified into a few types largely based on shape, including elliptical (football shaped), irregular, and spiral. Our solar system is a part of a spiral-shaped galaxy called the **Milky Way Galaxy,** which has over 200 billion stars. Figure 3-3 illustrates the spiral shape of the Milky Way Galaxy. It also shows the position of our solar system between two spiral arms about two-thirds of the distance out from the galactic center.

Stars

Along with dust and gas clouds, stars make up the majority of the visible matter in a galaxy. A **star** is usually a large ball of gas held together by gravity that produces tremendous amounts of energy and shines. There are many exceptions to this definition—some very old stars are the size of planets or moons, and some stars no longer emit much radiation. The star called the sun is the dominant gravitational force associated with Earth and the rest of our solar system.

Energy Production in Stars Most of the tremendous amounts of energy produced by most stars is the result of nuclear fusion in their cores. **Nuclear fusion** is the combining of the nuclei of smaller elements to form the nuclei of larger elements with some of the mass being converted into energy. As an example, the sun converts hydrogen nuclei into helium nuclei with about 0.07 percent of the mass forming energy. There are many other types of nuclear fusion that occur in stars of different ages or sizes than the sun. Nuclear fusion can only occur in extremely high temperature and high pressure conditions like those found in star interiors. The energy of nuclear fusion in most stars is eventually radiated into space as types of electromagnetic energy.

The Characteristics of Stars Diagram The classification scheme of grouping stars by surface temperature compared to their luminosity is shown in the Characteristics of Stars diagram in the *Earth Science Reference Tables.* **Ⓡ** **Luminosity** is the actual brightness of a star or rate of total energy emitted compared to the Sun. It is measured as absolute magnitude, which is a star's brightness at a standard distance. What we directly observe when we look at stars is the apparent brightness, which is dependent upon the star's absolute luminosity and its distance away from us.

An analysis of a Characteristics of Stars diagram indicates that star properties are not random. Of the hundreds of thousands of stars plotted on the diagram, stars appear to be grouped by differences in luminosity and surface temperature as reflected by color. Just as the filament in a light bulb or the coil in an electric heater changes color with increasing temperatures, stars change color from red to blue as their surface temperatures increase.

Star Types Figure 3-4 illustrates the relative size differences in some of the star groups. The diameter of the sun—a medium-sized star—is 109 times the diameter of Earth. Most stars are much bigger than Earth, but some—such as neutron stars, black holes, and some dwarfs—are smaller than Earth. These smaller stars are actually shown too big in this diagram compared to the sun. Giant stars are 10 to 100 times the diameter of the sun, and super giants are 100 to 1000 times the diameter of the sun. Some of the star types commonly identified on a Characteristics of Stars diagram are described here.

Main Sequence Stars About 90 percent of studied stars are located on the Characteristics of Stars diagram in a broad band called the main sequence. Most stars spend the majority of their life span as a main sequence star. Most of these stars are average size, and as the surface temperatures of the stars increase, the luminosity increases. The luminosity increase from red to blue-white is mostly related to an increase in star size and the resulting higher temperatures. Our sun is a main sequence star of yellow color. The smallest and coolest stars of the main sequence are the very common type of star—the red dwarfs.

Giant Stars Red, orange, and yellow giant stars are a rare type of star but are commonly seen in the night sky because of their large size—10 times or more the diameter of the sun—and their high luminosity. These low-temperature stars represent a late stage in the evolution of medium to small-size main sequence stars—when they greatly expand in size.

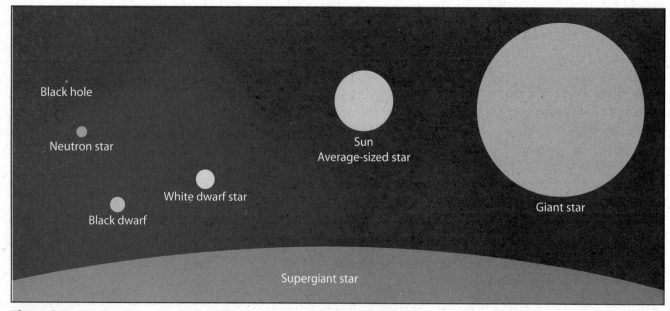

Figure 3-4. Relative sizes of stars: The smaller stars are not drawn to scale.

Super Giants Super giant stars can be anywhere from 100 to 1000 times the diameter of the sun. (See Figure 3-4.) These highly luminous stars represent the late evolution of stars much more massive than the sun. Super giants usually explode in a tremendous event called a supernova. The super giant stars that are the brightest and exhibit the highest temperature are the blue super giants.

White Dwarfs Not all white dwarf stars are white, but they are all small—around the size of Earth. They are hot on the surface and low in luminosity. They represent the last luminous or shining stage of low- to medium-mass stars.

Black Dwarfs When a white dwarf cools and no longer emits much electromagnetic energy, it is a "dead" star—a black dwarf. Black dwarfs are probably very common in the universe because in the many billion years of the existence of white dwarf stars, many trillions of them have stopped nuclear fusion and no longer produce nuclear energy.

Star Origin and Evolution Stars, like many objects on Earth, have an origin, an evolution of features, and an ending. Figure 3-5 models star evolution as partly shown in the Characteristics of Stars chart in the *Earth Science Reference Tables*. It is believed that stars originate from clouds of gas and dust molecules. These clouds were created from the masses that evolved from the original Big Bang and/or from the mass given off by stars that have expanded, exploded, or otherwise given off mass to space. Gravity causes these gas and dust clouds to clump up, forming larger and larger balls of gas and dust molecules. When the mass of these spherical balls becomes slightly larger than the planet Jupiter, the gravitational contraction results in high enough temperatures and pressure to start nuclear fusion. Then the ball begins to shine, or radiate large amounts of electromagnetic energy, and a star is born.

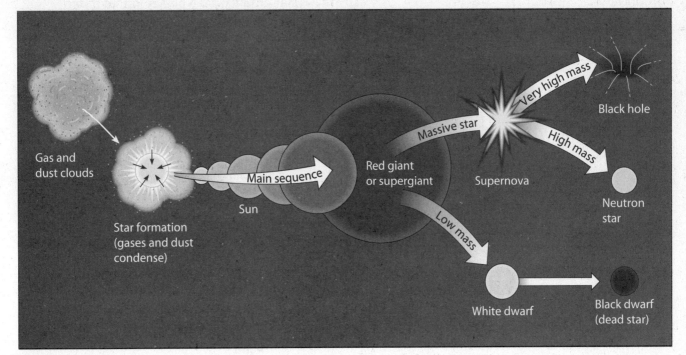

Figure 3-5. Model of star origin and evolution: The original mass of a star largely determines its evolutionary stages and how long it lasts.

The evolutionary stages of stars—after they spend most of their lives as a main sequence star—depends upon their original mass. Most stars with masses similar to the sun spend billions of years as a main sequence star and eventually expand to become a red giant. As the bottom part of Figure 3-5 shows, these stars use up most of their nuclear fuel and collapse to form a white dwarf, and then slowly "die" becoming a black dwarf. This process may take many billions of years, and some stars created soon after the Big Bang may still exist.

The evolution of stars with an original mass greater than one and a half times the mass of the sun is substantially different. These stars exist for much shorter periods of time—approximately 100,000,000 years. As the upper part of Figure 3-5 indicates, these massive stars evolve into super giants after spending time as a large main sequence star. They eventually explode in a supernova event and then rapidly collapse, forming a body much smaller than a white dwarf. They are so dense that only neutrons can exist, and a neutron star is formed. When even more massive stars collapse, the density is so great that it creates an extreme gravity field that allows no visible light or any other form of energy to escape, and a black hole is formed.

Review Questions

7. Billions of stars in the same region of the universe are called

(1) solar systems   (3) constellations
(2) asteroid belts   (4) galaxies

8. The following symbols represent the Milky Way Galaxy, the solar system, the sun, and the universe.

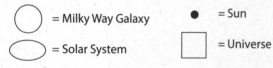

Which arrangement of symbols is most accurate?

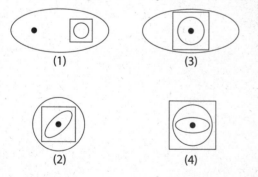

9. In which group are the parts listed in order from oldest to youngest?

(1) solar system, Milky Way Galaxy, universe
(2) Milky Way Galaxy, solar system, universe
(3) universe, solar system, Milky Way Galaxy
(4) universe, Milky Way Galaxy, solar system

10. The great system of 200 billion stars to which the sun and our solar system belong is the

(1) Andromeda Galaxy
(2) Large Magellanic Galaxy
(3) Milky Way Galaxy
(4) Orion Nebula Galaxy

11. A star differs from a planet in that a star

(1) has a fixed orbit
(2) is self-luminous
(3) revolves about the sun
(4) shines by reflected light

12. The sun's energy is most likely the result of the

(1) fusion of hydrogen atoms
(2) transformation of the sun's gravitational potential energy to heat energy
(3) burning fossil fuels
(4) radioactive decay of uranium and thorium atoms

13. Nuclear fusion can only occur in areas of

(1) high temperature and low pressure
(2) high temperature and high pressure
(3) low temperature and low pressure
(4) low temperature and high pressure

14. As star color changes from blue to red, the surface temperature of the star

(1) decreases
(2) increases
(3) remains the same

15. A luminosity and temperature of stars diagram classifies a star of high temperature and low luminosity as a

(1) giant
(3) supergiant
(2) main sequence star
(4) white dwarf

Base your answers to questions 16 through 23 on the Characteristics of Stars diagram in the *Earth Science Reference Tables*.

16. A main sequence star is 1000 times more luminous than the sun. The temperature is likely to be most nearly

(1) 3000 K
(3) 12,000 K
(2) 5000 K
(4) 25,000 K

17. A giant star has a luminosity of 300. Its color is most likely to be

(1) yellow-red
(3) white
(2) black
(4) blue-white

18. A white dwarf star has a temperature of 13,000 K. What is the probable luminosity of the star?

(1) 100   (2) 10   (3) 0.1   (4) 0.01

19. An orange star has a temperature of 4000 K and is 500,000 times as luminous as the sun. To which group does it belong?

(1) giants
(3) white dwarfs
(2) supergiants
(4) main sequence

20. The nearest star to the sun is Alpha Centauri. How does this star compare to the sun?

(1) It is much hotter.
(2) It has a different color.
(3) It has a higher luminosity.
(4) It is much smaller in diameter.

21. The sun is best described as a

(1) very large star
(3) red star
(2) medium-sized star
(4) cool star

22. The sun is brighter than any star in the group of

(1) supergiants
(3) main sequence stars
(2) giants
(4) white dwarfs

23. Which type of star is associated with the last stage in the evolutionary development of most stars?

(1) main sequence star
(3) giant
(2) supergiant
(4) white dwarf

Solar System

In the last few years, powerful telescopes on Earth and in space have found evidence of planets around more than 100 stars. This means that "solar system" really can refer to any star or group of two or three stars that has non-star objects orbiting it. However, in this book, the solar system is our **solar system**—the sun and all objects that orbit the sun under its gravitational influence.

Parts of the Solar System

Most of the solar system is space devoid of much mass. However, about 99 percent of the mass that does exist is contained in the sun. The sun is a medium-sized, main sequence star about 5 billion years old that is the gravitational center of our solar system. A satellite is any object that orbits or revolves around another object. The planets, asteroids, meteoroids, and comets are satellites of the sun, and the moons are satellites of planets or asteroids. Earth has one natural satellite—the moon—and more than 2,500 artificial ones.

Planets The eight planets are the largest objects that independently orbit the sun and don't share their environment with other large objects. Planets are generally spherical in shape. Recently, over 1000 planets—called exoplanets—have been found revolving around stars other than our sun.

Digging Deeper

In recent years astronomers have discovered two portions of our solar system beyond the orbit of Neptune. The Kuiper Belt is a region of the solar system that is generally in the plane of the planets beyond Neptune that includes Pluto and many other dwarf planets, some even larger than Pluto, moons, and comets. Many of the comets that come into the inner parts of the solar system are believed to originate in the Kuiper Belt. The Kuiper Belt is believed to extend out about 1000 times Earth's distance from the sun.

The Oort Cloud is a vast "cloud" or sphere of likely millions of comet-like bodies that surround the rest of the solar system, and may extend out from Neptune's orbit 50,000 to 100,000 times the distance of the Earth to the sun. It may even reach out to where the influence of the sun blends with that of other stars.

Figure 3-6. Composite images of 3 asteroids: These three images are at different scales. The three asteroids are all in the main asteroid belt located between the orbits of Mars and Jupiter. Ceres, the largest asteroid at the bottom, with an average diameter of about 940 km, has recently been classified as a dwarf planet due to its size and spherical shape. Vesta's average diameter is about 535 km, and is shown in the middle. Ida, the smallest at the top, has a more typical irregular asteroid shape and its largest "diameter" is about 56 km. Note the high density of impact craters on all three asteroids.

Figure 3-7. Comet near the sun: When the orbit of a comet brings it near the sun some of the solids are vaporized or are blown off the comet forming one or more tails.

Asteroids An **asteroid** is a solid rocky and/or metallic body that independently orbits the sun. Asteroids have an irregular shape, except for the larger ones which are spherical, and no atmosphere. (See Figure 3-6.) A large percentage of the thousands of known asteroids are in orbits between Mars and Jupiter. Asteroids are smaller than planets (from about 100 to 1000 kilometers in diameter) and are often called minor planets.

Moons A **moon** is a body that orbits a planet or an asteroid as those objects orbit the sun. There are approximately 175 known moons, which vary in size from larger than the smallest planets to only a few kilometers in diameter.

Comets A **comet** is often compared to a snowball made from snow found along a road that has just been sanded—a dirty snowball. Comets are mainly composed of solids that easily change to gases when heated. They are largely ices of substances such as water and methane mixed with rocky or metallic solids. Most comets are only 1 to 100 kilometers in diameter. When comets get near the sun, some of their ices turn to gases. Some solids are released, forming spectacular tails visible in Earth's sky, sometimes for weeks at a time. (See Figure 3-7.)

Meteoroids Very small solid fragments that orbit the sun are called meteoroids. Most meteoroids are only the size of a dime or sand grain. When meteoroids burn up or vaporize, they leave a brief visual streak as they pass through Earth's atmosphere and are called **meteors.** If a meteoroid survives its trip through Earth's atmosphere and lands on Earth's surface, it is then called a meteorite. Some meteorites have sufficient mass to create a depression in Earth's crust called an **impact crater.**

Evolution of the Solar System

Scientists infer that our solar system started to form approximately 5 billion years ago. At first there was a gas dust cloud many times the size of the present solar system. This cloud contained remnants of stars that had exploded, giving to the cloud heavier elements to mix with the more common lighter ones. Gravitation, perhaps aided by a shock wave from an exploding star, caused the cloud to condense into one or more mass concentrations. Look at Figure 3-8 and read the caption to see how these masses may have formed our solar system.

Even after Earth and other planets formed, their gravitational forces pulled on the smaller clumps of matter to cause comets, asteroids, and meteoroids to collide with the planets in what is called an **impact event.** The planets, asteroids, and moons with solid surfaces bear witness to these impact events in the form of craters. Impact events have also been linked to global climate changes and mass extinctions.

Meteorites still hit Earth, and there is concern that this type of natural disaster could destroy a large portion of the life on our planet. Presently, an intensive scientific search is being conducted to find comets, asteroids, and meteoroids that could collide with Earth and have enough mass to result in loss of life, injury, and loss of property.

Figure 3-8. Theory of our solar system's formation: At stage A, a shock wave started a gravitational contraction of a gas-dust cloud. At stage B, most of the matter was pulled to the center to form the sun, which started nuclear fusion. Clumping of gas and dust around the sun occurred at the same time. At stage C, larger and larger clumps formed still larger masses—forming planets, moons, and asteroids. Elements having a small mass were driven out of the inner solar system leaving the terrestrial planets with only small amounts of light elements. By stage D, the solar system was similar to what it is today.

The gravitational contraction of the planets, larger asteroids, and larger moons produced heat. This heat, along with the heat from radioactive decay and frictional heat from impacting meteorites, caused the newly formed planets, larger asteroids, and moons to largely melt. As a result, these bodies became layered into zones based on the density of their various elements and compounds.

Review Questions

24. Comets are considered to belong to the solar system if they

(1) glow by reflected light
(2) revolve about the sun
(3) have elliptical orbits
(4) have uniform periods of revolution

25. A person observes that a bright object streaks across the nighttime sky in a few seconds. What is this object most likely to be?

(1) a comet
(2) a meteor
(3) an explosion on the sun
(4) an orbiting satellite

26. A belt of asteroids is located an average distance of 503 million kilometers from the sun. Between which two planets is this belt located?

(1) Mars and Jupiter   (3) Jupiter and Saturn
(2) Mars and Earth   (4) Saturn and Uranus

27. Which is not included in our solar system?

(1) Polaris   (3) meteors
(2) the moon   (4) asteroids

28. In the last billion years when meteorites, asteroids, or comets collided with Earth, which has occurred?

(1) Craters have formed.
(2) The whole Earth's surface has melted.
(3) All life has been destroyed.
(4) The oceans have largely evaporated.

29. Today it is most commonly believed that our solar system formed

(1) by gravitational collapse of a gas-dust "cloud"
(2) from material exploded from the sun
(3) at the time of the Big Bang that formed the present universe
(4) by fusion of matter between the sun and a passing star

Planet Characteristics

A planet's distance from the sun has a major effect on its characteristics. ⓡ See the Solar System Data in the *Earth Science Reference Tables* to find each planet's distance from the sun and other significant features and events. When the planets were forming, the sun probably radiated more energy than it does today. The high temperatures and pressure from particles emitted by the sun drove the less dense elements and compounds away from the inner solar system. The outer parts of the solar system were not nearly so hot, and the particle pressure from the sun not nearly so great. These differences in the inner and outer solar system provide characteristics that allow the planets to be classified into the inner terrestrial planets and outer Jovian planets. The former planet Pluto, because of its small size and its composition similar to comets and other distant solar system members, doesn't fit either planet classification and is now called a "dwarf planet."

Terrestrial Planet Properties The **terrestrial planets** are close to the sun and mostly solid. They have relatively small diameters and high densities. Their rocky surfaces are dotted with impact craters. They have few or no moons and have no rings. Terrestrial planets are the planets similar to Earth and include Mercury, Venus, Earth, and Mars.

Jovian Planet Properties The **Jovian planets** are far from the sun and are largely gaseous. They have relatively large diameters and low densities. They have no solid surfaces (though they may have a solid core) and thus no craters. These planets have many moons and have rings. The Jovian planets are the planets similar to Jupiter and include Jupiter, Saturn, Uranus, and Neptune.

Motions of the Planets

The planets have many different motions. They move with the solar system around the Milky Way Galaxy in periods of about 225 million years.

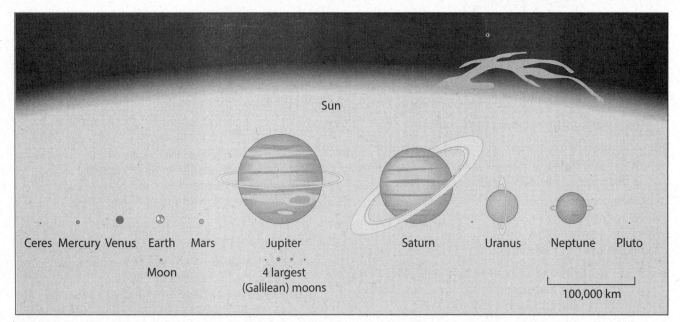

Figure 3-9. **Comparison of the size (diameters) of the planets and some other solar system members:** The diameter of Jupiter is about 10 times that of Earth, and the diameter of the sun is a little over 100 times that of Earth. The largest moon of Jupiter is larger than Mercury. The former planet Pluto and former largest asteroid Ceres are now called dwarf planets.

They rotate, or spin around an imaginary axis, and they revolve around the sun in an orbit, or path.

Planet Rotation Planets spin on an imaginary axis in a motion called **rotation.** The period of rotation is the amount of time it takes for a planet to make one spin around its imaginary axis and determines the length of a planet's day. Six of the eight planets rotate in the same direction as they revolve around the sun. You can tell that planets rotate through observations of surface features made at different times. The Solar System Ⓡ Data Table in the *Earth Science Reference Tables* lists the periods of rotation of the planets.

Memory **Jogger**

You may recall that the length of a day on Earth is not the same as the length of a day on other planets. Since each planet has a different period of rotation, the length of a day varies from planet to planet.

Planet Revolution A planet's **revolution** is its movement around the sun in a path called an orbit. The planets revolve around the Sun in a counterclockwise direction as viewed from Polaris. Earth's orbit (and those of the other planets) is an oval shape called an **ellipse.** Within the ellipse are two fixed points called **foci** (singular, **focus**). The sum of the distances between any point on the ellipse and the two foci is a constant; that is, the sum of those distances for one point is equal to the sum for any other point on the curve. The sun is at one of the foci of each planetary orbit in the solar system. (See Figure 3-10.) The major axis of an ellipse is the longest straight-line distance across an ellipse—the biggest diameter—and it cuts through the two foci.

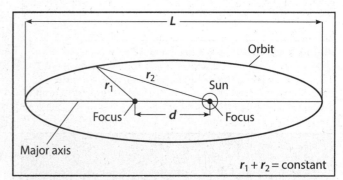

Figure 3-10. An elliptical orbit of a solar system member with the sun at one focus: Except for Mercury, the orbits of the planets would appear to look like a circle at this scale. The eccentricity of the ellipse is 0.26 (d = 2.0 cm and L = 7.7 cm; $\frac{2}{7.7}$ = 0.26).

Eccentricity of Planet Orbits The degree of flattening or "ovalness" of an ellipse is measured by its **eccentricity.** Eccentricity can also be described as the amount of difference between an ellipse as compared to a special type of ellipse called a circle. The formula to compute eccentricity is listed Ⓡ below and also in the *Earth Science Reference Tables.*

$$\text{eccentricity of an ellipse} = \frac{\text{distance between foci}}{\text{length of major axis}} = \frac{d}{L}$$

If you measure d and L in the ellipse of Figure 3-10 and apply the formula, you should find the eccentricity to be 0.26. As the foci of an ellipse are brought closer together, the ellipse becomes more like a circle and the eccentricity decreases toward zero. The eccentricities of the planets are Ⓡ listed in the Solar System Data in the *Earth Science Reference Tables.* If you were to draw the orbits of the planets to scale they would look like circles to the human eye, except for Mercury. As an example, Figure 3-11 shows Earth's orbit nearly drawn to scale, and it appears to be a circle.

Varying Distance of Planets from the Sun and Apparent Solar Size The elliptical shape of planetary orbits causes the planets to vary in distance from the sun during a revolution. For example, Earth is 147,000,000 kilometers from the sun when closest (occurring on or about January 3). Earth is 152,000,000 kilometers from the sun when farthest away (occurring on or about July 4). The difference between these two distances is only about 5,000,000 km. It is important to note that this is NOT the factor that causes seasons on Earth.

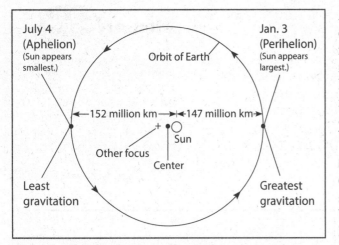

Figure 3-11. **Earth's orbit drawn close to true scale:** If the orbit were drawn to true scale, the two foci would be about 1 mm apart. Even at this exaggerated scale, with a greater eccentricity, the orbit appears to be a circle—thus Earth's orbit of the sun is a slightly eccentric ellipse.

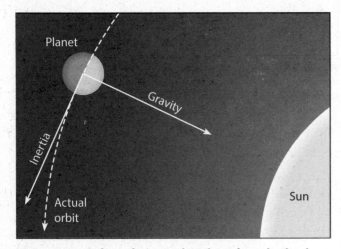

Figure 3-12. **Balance between inertia and gravitation in revolution:** Inertia would make a planet travel in a straight line. The mutual gravitation between the sun and a planet would pull the planet towards the sun. The actual orbit is a balance between the actions of inertia and gravity.

As Earth revolves around the sun the varying distance between the two bodies results in changes in the apparent size (diameter) of the sun as viewed from Earth. Photographs taken of the sun when Earth is closest to the sun, around January 3, illustrate that the sun appears largest on this date and smallest around July 4, when the distance between Earth and the sun is the longest.

Inertia, Gravitation, Orbital Velocity/Speed, and Planet Orbits The planets and all other bodies that orbit the sun, or any revolving body, operate under a balance between inertia and gravitation as shown in Figure 3-12. **Inertia** is the concept that an object at rest will tend to remain at rest, and that an object in motion will maintain the direction and speed of that motion unless an opposing force affects it. **Gravitation** is the attractive force that exists between any two objects in the universe. The gravitational force is proportional to the product of the masses of the objects and inversely proportional to the square of the distance between their centers. In simple terms, the greater the mass of one or both objects (such as a star and a planet), the more gravitational attraction there is between the objects. Also the closer together two objects are, the greater the gravitational attraction between them. Conversely, the farther apart two objects are, the lower the gravitational attraction between them.

The orbit of a planet around the sun, or that of any other satellite, is an example of the dynamic equilibrium, or balance, between inertia and gravitation. The shape and size of the orbit is a compromise, or balance, between the forces as illustrated in Figure 3-12.

Since each planet's orbit has some eccentricity, its distance from the sun varies during its yearly revolution. The result is that each planet's orbital speed velocity varies during its year. When a planet is closer to the sun, its orbital speed velocity is greatest, and when a planet is farthest from the sun, its orbital speed velocity is slowest.

The period of revolution for a planet is the amount of time it takes the planet to make one orbit, or revolution, around the sun. This amount of time equals one <u>year</u> for that planet. The period of revolution of a planet is related to the planet's distance from the sun. The closer a planet is to the sun, the smaller its orbit, the shorter its period of revolution, and the faster its speed of revolution. Thus the time it takes for a planet, or any other member of the solar system, to orbit the sun is affected by two factors. The farther a planet is from the sun, the longer the orbital path that must be traveled in one year. Also, the farther a planet is from the sun, the less mutual gravitational attraction between the two objects and thus a slower orbital velocity.

30. The Jovian planets have more gravitational pull than the terrestrial planets. Therefore, they have

(1) a shorter year
(2) higher average density
(3) higher surface temperatures
(4) more low-density gases in their atmosphere

Base your answers to questions 31 and 32 on the following graphs. The first variable mentioned is on the Y-axis and the second is on the X-axis.

31. Which graph best illustrates the relationship between the diameter of a planet versus the distance of the planet from the sun?

32. Which graph best illustrates the relationship between the time it takes a planet to make one revolution around the sun versus the distance of the planet from the sun?

33. The planet that has the shortest day is

(1) Mercury   (3) Jupiter
(2) Earth   (4) Uranus

34. Which member of the solar system has an equatorial diameter of 3.48×10^3 kilometers?

(1) the moon   (3) the sun
(2) Earth   (4) Mercury

35. The planets known as "gas giants," or Jovians, include Jupiter, Uranus, and

(1) Mercury   (3) Mars
(2) Saturn   (4) Earth

36. Which three planets are known as terrestrial planets because of their high density and rocky composition?

(1) Venus, Neptune, and Mercury
(2) Venus, Saturn, and Neptune
(3) Jupiter, Saturn, and Uranus
(4) Mercury, Mars, and Venus

37. Astronomers have observed a reddish spot on the surface of Jupiter. From observations of this spot, it is possible to estimate the

(1) period of Jupiter's rotation
(2) period of Jupiter's revolution
(3) pressure of Jupiter's atmosphere
(4) temperature of Jupiter's surface

38. Which planet takes longer for one spin on its axis than for one orbit around the sun?

(1) Mercury   (3) Earth
(2) Venus   (4) Mars

39. Which planet revolves fastest in its orbit?

(1) Earth   (3) Mercury
(2) Jupiter   (4) Neptune

40. In our solar system, the orbits of the planets are best described as

(1) circular, with the planet at the center
(2) circular, with the sun at the center
(3) elliptical, with the planet at one of the foci
(4) elliptical, with the sun at one of the foci

41. Which diagram best approximates the shape of the path of Earth as it travels around the sun?

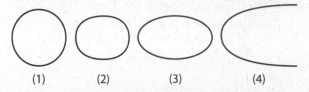

42. Based on the following diagram, what is the eccentricity of the ellipse in the diagram?

F, F₁ = foci
AB = major axis

(1) 1.0   (2) 0.5   (3) 0.30   (4) 0.13

43. If the pins in the following diagram were placed closer together, the eccentricity of the ellipse being constructed would

(1) decrease   (2) increase   (3) remain the same

44. The following diagram represents a student's constructed laboratory drawing.

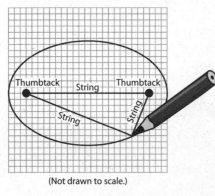

(Not drawn to scale.)

The student's drawing best represents the

(1) shape of Earth's moon
(2) shape of an elliptical orbit
(3) path of an earthquake wave
(4) path of a projectile deflected by Earth's rotation

45. The following diagram represents the construction of a model of an elliptical orbit of a planet traveling around a star.

The focal point and the center of the star represent the foci of the orbit. The eccentricity of this orbit is approximately

(1) 1.3   (2) 0.8   (3) 0.5   (4) 0.3

46. The following diagram shows the orbits of planets A and B in a star-planet system. The period of revolution for planet B is 40 days.

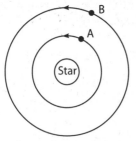

The period of revolution for planet A most likely is

(1) less than 40 days
(2) greater than 40 days
(3) 40 days

47. Which planet's orbit is most nearly circular?

(1) Earth
(2) Venus
(3) Neptune
(4) Jupiter

48. As the distance between two objects in the universe increases, the gravitational attraction between these two objects

(1) decreases
(2) increases
(3) remains the same

49. The diagram shows Earth (E) in orbit about the sun.

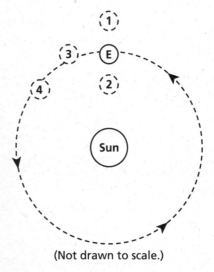

(Not drawn to scale.)

If the gravitational force between Earth and the sun were suddenly eliminated, toward which position would Earth then move?

(1) 1
(2) 2
(3) 3
(4) 4

50. The force of gravity between two objects is greatest when

(1) masses are small and the objects are close together
(2) masses are small and the objects are far apart
(3) masses are large and the objects are close together
(4) masses are large and the objects are far apart

Directions

Review the Test-Taking Strategies section of this book. Then answer the following questions. Read each question carefully and answer with a correct choice or response.

Part A

1 Which theory is best supported by a Doppler shift of spectral lines toward the red end of the spectrum?
(1) creation of the solar system
(2) expanding universe
(3) nature of light energy
(4) formation of impact craters

2 According to the Big Bang theory, the universe began as an explosion and is still expanding. This theory is supported by observations that the stellar spectra of distant galaxies show a
(1) concentration in the yellow portion of the spectrum
(2) concentration in the green portion of the spectrum
(3) shift toward the blue end of the spectrum
(4) shift toward the red end of the spectrum

3 The following diagram shows the home galaxy of our sun and solar system and four other galaxies that are trillions of miles away.

(Not drawn to scale)

Which galaxy is most likely moving away from the sun at the greatest velocity?
(1) A
(2) B
(3) C
(4) D

4 The following diagram represents the Milky Way Galaxy.

Which letter best represents the location of Earth's solar system?
(1) A   (2) B   (3) C   (4) D

5 A star of high surface temperature and low luminosity (relative absolute magnitude) is most likely a
(1) giant star   (3) supergiant star
(2) main sequence star   (4) white dwarf star

6 Why does a star with a high amount of matter tend to have a short life?
(1) It rotates rapidly.
(2) It consumes its fuel rapidly.
(3) It has a core of heavy elements.
(4) It collapses to form a white dwarf.

7 What is the single most important factor controlling the evolution of a star?
(1) mass   (3) element composition
(2) rotation rate   (4) temperature

8 Which of the following pairs of characteristics is most important in determining the type of a planet's atmosphere?
(1) orbital speed and volume
(2) rate of rotation and diameter
(3) mass of the planet and distance from the sun
(4) density of the planet and the number of moons

9 Which planet has traveled around the sun more than once in your lifetime?
(1) Mars   (3) Neptune
(2) Uranus   (4) Jupiter

10 As the distance from the sun increases, the diameter of the planets
(1) increases only
(2) decreases only
(3) both increases and decreases
(4) remains the same

11 In a scale model of the solar system, if Earth's diameter were 1 meter, the sun's diameter would be about
(1) 10 meters
(2) 100 meters
(3) 1,000 meters
(4) 10,000 meters

12 The diagram below represents Earth.

Which diagram best represents Mars, drawn to the same scale?

(1) (2) (3) (4)

13 If the planets were all on the same side of the sun, which line best shows the correct spacing between the inner planets and their distances from the sun at a scale of 1 centimeter = 0.2 AU? (An AU or astronomical unit is Earth's average distance from the sun; the sun and planets are represented by points of identical sizes, but distances between them are drawn to scale.)

(1) Sun   Mercury Venus   Earth   Mars

(2) Sun   Mercury   Venus   Earth Mars

(3) Sun Mercury   Venus Earth   Mars

(4) Sun Mercury   Venus   Earth   Mars

14 A planet was viewed from Earth for several hours. The following diagrams represent the appearance of the planet at four different times.

Diagram   Diagram   Diagram   Diagram
   A   B   C   D

The inference that can be made based on the diagrams is that this planet is
(1) tilted on its axis   (3) revolving
(2) changing seasons   (4) rotating

15 The period of time a planet takes to make one revolution around the sun is most dependent on what other characteristic of the planet?
(1) rotation rate
(2) mass
(3) diameter
(4) distance from the sun

16 Which diagram shows a planet with the least eccentric orbit?

Key:
• planet
✳ star

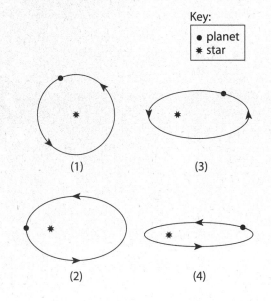

(1)   (3)

(2)   (4)

17 The following diagram shows a planet's orbit around the sun.

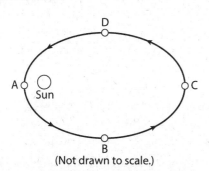

(Not drawn to scale.)

At which location is the planet's orbital speed greatest?
(1) A   (2) B   (3) C   (4) D

18 The diagram below represents a planet revolving in an elliptical orbit around the star.

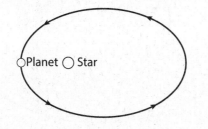

As the planet makes one complete revolution around the star, starting at the position shown, the gravitational attraction between the star and the planet will
(1) decrease, then increase
(2) increase, then decrease
(3) continually decrease
(4) remain the same

19 Planet A has a greater mean distance from the sun than planet B. On the basis of this fact, which further comparison can be correctly made between the two planets?
(1) Planet A is larger.
(2) Planet A's revolution period is longer.
(3) Planet A's speed of rotation is greater.
(4) Planet A's day is longer.

Part B

20 What is the difference between a galaxy and a constellation? [1]

21 How is a planet different from a moon? [1]

Base your answers to questions 22 through 24 on the passage below and on your knowledge of Earth science.

A Newly Discovered Planet

Scientists studying a Sun-like star named *Ogle-Tr-3* discovered a planet that is, on the average, 3.5 million kilometers away from the star's surface. The planet was discovered as a result of observing a cyclic decrease in the brightness of *Ogle-Tr-3* every 28.5 hours. The changing brightness is the result of the planet blocking some of the starlight when it is between *Ogle-Tr-3* and Earth. This observation allowed scientists to find not only the planet, but also to determine the planet's mass and density. The mass has been calculated to be approximately 159 times the mass of Earth. The planet is only 20% as dense as Jupiter. Scientists think that this low density is the result of being very close to *Ogle-Tr-3*.

22 Compared to the periods of revolution of Mercury and Venus, this newly discovered planet's period of revolution is
(1) shorter than both Mercury's and Venus's
(2) longer than both Mercury's and Venus's
(3) shorter than Mercury's but longer than Venus's
(4) longer than Mercury's but shorter than Venus's

23 The density of the discovered planet has been estimated to be approximately
(1) 5.5 g/cm^3 (3) 1.3 g/cm^3
(2) 2.0 g/cm^3 (4) 0.3 g/cm^3

24 The planet was discovered when it passed between Earth and the star *Ogle-Tr-3*.
Which event in our solar system results from a similar type of alignment of the Moon between Earth and the Sun?
(1) summer solstice   (3) solar eclipse
(2) winter solstice   (4) lunar eclipse

Base your answers to questions 25 through 28 on Table 1 and Table 2 that follow.

Table 1		
Planet	Average Distance From the Sun (AU)	Average Orbital Speed (km/s)
Mercury	0.4	48.0
Venus	0.7	35.0
Earth	1.0	30.0
Mars	1.5	24.0
Jupiter	5.2	13.0
Saturn	9.6	10.0
Uranus	19.0	7.0
Neptune	30.0	5.1
Pluto	39.0	4.7

Table 2	
Asteroid	Average Distance From Sun (AU)
Ceres	2.8
Pallas	2.8
Vesta	2.4
Hygiea	3.2
Juno	2.7

25 On the following grid, plot the average distance from the sun and the average orbital speed for each of the eight planets and the dwarf planet Pluto listed in Table 1. Connect the nine points with a line. [2]

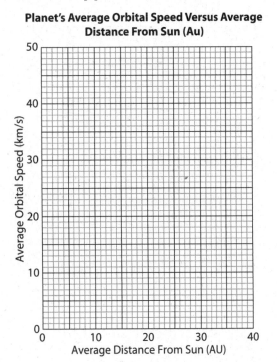

Planet's Average Orbital Speed Versus Average Distance From Sun (Au)

26 Describe the relationship between a planet's average distance from the sun and the planet's average orbital speed. [1]

27 The orbits of the asteroids listed in Table 2 are located between two adjacent planetary orbits. State the names of the two planets. [1]

28 Based on its distance from the sun, which of the asteroids listed in Table 2 has the greatest average orbital speed? [1]

---

29 The following diagram represents the elliptical orbit of a spacecraft around the sun.

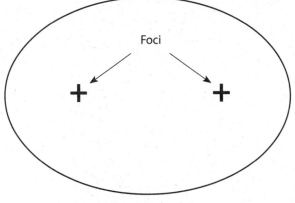

(Drawn to scale.)

Calculate the eccentricity of the spacecraft's orbit following these directions:
(a) Write the equation for eccentricity. [1]
(b) Substitute measurements of the diagram into the equation. [1]
(c) Calculate the eccentricity and record your answer in decimal form. [1]
(d) State how the eccentricity of this elliptical orbit compares to the eccentricity of Earth's orbit. [1]

Base your answers to questions 30 and 31 on the calendar model shown below of the inferred history of the universe and on your knowledge of Earth science. The 12-month time line begins with the Big Bang on January 1 and continues to the present time, which is represented by midnight on December 31. Several inferred events and the relative times of their occurrence have been placed in the appropriate locations on the time line.

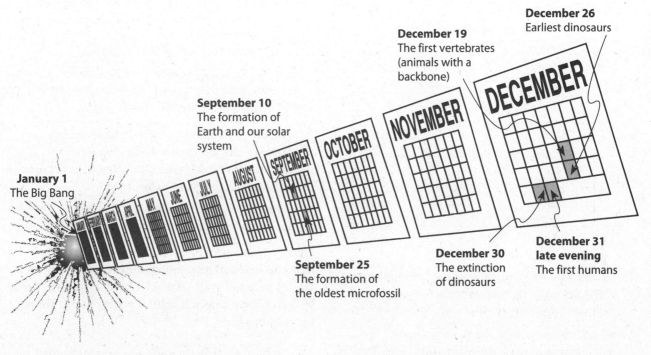

30 State *one* piece of evidence used by scientists to support the theory that the Big Bang event occurred. [1]

31 How many millions of years of Earth's geologic history elapsed between the event that occurred on September 10 and the event that occurred on September 25 in the model? [1]

32 Using the "Characteristics of Stars" graph in the *Earth Science Reference Tables*, list the five stars below in order of *decreasing* relative luminosity, with letter *a* being the brightest. [1]

Aldebaran, Betelgeuse, Polaris, Sirius, the Sun

Part C

33 Describe how the Big Bang theory can explain the observed Doppler effect of most galaxies. [1]

Use the following information and your knowledge of earth science to answer questions 34 through 41.

A tenth planet, called Thelma, is located exactly between the orbits of Earth and Mars. Its density and diameter are halfway between those of Earth and Mars.

34 State a probable distance of the planet Thelma from the sun in kilometers. [1]

35 State a probable period of revolution of the planet Thelma using proper units. [1]

36 What is the most likely shape of the planet Thelma? [1]

37 In years, what is the oldest possible rock that would likely be found on planet Thelma? [1]

38 What information would you need to know to be able to determine the length of a day on the planet Thelma? [1]

39 Explain why the planet Thelma would likely be considered a terrestrial planet and NOT a Jovian planet. [1]

40 Explain how the magnitude of gravitation between the sun and planet Thelma compares to the gravitation between the sun and Mars. State a reason for the difference in the gravitations. [2]

41 Describe the landscape feature you would expect to find on the solid surface of the planet Thelma if a 5-mile-wide asteroid had recently collided with the planet. [1]

Base your answers to questions 42 and 43 on the graph below and on the "Characteristics of Stars" graph in the *Earth Science Reference Tables*. The graph below shows the inferred stages of development of the Sun, showing luminosity and surface temperature at various stages.

Inferred Stages of Development

42 Describe the changes in luminosity of the Sun that will occur from its current Main Sequence stage to its final White Dwarf stage. [1]

43 Which star shown on the "Characteristics of Stars" graph in the *Earth Science Reference Tables* is currently at the Sun's final predicted stage of development? [1]

Base your answers to questions 44 and 45 on your knowledge of Earth science and on the newspaper article shown below, written by Paul Recer and printed in the *Times Union* on October 9, 1998.

Astronomers peer closer to Big Bang

WASHINGTON—The faintest and most distant objects ever sighted—galaxies of stars more than 12 billion light years away—have been detected by an infrared camera on the Hubble Space Telescope.

The sighting penetrates for the first time to within about one billion light years of the very beginning of the universe, astronomers said, and shows that even at that very early time there already were galaxies with huge families of stars.

"We are seeing farther than ever before," said Rodger I. Thompson, a University of Arizona astronomer and the principal researcher in the study.

Thompson and his team focused an infrared instrument on the Hubble on a narrow patch of the sky that had been previously photographed in visible light. The instrument detected about 100 galaxies that were not seen in the visible light and 10 of these were at extreme distance.

He said the galaxies are seen as they were when the universe was only about 5 percent of its present age. Astronomers generally believe the universe began with a massive explosion, called the "Big Bang," that occurred about 13 billion years ago.

Since the Big Bang, astronomers believe that galaxies are moving rapidly away from each other, spreading out and becoming more distant.

44 The Big Bang theory is widely believed by astronomers to explain the beginning of the universe. Why does the light from distant galaxies support the Big Bang theory? [1]

45 Compare the age of Earth and our solar system to the age of these distant galaxies of stars. [1]

Base your answers to questions 46 through 48 on the diagram below. The diagram shows the positions of Halley's Comet and Asteroid 134340 at various times in their orbits. Specific orbital positions are shown for certain years.

Orbit of Asteroid 134340

46 The eccentricity of the asteroid's orbit is 0.250. On the orbital diagram above mark the position of the second focus of the asteroid's orbit by placing an **X** on the major axis at the proper location. [1]

47 Determine which was traveling faster, Halley's Comet or the asteroid, between the years 1903 and 1908. State *one* reason for your choice. [1]

48 Explain why Halley's Comet is considered to be part of our solar system. [1]

Motions of Earth, Moon, and Sun

How **Scientists** **Study** Motions of Earth, Moon, and Sun

? *Does the man on the moon change his facial expressions?* **?**

There is a common misconception that Earth's moon does *not* rotate. Most people likely believe that the moon revolves around Earth as Earth revolves around the sun. The revolution period of the moon's orbit around Earth is about 27 ⅓ days. When you observe the moon over a period of a month or more, you may notice that even though you see varying amounts of the moon (due to the changing phases), you always see the same features of the full moon, which makes it seem as if the moon does not spin on its own axis.

Try the following: Use your desktop as a model of the moon's orbital plane about Earth. Use a Roosevelt dime as a model of the moon, and a half dollar a model of Earth. Point the top of Roosevelt's head (moon) towards the half-dollar (Earth) and revolve the moon around Earth. Now try it again but always keep Roosevelt's head pointed toward Earth. What action occurs? Right! The dime rotates, but just once as it travels around the half-dollar. Thus, the same side of the moon must point toward Earth all the time. In other words, the man on the moon has the same face all the time, because the moon rotates once per revolution in 27 ⅓ days.

Motions of Earth, Moon, and Sun

Vocabulary

axis (of rotation)	Foucault pendulum	phases (of the moon)
constellation	geocentric model	tides
Coriolis effect	heliocentric model	time zone
eclipse	local time	

Topic Overview

Throughout time, most cultures have attempted to understand the nature and the motions of celestial objects—the stars, sun, moon, and planets. Many of the explanations of the nature and cause of motions of celestial objects have become part of the belief systems of past and present cultures.

In this topic you will study the nature and motion of celestial objects in relationship to Earth and our satellite, the moon. Some scientists consider Earth and its moon to be a double planet, but for the purpose of this book, the moon will be considered a satellite of Earth, and Earth a satellite of the sun.

Apparent Motions of Celestial Objects

An apparent motion is a motion that an object appears to make. Apparent motions can be real or illusions. When you observe a person spinning around, that motion is real. However, when the spinning person sees the room as spinning, that is an illusion and not a real motion. It has always been difficult for people looking into space to distinguish real motions of celestial objects from illusions. For example, the stars appear to move across the sky from east to west. However, this apparent motion is caused by Earth's rotation.

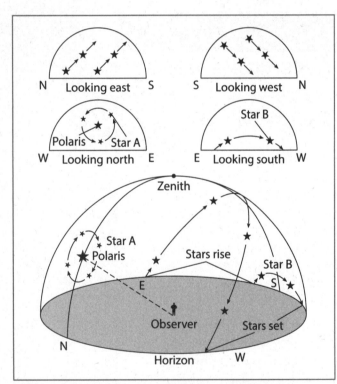

Figure 4-1. Apparent daily motion of stars in middle northern latitudes: To an observer in the mid-latitudes of the Northern Hemisphere—such as New York State—most stars appear to move from east to west in circular paths, or along arcs. The complete circular path can be seen for stars in the northern part of the sky around Polaris. Other stars rise over the eastern horizon and set at the western horizon in the middle latitudes.

Daily Motion and Stars

Most celestial objects appear to move across the sky, rising in the eastern part of the sky and setting in the western part of the sky. The vast majority of the 6000 or so celestial objects visible with the unaided eye at any location are stars.

Some of the stars near the North Star, or Polaris, appear to move in a complete circle in 24 hours. The paths of all celestial objects moving in the sky are circular, or parts of a circle called an arc. All the motion occurs at a constant rate of approximately 15° per hour or 360° in 24 hours. These movements of celestial objects over a 24-hour period are called daily motion. (See Figure 4-1.)

Apparent Motions of the Planets

As seen from Earth, the planets exhibit daily motion similar to that of the stars. However, over extended periods of time (weeks to months), the planets appear to change position with respect to the background field of stars around them. As illustrated in Figure 4-2, this apparent movement of the planets relative to the stars is not uniform and often appears complicated. Each year, a similar motion would be observed, but in a different region of the sky. From a central sun perspective, the complicated motion of the planets is the result of Earth and other planets revolving around the sun in different orbits at different speeds. This causes other planets viewed from Earth to sometimes appear to make loops and move back and forth.

Apparent Motions of Earth's Moon

The moon also follows the daily east-to-west motion of the stars. However, it appears to rise about 50 minutes later each day and shifts eastward each day compared to the background field of stars.

Apparent Sun Motions in Northern Mid-Latitudes

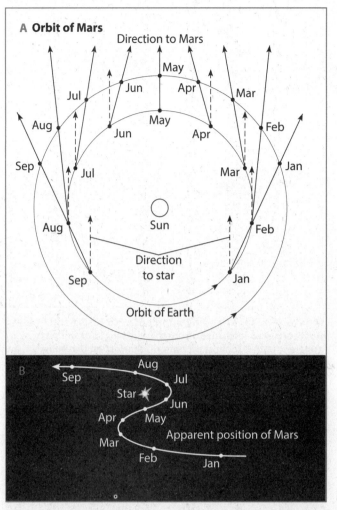

Figure 4-2. **Apparent motions of a planet:** Diagram A shows successive positions of Earth and Mars along their orbits at monthly intervals during part of a given year. The dashed arrows show the sight lines from Earth to a certain star. These sight lines are practically parallel because of the great distance of the star. The solid arrows are the sight lines toward Mars. As the diagram shows, the sight line changes in relation to the star each month. Diagram B shows how the apparent position of Mars changed with respect to the star.

Like all other visible celestial objects, the sun also seems to move in the sky. The sun's apparent path, from sunrise to sunset, has the shape of an arc. As shown in Figure 4-3, the sun's path changes both its position and its length with the seasons. The greater the length of the sun's path over an area, the more hours of daylight the area has. In summer, daylight is longest, in winter shortest, and in spring and fall in-between—approximately 12 hours. Figure 4-3 also shows how the position of the sun at sunrise and sunset varies predictably with the seasons. In spring and fall, the sun rises due, or exactly, east and sets due west. In summer, the sun rises north of east and sets north of west. In the winter, the sun rises south of east and sets south of west.

Changes in the Altitude of the Sun at Noon Figure 4-3 indicates that the daily altitude of the sun is lowest at sunrise and increases in altitude until noon, when the sun then decreases to its sunset position. The sun always reaches its highest position in the sky at local solar noon. However, the altitude of

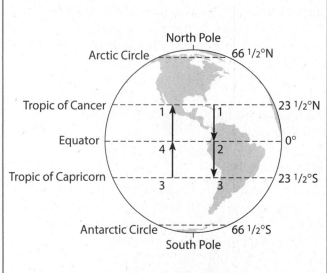

Figure 4-3. The changing apparent path of the sun in the northern mid-latitudes: Note that the length of the sun's apparent path is longest on June 21, shortest on December 21, and in-between on March 21 and September 23. Also, the altitude of the sun at noon is highest on June 21, shortest on December 21, and in-between on September 23 and March 21. (See Appendix 4.)

Figure 4-4. The yearly changes in latitude where the sun is directly overhead at noon—at an altitude of 90°: Point 1 is June 21, point 2 is September 23, point 3 is December 21, and point 4 is March 21.

(A4) the sun at noon depends on the time of year and the latitude of the observer. Only between latitudes $23\frac{1}{2}°$ N and $23\frac{1}{2}°$ S can the noon sun be directly overhead at an altitude of 90°. Thus, the noon sun is never directly overhead anywhere in the continental United States. Figure 4-4 shows how the latitude at which the sun is overhead at noon changes during a year.

Review Questions

1. If Earth rotated from north to south, the North Star would appear to

(1) set in the south
(2) set in the north
(3) move in a circle in the sky
(4) remain stationary

2. How would a three-hour time exposure photograph of stars in the northern sky appear if Earth did not rotate?

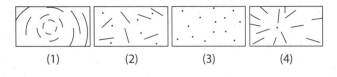

(1)　　　(2)　　　(3)　　　(4)

3. An observer took a time-exposure photograph of Polaris and five nearby stars. How many hours were required to show these star paths?

(1) 6　　　(2) 2　　　(3) 8　　　(4) 4

4. When observed from a location in New York State for an entire night, the North Star (Polaris) appears to

(1) rise in the east and set in the west
(2) rise in the west and set in the east
(3) move southward along an arc-shaped path
(4) remain stationary in the sky

5. Explain why most stars seem to move from east to west across the sky in New York State.

6. The star Sirius is observed in the evening sky during the month of January. At the end of 3 hours, Sirius will appear to have moved

(1) 60°   (2) 45°   (3) 3°   (4) 0°

7. On December 21, at which latitude would an observer find the sun directly overhead?

(1) 0°
(2) 23½° North
(3) 23½° South
(4) 90° South

8. The sun's apparent daily movement across the sky is caused by

(1) the sun's revolution around Earth
(2) Earth's revolution around the sun
(3) the sun's rotation on its axis
(4) Earth's rotation on its axis

9. At which location below would the sun produce an angle of 23.5° relative to an observer's head, at noon on June 21?

(1) 0°
(2) 23.5°N
(3) 23.5°S
(4) 66.5°N

10. At 40° N latitude, for how many days a year is the sun directly overhead at noon?

(1) 1   (2) 2   (3) 3   (4) 0

11. In New York State, to see the sun at noon, one would look towards the

(1) north   (3) east
(2) south   (4) west

12. A student in New York State obtained the data below by noting the altitude of the sun at noon for three consecutive months.

Month	Altitude of Sun at Noon
X	27.0°
Y	23.5°
Z	25.5°

The data for month Y were obtained during

(1) March   (3) September
(2) June   (4) December

13. To a person located at 43° North latitude, the sun appears to rise due east on

(1) December 22   (3) March 21
(2) March 1   (4) June 22

14. From September 21 to December 20 in the United States, the direction in which the sun sets

(1) is always directly east
(2) is always directly west
(3) moves from the east towards the north
(4) moves from the west towards the south

Models that Help Explain Apparent Celestial Motions

For thousands of years, people have developed theories to explain their observations of the movements of celestial objects. An explanation of two of these theories follows.

Geocentric Models

A majority of early cultures believed the most obvious way to explain the daily motion of celestial objects. They assumed that Earth is stationary, and that most celestial objects revolve around it. This Earth-centered model is called the **geocentric model.** In many geocentric models, the moon and sun were thought to travel at slightly different speeds in their orbits of Earth. The geocentric model explained most of the motions of the stars, sun, and moon, but it did not explain the apparent motions of the planets. One version of the geocentric model proposed that the planets moved around in circles as the planets revolved around Earth. The geocentric model also could not explain some Earth motions and the behavior of a freely

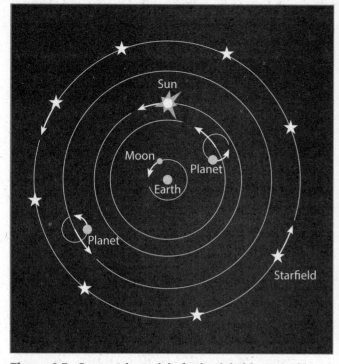

Figure 4-5. **Geocentric model of celestial objects:** In this model, Earth neither rotates nor revolves. The moon, sun, and other stars orbit Earth in circular paths at different speeds. All stars are the same distance from Earth. The planets revolve in small circles, while the centers of these circles revolve around Earth in circular orbits. These additional small circles for the planets are needed to explain the planet's irregular motions. The small circles are much more complicated than those shown here.

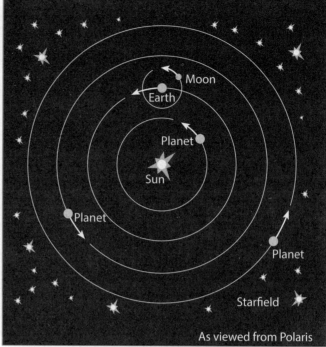

As viewed from Polaris

Figure 4-6: **A modern heliocentric model:** The sun is the center of motion. Earth and other planets rotate and revolve around the sun at different speeds in elliptical orbits with some eccentricity. Note the counterclockwise revolution of the planets as viewed from Polaris. The stars don't revolve around Earth and are at varying distances from the solar system.

Memory Jogger

Recall that <u>eccentricity</u> can be described as the amount of difference between an ellipse as compared to a circle. With the exception of Mercury, the slightly elliptical orbits of the planets, drawn to scale, look like circles to the human eye.

swinging pendulum. In European cultures, the geocentric model was largely accepted up to the 16th century.

Heliocentric Models

Some ancient cultures and most modern societies use a **heliocentric model**—sun-centered model—to explain the apparent motions of celestial objects in Earth's sky. In all heliocentric models, Earth both rotates on an imaginary axis and revolves around the sun in an orbit. The moon revolves around Earth as Earth revolves around the sun. The daily motion of stars is explained by the rotation of Earth. The motions of the moon are explained by the rotation of Earth, the revolution of Earth around the sun, and the revolution of the moon around Earth. The apparent motions of the sun are explained by the rotation of Earth on a tilted axis and the revolution of Earth around the sun.

Because they used circular orbits for the planets, most early heliocentric models did no better in predicting the motions of the planets than did the geocentric views. When elliptical orbits and varying orbital speeds were added to the heliocentric model, the motions of the planets could be predicted. The heliocentric model did explain the behavior of a freely swinging pendulum.

15. In the geocentric model, which motion would occur?

(1) Earth would revolve around the sun.
(2) Earth would rotate on its axis.
(3) The moon would revolve around the sun.
(4) The sun would revolve around Earth.

16. Which diagram represents a geocentric model?

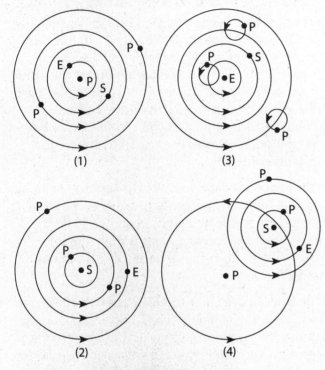

(1)   (3)

(2)   (4)

Key: E = Earth, P = Planet, S = Sun

17. The apparent rising and setting of the sun as seen from Earth are caused by the

(1) rotation of the sun
(2) rotation of Earth
(3) revolution of Earth
(4) revolution of the sun

18. Which diagram best represents a portion of the heliocentric model of the solar system?

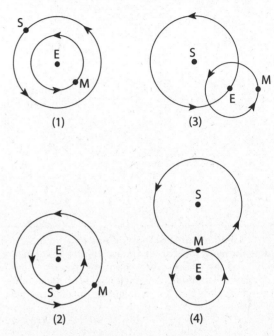

(1)   (3)

(2)   (4)

S = Sun, E = Earth, and M = Moon

19. Which planetary orbit model allows a scientist to predict the exact positions of the planets in the night sky for many years?

(1) The planets' orbits are circles in a geocentric model.
(2) The planets' orbits are ellipses in a geocentric model.
(3) The planets' orbits are circles in a heliocentric model.
(4) The planets' orbits are ellipses in a heliocentric model.

Actual Earth Motions

Earth moves constantly in a variety of motions. Earth moves with the Milky Way Galaxy as the universe expands. It moves around the center of the Milky Way Galaxy with our solar system in a 225-million-year period. Earth also rotates and revolves around the sun in an orbit.

Rotation of Earth

The spinning of Earth on its **axis**—the imaginary line through the planet from the North Pole to the South Pole—is its rotation. The axis of Earth is tilted $23\frac{1}{2}°$ from a line perpendicular to the plane of its orbit of the sun.

Figure 4-7. Circle of rotation—meridians of longitude—showing local solar times: Angular rotation rate is 15° per hour at any latitude. Local solar time changes 1 hour for each 15 degrees of longitude. When it is local solar noon on the side of Earth facing the sun, it is midnight on the opposite side.

As Earth orbits the sun, Earth's axis remains tilted at 23 $\frac{1}{2}$°. The north end of the axis points towards the North Star, or Polaris.

Earth rotates 360° from west to east in 24 hours, at an angular rate of 15° per hour. This angular rate is the same at all locations on Earth. Looking down over the North Pole, the direction of Earth's rotation is west to east—counterclockwise—as shown in Figure 4-7.

Evidence of Earth's Rotation

Throughout much of human history, scientists have searched for evidence that Earth rotates. Earth's movement is not apparent because people don't feel very smooth motions the same way that they are aware of abrupt motions. Also, there is nothing near Earth with which to compare its motion. Only in recent history have people and satellites been able to observe the rotation of Earth.

The Foucault Pendulum When a **Foucault pendulum** is allowed to swing freely (first observed in 1851), its path will appear to change in a predictable way, as shown in Figure 4-8. This is evidence of Earth's rotation because the pendulum—due to inertia—would continue to swing in the original path if Earth did not rotate. (See A-A´ in Figure 4-8.)

The path of the Foucault pendulum only appears to change. Actually, the pendulum swings in a fixed direction in space, while Earth, carrying the observer with it, rotates under the pendulum. If you could observe the pendulum moving through a powerful telescope in space, you would see no apparent change in its path. Foucault pendulums can be found in a number of museums to recreate the experiment.

Figure 4-8: Apparent motion of a Foucault pendulum: An observer sees a pendulum swing in the direction A-A´. Several hours later, the pendulum has changed its direction of swing to the line B-B´.

The Coriolis Effect The tendency of all particles of matter moving at Earth's surface to be deflected, or curve away, from a straight-line path is the **Coriolis effect.** The deflection is to the right in the Northern Hemisphere and to the left in the Southern Hemisphere. This deflection occurs because Earth is rotating, and therefore Earth's surface is moving with respect to the path of the particles.

The following example can help to explain the effect. Imagine that you are at the center of a merry-go-round that is rotating counterclockwise. Your friend is near the rim of the merry-go-round. You throw a ball directly at your friend. By the time the ball reaches the rim of the merry-go-round, your friend has been carried to the left. The ball reaches the rim at a point that is now to the right of your friend. With respect to the moving merry-go-round, the ball has been deflected to the right. In a similar manner, rockets, ocean currents, large storms, and winds are deflected with respect to Earth's surface. Since the only reasonable explanation of the Coriolis effect is that Earth rotates, the Coriolis effect is good evidence for Earth's rotation.

Evidence of Earth's Revolution Around the Sun

Earth revolves around the sun in a slightly eccentric elliptical orbit, or path, once a year. Earth revolves in a counterclockwise direction (as viewed from Polaris) at a rate of approximately 1 degree per day (360 degrees in 365 days). Just as scientists had trouble providing proof that Earth rotates, they also had difficulty finding solid evidence of Earth's revolution around the sun.

If you understand that Earth's limited change in distance from the sun during the year does not cause seasons, then the seasonal changes associated with changes of the sun's path is evidence of revolution. If Earth did not revolve around the sun, the same part of Earth would tilt toward the sun all the time. Therefore, the same part of Earth would receive the more direct rays of sunlight. The seasons would not change; each part of Earth would have the same season all the time.

Having different constellations associated with each of the four seasons is further evidence of Earth's revolution. A **constellation** is a group of stars that form a pattern and are used to help people locate celestial objects. At night you can see different constellations at different times of the year, as shown in Figure 4-9.

Earth's revolution around the sun produces other effects that can be used as evidence of revolution. During the year the apparent diameter of the sun changes in a cyclic fashion. Earth's changing distance from the sun as Earth revolves in its slightly elliptical orbit causes the size of the sun to appear to change. The sun appears the largest when Earth is closest to the sun around January 3. The sun appears the smallest when it is farthest away from Earth on about July 4.

Slight changes in the Doppler effect of stars can also be used as evidence of revolution. As Earth revolves around the sun, Earth is traveling toward a given star for about half the year, and the other half of the year it is moving

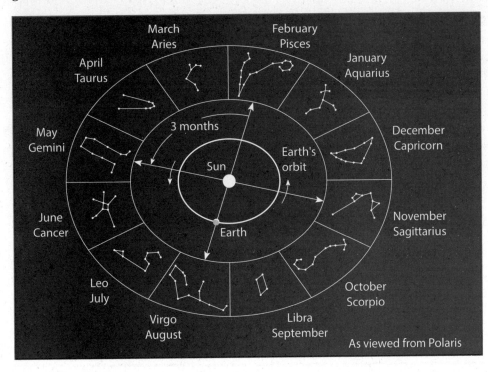

Figure 4-9. Changes in the constellations during the year: The fact that you observe different constellations in different seasons is evidence of Earth's revolution around the sun. Constellations are visible when the dark side of Earth (away from the sun) faces toward the constellation.

away from a given star. These movements toward or away from a star result in small yearly cyclic changes in blue and red shifting of starlight.

Review Questions

20. The following diagram represents part of the night sky, including the constellation Leo. The black circles represent stars. The unshaded circles represent the changing positions of one celestial object over a period of a few weeks.

The celestial object represented by the unshaded circles most likely is

(1) a galaxy (3) Earth's moon
(2) a planet (4) another star

21. Why are different constellations visible in the night sky at different seasons of the year?

22. An angle of $23\frac{1}{2}°$ is formed between the axis of Earth and a line

(1) from the center of Earth to Polaris
(2) from the center of Earth to the sun
(3) perpendicular to the plane of Earth's orbit
(4) perpendicular to the plane of the moon's orbit

23. The Foucault pendulum provides evidence of Earth's

(1) rotation (3) insolation
(2) revolution (4) inclination

24. On Earth, surface ocean currents rotate clockwise in the Northern Hemisphere and counterclockwise in the Southern Hemisphere because of the

(1) Coriolis effect
(2) Seasonal effect
(3) Tidal effect
(4) Doppler effect

Base your answers to questions 25 and 26 on the following diagram. The diagram shows, over the course of a year, twelve constellations that are visible in the night sky to an observer in New York State. Different positions of Earth are represented by letters A through D. The arrows represent the direction of Earth's motion around the sun.

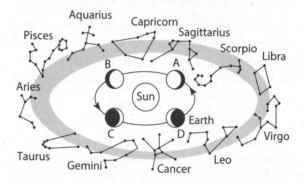

(Not drawn to scale.)

25. Which constellations are both visible at midnight to an observer in New York State when Earth is located at position D?

(1) Aries and Taurus (3) Leo and Virgo
(2) Pisces and Libra (4) Aquarius and Scorpio

26. The constellations observed from New York State when Earth is at position A are different from the constellations observed from New York State when Earth is located at position C because

(1) Earth moves in its orbit
(2) Earth is tilted on its axis
(3) the lengths of day and night are different
(4) the stars move around Earth as shown by star trails

27. Which statement provides the best evidence that Earth revolves around the sun?

(1) The sun follows an apparent daily path, rising in the east and setting in the west.
(2) A Foucault pendulum appears to shift its direction of swing in a predictable manner.
(3) The stars appear to follow circular paths around the North Star (Polaris).
(4) The seasons of spring, summer, fall, and winter repeat in a pattern.

Earth and Moon Motions and Time

Throughout the ages most cultures have used the actual motions of Earth and/or the moon as a frame of reference to determine time. The concept of the month is based on the length of one cycle of our moon's phases. The day is based on one rotation of Earth as measured by apparent motions of the sun. The year is based on one revolution of Earth around the sun as measured by changes in the apparent motions of the sun or other stars. Specific time within a day is more difficult to determine.

Figure 4-10. Local time is measured by a sundial: The position of a shadow on a sundial provides local solar time. The present reading is 12:00 noon—when the sun is highest in the sky for that day. Note that the sun's shadow at solar noon points directly to geographic north.

Local Time

Time based on the rotation of Earth as reflected in motions of the sun is **local time.** All places on the same north-south line, or meridian of longitude, have the same local time. However, locations even slightly east or west of any meridian have different local times, due to Earth's rotation. There are two types of time based on observations of the sun at a single location.

Local Solar Time For any location, the sun reaches its highest point in the sky once each day at solar noon. The time it takes for Earth to rotate from solar noon to solar noon on two successive days at any fixed location on Earth is the solar day. This type of local time, based on the motions of the sun in the sky, is solar time, apparent solar time, or sundial time, because a sundial is used to measure it. (See Figure 4-10.)

If Earth moved around the sun in a circular orbit at a constant speed, the apparent solar day would have a constant length. However, Earth's speed around the sun varies in a cyclic manner in the course of the year. As a result, the length of the apparent solar day also varies during the year. Days of varying length make it very difficult to measure time using clocks and watches. Therefore, for convenience in timekeeping, a solar day of average length—the mean solar day—has been established. This second type of local time is mean solar time, which is based on the mean solar day. It has been divided into exactly 24 hours. On most days of the year, the solar day is either slightly more or slightly less than 24 hours in length.

Time Zone or Standard Time

Time zones have been created to standardize time for regions. Because there is no limit to the number of meridians of longitude that could exist, there could be a different local time for each meter or kilometer where you live. To solve this problem, 24 separate **time zones** in 15-degree-wide east-to-west bands have been established. All parts of Earth within each of these 15-degree longitude bands maintain the same time, as shown in Figure 4-11. Since Earth rotates 360 degrees in a 24-hour period, each 15-degree band has a difference of one hour in time. Each time zone keeps the local mean solar time of the meridian that is in the middle of that particular time zone.

Figure 4-11. Time zones on Earth: There are 24 time zones, each 15 degrees of longitude in width. In the United States and other land areas, the actual time zone boundaries are adjusted so as not to split states, counties, and communities into two time zones.

Review Questions

28. Traditionally, most units of time are based upon

(1) the motions of Earth
(2) the longitude of an observer
(3) the motions of the moon
(4) the real motions of the sun

29. If Earth's rate of rotation decreased, there would be an increase in the

(1) length of the seasons
(2) sun's angle of insolation at noon
(3) number of observable stars seen at night during the year
(4) length of an Earth day

30. How long does Earth take to complete one orbit around the Sun?

(1) 1 day   (3) 1 year
(2) 1 month   (4) 1 decade

31. Units of time are based on Earth's motion relative to other celestial objects. The year is best defined as Earth's motion relative to the

(1) asteroids   (2) sun   (3) moon   (4) planets

32. According to the diagram below, the time at point C is closest to

(1) 6 A.M.   (3) 6 P.M.
(2) 12 noon   (4) 12 midnight

33. Cities located on the same meridian must have the same

(1) altitude   (3) length of daylight
(2) latitude   (4) local solar time

34. When does local solar noon always occur for an observer in New York State?

(1) when the clock reads 12 noon
(2) when the sun reaches its maximum altitude
(3) when the sun is directly overhead
(4) when the sun is on the prime meridian

Base your answers to questions 35 through 37 on the following diagram of Earth. Some of the latitude and longitude lines have been labeled. Points A through E represent locations on Earth's surface.

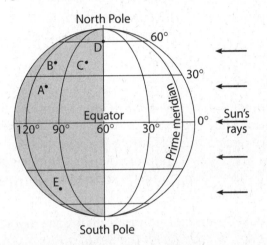

35. What do locations A, B, and E have in common?

(1) They are in the same season.
(2) They have the same local time.
(3) They have the same prevailing wind direction.
(4) They are at the same latitude.

36. The latitude and longitude of which location are closest to those of New York State?

(1) A   (2) B   (3) C   (4) D

37. What is the approximate time at location D?

(1) 6 A.M.   (3) 9 P.M.
(2) 12 noon   (4) 12 midnight

38. Ship X and ship Y are sailing along the equator. The difference in local solar time between their locations is 2 hours. What is their difference in longitude?

(1) 0°   (2) 15°   (3) 30°   (4) 45°

Base your answers to questions 39 and 40 on the following time zone map.

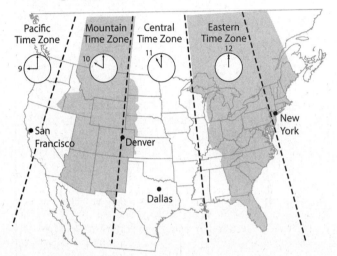

39. What is the time in San Francisco when it is 6 A.M. in Dallas?

(1) 5 A.M.   (2) 7 A.M.   (3) 3 A.M.   (4) 4 A.M.

40. The dashed boundaries between time zones are how many degrees of longitude apart?

(1) 10°   (2) 15°   (3) $23\frac{1}{2}°$ (4) 24°

Actual Motions of Earth's Moon

The revolution of the moon around Earth as Earth revolves around the sun results in many common observable events, including phases of the moon, tides, and eclipses. The moon revolves around Earth in an elliptical orbit that is tilted about 5° from Earth's orbit and that has a period of $27\frac{1}{3}$ days. Besides revolving around Earth in $27\frac{1}{3}$ days, the moon also rotates on its axis in $27\frac{1}{3}$ days. Thus as the moon revolves once, it rotates once. This is the reason why the same "face" or side of the moon always points towards Earth. Figure 4-12 provides some details of the orbital motions of Earth and its moon.

Moon Phases

Half of the moon is always receiving light from the sun at any given time—except during lunar eclipses. Since the moon revolves around Earth, an observer on Earth sees varying amounts of this lighted half as the moon moves through its orbit. The varying amounts of the lighted moon as seen

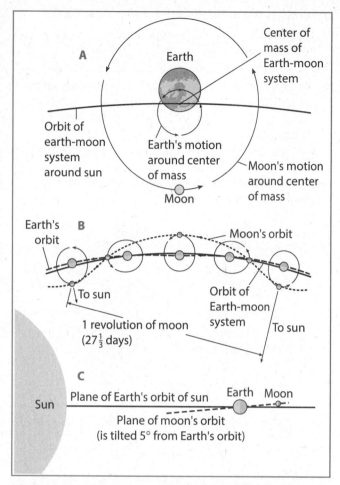

Figure 4-12. The moon's orbit: (A) The revolution of the moon around Earth is due to a balance between the inertia of the moon and the gravitational attraction of the moon to the center of the Earth-moon system. (B) The movements of the moon are exaggerated. (C) The moon's orbit of Earth is tilted 5° from Earth's orbital plane of the sun.

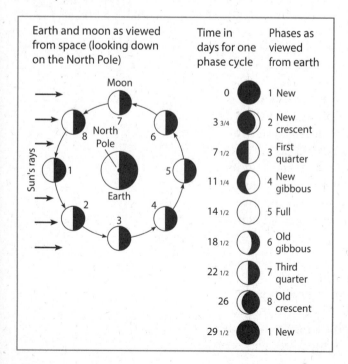

from Earth are known as the moon's **phases.** (See Figure 4-13.)

Because the revolution of the moon around the center of the Earth-moon system is cyclic, the phases of the moon are also cyclic. However, because of the revolution of the Earth-moon system around the sun, the cycle of phases is somewhat longer than the time of one revolution of the moon. The period from one full moon to the next is $29\frac{1}{2}$ days, whereas the moon's period of revolution and rotation is just $27\frac{1}{3}$ days. This difference in time is explained in Figure 4-14.

Tides

The gravitation between Earth, the moon, and the sun results in a cyclic rise and fall of ocean waters on Earth called **tides.** Figure 4-15 illustrates a typical tide pattern and how the varying positions of Earth, the moon, and the sun result in different levels of ocean water.

The tidal effect is caused primarily by the moon not the sun. Even though the moon is much smaller than the sun, it is about 400 times closer to Earth. Figure 4-15 illustrates that there is a bulge of water—a <u>high tide</u>—on Earth directly under the moon's position. There is also a high tide on the opposite side of Earth because the solid Earth is closer to the Earth-moon center of gravitation than the ocean water. This causes Earth to be pulled away from the water, leaving the high tide. At right angles to the positions of high tide, the gravitational pull of the moon is least, and the levels of ocean water are low, resulting in a <u>low tide.</u>

Because Earth is rotating, the low and high tides follow the straight-line alignment between Earth and the moon. The timing of high and low tides is not only affected by the rotating Earth, it is also influenced by the moon revolving around Earth. Thus, the ideal time between two high tides or two low tides would be about 12 hours and 25 minutes. A complete ideal cycle of two high tides and two low tides at a location would then take about 24 hours and 50 minutes. Few ocean shores experience an ideal cycle of tides, due to many factors.

Figure 4-13. The phases of the moon: The half of the moon facing the sun is always illuminated by light from the sun. The right side of the diagram shows how the moon appears as viewed from Earth for each phase of the moon.

The effect of the sun on tides is largely that of reducing or enhancing their heights. When Earth, the moon, and the sun are in a straight line, the sun enhances the tidal effect, and high tides are higher and low tides are lower. This large tidal range happens during new and full moon phases. When the moon is in one of the quarter phases, the sun is pulling at right angles to the moon. As a result, high tides are then lower, and low tides are higher, producing a smaller tidal range.

Eclipses

Earth and the moon, like all other opaque objects that don't produce their own light, cast long shadows into space. When a celestial object partly or completely comes into the shadow of another celestial object, there is an event called an **eclipse.**

Lunar Eclipse When the moon revolves into the shadow of Earth at the full moon phase, a lunar eclipse, or eclipse of the moon, can occur. (See Figure 4-16.) A lunar eclipse doesn't happen during most full moons because the moon's orbit of Earth is tilted about 5 degrees compared to Earth's orbit. If Earth's shadow (umbra) covers only part of the moon, there is a partial eclipse. The curved shadow of Earth on the moon during a partial lunar eclipse is evidence for Earth's spherical shape.

When there is a total lunar eclipse, the moon is completely covered by Earth's shadow and all people on the dark half of Earth can view the eclipse for up to about 100 minutes. The complicated cycle of lunar eclipses results in an average of two total lunar eclipses a year.

Solar Eclipse Under rare ideal conditions at the new moon phase, the moon can just barely block out the sun, casting a shadow on Earth that causes a solar eclipse. As seen in Figure 4-17, the moon's shadow can just barely reach Earth, making solar eclipses a rare event. A total eclipse of the sun can only be observed at any one location on Earth for up to $7\frac{1}{2}$ minutes once every 200 years or so.

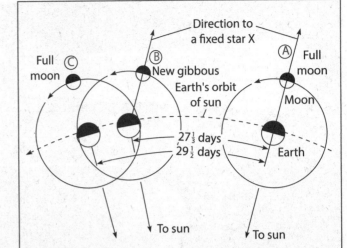

Figure 4-14. Different lengths of the moon's period of revolution and one phase cycle: The moon takes about $27\frac{1}{3}$ days to revolve around Earth, but one phase cycle, such as from full moon to full moon, takes $29\frac{1}{2}$ days.

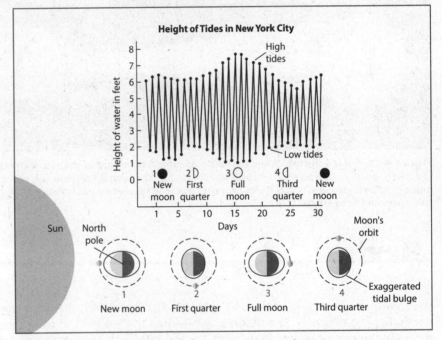

Figure 4-15. Ideal tide pattern in New York City: When the moon is in the new or full moon phase (positions 1 and 3), the gravity of the moon and sun are in a straight line. This causes higher high tides and lower low tides—a large tidal range. When the moon is in the quarter phase (positions 2 and 4), the gravitational force of the sun is at a 90° angle to the moon's force. This causes lower high tides and higher low tides—a smaller tidal range.

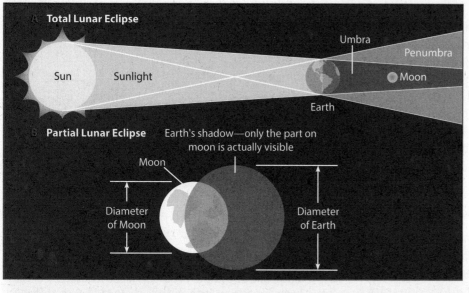

Total Lunar Eclipse

Sun

Sunlight

Umbra

Penumbra

Moon

Earth

Partial Lunar Eclipse

Earth's shadow—only the part on moon is actually visible

Moon

Diameter of Moon

Diameter of Earth

Figure 4-16. Lunar eclipse: Diagram A shows the condition of a total eclipse when the moon is completely covered by Earth's shadow (umbra). Diagram B shows a partial lunar eclipse as viewed from Earth when the moon is only partly in Earth's shadow. (Distance and size are not drawn to scale.)

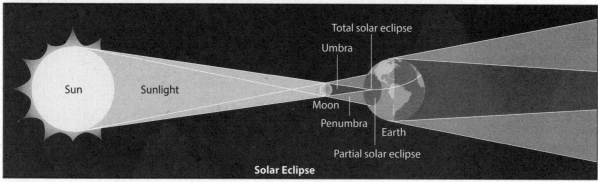

Total solar eclipse

Umbra

Sun

Sunlight

Moon

Penumbra

Earth

Partial solar eclipse

Solar Eclipse

Figure 4-17. Solar eclipses: When the new moon revolves in front of the sun, the diagram shows that the moon's shadow (umbra) just barely reaches Earth and the path of the total eclipse is small. When only the lighter part of the moon's shadow (penumbra) hits Earth, people in this shadow see the sun only partly blocked out—a partial solar eclipse. (Distances and sizes are not to scale.)

Review Questions

Base your answers to questions 41 through 47 on the following diagram. The diagram represents the moon in various positions in its orbit around Earth. Letters A through E represent five of the moon's positions.

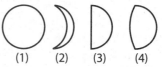

(Not drawn to scale.)

41. Which diagram best represents the appearance of the moon to an observer on Earth when the moon is at position B?

(1) (2) (3) (4)

42. The moon would not be visible from Earth when the moon is at position

(1) A (2) E (3) C (4) D

43. Why would an observer on Earth see a complete cycle of phases of the moon in approximately one month?

(1) The moon rotates on its axis.
(2) The moon revolves around Earth.
(3) Earth rotates on its axis.
(4) Earth revolves around the sun.

44. If the distance of the moon from Earth were to increase, the length of time the moon would take to complete one revolution around Earth would

(1) decrease   (2) increase   (3) remain the same

45. How does the moon appear to an observer in New York State when the moon is located at position E?

   (1)   (2)   (3)   (4)

46. The shadow of the moon may fall on Earth at position

(1) A   (2) B   (3) C   (4) D

47. At which positions of the moon do the smallest high tides occur on Earth?

(1) C and E   (3) B and C
(2) A and D   (4) A and B

48. If a full moon occurs on November 1, the next full moon phase will occur about

(1) November 22   (3) December 6
(2) November 30   (4) December 13

49. In the open ocean, a bulge of water two to three feet high that follows the moon's movement around Earth is a

(1) tide
(2) tsunami
(3) wind wave
(4) surface ocean current

50. The following diagram represents a north polar view of Earth in relation to the moon and the sun.

(Not drawn to scale.)

The tides that occur when the sun, moon, and Earth are in the relative positions indicated by the diagram are best described as

(1) the highest high tides and the lowest low tides
(2) the highest high tides and the highest low tides
(3) the lowest high tides and the lowest low tides
(4) the lowest high tides and the highest low tides

51. A high tide occurs at Boston on a certain day at 3 P.M. The next high tide may be expected to occur at

(1) 9:26 P.M. the same day
(2) 3:26 A.M. the following day
(3) 9:52 A.M. the following day
(4) 3:52 P.M. the following day

52. During which event does our moon receive the least amount of sunlight?

(1) a Jupiter eclipse   (3) a solar eclipse
(2) an Earth eclipse   (4) a lunar eclipse

53. During which phase of the moon do solar eclipses occur?

(1) new moon   (3) last quarter moon
(2) first quarter moon   (4) full moon

The following diagram represents the landscape on the moon with Earth shown in the background. Use this diagram to answer questions 54 through 57.

54. As viewed from Earth, what is the phase of the moon?

(1) new   (3) quarter
(2) full   (4) gibbous

55. With respect to the diagram, which statement is true?

(1) No eclipse could occur.
(2) A lunar eclipse might occur.
(3) A partial solar eclipse might occur.
(4) A total solar eclipse might occur.

56. In the week following the period shown in the diagram, the amount of the moon's surface that is illuminated by the sun will

(1) increase
(2) decrease
(3) remain the same
(4) increase, then decrease

57. What is the most probable cause of the lunar features indicated by A?

Directions

Review the Test-Taking Strategies section of this book. Then answer the following questions. Read each question carefully and answer with a correct choice or response.

Part A

Base your answers to questions 1 through 4 on the following diagram. The diagram represents a plastic hemisphere upon which lines have been drawn to show the apparent paths of the sun on four days at a location in New York State. Two of the days are December 21 and June 21. The protractor is placed over the north-south line.

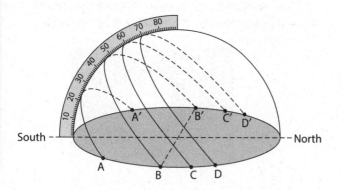

1 On which two dates could the sun have followed path C-C´?
   (1) October 22 and March 28
   (2) September 9 and January 7
   (3) January 27 and August 21
   (4) May 7 and August 1

2 Which path was recorded on a day that had 12 hours of daylight and 12 hours of darkness?
   (1) A-A´   (2) B-B´   (3) C-C´   (4) D-D´

3 Which would be the approximate length of daylight for the observer, when the sun travels along the entire length of path A-A´?
   (1) 9 hours   (3) 15 hours
   (2) 12 hours   (4) 18 hours

4 Which observation about the sun's apparent path on June 21 is best supported by the diagram?
   (1) The sun appears to move across the sky at a rate of 1° per hour.
   (2) The sun's total daytime path is shortest on this date.
   (3) Sunrise occurs north of east.
   (4) Sunset occurs south of west.

5 Which motion causes the apparent rising and setting of the moon each day as seen from a location in New York State?
   (1) Earth revolving around the sun
   (2) the moon revolving around Earth
   (3) Earth rotating on its axis
   (4) the moon rotating on its axis

6 As Earth revolves in orbit from its January position to its July position, the angle between its axis and orbital plane will
   (1) decrease
   (2) increase
   (3) remain the same

7 The following diagram represents a Foucault pendulum in a building in New York State. Points A and A´ are fixed points on the floor.

As the pendulum swings for six hours, it will
   (1) appear to change position due to Earth's rotation
   (2) appear to change position due to Earth's revolution
   (3) continue to swing between A and A´ due to inertia
   (4) continue to swing between A and A´ due to air pressure

Base your answers to questions 8 through 12 on the following diagram.

8 Earth will travel from A to B in
(1) 1 day   (3) $27\frac{1}{3}$ days
(2) 2.5 days   (4) $29\frac{1}{2}$ days

9 In respect to Earth at position B, in which phase is the moon?
(1) full   (3) gibbous
(2) new   (4) crescent

10 When Earth is at position B, how long must the moon travel beyond where it is shown to be in the same phase as it was in position A?
(1) 1 day   (3) 6 hours
(2) 2 days   (4) 7 days

11 What is the main reason why the moon must travel a greater distance to be in the same phase at position B as it was at position A?
(1) The sun's rays are essentially parallel when they reach Earth.
(2) The moon's periods of revolution and rotation are the same.
(3) Earth is constantly revolving around the sun.
(4) Earth's axis is inclined to the plane of its orbit.

12 At position B, the highest tides on Earth will occur when the moon is at points
(1) 1 and 2   (3) 2 and 4
(2) 1 and 3   (4) 3 and 4

13 The Coriolis effect provides evidence that Earth
(1) has a magnetic field
(2) has an elliptical orbit
(3) revolves around the sun
(4) rotates on its axis

14 A projectile is launched from a point near the North Pole toward the equator. Which diagram best represents the apparent path of the projectile, if it were viewed from Earth?

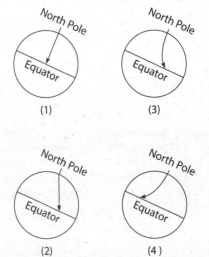

15 Some stars that can be seen in New York State on a summer night cannot be seen on a winter night. This fact is a result of the
(1) rotation of Earth on its axis
(2) rotation of the stars around Polaris
(3) revolution of Polaris around Earth
(4) revolution of Earth around the sun

16 To an observer on Earth, the planet Venus does not appear at one fixed position among the stars because Venus
(1) rotates on its axis
(2) revolves around the sun
(3) shows an apparent motion around Earth
(4) shows a complete cycle of phases

17 The diagram below shows the rotation of Earth as it would appear from a satellite over the North Pole. The time at point X is closest to

(1) 6 A.M.   (3) 6 P.M.
(2) 12 noon   (4) 12 midnight

18 The new moon phase occurs when the moon is positioned between Earth and the sun. However, these positions do not always cause an eclipse of the sun because the
  (1) moon's orbit is tilted relative to Earth's orbit
  (2) new moon phase is visible only at night
  (3) night side of the moon faces toward Earth
  (4) apparent diameter of the moon is greatest during the new moon phase

Part B

Base your answers to questions 19 through 23 on the following table and information.

Tidal Record for Reversing Falls, St. John River				
Date	Time of First High Tide	Time of First Low Tide	Time of Second High Tide	Time of Second Low Tide
June 26	2:25 A.M.	8:45 A.M.	2:55 P.M.	9:05 P.M.
June 27	3:15 A.M.	9:35 A.M.	3:45 P.M.	9:55 P.M.
June 28	4:05 A.M.	10:25 A.M.	4:35 P.M.	10:45 P.M.

The Bay of Fundy, located on the east coast of Canada, has the highest ocean tides in the world. The St. John River enters the Bay of Fundy at the city of St. John, where the river actually reverses direction twice a day at high tides. Data for the famous Reversing Falls of the St. John River are given for high and low tides on June 26–28, 1994.

19 Which graph best represents the tides recorded on June 28?

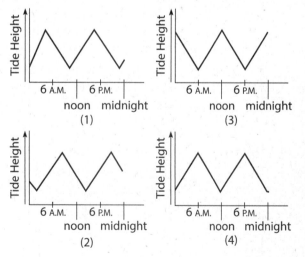

20 Compared to the first high tide on June 26, how much later in the day did the first high tide occur on June 27? [1]

21 Tides in the Bay of Fundy are best described as
  (1) predictable and noncyclic
  (2) predictable and cyclic
  (3) unpredictable and noncyclic
  (4) unpredictable and cyclic

22 Complete the following sentence: The moon has a greater effect on Earth's ocean tides than the sun has because the

23 Which model of the sun, Earth (E), and moon (M) best represents a position that would cause the highest ocean tides in the Bay of Fundy?

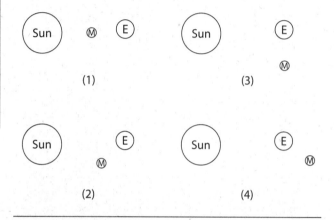

24 On the United States time zone map provided below, indicate the standard time in each time zone when it is 9 A.M. in the Central Time Zone. The dashed lines represent the standard time meridians for each time zone. Be sure to indicate the time for all three zones.

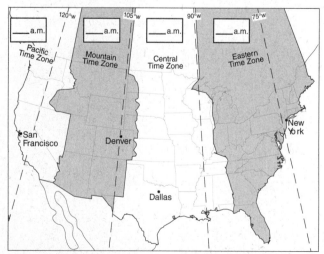

25 Draw and fully label a diagram showing a total eclipse of the sun. Include labels for the shadows, all solar system members shown, and phase of the moon. [4]

Use this information to answer questions 26 through 29. The following diagram represents the apparent path of the sun for an observer in New York State on the dates indicated. The diagram also shows the angle of Polaris above the horizon.

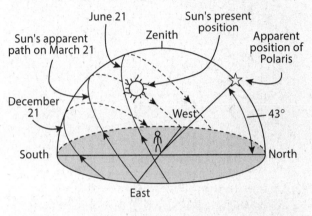

(Not drawn to scale)

26 On the diagram, draw the apparent path of the sun on May 21. [1]

27 On the diagram, mark and label the position of sunrise on May 21. [1]

28 State the latitude of the location represented by the diagram to the nearest degree. Include the latitude direction in your answer. [1]

29 At approximately what hour of day would the sun be at the position shown in the diagram? [1]

Part C

Using the following statement, answer questions 30 through 33.

Suppose that Earth does not have and has never had a moon.

30 Why would Earth still have ocean water tides? [1]

31 How would Earth's ocean tides be different than they are with the presence of the moon? [1]

32 Would people on Earth experience lunar and/or solar eclipses? Explain why or why not. [2]

33 Infer how the lack of a moon would have affected time keeping throughout the history of humans. What specific time period would have been affected? [1]

Using the following statement, answer questions 34 and 35.

Through accurate measurements of time and studies of growth patterns of fossil life forms, it has been determined that Earth's rate of rotation is slowing down.

34 What unit of time would be most altered by this change in Earth's rotation? [1]

35 List two completely different types of apparent motions observed on Earth today that would not exist if Earth were to stop rotating. [2]

36 The diagram provided below represents the Sun and Earth as viewed from space on a certain date.

(Not drawn to scale)

(a) Using a symbol for the Moon of approximately this size (◯), draw the position of the Moon on the diagram provided *above* at the time when the full-Moon phase is observed from Earth. [1]

(b) Draw an arrow on the diagram provided *above* that shows the motion of Earth that causes surface ocean currents and surface winds to curve (Coriolis effect). [1]

37 The drawing below shows the mile-wide Barringer impact crater located in Diablo Canyon, Arizona. Describe the event that produced this crater. [1]

Base your answers to questions 38 through 40 on the reading passage below and on your knowledge of Earth science.

The Blue Moon

A "Blue Moon" is the name given to the second full moon in a calendar month. Because there are roughly 29.5 days between full moons, it is unusual for two full moons to "fit" into a 30 or 31 day month (and impossible to fit into a 28 or 29 day month, so February can never have a Blue Moon). The saying "Once in a Blue Moon" means a rare occurrence, and predates the current astronomical use of the term, which is quite recent. In fact, Blue Moons are not all that rare, on average there will be one Blue Moon every 2.5 years. After 1999, the next Blue Moons will be in November 2001; July 2004; and June 2007. The last one before 1999 was in July 1996.

The term Blue Moon is believed to have originated in 1883 after the eruption of Krakatoa. The volcano put so much dust in the atmosphere that the Moon actually looked blue in color. This was so unusual that the term "once in a Blue Moon" was coined.

"The Blue Moon"
David R. Williams
nssdc.gsfc.nasa.gov/planetary/lunar/blue_moon.html

38 Explain why a Blue Moon never occurs during the month of February. [1]

39 What is the greatest number of full-Moon phases, visible from Earth, that are possible in a span of 1 year? [1]

40 Draw the relative positions of Earth, the Moon, and the Sun, as viewed from space, so that a full-Moon phase would be visible to an observer on Earth. Label Earth, the Moon, and the Sun in your drawing. [1]

Base your answers to questions 41 and 42 on the information below and on your knowledge of Earth science.

Accurate observations of the Sun were made by a New York State observer. This person observed the time of sunrise and the position of sunrise along the eastern horizon for each day during the month of May.

41 Describe how the time of sunrise changed for the observer each day during the month of May. [1]

42 State the actual Earth motion that causes the Sun to appear to rise each day. [1]

Base your answer to questions 43 through 45 on the diagram provided below and on your knowledge of Earth science. The diagram shows the Sun, Earth, and the Moon's orbit around Earth as viewed from space.

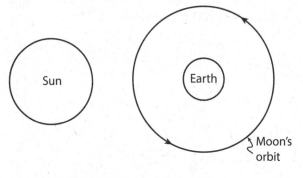

(Not drawn to scale)

43 On the diagram above draw a circle of approximately this size (◯) to represent the Moon's position in its orbit when a solar eclipse is viewed from Earth. [1]

44 Approximately how many complete revolutions does the Moon make around Earth each month? [1]

45 Explain why solar eclipses do not occur every time the Moon revolves around Earth. [1]

Base your answers to questions 46 and 47 on the data table below, which provides information about four of Jupiter's moons.

Data Table			
Moons of Jupiter	**Density (g/cm³)**	**Diameter (km)**	**Distance from Jupiter (km)**
Io	3.5	3630	421,600
Europa	3.0	3138	670,900
Ganymede	1.9	5262	1,070,000
Callisto	1.9	4800	1,883,000

46 Identify the planet in our solar system that is closest in diameter to Callisto. [1]

47 In 1610, Galileo was the first person to observe, with the aid of a telescope, these four moons orbiting Jupiter. Explain why Galileo's observation of this motion did *not* support the geocentric model of our solar system. [1]

Energy in Earth Processes

What You Know About Heat and Temperature

? *What would happen if you stepped outside the Space Shuttle into Earth's thermosphere without wearing an astronaut suit?* **?**

The outer most portion of Earth's atmosphere is called the thermosphere, because it has such high temperatures in the thousands of degrees. Even though the thermosphere is so hot, you would instantly freeze to death if exposed to this environment. Why? While the average atom or molecule in the thermosphere is moving extremely fast (thus a high temperature) the density of the atoms or molecules is extremely low, so there is little thermal energy and available heat. Your unprotected body, having a relatively high amount of thermal energy, would give up its thermal energy as heat to the surrounding thermosphere. When the thermal energy moves out of your body, you freeze.

Find out about how thermal energy, heat, and temperature differ in this topic.

5 Energy in Earth Processes

Vocabulary

condensation	energy	solidification
conduction	heat energy	specific heat
convection	joules	temperature
crystallization	mechanical energy	texture
electromagnetic energy	nuclear decay	vaporization
electromagnetic spectrum	radiation	wavelength

Topic Overview

Energy, like mass, time, or distance, is one of the basic attributes of the universe. **Energy** is the ability to do work. Everything you do—in fact, everything that is done in the universe—involves the use or transfer of energy. Earth can be described as a huge machine driven by two major heat engines—one external and one internal. Earth's external engine—the one that drives most Earth surface processes—is powered mainly by energy from the sun. Heat from the interior of Earth and the resulting mechanical energy powers Earth's internal heat engine.

Electromagnetic Energy

Visible light is the type of electromagnetic energy you are probably most familiar with. Visible light waves are the parts of the electromagnetic energy that is radiated by the sun and observed with the human eye. **Electromagnetic energy** is a type of energy that is radiated, or given off, in the form of transverse waves from all matter not at absolute zero. Absolute zero, that is, 0 Kelvin or −273° Celsius, is theoretically the lowest possible temperature and the one at which particles of matter have no motion. Transverse waves vibrate at right angles to the direction in which they are moving. (See Figure 5-1.)

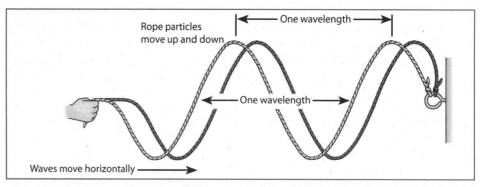

Figure 5-1. A rope model of an electromagnetic transverse wave: As particles of the rope move up and down, the wave moves along the length of the rope. In an electromagnetic wave, there are no moving particles. Instead, the wave vibrates at right angles to the direction in which the wave is moving.

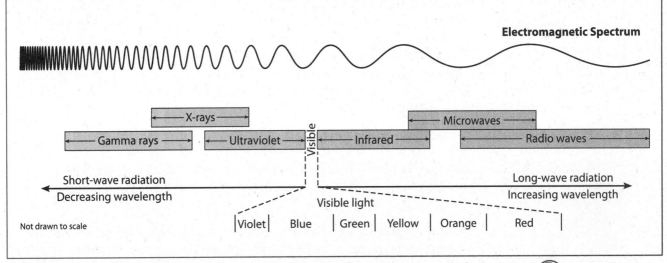

Figure 5-2. An electromagnetic spectrum. Also see a similar chart in the *Earth Science Reference Tables.* Ⓡ

Characteristics and Types of Electromagnetic Energy

Different types of electromagnetic energy are distinguished by their different wavelengths. The **wavelength** is the distance from one crest of a wave to the next crest. A wavelength may also be described as the distance between any two corresponding points on successive cycles, as shown in Figure 5-1. Figure 5-2 shows the various types of electromagnetic energy in order of increasing wavelength. Any model that shows the types of electromagnetic energy is known as an **electromagnetic spectrum.**

Visible light is the only part of the electromagnetic spectrum that can be seen by the human eye. Infrared energy is often felt due to its heating effects. Instruments must be used to observe most forms of electromagnetic energy, including ultraviolet energy, which tans or burns the skin. Electromagnetic energy can be separated into two groups by comparing its wavelengths to those of visible light. Electromagnetic energy with a wavelength longer than visible light is called <u>long-wave electromagnetic energy.</u> Electromagnetic energy with a wavelength shorter than visible light is called a short wave. Some scientists include visible light as a type of short-wave radiation.

Interactions Between Electromagnetic Energy and an Environment

When electromagnetic energy comes in contact with a material, the waves interact with the material. The waves may be

- <u>refracted,</u> or bent, in their passage through materials of varying density so that the direction of the waves is changed
- <u>reflected,</u> or bounced off the material
- scattered, or refracted and/or reflected in various directions
- transmitted, or passed through the material
- <u>absorbed,</u> or taken into the material

Surface Properties and Absorption Characteristics of a surface determine the amount of electromagnetic energy that can be absorbed. For example, the darker the color of the surface of a material, the more visible light it will absorb. This is the reason that a dark-colored asphalt road feels hotter to the bare foot on a sunny day than a light-colored concrete road. Color is the way the human eye distinguishes the various wavelengths of visible light.

The **texture**—roughness or smoothness—of a surface also affects the amount of electromagnetic energy absorbed. The rougher a surface is, the more energy it will absorb and the less it will reflect. For example, mirrors are shiny because they are smooth and reflect most of the incoming visible light.

The more effective a material is at absorbing electromagnetic energy, the better it also is at radiating, or giving off, electromagnetic energy. Thus a dark-colored object will heat up quickly in sunlight, but it will also cool off quickly after sunset because it rapidly radiates electromagnetic energy. The result is that a concrete road will be warmer a few hours after sunset on a sunny day than will a road made of asphalt.

Review Questions

1. Which is the major source of energy for most of Earth's processes?

   (1) radioactive decay within Earth's interior
   (2) convection currents in Earth's mantle
   (3) radiation received from the sun
   (4) earthquakes along fault zones

2. All objects warmer than 0 Kelvin (absolute zero) must be

   (1) radiating electromagnetic energy
   (2) condensing to form a gas
   (3) warmer than 0°C
   (4) expanding in size

3. The various types of electromagnetic energy are distinguished from one another by their

   (1) temperature
   (2) wavelengths
   (3) height of waves
   (4) speed of travel in space

4. Which type of electromagnetic energy has the shortest wavelength?

   (1) ultraviolet   (3) gamma rays
   (2) visible light   (4) radio waves

5. In the visible spectrum, which color has the longest wavelength?

   (1) red   (3) orange
   (2) green   (4) violet

6. Which statement about electromagnetic energy is correct?

   (1) Violet light has a longer wavelength than red light.
   (2) X-rays have a longer wavelength than infrared waves.
   (3) Radio waves have a shorter wavelength than ultraviolet rays.
   (4) Gamma rays have a shorter wavelength than visible light.

7. As electromagnetic energy from a heat source interacts with its environment, it is being

   (1) reflected only
   (2) refracted only
   (3) absorbed only
   (4) reflected, refracted, and absorbed

8. When electromagnetic energy travels from air into water, the waves are bent due to the density differences between the air and water. What is this bending called?

9. Which would absorb the most solar radiation, if you assume that each covers an equal geographic area?

   (1) a freshwater lake
   (2) a snow field
   (3) a sandy beach
   (4) a forest

10. Which type of surface would most likely be the best reflector of electromagnetic energy?

    (1) dark-colored and rough
    (2) dark-colored and smooth
    (3) light-colored and rough
    (4) light-colored and smooth

11. An object that is a good radiator of electromagnetic waves is also a good

    (1) insulator from heat
    (2) reflector of heat
    (3) absorber of electromagnetic energy
    (4) refractor of electromagnetic energy

12. A homeowner decides to install carpet in a room that receives the most sunlight. A carpet with which characteristics will absorb the most radiation from the sun?

    (1) smooth texture and light color
    (2) smooth texture and dark color
    (3) rough texture and light color
    (4) rough texture and dark color

Transfer of Energy

Energy moves away from a region of high concentration, or <u>source,</u> to a region of low concentration, or sink. Energy transfer from a region of higher temperature to a region of lower temperature is called **heat energy.** Heat transfers thermal energy, the energy of the motions of atoms and molecules.

Achieving Dynamic Equilibrium

Heat will continue to move from the source to the sink until their energies are equal, establishing a <u>dynamic equilibrium.</u> At dynamic equilibrium a region loses and gains equal amounts of energy. If the dynamic equilibrium is between all forms of energy, then the temperature of the region or system will remain constant.

Methods of Energy Transfer

Heat is transferred from an area of high concentration to an area of low concentration by one of three methods—conduction, convection, or radiation.

Conduction The transfer of heat energy from atom to atom or molecule to molecule when vibrating atoms or molecules collide is **conduction.** Conduction is most effective in solids—especially metals—because the atoms or molecules are closer together than in gases and liquids. However, some heat conduction can take place in liquids and gases. In Figure 5-3 conduction is the main method of heat transfer from the source to the sink through the metal bar.

Convection The transfer of heat by movement in fluids—gases and liquids—caused by differences in density within the fluids is **convection.** Warmer portions of the fluid usually have lower density and tend to rise above the cooler portions. The reason for the rise of less dense fluids is that gravity pulls less on objects that are lower in density and pulls more on objects of higher

> **Digging** Deeper
>
> The portion of space that separates regions of different properties is called an interface, or boundary. Energy is transferred across interfaces, such as the metal bar shown in Figure 5-3, or the region of space between the sun and Earth.

Figure 5-3. An experiment in heat energy transfer: In this experiment, the amounts of heat transferred from the hot calorimeter (the source) to the cold calorimeter (the sink) and the methods of that transfer are investigated. A calorimeter is an insulated container used in energy experiments.

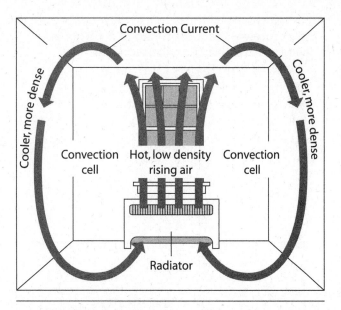

Convection Current

Cooler, more dense

Cooler, more dense

Convection cell

Hot, low density rising air

Convection cell

Radiator

Figure 5-4. **Heating a room by convection:** The air around a radiator is heated by conduction and by infrared radiation emitted by the radiator. Greenhouse gases (carbon dioxide and water vapor) in the room absorb the radiation. The heat is then carried around the room by convection currents.

density. Higher-density portions of a fluid are pulled down and displace less dense objects, pushing them upward. The result is a convection current—a circulatory motion—that transfers heat energy from one place to another. (See Figures 5-3 and 5-4.) Convection currents transfer heat throughout Earth's atmosphere, hydrosphere, and most likely below the lithosphere.

Radiation The method by which heat is transferred via electromagnetic waves is **radiation.** No medium is needed to transfer the transverse waves that carry electromagnetic energy; this energy can radiate from its source across empty space. Radiation can also occur in liquids, solids, and gases—such as sunlight being transmitted through the atmosphere (gas) or through window glass (solid). X-ray electromagnetic radiation can pass through all but the densest materials. Radiation is also the method by which the sun's electromagnetic energy moves through space to other objects in the solar system. The higher an object's temperature, the more electromagnetic energy it gives off. In Figure 5-3, the higher the temperature of the metal bar, the more infrared energy it will radiate to the hand. (See Figure 5-2 and the Electromagnetic Spectrum in the ⓡ *Earth Science Reference Tables.*)

Review Questions

For questions 13 through 16, refer to the following diagram. A student is using the apparatus shown to perform an investigation. The two calorimeters contain equal amounts of water, and the metal bar is touching the water inside each calorimeter. At the beginning of the investigation, the temperature of the water was 100°C in calorimeter A and 20°C in calorimeter B. The room temperature is 20°C.

Thermometer

Metal bar

Insulated cap

Water at 100°C

Water at 20°C

Calorimeter A

Calorimeter B

13. If this were a closed system, what would be the temperature when the system reaches equilibrium?

    (1) 100°C   (2) 75°C   (3) 60°C   (4) 40°C

14. Which conclusion should the student make after performing this investigation?

    (1) The energy gained by the cold water equaled the energy lost by the hot water.
    (2) The energy gained by the cold water was less than the energy lost by the hot water.
    (3) The change in temperature of the cold-water thermometer equaled the change in temperature of the hot-water thermometer.
    (4) Energy was transferred between the two calorimeters primarily by radiation.

15. Which procedure would best increase the amount of heat energy that is actually gained by calorimeter B?

    (1) increasing the length of the metal bar
    (2) increasing the thickness of the metal bar
    (3) circulating air over the metal bar
    (4) placing insulation around the metal bar

16. Which graph best represents the probable relationship between the temperatures of the two calorimeters and the time for this heat transfer investigation?

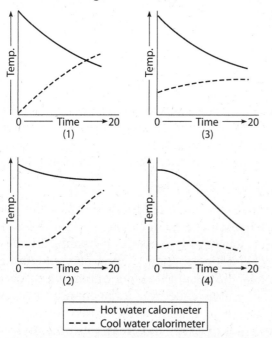

(1)

(3)

(2)

(4)

```
——— Hot water calorimeter
- - - - Cool water calorimeter
```

17. The environment is in dynamic equilibrium when it is gaining

(1) less energy than it is losing
(2) more energy than it is losing
(3) the same amount of energy it is losing

18. Differences in density cause energy to be transferred by which method?

(1) absorption   (3) convection
(2) conduction   (4) radiation

19. Water is being heated in a beaker as shown.

Heat Source

Which of the following drawings shows the most probable movement of water in the beaker due to the heating?

(1)   (2)   (3)   (4)

20. At which temperature will an object radiate the greatest amount of electromagnetic energy?

(1) 0°F
(2) 5°C
(3) 10°F
(4) 230 K

21. What method of energy transfer requires no medium for transfer?

(1) conduction
(2) convection
(3) refraction
(4) radiation

22. By which process does starlight travel through space?

(1) absorption
(2) conduction
(3) vaporization
(4) radiation

23. By which process do light rays pass through window glass?

(1) conduction
(2) convection
(3) radiation
(4) compression

24. Which diagram correctly indicates why convection currents form in water when water is heated?

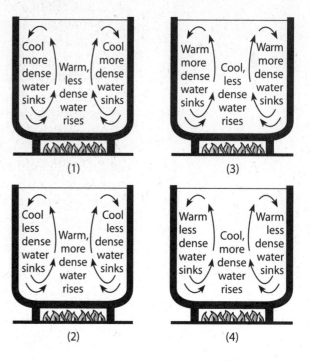

(1)

(3)

(2)

(4)

Transformation of Energy

A transformation of energy is the changing of one type of energy into another type of energy. Some of these transformations are discussed in the following paragraphs.

Heat Production

Transformations of energy often occur when there is friction. For example, as a glacier flows, some of its kinetic energy is transformed into heat energy at the interface of the glacier and its valley walls. This transformation occurs because of friction between the moving glacier and the rock of the valley walls. Transformation of energy also occurs when wind blows over the ocean, creating waves and surface ocean currents. At the interface of the atmosphere and hydrosphere, heat is formed.

Transformations of Mechanical Energy

All the energy of an object or system not related to the individual motions of atoms and molecules is **mechanical energy.** It can also be defined as the total of the potential and kinetic energy of an object or system. An object in motion has a kind of energy called <u>kinetic energy.</u> The faster something moves and the more mass it has, the greater its kinetic energy. Objects or systems can also have a kind of energy called <u>potential energy</u>—energy related to position or phase. It may be thought of as "stored" energy. The higher an object is above the center of Earth, the greater its potential to fall—the greater its potential energy. The more mass that is involved, the more potential energy that is present.

Either kinetic or potential energy can be transformed into the other. For example, water at the top of a waterfall has potential energy because of its position relative to Earth's center. As the water falls to a lower level, some of its potential energy is transformed into kinetic energy, resulting in an increase in speed.

Transformation of Electromagnetic Wavelength

One example of wavelength transformation is when electromagnetic energy is absorbed by an object and reradiated at a longer wavelength. This occurs because energy moves from regions of greater to lower concentrations, and the region of greater concentration usually has a higher temperature and emits shorter wavelengths. This type of transformation is very common at Earth's surface. There the relatively short-wavelength ultraviolet and visible radiations from the sun are absorbed and reradiated as longer wavelength infrared radiations. Since Earth's surface is much lower in temperature than the sun, it emits longer wavelengths than the sun's surface.

Temperature and Heat

The temperature of an object or region is directly related to the amount of heat, or thermal energy, in the object or region.

Temperature

Temperature is a measure of the average kinetic energy of the particles of a body of matter—and is NOT a type of energy. According to the theory of matter, the particles of every material are in continuous, random motion, and therefore have kinetic energy. At any moment, some of the particles have more kinetic energy than others. The greater the average kinetic energy of the particles of matter, the higher the temperature.

Your senses respond to temperature by sensations of hot and cold. However, to accurately measure temperature you need to use a thermometer. A thermometer indicates temperature on a scale marked in degrees. Three different temperature scales are in use in the United States. Relationships among the three temperature scales—Fahrenheit, Celsius, and Kelvin—are given in the *Earth Science Reference Tables*. Figure 5-5 illustrates the method of converting among the three temperature scales.

Heat and Thermal Energy

As explained earlier, thermal energy is the energy of the motion of atoms and molecules. When the thermal energy of one object is greater—has a higher temperature—than another, some of the thermal energy will be transferred from the hotter body to the colder one. The type of energy that is transferred from hotter to colder objects is heat energy. It is measured in **joules**—a metric unit of energy or work.

Specific Heat

It takes 4.18 joules to raise the temperature of one gram of liquid water one degree Celsius. It takes only about 0.84 joules (one fifth as much) to raise the temperature of one gram of a typical rock (basalt) one degree Celsius. The quantity of heat needed to raise the temperature of one gram of any substance one degree Celsius is called the **specific heat** of that substance. In simpler terms, specific heat is the resistance a material presents to heating up or cooling off.

Liquid water has the highest specific heat of naturally occurring substances, which is why large bodies of water have a major moderating effect on weather and climate. All other naturally occurring substances have a specific heat less than that of liquid water. Therefore, gaining or losing the same amount of heat causes equal masses of these other substances to heat up or cool off, respectively, faster than water. See Specific Heats of Some Common Materials in the *Earth Science Reference Tables*.

Figure 5-5. Converting among the three temperature scales: Note that each line on the thermometer scales is two degrees for Fahrenheit and one degree for Celsius and Kelvin. The lines are so close that a reading within one degree of Fahrenheit and 0.5 degree of Celsius or Kelvin is acceptable. To convert among the scales, hold a straight edge on the value you are converting from. Then read the value of the other temperature scale on the line. For example, room temperature is 68°F, which converts to 20°C and 293 K. Ice melts at 32°F, 0°C, and 273 K. Water boils at 212°F, 100°C, and 373 K.

Review Questions

25. How do the wavelengths of electromagnetic energy absorbed by materials on Earth compare to the wavelengths radiated by materials on Earth?

(1) The reradiated wavelengths are shorter.
(2) The reradiated wavelengths are longer.
(3) The absorbed and reradiated wavelengths are the same.

26. The temperature of an object is determined by the

(1) average kinetic energy of its molecules
(2) average potential energy of its molecules
(3) total kinetic energy of the object
(4) total potential energy of the object

27. The temperature of a stovetop is 65°C. What is the equivalent Fahrenheit temperature?

(1) 126°F   (2) 132°F   (3) 144°F   (4) 149°F

28. A boulder falls freely from point A to point B, as shown in the following diagram.

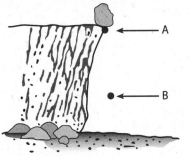

Which statement best explains the relationship between the height of the boulder and its potential and kinetic energy as it falls?

(1) Its potential energy decreases, and its kinetic energy increases.
(2) Its potential energy increases, and its kinetic energy decreases.
(3) Its potential energy and kinetic energy both decrease.
(4) Its potential energy and kinetic energy both increase.

29. Equal masses of lead, granite, basalt, and water at 5°C are exposed to equal quantities of heat energy. Which would be the first to show a temperature rise of 10°C?

(1) lead
(2) granite
(3) basalt
(4) water

30. During some winters in the Finger Lakes region of New York State, the lake water remains unfrozen even though the land around the lakes is frozen and covered with snow. The primary cause of this difference is that water

(1) gains heat during evaporation
(2) is at a lower elevation
(3) has a higher specific heat
(4) reflects more radiation

Heat Energy and Changes of State

Matter may exist in the solid, liquid, or gaseous states, or phases. An increase or decrease in energy and temperature of matter can cause the matter to go from one state to another.

Types of Change of State

The following are some changes of state.

- Melting is the changing of a solid to a liquid.
- **Solidification,** or freezing, is the changing of a liquid to a solid. If solidification results in a solid with an ordered pattern of atoms, the process is **crystallization.**
- Evaporation, or **vaporization** is the changing of a liquid to a gas, or vapor.
- **Condensation** is the changing of a gas, or vapor, to a liquid.
- Sublimation is the changing of a gas directly to a solid (also called deposition), or from a solid directly to a gas—without going through a liquid state.

The changes in state of water are shown in Figure 5-6. When water changes state from a solid to a liquid to a gas, it absorbs heat, molecular movement speeds up, and the tightly bound water molecules become less and less tightly bound. When water changes state from a gas to a liquid to a solid, water releases stored heat, molecular movements slow down, and molecules become more tightly bound.

Stored Heat and Changes of State

When a material is in one of the three states, its temperature rises as heat is added to it. If, however, the material is in the process of changing state,

Figure 5-6. Changes in state of water: When water changes phase from a solid to a liquid to a gas, it absorbs heat and changes tightly bound water molecules of a solid to less tightly bound molecules of liquid water and gaseous water. To go from a gas to a liquid to a solid, water releases stored heat and the molecular movements slow down.

its temperature remains the same as it is heated. During the change of state, the added heat energy is not increasing the kinetic energy of the atoms or molecules, and therefore, the temperature does not change. The added heat energy is being converted to a kind of potential energy, or stored heat.

In order for a change of state from a solid to a liquid, or from a liquid to a gas to occur, the substance must gain heat. When the change of state is from a gas to a liquid, or from a liquid to a solid, the substance must lose stored heat. The amount of stored heat, gained or lost, varies with the particular substance and type of change of state.

Stored Heat and Changes of State of Water

Figure 5-7 shows how the temperature of a fixed amount of water changes as it is heated at a constant rate from ice—solid water—at –100°C to gaseous water—water vapor—at 200°C. The temperature is plotted against time in minutes (upper scale of the graph) and the corresponding amount of added heat (lower scale of the graph). You can see that the temperature remains constant at 0°C for almost 2 minutes while the water is changing from the solid state to the liquid state. There is another constant-temperature interval, of more than 10 minutes, at 100°C while the water is changing from the liquid state to the gaseous phase. The reason for these intervals of constant temperature is that the heat being added at those times is being changed to stored heat (potential energy). To find the amount of energy gained or released by water as it changes state, refer to Ⓡ Figure 5-6 or to Properties of Water in the *Earth Science Reference Tables.*

Figure 5-7. Heating or cooling of water: When read from left to right, the graph shows the temperature change of one gram of water as heat is added at a constant rate—209.3 joules per minute. When read from right to left, the graph shows the temperature change if 209.3 joules per gram is released from the water. The flat portion of the graph shows data as water absorbs or releases stored heat associated with a change of state. The steeply sloped portions of the graph show data as water is increasing or decreasing in temperature, but not experiencing a change of state.

Earth's Energy Supply

The energy for some of Earth's processes comes from Earth's interior. However, most of the energy Earth needs comes from the sun's electromagnetic radiation.

Solar Energy

The sun radiates, or gives off, and Earth receives a wide range of electromagnetic energy of various wavelengths. This solar electromagnetic spectrum includes X-rays, ultraviolet rays, visible light, and infrared rays. Of all the types of electromagnetic radiation from the sun, the one with the greatest intensity is visible light.

Solar energy is produced by <u>nuclear</u> <u>fusion</u>—a process in which the nuclei (centers) of atoms are combined to form larger atomic nuclei—releasing great amounts of energy in the process. Nuclear fusion can only occur under the conditions of very high temperature and pressure, for example, in the interior of a star. Figure 5-8 illustrates the type of fusion believed to be most common in the sun. A small fraction of the energy produced by nuclear fusion is radiated as electromagnetic energy and received by Earth—thus "fueling" most Earth processes.

Earth's Own Energy

Heat energy from Earth's interior is converted into mechanical energy for mountain building, volcanic eruptions, plate movements, and other internal movements. Some of this heat remains from when Earth formed, and some is produced as the result of materials being pulled by gravity towards Earth's center. Probably most of Earth's interior energy comes from the nuclear decay of radioactive materials within Earth. **Nuclear decay,** also called nuclear fission or radioactive decay, is the process by which unstable or radioactive atomic nuclei of elements, such as uranium and radium, split to form lighter elements. In the process, large amounts of

Figure 5-8. A simple model of nuclear fusion in our sun: The high heat and pressure of our sun combine the nuclei of hydrogen to produce helium, energy, and subatomic particles.

Figure 5-9. The process of nuclear decay (of uranium-235): The nuclei of radioactive elements are unstable, and they can split to form elements with smaller nuclei, subatomic particles, and large amounts of energy.

energy are released. Nuclear decay is the process employed in the atomic reactors used to produce a portion of the nation's electric supply. Figure 5-9 illustrates the process of nuclear decay.

Another source of Earth's energy is the energy created by the impact of meteoroids, asteroids, and comets with Earth's atmosphere and Earth's surface. These impacts continue today although they are likely not as frequent as in ancient Earth history. There are many other minor sources of Earth energy, including the gravitational energy of the Sun and Moon creating the tidal energy of the oceans and many sources of friction.

Review Questions

31. At which temperature will ice melt under normal conditions?

(1) 0 K (2) 32 K (3) 212 K (4) 273 K

32. The change from the gas, or vapor phase, to the liquid phase is called

(1) evaporation   (3) precipitation
(2) condensation   (4) transpiration

33. Which diagram correctly shows the processes that change the phases of matter?

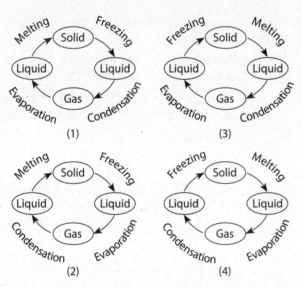

(1)   (3)

(2)   (4)

34. Two identical towels are hanging on a clothesline in the sun. One towel is wet; the other is dry. The wet towel feels much cooler than the dry towel because the

(1) dry towel receives more heat energy from the sun
(2) dry towel has more room for heat storage than the wet towel
(3) presence of water in the wet towel requires an additional amount of heat energy to bring about a temperature change
(4) water in the wet towel prevents absorption of heat energy

35. Water loses energy when it changes phase from

(1) liquid to solid
(2) solid to liquid
(3) liquid to gas
(4) solid to gas

Base your answers to questions 36 through 42 on the following graph. The graph shows the temperatures recorded when a sample of water was heated from –100°C to 200°C. The water received the same amount of heat every minute.

36. For the time on the graph represented by the line from point B to point C, the water was

(1) freezing
(2) melting
(3) condensing
(4) boiling

37. At which point in time would most of the water be in the liquid phase?

(1) 1 minute
(2) 14 minutes
(3) 16 minutes
(4) 4 minutes

38. What is the rate of temperature change between points C and D?

(1) 10°C/min
(2) 25°C/min
(3) 50°C/min
(4) 150°C/min

39. The greatest amount of energy was absorbed by the water between points

(1) A and B
(2) B and C
(3) C and D
(4) D and E

40. During which time interval was the rate of temperature change the greatest?

(1) A to B
(2) B to C
(3) C to D
(4) D to E

41. What is the most probable explanation for the constant temperature between points D and E on the graph?

(1) The added heat was radiated as fast as it was absorbed.
(2) The added heat was lost to the surroundings.
(3) The added heat changed liquid water to water vapor.
(4) The added heat changed water vapor to liquid water.

42. Which change occurred between point A and point B?

(1) Ice melted.
(2) Ice warmed.
(3) Water froze.
(4) Water condensed.

43. What is the major source of energy for Earth's surface?

(1) convective motion within the mantle
(2) energy released during the collision of tectonic plates
(3) interaction of major air masses as Earth rotates on its axis
(4) electromagnetic energy from the sun

44. The sun's energy is most likely the result of

(1) the burning of fossil fuels
(2) gravitational contraction of the sun
(3) a nuclear reaction involving the combination of atoms
(4) a nuclear reaction involving a radioactive decay

45. A source of energy for the high temperatures found deep within Earth is

(1) tidal friction
(2) incoming solar radiation
(3) nuclear decay of radioactive materials
(4) meteorite bombardment of Earth

46. As the lake surface freezes in the winter, how many joules of heat are released by each gram of water?

47. Which process requires water to gain 2260 joules of energy per gram?

(1) vaporization   (3) melting
(2) condensation   (4) freezing

48. Describe two sources of Earth's energy that are not produced in Earth's interior or produced by the sun.

Directions

Review the Test-Taking Strategies section of this book. Then answer the following questions. Read each question carefully and answer with a correct choice or response.

Part A

1 A concrete play area is resurfaced with dark-colored asphalt. Compared with the amount of heat energy that was absorbed by the old concrete surface, the amount of heat energy absorbed by the dark-colored asphalt surface will most probably be
   (1) less
   (2) greater
   (3) sometimes the same and sometimes less
   (4) sometimes greater and sometimes less

2 The following diagram represents the path of visible light as it travels from air to water to air through a glass container of water.

The light does not travel in a straight line because of
   (1) convection
   (2) scattering
   (3) absorption
   (4) refraction

3 An ice cube is placed in a glass of water at room temperature. Which heat exchange occurs between the ice and the water within the first minute?
   (1) The ice cube gains heat and the water loses heat.
   (2) The ice cube loses heat and the water gains heat
   (3) Both the ice cube and the water gain heat.
   (4) Both the ice cube and the water lose heat.

4 The following map shows four locations in a temperature field. The temperature of each location is given in degrees Celsius.

Heat energy will normally flow from
   (1) A to B   (2) A to C   (3) B to D   (4) D to C

5 A barefoot student steps on a hot concrete surface. Most of the heat transferred to the student's skin by this contact is by the process of
   (1) convection   (3) vaporization
   (2) conduction   (4) radiation

6 During a volcanic eruption, a rock is thrust upward into the air from point A to point B as shown in the following diagram.

Which graph best represents the relationship between the height of the rock and its potential energy (PE) as it rises?

7 The transfer of heat from the sun to Earth takes place by
(1) conduction
(2) convection
(3) radiation
(4) evaporation

8 A camper takes a 100-gram piece of basalt rock from a campfire and places it in a cup holding 250 milliliters of water. The temperature of the rock is 300°C and the temperature of the water is 20°C. Air temperature is 20°C. In the process of heating the water with the basalt, the temperature of the basalt decreased more than the temperature of the water increased. This difference most likely occurred because
(1) water has a higher specific heat than basalt
(2) water has a higher density than basalt
(3) the basalt had a greater mass than the water did
(4) the basalt had a higher starting temperature than the water did

9 Water vapor solidifies in the atmosphere to form ice crystals in clouds. Which statement best describes the exchange of heat energy during this process?
(1) Heat energy is transferred from the atmosphere to the water vapor.
(2) Heat energy is released from the water vapor into the atmosphere.
(3) Heat energy is transferred equally to and from the water vapor.
(4) No heat energy is exchanged between the atmosphere and the water vapor.

10 Which process results in a release of stored heat energy?
(1) melting ice
(2) heating of liquid water
(3) condensation of water vapor
(4) evaporation of water

11 Which process requires the most absorption of energy by water?
(1) melting 1 gram of ice
(2) condensing 1 gram of water vapor
(3) vaporizing 1 gram of liquid water
(4) freezing 1 gram of liquid water

12 The sun's energy is often converted into potential energy by
(1) evaporation of water from the oceans
(2) formation of fog in a valley
(3) freezing of water droplets on a highway
(4) precipitation of rain from a thunderstorm

Base your answers to questions 13 through 15 on the following graph. The graph shows the amount of heat energy (joules) needed to raise the temperature of 1-gram samples of four different materials.

13 Which of these materials has the highest specific heat?
(1) liquid water   (3) basalt
(2) dry air   (4) iron

14 If all four materials were heated to 100°C and then allowed to cool, which material would show the most rapid drop in temperature?
(1) basalt   (3) dry air
(2) iron   (4) liquid water

15 Which statement is best supported by the graph?
(1) The same amount of heat energy is required to raise the temperature of each material by 10°C.
(2) The temperature of a material with a high specific heat is raised faster than that of a material with a low specific heat.
(3) Three of the four materials have the same specific heat.
(4) The amount of heat energy needed to produce an equal temperature change varies with the materials heated.

Part B

Base your answers to questions 16 through 24 on the following diagram and data tables. The diagram represents a light source located equal distance from two air-filled metal cans. One can is shiny, and the other is black. Both cans were heated for 10 minutes. The lamp was removed, and both cans were allowed to cool for 10 minutes. Temperature readings of the cans' interiors were recorded each minute for the 20 minutes of heating and cooling. The data tables show these temperatures. A graph is provided to allow you to plot the given data and to assist you in answering the questions.

Black can   Shiny can

Lamp On											
Time (min)	0	1	2	3	4	5	6	7	8	9	10
Temperature of Shiny Can (°C)	20	20	21	22	23	24	24.5	25	25.5	26	26.5
Temperature of Black Can (°C)	20	21	23	25	27	28.5	29.5	30.5	31	31.5	32
Lamp Off											
Time (min)	11	12	13	14	15	16	17	18	19	20	
Temperature of Shiny Can (°C)	26.5	26	25.5	25	24.5	24	24	23.5	23.5	23	
Temperature of Black Can (°C)	31.5	31	30.5	29.5	28.5	27.5	26.5	25.5	25	24.5	

16 On the graph at the right, plot the data given in the tables for each can. [4]

17 At which time during the investigation was the temperature in the black can 31°C and the temperature in the shiny can 25.5°C? [1]

18 At what rate did the temperature of the black can change during the first 10 minutes of the investigation? [1]

19 By which process was most of the heat energy transferred from the light source to the cans during the first 10 minutes of the investigation? [1]

20 Why did the black can become warmer than the shiny can during the heating period? [1]

21 By what method does most of the energy travel through the cans?

22 Explain what could be done to the black can to increase its absorption of energy given off by the light source.

23 How would the specific heat of the iron in the cans compare to the specific heat of the dry air in the cans?

24 List the can type and the time when the most energy would be emitted by a can in the experiment.

Base your answers to questions 25 through 28 on the following temperature field map. The map shows 25 measurements (in °C) that were made in a temperature field and recorded as shown. The dots represent the exact locations of the measurements. A and B are locations within the field.

Temperature Field Map (°C)

```
• 23    • 24    • 25    A • 27    • 26

• 23    • 24    • 25    • 26      • 26

• 22    • 23    B • 24    • 25    • 25

• 21    • 22    • 24    • 24      • 24

• 20    • 22    • 21    • 22      • 22
```

```
0      1.0     2.0     3.0     4.0
└───────┴───────┴───────┴───────┘
              meters
```

25 On the temperature field map provided, draw three isotherms—the 23°C isotherm, the 24°C isotherm, and the 25°C isotherm. [2]

26 Calculate the temperature gradient between locations A and B on the temperature field map, following the directions given.
  a. Write the equation for the gradient. [1]
  b. Substitute data from the map into the equation. [1]
  c. Calculate the gradient, and label it with proper units. [1]

27 Place a capital letter S on the map at the location that would be considered an energy source. [1]

28 Place a capital letter L on the map at the location that has the least amount of kinetic energy. [1]

Part C

The following paragraph provides information about geothermal energy as an alternate energy source. Use data from the paragraph and your knowledge of earth science to answer questions 29 through 32.

One alternate source of energy humans can substitute for declining supplies of fossil fuels is geothermal energy. Geothermal energy is the heat energy usually stored in rocks and water beneath Earth's solid surface. It is generally believed that hot rocks are available at any location if you drill deep enough, but drilling more than few thousand feet is usually too expensive and not economically practical. Where hot rocks with hot gaseous water (steam) and/or hot liquid water are found in large quantities, within a few thousand feet of Earth's surface, the geothermal energy may be used in place of fossil fuels. The hot gaseous or liquid water is either used directly to heat homes and industries, or it is used to generate electricity in a facility similar to ones that use fossil fuels to heat water to produce electricity.

29 Explain what nuclear, or atomic, process most likely results in geothermal energy. Also state why this nuclear energy will last longer than the supply of fossil fuels. [2]

30 Explain how the nuclear process that results in geothermal energy is different from the process that produces energy within the sun. [1]

31 What evidence in the *Earth Science Reference Tables* suggests the existence of geothermal energy? [1]

32 There are two geothermal deposits of equal mass and depth. One deposit is all steam and the other is all hot liquid water. Which deposit would most likely produce the greater amount of geothermal energy? Why? [1]

33 About 5 percent of the energy used by people in the United States comes from hydroelectric facilities. These facilities use the power of falling water from streams and lakes to turn mechanical devices to generate electricity. Using the information above and your knowledge of earth science, explain how energy produced by hydroelectric facilities can be considered the result of both solar energy and gravitational energy. [2]

Insolation and the Seasons

What You Know About Incoming Solar Radiation

? *Where on Earth would you have to use blackout shades to get a good night's sleep in July?* **?**

Consider three different locations—Quito, Ecuador, near the equator, Syracuse, New York, and the North Pole. Where would you get the most daylight every year?

You might think the tropical equator is the place, with its 12 hours of daylight each day. But is that more than anyone in the other locations?

It certainly is for the winter residents of Syracuse, New York, who get only nine hours of daylight each day in late December. But in June, they have over 15 hours of daylight each day.

If you lived at the North Pole, you would have daylight 24 hours each day from March 21 until September 21! But during the other half of the year, you would have zero hours of daylight each day. But it all averages out, just like it does everywhere else on Earth. No matter where you are, you have one-half year's worth of daylight every year.

6 Insolation and the Seasons

Vocabulary

angle of incidence	greenhouse gases	ozone
deforestation	heat budget	sunspot
El Niño	ice ages	transpiration
global warming	insolation	

Topic Overview

Without energy from the sun, conditions on Earth would be drastically different. Energy from the sun drives global wind patterns, ocean currents, and the water cycle. Life processes of plants and animals also depend almost entirely on energy from the sun. Without solar energy, Earth would be a frozen wasteland, as all water and all the gases of Earth's atmosphere would exist only in the solid state. There would be no life and no rock cycle as it is now known. Very little weathering and erosion would occur. Both Earth and its moon would be almost totally dark.

Solar Radiation and Insolation

A body of matter that is not at absolute zero emits electromagnetic energy. This energy is radiated over a portion of the electromagnetic spectrum, with more of the energy radiated at some wavelengths than at others. The rate at which energy is radiated is called the intensity of radiation. In general, the higher the temperature of a body of matter, the shorter the wavelength at which the maximum intensity of radiation occurs. At the

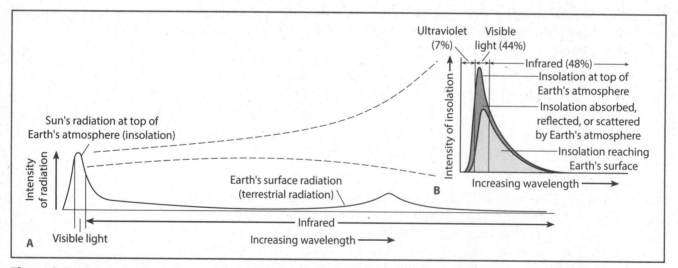

Figure 6-1. Intensity of insolation received by Earth and energy radiated from Earth into space: (A) The sun, being much hotter than Earth (sun 5800°C; Earth 15°C) emits shorter wavelengths of radiation than Earth does. Earth's surface emits only long wavelengths—infrared radiation. (B) The total amount of energy received by Earth's surface equals approximately 50 percent of the insolation that reaches the outermost part of Earth's atmosphere.

sun's temperature, the maximum intensity of radiation occurs in the range of visible wavelengths of electromagnetic energy. (See Figure 6-1.)

Insolation (**IN**coming **SOL**ar radi**ATION**) is the portion of the sun's output of electromagnetic radiation that is received by Earth at the outermost part of our atmosphere. The intensity of insolation is the relative strength of the sun's radiation that reaches a specific area of Earth in a specific amount of time. Figure 6-1 shows how the intensity of insolation varies with wavelength. The maximum intensity of insolation occurs in the range of wavelengths of visible light. However, approximately 48 percent of the total energy received at the outermost part of our atmosphere is infrared, a type of long-wave radiation.

Memory Jogger

Recall that a wavelength in an electromagnetic wave, as in other waves, is the distance between two successive peaks.

Effects of Earth's Atmosphere on Insolation

The insolation reaching Earth's surface is different from the insolation entering Earth's upper atmosphere, as shown in Figure 6-1. Since the atmosphere is mostly transparent to visible light, it transmits most of the visible light from the sun. However, insolation may be absorbed, reflected, or scattered before reaching Earth's surface. The atmosphere affects insolation in several ways as summarized in Figure 6-3.

Absorption of Ultraviolet and Infrared Most incoming ultraviolet radiation and other short wave radiation are absorbed by Earth's atmosphere. Nearly all ultraviolet radiation is absorbed in Earth's upper atmosphere (stratosphere) by **ozone** (O_3), a form of oxygen gas. In recent years, the amount of ozone in the upper atmosphere has been reduced by the chlorine and fluorine that have escaped into the atmosphere—mostly due to human activities. The result is that more ultraviolet radiation has been reaching Earth's surface. Ultraviolet radiation can be lethal to many forms of life and is a direct cause of skin cancer in humans. Regions in which the amount of ozone has been greatly reduced—popularly called "ozone holes"—occur near Earth's poles, especially the South Pole. (See Figure 6-2)

Other gases found in the atmosphere can absorb long-wave infrared radiation. Water vapor, carbon dioxide (CO_2), and methane (CH_4) are three gases that absorb much incoming infrared radiation.

Reflection and Scattering When clouds are present, much of the incident, or incoming, solar energy is reflected back into space. However, some of it, including some visible light, is reflected to the atmosphere or toward Earth's surface.

Random reflection, or scattering, of insolation is caused by aerosols—finely dispersed solids and liquids suspended in air. Besides ice crystals and water droplets, the dispersed materials include dust, bacteria, meteor fragments, volcanic ash, and various other air pollutants. As the concentration of aerosols increases, the scattering of insolation also increases, thus reducing the amount of insolation that reaches Earth's surface.

Balance of Energy from Insolation and Earth's Surface Radiation

About half of the insolation that strikes Earth's upper atmosphere reaches Earth's land and water surfaces, as shown in Figure 6-3. Some of the insolation is reflected and some is absorbed. Insolation that is absorbed by

1979

1992

Area where hole is growing

Ozone level
500

100

Figure 6-2. The "hole" in the ozone shield: These satellite maps show how much the "hole" in the ozone shield above the South Pole grew in just over a decade.

Earth's surface is partly converted to heat and tends to raise the temperature of the surface. However, Earth's surface also radiates electromagnetic energy, thus tending to lower its temperature. Over time, the amount of energy absorbed from insolation is generally equal to Earth's surface radiation, and thus temperature and heat are balanced.

Factors Affecting Absorption and Reflection of Insolation

When insolation reaches Earth's surface, many factors affect whether it is absorbed or reflected. These factors include the angle at which the insolation reaches Earth's surface, the characteristics of the surface, and how the energy of the insolation interacts with Earth's surface materials and living things.

Angle of Incidence One important factor affecting the absorption of insolation is the angle at which the insolation strikes Earth's surface—called the **angle of incidence**. The altitude of the sun—which varies with time of day, latitude, and season—determines the angle of incidence. The higher the sun is in the sky, the higher the angle of incidence, and the more insolation is absorbed. Generally, a lower angle of incidence means that more insolation is reflected and less is absorbed. (See Table 6-1.)

Surface Characteristics Texture and color also affect the absorption of insolation by Earth's surfaces. When a surface has a rough or uneven texture, more insolation is absorbed and less is reflected. Surfaces with darker colors tend to absorb more insolation than they reflect. Surfaces with lighter colors tend to reflect more insolation than they absorb. For example, ice and snow reflect almost all of the insolation that strikes them. This is one reason the polar regions stay cool even during summer's six months of continuous sunshine.

Change of State and Transpiration When energy from insolation reaches Earth's surfaces, it interacts with the materials and living things found there. For example, energy from insolation can cause water to change state—melting of ice or snow into liquid water or evaporating liquid water to form water vapor. Energy from insolation also fuels plant growth and increases **transpiration**—a process by which plants release water vapor into the atmosphere as part of their life functions. When energy from insolation is involved in change of state and transpiration, it is not available to raise the temperature of Earth's surface. Instead, it is transformed into potential energy.

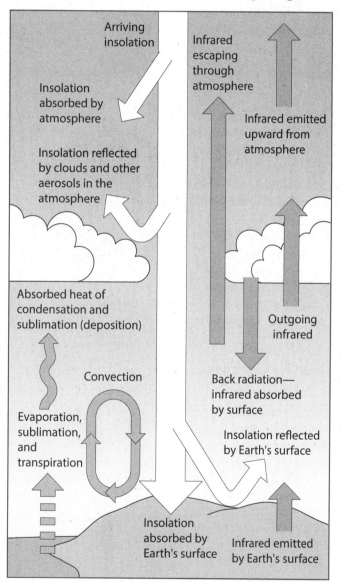

Figure 6-3. Energy balance for Earth's surface and atmosphere: About half of the insolation is absorbed by Earth's land and water surfaces. The remainder is reflected back into space or absorbed by Earth's atmosphere. Earth's surface and atmosphere also absorb energy from reradiation, which occurs as some of the infrared radiation emitted by Earth's surface is radiated back by greenhouse gases in the atmosphere.

Land and Water Heating

With equal amounts of insolation, an area of Earth's surface made up of liquid water will heat up and cool off more slowly than an equal area of land. These rates in heating and cooling differ for the following reasons:

- Water has a much higher specific heat than the rocks and soil that make up land.
- Water is highly transparent to insolation. Some insolation penetrates up to 300 feet in clear water but usually to less than a foot in rocks and soil. Rocks and soil heat rapidly because the energy of insolation is concentrated in a thin zone.
- Water can flow freely, so convection can occur. Convection currents in water can distribute absorbed energy through a large volume.
- When insolation strikes water surfaces, much of its energy is converted to stored heat as some water evaporates. Thus, less energy is available to increase the water temperature.

The Greenhouse Effect

Although Earth's atmosphere allows much insolation to pass through to Earth's surface, most of the radiation from Earth's surface does not escape into outer space. Instead, it is absorbed by the atmosphere. This occurs because Earth's surface radiation consists mostly of long infrared radiation, which can be absorbed by carbon dioxide, water vapor, methane, and other gases in the atmosphere. These gases are called **greenhouse gases.** This absorption warms the atmosphere and causes it to act as a heat "blanket." This blanket reduces energy loss to outer space and makes Earth's surface about 59°F (33°C) warmer than it would otherwise be. Without any greenhouse gases, the average temperature of Earth would be about 0°F (–18°C).

Figure 6-4 models the process by which the atmosphere transmits short-wave radiation from insolation and absorbs long-wave reradiation called

Energy radiated at longer wavelengths

Glass traps infrared rays

Sunlight passes through glass

Figure 6-4. The greenhouse effect: Insolation is transmitted through the glass of a greenhouse, just as it is transmitted through Earth's atmosphere. Objects inside a greenhouse absorb energy from the insolation and are heated. The heated objects then give off long wave infrared radiation, which cannot pass outward through the glass. The infrared radiation is trapped by the glass, and is partly absorbed by the air and by objects inside the greenhouse—raising their temperatures. Comparatively, radiation emitted from Earth's surface is trapped in the atmosphere by greenhouse gases—increasing Earth's surface temperatures.

the greenhouse effect. In recent years there has been a major concern that an increased greenhouse effect is causing a type of climate change called **global warming**—an increase in average Earth temperatures. The burning of wood and fossil fuels releases additional carbon dioxide and other greenhouse gases into the atmosphere. This increase in carbon dioxide and other greenhouse gases is thought to intensify the greenhouse effect—thus raising Earth's surface temperatures. Global warming could result in environmental problems such as rising sea levels caused by melting glaciers and sea ice, and the shifting of Earth's climatic zones. (See Figure 6-12.)

Review Questions

1. Electromagnetic energy that reaches Earth from the sun is called
   (1) insolation
   (2) conduction
   (3) specific heat
   (4) terrestrial radiation

2. The graph below represents the relationship between the intensity and wavelength of the sun's electromagnetic radiation.

Which statement is best supported by the graph?
   (1) The infrared radiation given off by the sun occurs at a wavelength of 2000 angstroms.
   (2) The maximum intensity of radiation given off by the sun occurs in the visible region.
   (3) The infrared radiation given off by the sun has a shorter wavelength than ultraviolet radiation.
   (4) The electromagnetic energy given off by the sun consists of a single wavelength.

3. Water vapor and carbon dioxide in Earth's atmosphere are good absorbers of
   (1) visible radiation
   (2) infrared radiation
   (3) ultraviolet radiation
   (4) X-rays

4. If dust particles are added to the atmosphere, the amount of insolation reaching the ground will probably
   (1) decrease
   (2) increase
   (3) stay the same
   (4) increase, then decrease

5. Ozone is important to life on Earth because ozone
   (1) cools refrigerators and air conditioners
   (2) absorbs energy that is radiated by Earth
   (3) absorbs harmful ultraviolet radiation
   (4) destroys excess atmospheric carbon dioxide

6. Which form of electromagnetic energy is radiated from Earth's surface with the greatest intensity?
   (1) X-rays
   (2) infrared rays
   (3) ultraviolet rays
   (4) visible light rays

7. In land areas of equal size located at the same latitude, the most solar radiation would probably be reflected by a
   (1) snow field
   (2) sandy desert
   (3) grassy field
   (4) forest

8. Insolation is changed into potential energy by
   (1) evaporation and transpiration of water from Earth's surface
   (2) formation of clouds and fog
   (3) freezing of lake and ocean water
   (4) rain and snow forming in clouds

9. How do the rates of warming and cooling of land surfaces compare to the rates of warming and cooling of ocean surfaces?

(1) Land surfaces warm more quickly and cool more slowly.

(2) Land surfaces warm more slowly and cool more quickly.

(3) Land surfaces warm more quickly and cool more quickly.

(4) Land surfaces warm more slowly and cool more slowly.

10. Which model best represents how a greenhouse remains warm as a result of insolation from the sun?

Variation of Insolation

Insolation varies from place to place on Earth's surface. It also varies in any given place over the course of a year. Insolation can vary in two general ways—by intensity (strength) and by duration (length of time).

Variation in Intensity and Angle of Insolation

The rate at which solar energy is received by a given area per unit time is the intensity of insolation. Intensity of insolation can be measured in joules per square meter per second. The intensity of insolation received at a particular area of Earth's surface varies for several reasons because of the angle of incidence. When insolation strikes a surface at an angle of 90°, or perpendicular, it has maximum intensity, because the insolation is concentrated in the smallest possible area. As the angle of incidence decreases from 90° toward 0°, the same amount of insolation is spread out over greater and greater areas, as shown in Figure 6-5. Therefore, at smaller angles of incidence, the intensity of insolation decreases the heating effect.

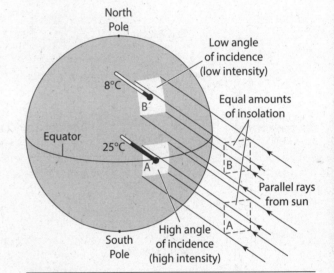

Figure 6-5. Earth's shape and the intensity of insolation: Because of Earth's spherical shape, the parallel rays from the sun strike different parts of Earth's surface at different angles. Near Earth's poles where the angle of incidence is smaller, the same amount of insolation spreads out over a larger area. As a result, the intensity of insolation is much less than that in regions with a higher angle of incidence of the sun's rays.

Effect of Earth's Shape and Thickness of the Atmosphere The sun's energy reaches Earth as a bundle of parallel rays. If Earth were flat and positioned perpendicular to these rays, the intensity of insolation would be the same everywhere on Earth's surface. However, Earth is shaped like a sphere. As a result, at any given time, there is just one place where insolation arrives perpendicular to Earth's surface. At all other places on Earth the angle of incidence is less than 90°. Generally, for each degree of latitude North or South of the place where insolation is perpendicular to Earth's surface, the angle of incidence is one degree less.

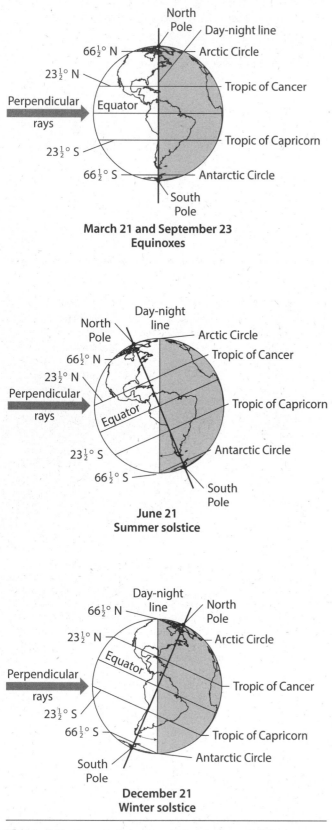

March 21 and September 23 Equinoxes

June 21 Summer solstice

December 21 Winter solstice

Figure 6-6. Seasonal changes in insolation at different latitudes: At any given time, the intensity of insolation is at a maximum at the latitude where the angle of incidence is 90°. The latitude of maximum intensity of insolation shifts with the seasons between $23\frac{1}{2}°$ N on June 21 to $23\frac{1}{2}°$ S on December 21.

The thickness of Earth's atmosphere, which the Sun's rays have to pass through to reach Earth's surface, varies greatly during the day and year, and with changes in latitude. When the Sun is straight overhead at a 90 degree angle of insolation, the intensity of the insolation is about 80 times stronger than when the Sun is on the horizon at a zero angle of insolation. (See Table 6-1.) This is due partly to the changes in the thickness of atmosphere that the Sun's rays must pass through. The more atmosphere the Sun's rays must pass through, the greater the absorption, reflection, refraction, and scattering of the rays, and the less the transmission of the rays to Earth's surface.

Effect of Latitude The intensity of insolation is greatest at the equator at each equinox, and decreases with increasing latitude (north or south). As shown in Figure 6-6, insolation is perpendicular to Earth's surface at the equator at the time of each equinox. The spring equinox is March 21, and the fall equinox is September 23.

On the first day of summer in the Northern Hemisphere (summer solstice), insolation is perpendicular to Earth's surface at $23\frac{1}{2}°$ N latitude. The intensity of insolation is at its maximum at this latitude—the Tropic of Cancer. On the first day of winter in the Northern Hemisphere (winter solstice), insolation is perpendicular to Earth's surface at $23\frac{1}{2}°$ S latitude. The intensity of insolation is at its maximum at this latitude—the Tropic of Capricorn. (See Appendix 4.)

Effect of Seasonal Changes As Earth travels in its yearly orbit around the sun, the angle of incidence for insolation at any given latitude varies with the seasons. As shown in Figure 6-7, the lowest angle of incidence at 42° N latitude occurs at the winter solstice and the highest angle at the summer solstice. As shown in Table 6-2, the angle of incidence for insolation decreases by one degree for each degree of latitude away from the point of perpendicular insolation.

Effect of Time of Day On any given day, the altitude of the sun varies from zero at sunrise, to a maximum at apparent solar noon, and back to zero again at sunset. In a similar way, the angle of incidence and the intensity of insolation also vary during the day as shown in Figure 6-8. The maximum angle and intensity occur at solar noon.

Table 6-1. Effect of Sun's Altitude on Insolation Intensity		
Altitude of the Sun	Relative Length of the Path of Sun's Rays through Earth's Atmosphere	Relative Intensity of Insolation on a Horizontal Surface of Earth
90°	1.00	0.78
60°	1.15	0.65
30°	2.00	0.31
0°	45.00	0.00

Variation in Duration of Insolation

The length of time that insolation is received each day—or the time between sunrise and sunset—is called the <u>duration</u> of <u>insolation</u>. The duration of insolation at a given location corresponds to the number of hours that the sun is visible each day. As shown in Table 6-2, the duration of insolation varies with latitude and with the seasons. In the continental United States, duration of insolation is longest on the summer solstice (June 21) and shortest on the winter solstice (December 21). On the equinoxes (March 21 and September 23), the average duration of insolation is 12 hours.

Effects of Latitude and Season A review of Table 6-2 will reveal how duration of insolation varies with latitude and season. At the time of the summer solstice, northern areas of the contiguous United States have more hours of daylight than do southern areas. The reverse happens at the time of the winter solstice when southern areas of the contiguous United States have more hours of daylight than the northern areas. Only during the equinoxes is the duration of insolation the same everywhere—12 hours.

Relationship of Surface Temperatures to Insolation

The temperature of Earth's surface at a given location varies throughout the day. Similarly, the average daily temperature varies throughout the year. These variations depend on the balance between energy being gained from insolation and the energy being lost by Earth's surface radiation. When energy is being gained at a greater rate than it is being lost, Earth's surface temperature rises. When energy is being lost faster than it is being gained, Earth's surface temperature falls. Temperatures are generally higher when the intensity of insolation is greater. Temperatures also tend to be higher at a location for which the duration of insolation is longer.

Figure 6-7. Maximum angles of incidence at 42° N latitude in different seasons: Values were measured at solar noon in New York State on the first day of each of the four seasons.

Figure 6-8. Changes in the altitude of the Sun during an average day and the resulting changes in the length and directions of shadows: The data is for an equinox day in the middle latitudes of the Northern Hemisphere. The time of day can be determined by observing the height and direction to the Sun's location in the sky. The shadow of a vertical post indicates how the angle of incidence of insolation varies throughout the day. A higher angle of incidence produces a shorter shadow and a greater intensity of insolation. The shortest shadow is at solar noon and it points directly north.

Table 6-2. Variation in Insolation by Latitude and Season

Latitude	Summer Solstice June 21		Equinoxes: March 21, September 23		Winter Solstice December 21	
	Angle of Incidence at 12:00 Noon	Duration of Insolation	Angle of incidence at 12:00 Noon	Duration of Insolation	Angle of Incidence at 12:00 Noon	Duration of Insolation
90° N	23½°	24 Hours	0°	12 Hours	—	0 Hours
80° N	33½°	24	10°	12	—	0
70° N	43½°	24	20°	12	—	0
66½° N	47°	24	23½°	12	0°	0
60° N	53½°	18½	30°	12	6½°	5½
50° N	63½°	16¼	40°	12	16½°	7¾
40° N	73½°	15	50°	12	26½°	9
30° N	83½°	14	60°	12	36½°	10
23½° N	90°	13½°	66½°	12	43°	10½
20° N	86½°	13¼	70°	12	46½°	10¾
10° N	76½°	12½	80°	12	56½°	11½
0°	66½°	12	90°	12	66½°	12
10° S	56½°	11½	80°	12	76½°	12½
20° S	46½°	10¾	70°	12	86½°	13¼
23½° S	43°	10½	66½°	12	90°	13½
30° S	36½°	10	60°	12	83½°	14
40° S	26½°	9	50°	12	73½°	15
50° S	16½°	7¾	40°	12	63½°	16¼
60° S	6½°	5½	30°	12	53½°	18½
66½° S	0°	0	23½°	12	47°	24
70° S	—	0	20°	12	43½°	24
80° S	—	0	10°	12	33½°	24
90° S	—	0	0°	12	23½°	24

Times of Yearly Maximum and Minimum Temperatures Each year, the times of maximum and minimum temperatures in a given place occur somewhat later than the times of maximum and minimum insolation. For example, in mid-latitude areas of the contiguous United States (49° N to 25° N) the maximum intensity of insolation and the maximum duration of insolation occur on June 21. However, the period of highest daily temperatures occurs later—toward the end of July or early in August. (See Figure 6-9.)

The reason for this delay relates to the changing balance between energy gain from insolation and energy loss from Earth's surface radiation. During spring and early summer in the contiguous United States, the intensity and duration of insolation increase. Each day the surface receives more energy of insolation than it loses by radiation and the average temperature goes up slightly. After June 21, a little less energy is received, but the amount of energy received is still more than the amount lost. Therefore, the temperature continues to go up until the rate of incoming energy

Memory Jogger

Recall that the length of the sun's apparent path through the sky varies during the year. Day length, or duration of insolation, is proportional to the length of the sun's path. There is one hour of insolation for each 15° of path.

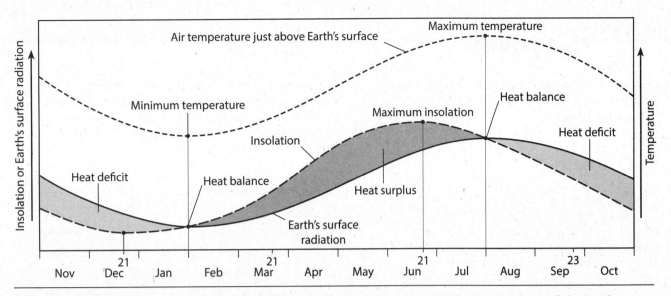

Figure 6-9. Average daily temperatures, insolation, and Earth's surface radiation for mid–latitudes of the Northern Hemisphere during a year

finally drops below the rate of energy loss by Earth's surface radiation. Similarly, mid-latitude areas of the contiguous United States are not at their coldest when the duration of insolation and angle of incidence are at their minimum on December 21. These areas continue to lose more energy from surface radiation than they gain by insolation until late January or early February—when the coldest temperatures occur.

Times of Daily Maximum and Minimum Temperatures The hottest part of an average day is some time in mid-afternoon, not at solar noon when the intensity of insolation is greatest. (See Figure 6-10.) Each day, although insolation is greatest at solar noon, Earth's surface continues to gain more energy from the sun than it loses from surface (terrestrial) radiation until mid-afternoon. In a similar way, the coolest temperatures on an average day usually occur just slightly after sunrise. Earth's surface continues to lose heat throughout the night until after insolation begins at sunrise.

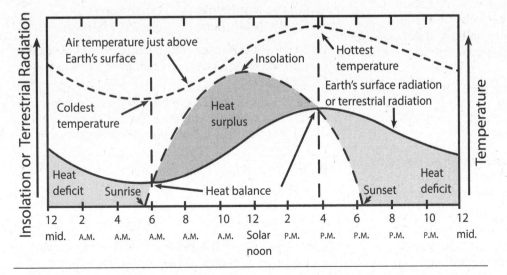

Figure 6-10. Typical daily variations in insolation, surface radiation, and near-surface air temperature

11. In which diagram does the incoming solar radiation reaching Earth's surface have the greatest intensity?

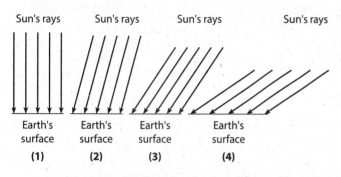

Sun's rays	Sun's rays	Sun's rays	Sun's rays
Earth's surface	Earth's surface	Earth's surface	Earth's surface
(1)	(2)	(3)	(4)

12. The following diagram represents a portion of Earth's surface that is receiving insolation. Positions A, B, C, and D are located on Earth's surface.

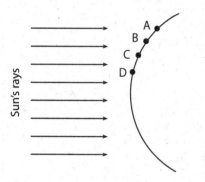

At which position would the intensity of insolation be greatest?

(1) A　　(2) B　　(3) C　　(4) D

13. Over a period of one year, which location would probably have the greatest average intensity of insolation per unit area? Assume that there is equal atmospheric transparency at each location.

(1) Tropic of Cancer, $23\frac{1}{2}°$ N
(2) New York City, 41° N
(3) the Arctic Circle, $66\frac{1}{2}°$ N
(4) the North Pole, 90° N

14. The most logical conclusion that can be made from the relationship between the altitude of the sun throughout the day and the amount of insolation is that, as the sun's altitude

(1) increases, the insolation increases
(2) increases, the insolation decreases
(3) decreases, the insolation increases
(4) decreases, the insolation remains the same

Base your answers to questions 15 through 18 on the following diagrams. The diagrams represent models of the apparent path of the sun across the sky for observers at four different locations, A through D, on Earth's surface.

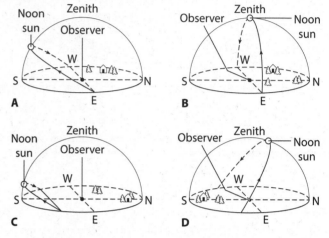

15. At location A, on which side would an observer's shadow cast by the sun fall at local noon?

(1) south side　　(3) east side
(2) north side　　(4) west side

16. If the model of location B represents the apparent path of the sun observed at the equator, what is the date at location B?

(1) March 21　　(3) October 21
(2) June 21　　(4) December 21

17. If the model of location D represents the apparent path of the sun on December 21, where is location D?

(1) the North Pole　　(3) the equator
(2) 45° N latitude　　(4) 45° S latitude

18. At location B three months later, how would the altitude of the noon sun compare to its present altitude?

(1) The altitude would be less than shown.
(2) The altitude would be greater than shown.
(3) The altitude would be the same as shown.

19. At which time of day would an observer's shadow cast by the sun be shortest?

(1) 6:00 A.M.　　(3) 3:00 P.M.
(2) 12:00 noon　　(4) 6:00 P.M.

20. At the time of the fall equinox, the number of hours of daylight in New York City is generally about

(1) 9　　(2) 12　　(3) 15　　(4) 18

Base your answers to questions 21 through 25 on the following diagram. The diagram represents Earth at a specific time in its orbit. The dashed lines indicate radiation from the sun. Points A through H are locations on Earth's surface.

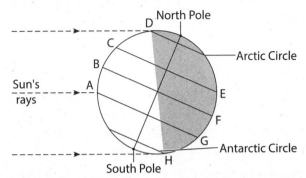

21. Which line represents the equator?

(1) AB   (2) BF   (3) CE   (4) DH

22. What is the season in the Northern Hemisphere when Earth is in the position shown in the diagram?

(1) spring   (3) fall
(2) summer   (4) winter

23. When the sun is in the position shown in the diagram, how many hours of daylight would occur at the North Pole during one complete rotation?

(1) 0   (2) 8   (3) 12   (4) 24

24. In which direction would a person located at position H have to look to see the sun at the time shown in the diagram?

(1) north   (2) east   (3) south   (4) west

25. Six months after the date indicated by the diagram, which point would receive the sun's vertical rays at noon?

(1) A   (2) B   (3) C   (4) D

26. The length of time that daylight occurs at a location during one day is called the location's

(1) angle of incidence
(2) intensity of insolation
(3) duration of insolation
(4) eccentricity of insolation

27. What is the primary reason New York State is warmer in May than in February?

(1) Earth is traveling faster in its orbit in February.
(2) The altitude of the noon sun is greater in February.
(3) The insolation in New York is greater in May.
(4) Earth is closer to the sun in May.

28. Which graph best represents the duration of insolation during the year at Earth's equator?

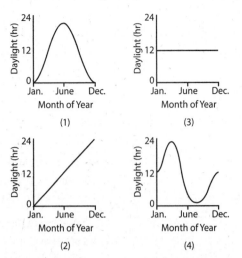

29. The following graph illustrates the relationship between insolation and Earth's surface radiation during a 24-hour period in New York State on March 21.

At what time did the maximum air temperature probably occur?

(1) 6 A.M.   (3) 4 P.M.
(2) 12 noon   (4) 6 P.M.

30. What is the usual cause of the drop in temperature that occurs between sunset and sunrise at most New York State locations?

(1) strong winds   (3) cloud formation
(2) ground radiation   (4) heavy precipitation

31. In New York State, the maximum total daily insolation occurs during June. Which statement best explains why the maximum annual temperature is usually observed about a month later, in July?

(1) Earth is closer to the sun in June than it is in July.
(2) Earth is farther from the sun in June than it is in July.
(3) New York State loses far more energy than it receives from the sun during most of July.
(4) New York State receives more energy from the sun than it loses during most of July.

Heat Budget and Climate Change

An object's **heat budget** is the result of the balance between the total amount of energy it receives and the total energy it emits or loses. Heat budget can be measured as the average temperature of an object. Earth's heat budget is the result of a radiation balance between the radiation from the sun and Earth's interior compared to the radiation Earth gives off to space.

Examples of Climate Change

Long-term changes in Earth's heat budget caused by Earth heating up or cooling off can result in climatic changes. The sections that follow describe some of the types of changes in Earth's heat budget and climate and some possible reasons for these changes.

Ice Ages and Long, Warm Periods on Earth Earth's heat budget has shifted in the past for long periods of time. Some of these shifts in heat balance

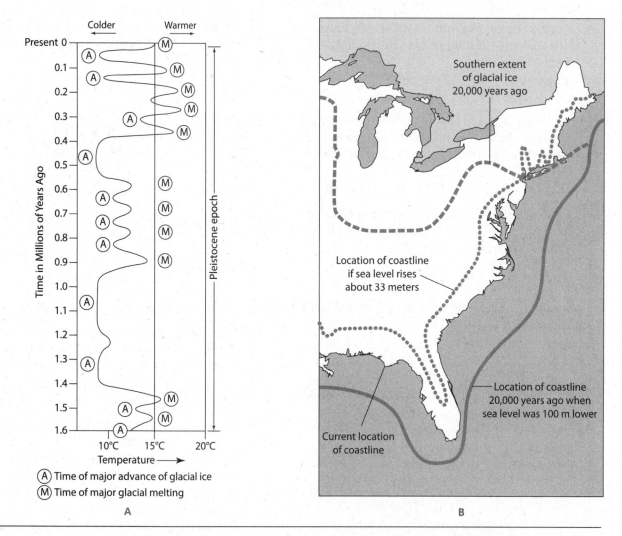

Figure 6-11. Changes in temperature, sea level, and position of glaciers associated with the Pleistocene Ice Age and present times: Diagram A shows estimated temperature variations from today's average Earth temperature of 15°C. Times of advances and melting of glaciers are estimates. Diagram B shows the maximum extent of glaciation about 20,000 years ago and the extended coastline of the area that is now the eastern United States. Sea levels 20,000 years ago were 100 meters lower, due to the large amounts of water stored as ice. Diagram B also shows how sea levels would rise if global warming continues—melting today's glaciers and ice caps.

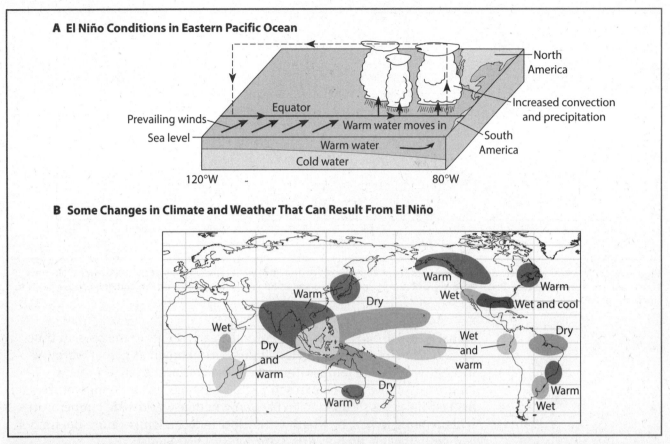

A El Niño Conditions in Eastern Pacific Ocean

North America

Increased convection and precipitation

Equator

Prevailing winds

Sea level

Warm water moves in

South America

Warm water

Cold water

120°W

80°W

B Some Changes in Climate and Weather That Can Result From El Niño

Warm

Dry

Warm

Wet

Warm

Wet

Wet and cool

Dry and warm

Wet and warm

Dry

Dry

Warm

Warm

Wet

Figure 6-12. El Niño conditions: Diagram A shows how every 2 to 10 years, changes in prevailing winds push a huge mass of warm ocean water toward the west coast of South America—replacing the normally cold waters of the eastern Pacific Ocean. The influx of warm water results in a temperature rise and an increase in air convection currents and precipitation in a region with a normally cool and dry climate. Map B shows some of the worldwide conditions linked to El Niño events, such as major flooding in southern California and droughts in southern Africa.

produced warm periods when Earth probably had few or no glaciers. Other shifts in heat balance produced periods called **ice ages** when glaciers advanced into the middle latitudes.

According to Geologic History of New York State in the *Earth Science Reference Tables*, the last ice age—the Pleistocene—lasted from about 1.8 million to approximately 10 thousand years ago. During the Pleistocene, glaciers advanced and retreated 10 or more times as shown in Figure 6-11. At times between the advances of the glaciers, there were warm interglacial periods when Earth was warmer than today. (See Figure 6-11.) Some scientists think that Earth is presently in one of these interglacial periods, but that in the future glaciers will again advance into the middle latitudes.

El Niño and La Niña Events Every 2 to 10 years, the normally cold waters of the eastern Pacific Ocean off western South America are replaced with a vast area of warmer waters. This warming event, known as **El Niño,** causes major climatic repercussions around the world. As shown in Figure 6-12, flooding, droughts, and heat waves are known to occur during an El Niño. Recently it has been noted that there are also periods of exceptionally cold water—called La Niña events—in the eastern Pacific Ocean, which also affect worldwide climate.

Figure 6-13. Worldwide average temperatures from 1880 to 2010: The increasing temperatures of the 1980s and 1990s have convinced many scientists that global warming is occurring and may worsen as human activities continue to add greenhouse gases to the atmosphere.

Global Warming and Heat Waves From the early 1980s to the present time, there has been a trend of rising temperatures known as global warming. In 1998, worldwide temperatures were the warmest ever recorded. Figure 6-13 shows the changes in Earth's average surface temperature over the last 120 years. It remains to be seen whether worldwide temperatures will continue to rise, or whether they just reflect a temperature fluctuation similar to the one that occurred during the 1930s and 1940s.

Many scientists believe that there are many weather consequences of global warming including increased numbers and strength of violent storms like hurricanes and tornadoes and an increase in heat waves. A heat wave is a series of days with abnormally and uncomfortably hot and unusually humid weather that lasts two or more days. Heat waves can make it difficult for humans to effectively cool their bodies, especially if they do not live in a normally hot and humid climate. Heat waves can result in hyperthermia (heat stroke) leading to death. In most years in the United States, more humans die of heat waves than any other weather event. On average, 170 heat-related deaths occurred each year from 1998 to 2007. That average decreased from the early 2000s, when the 10-year average was 237, perhaps due to increased awareness of the dangerous potential of heat waves. To protect yourself during a heat wave, don't over exercise outside, stay in shady areas, drink plenty of water, and try to stay in an air-conditioned location.

Causes of Heat Budget Shifts

There are many possible explanations for the shifts in Earth's heat budget that produce climate change. Some possible causes are described in the following paragraphs.

Changes in Solar Energy The sun's energy output and related sunspot activity follow an 11-year cycle, as shown in Figure 6-14. A **sunspot** is a darker region of the sun's visible surface. When there are large numbers of sunspots, the sun emits from 0.1 to 1.0 percent more electromagnetic energy. As a result, Earth receives more insolation at these times. Note that the high temperatures of the 1990s, shown in Figure 6-13, show a correlation with an increase in the number of sunspots as indicated in Figure 6-14.

Changes in Earth's Orbit and Axis Tilt Changes in Earth's axis and orbit over many thousands of years may be a major influence in climate change. Over periods of thousands of years, the tilt of Earth's axis changes a few degrees. The season during which Earth passes closest to the sun varies from its present winter occurrence in the Northern Hemisphere to a summer occurrence. The amount of eccentricity of Earth's orbit also changes a minor amount. When the cycles of these factors occur at the same time, summers may be cooler and winters warmer with more precipitation. The times of such occurrences seem to correspond with the advances of the glaciers during the Pleistocene Ice Age. (See Figure 6-11.)

Volcanic Eruptions and Climate Changes In the early 1990s, Earth's atmosphere underwent cooling that was probably related to the eruption of the Pinatubo volcano in the Philippines. (See Figure 6-13.) When there are major volcanic eruptions, aerosols such as volcanic ash and sulfur compounds are propelled into the stratosphere and stay there for months or years. The aerosols make Earth's atmosphere less transparent to insolation and reflect a greater than normal amount of insolation back into space. As a result, less energy arrives at Earth's surface, and cooler temperatures occur.

Memory Jogger

Recall that the <u>amount of eccentricity</u> of Earth's orbit refers to the amount of deviation from a circle, or the flattening of its elliptical shape.

Human Causes Many scientists who study climate have found evidence that human activities have an impact on climate change. For example, the expansion of deserts at the cost of grasslands—called desertification—is often related to overgrazing by livestock such as sheep and cattle. Since deserts heat up faster than grasslands, the temperature of these areas increases.

The cutting down of forests—called **deforestation**—in many tropical areas has resulted in these regions becoming hotter and drier. When deforestation occurs, the insolation once absorbed by the trees and converted into potential energy instead goes into heating Earth's surface. Additionally, without the trees, there is less transpiration of water vapor to increase the humidity of the atmosphere—resulting in less precipitation.

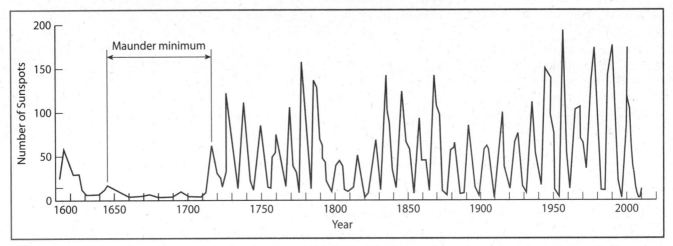

Figure 6-14. Graph of sunspot numbers for the years 1600–2010: This diagram shows the number of sunspots varies through a solar cycle of approximately 11 years.

As discussed previously, human activities that produce greenhouse gases may be a major reason for the present global warming. For example, the increase in atmospheric carbon dioxide in recent years is largely due to the burning of fossil fuels. The aerosol called soot, caused by coal and diesel fuel burning, can darken portions of Earth's surface increasing surface warming. Another human factor is the building of cities—urbanization—which results in clearing land of plants and trees to construct buildings. Cities also increase carbon dioxide because of an increased use of fossil fuels.

Review Questions

32. Between the years 1850 and 1900, records indicate that Earth's mean surface temperature showed little variation. This would support the inference that

(1) Earth was in heat balance
(2) another ice age was approaching
(3) Earth was gaining more energy than it was losing
(4) the sun was emitting more energy

33. Air temperature is regulated partly by the percentage of carbon dioxide (CO_2) in the air. Which of the following statements is correct?

(1) The CO_2 content of the air during the glacial period was very high because cold water absorbs more CO_2 than warm water.
(2) During periods of great volcanic activity, the CO_2 content of the air decreases because the clouds reduce plant growth.
(3) The CO_2 content of the air is increasing due to the burning of fossil fuels.
(4) The CO_2 content of the air is increasing due to the deposition of limestone from groundwater.

34. Some scientists predict that an increase in atmospheric carbon dioxide would cause a worldwide increase in temperature. Which of the following could result if a worldwide temperature increase occurred?

(1) Continental drift will increase.
(2) Isotherms will shift toward the equator.
(3) Additional landmasses will form.
(4) Ice caps at Earth's poles will melt.

35. A heating of the normally cold ocean waters of the eastern Pacific Ocean off the coast of South America is called

(1) the greenhouse
(2) El Niño
(3) ozone effect
(4) global warming

36. Which event would most likely cause a new ice age in North America?

(1) a decrease in the energy produced by the sun
(2) a decrease in the light reflected by Earth's surface
(3) an increase of carbon dioxide in Earth's atmosphere
(4) an El Niño event

37. When were large parts of North America covered by ice sheets?

(1) only once, early in Earth's geologic history
(2) only once, in the recent geologic past
(3) once early in Earth's geologic history and once in the recent geologic past
(4) many times during Earth's geologic history

38. Another ice age would probably result in a change in

(1) sea level
(2) moon phases
(3) the speed at which Earth moves in its orbit
(4) the time between high tides

Seasons

New York and other mid-latitude areas of the Northern Hemisphere experience four seasons—winter, spring, summer, and fall. These seasons are distinguished by differences in temperature, moisture, and vegetation. Some land regions near the equator have little seasonal change. There, the intensity of insolation remains relatively high, and the duration of insolation is about 12 hours per day throughout the year.

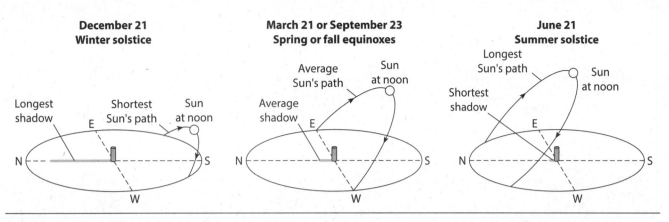

Figure 6-15. The direct causes of seasons: Shown for the mid-latitudes of the northern hemisphere include changes in angle of incidence or height of the sun in the sky and the changes in duration of the sun's daily motion path. Note how the length of the shadow of the sun at noon changes with the seasons.

Direct Causes of the Seasons

Seasonal changes in temperature, moisture, and other weather conditions result from the cyclic variations in the angle of incidence and the intensity and duration of insolation that occur during the year. (See Figure 6-15 and Appendix 4.) Generally the seasons follow the north-south shift in the direct rays of insolation. This shift, caused by the tilt of Earth's axis, occurs between $23\frac{1}{2}°$ N latitude and $23\frac{1}{2}°$ S latitude as discussed previously. This shifting of the sun's rays (A4) results in the seasons being the opposite of each other in the Northern and Southern Hemispheres.

Climate zones, and their associated wind patterns and surface ocean currents, also shift in a north-south pattern. However, this shift lags about a month behind the shift of direct rays of insolation. Figure 6-16 shows the effects of the shifting rays of the sun on the seasonal positions of the wind and moisture belts on Earth.

Astronomical Causes of the Seasons

The variations in insolation that directly cause the seasons are themselves the result of factors that may be called the astronomical, or indirect, causes of the seasons. These indirect causes of seasons include the tilt and parallelism of Earth's axis and Earth's revolution around the sun.

Tilt of Earth's Axis As shown in Figure 6-17, Earth's rotational axis is tilted at an angle of $23\frac{1}{2}°$ with respect to a line perpendicular to the plane of its orbit of the sun. This tilt, coupled with the other reasons described here, means that perpendicular insolation from the sun shifts between $23\frac{1}{2}°$ N and $23\frac{1}{2}°$ S latitudes. If the tilt of Earth's axis were greater, perpendicular insolation would reach farther

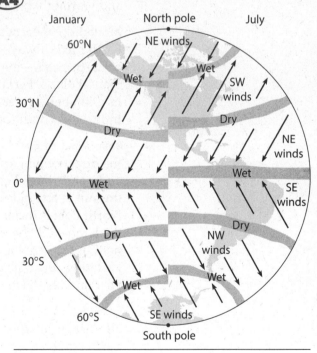

Figure 6-16. Seasonal shifting of Earth's wind and moisture belts: By comparing the latitudes of the wind and moisture belts in January and July, you can see how the wind and moisture belts shift north and south during the year following the direct rays of insolation. Also, look at the diagram Planetary Wind and Moisture Belts in the Troposphere in the *Earth Science Reference Tables* that represents conditions near the time of the equinoxes.

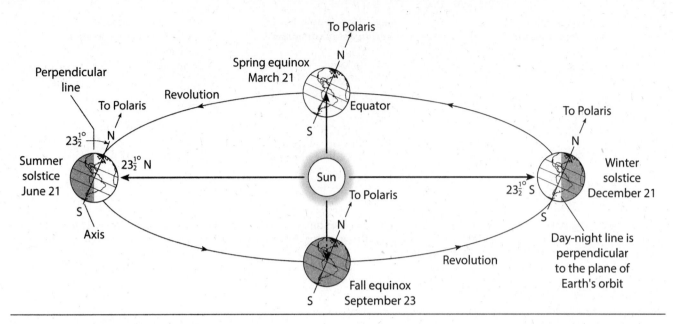

Figure 6-17. Indirect causes of the seasons: The astronomical, or indirect, causes for the seasons described in the text, result in the changes in angle, intensity, and duration of insolation.

north and south, resulting in generally warmer summers and colder winters for much of Earth. If the tilt of Earth's axis were less than $23\frac{1}{2}°$, then perpendicular insolation would not shift as much. As a result, seasonal effects would be less pronounced—there would be cooler summers and warmer winters.

Parallelism of Earth's Axis Regardless of the position of Earth in its orbit, Earth's axis always points in the same direction in space. The north end of Earth's axis—the North Pole—always points to the present-day North Star—Polaris. Figure 6-17 shows that as Earth orbits the sun, the position of its axis at any given time is always parallel to its position at any other time—this condition is called parallelism.

Revolution of Earth Around the Sun As Earth revolves around the sun, the direction of Earth's axis with respect to the sun varies because of its tilt and parallelism. For example, on June 21, the North Pole is inclined toward the sun at an angle of $23\frac{1}{2}°$ from the perpendicular. On December 21, the North Pole is inclined away from the sun at this angle. On March 21 and September 23, the axis is still inclined $23\frac{1}{2}°$ from the perpendicular, but neither toward nor away from the sun. This cycle of variations causes variations in angle of incidence and duration of insolation throughout the year and results in seasonal changes. (See Figures 6-15 and 6-17.)

Small Seasonal Effect of Earth's Elliptical Orbit Because of Earth's slightly elliptical orbit, there is a variation in distance between Earth and the sun as Earth revolves around the sun. The small changes in distance between Earth and the sun during the year are too small to have a significant effect on the seasons. For example, winter in the Northern Hemisphere occurs at a time when Earth is actually nearest the sun. Earth as a whole receives about seven percent more energy when it is closest to the sun than it does when it is farthest away. This seven percent difference would only be significant if Earth's axis was not tilted at an angle of $23\frac{1}{2}°$.

39. The factor that contributes most to the seasonal temperature changes during a year in New York State is the changing

(1) speed at which Earth travels in its orbit around the sun
(2) angle at which sun's rays strike Earth's surface
(3) the distance between Earth and the sun
(4) energy given off by the sun

40. On which two dates could all locations on Earth have equal hours of day and night?

(1) September 23 and December 21
(2) December 21 and March 21
(3) March 21 and June 21
(4) March 21 and September 23

41. At which latitude does Earth receive the greatest intensity of insolation on June 21?

(1) 0°
(2) 23 $\frac{1}{2}$° S
(3) 23 $\frac{1}{2}$° N
(4) 90° N

Base your answers to questions 42 and 43 on the following diagram, which shows Earth as viewed from space. The shaded side represents Earth's nighttime side.

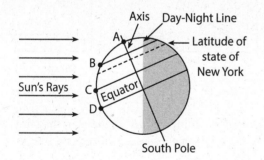

42. Which point on Earth's surface is receiving the greatest intensity of insolation?

(1) A   (2) C   (3) B   (4) D

43. The total number of hours of daylight received by New York State on the days represented in the diagram is closest to

(1) 9 hr   (2) 12 hr   (3) 15 hr   (4) 20 hr

44. Which position in the following diagram best represents Earth on the first day of summer in the Northern Hemisphere?

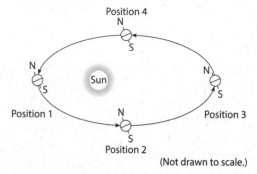

(Not drawn to scale.)

(1) 1
(2) 2
(3) 3
(4) 4

45. At which latitude would the duration of insolation be greatest on December 21?

(1) 23 $\frac{1}{2}$° S
(2) 0°
(3) 10° N
(4) 23 $\frac{1}{2}$° N

46. Which change would occur if Earth's axis were inclined at an angle of 33 $\frac{1}{2}$° instead of 23 $\frac{1}{2}$°?

(1) The equator would receive fewer hours of daylight on June 21.
(2) The sun's perpendicular rays would move over a larger area of Earth's surface.
(3) The average duration of insolation would be less at the equator.
(4) There would be less seasonal effect on Earth.

47. Which of the following is the best description of parallelism?

(1) Earth's daily rotation
(2) position of the moon with respect to Earth
(3) positions of Earth's axis as it revolves around the sun
(4) arrangement of galaxies in the universe

48. Which does NOT cause the changes of Earth's seasons?

(1) Earth's revolution
(2) inclination of Earth's axis
(3) variation of the distance to the sun
(4) parallelism of Earth's axis

Directions

Review the Test-Taking Strategies of this book. Then answer the following questions.
Read each question carefully and answer with a correct choice or response.

Part A

1 The radiation that passes through the atmosphere and reaches Earth's surface has the greatest intensity in the form of
   (1) visible light radiation
   (2) infrared radiation
   (3) ultraviolet radiation
   (4) radio-wave radiation

2 Compared with the temperature of land surfaces, temperatures of water surfaces change
   (1) faster because water has a higher specific heat
   (2) faster because water has a lower specific heat
   (3) slower because water has a higher specific heat
   (4) slower because water has a lower specific heat

3 Most of the energy radiated by Earth's surface at night is in the form of
   (1) infrared rays   (3) visible light rays
   (2) ultraviolet rays   (4) X-rays

4 Under which conditions will the greatest amount of cooling by Earth's surface radiation occur?
   (1) a clear night with low humidity
   (2) a clear night with high humidity
   (3) a cloudy night with low humidity
   (4) a cloudy night with high humidity

5 The sun's rays have a greater effect on land temperature than they have on water temperature. This difference can be explained partly by which of the following?
   (1) Some energy from the sun is used to evaporate ocean water.
   (2) Less energy is reflected by the water's surface than by the land's surface.
   (3) Land materials have a higher specific heat than water has.
   (4) Land materials require more heat energy than water does to raise their temperature 1°C.

6 Adding more carbon dioxide to the atmosphere increases the amount of
   (1) radiant energy reflected by Earth
   (2) radiation from the sun absorbed by the oceans
   (3) radiation from Earth absorbed by the atmosphere
   (4) ultraviolet rays striking Earth

7 Which graph best illustrates the relationship between the intensity of insolation and the angle of incidence?

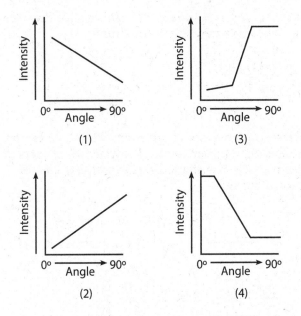

8 The seasonal temperature changes in the climate of New York State are most influenced by the changing
   (1) CO_2 content of the air
   (2) angle of incidence at which the sun's rays strike Earth's surface
   (3) distance from the sun to Earth
   (4) speed at which Earth revolves around the sun

9 The activity shown in the following diagram was used to test the effect of the angle of incidence on temperature. A student placed four thermometers—A, B, C and D—on a large globe. The bulb of each thermometer was placed against a black plastic square directly on a line representing latitude. The thermometers were then exposed to direct sunlight for 10 minutes at the angles shown.

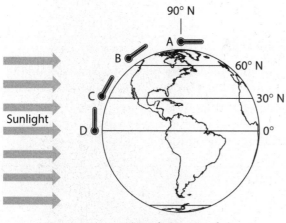

(Not drawn to scale.)

Which thermometer will show the greatest increase in temperature?
(1) A (2) B (3) C (4) D

10 In New York State at 3 P.M. on September 21, the vertical pole shown on the following diagram casts a shadow.

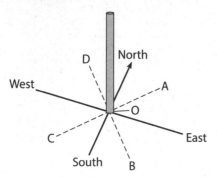

Which line best approximates the position of that shadow?
(1) OA (2) OB (3) OC (4) OD

11 The following diagram represents a model of the sun's apparent path across the sky in New York State for selected dates.

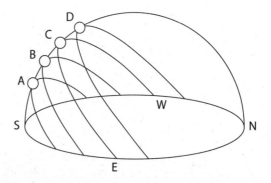

For which path would the duration of insolation be greatest?
(1) A (2) B (3) C (4) D

12 Which two factors determine the number of hours of daylight at a particular location?
(1) longitude and season
(2) longitude and Earth's average diameter
(3) latitude and season
(4) latitude and Earth's average diameter

13 When do maximum surface temperatures usually occur in the Northern Hemisphere?
(1) early June to mid-June
(2) mid-July to early August
(3) late August to mid-September
(4) mid-September to early October

14 Earth loses heat energy to outer space mainly by
(1) radiation   (3) convection
(2) reflection   (4) conduction

15 An increase in carbon dioxide in the atmosphere may lead to an increase in global temperatures because carbon dioxide
(1) absorbs infrared radiation, thus preventing it from escaping Earth's atmosphere
(2) blocks harmful ultraviolet radiation from reaching Earth's surface and being absorbed
(3) interferes with the formation of clouds that block sunlight and cause cooling
(4) enters the atmosphere at a high temperature from combustion and respiration

16 The diagram below shows trends in the temperature of North America during the past 200,000 years, as estimated by scientists.

What is the total number of major glacial periods that have occurred in North America in the last 200,000 years?

(1) 5   (2) 2   (3) 3   (4) 4

17 The diagram below shows the shadow cast by a telephone pole on March 21 at solar noon at a location in New York State.

Shadow Cast on March 21

Which shadow was cast by the same telephone pole on June 21 at solar noon?

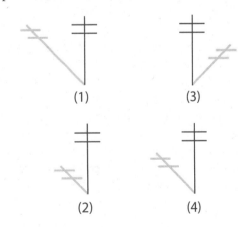

18 It is known that less ozone in Earth's stratosphere can result in

(1) ice ages
(2) an increase in carbon dioxide
(3) an increase in skin cancer
(4) a decrease in rock weathering caused by ultraviolet rays

19 Which angle of the sun above the horizon produces the greatest intensity of sunlight per unit area?

(1) 25°
(2) 40°
(3) 60°
(4) 70°

Part B

Base your answers to questions 20 and 21 on the following diagram. It represents a field showing the amount of insolation received at Earth's surface on a clear day in the morning—in joules per square centimeter per minute.

20 If the insolation value at the outer edge of Earth's atmosphere over New York State equals 7.75 joules per square centimeter per minute, why are the values lower at the surface in New York State? [1]

21 What change in atmospheric conditions within the dashed circle could cause the different pattern of isolines as indicated in that area in the following diagram? [1]

Base your answers to questions 22 and 23 on the table below, which provides information about several gases and their relationship to the greenhouse effect.

22 State one reason that a scientist would recommend restricting the emission of chlorofluorocarbon CFC-12 into the atmosphere. [1]

23 State which of the following actions would contribute more to the greenhouse effect and give a reason for your answer. [2]
  (1) releasing 1 kilogram of methane directly into the atmosphere, OR
  (2) burning 1 kilogram of methane, resulting in the release of about 3 kilograms of carbon dioxide into the atmosphere

24 Why is reflectivity of insolation at high latitudes greater in winter than in summer? [1]

25 In New York State, ski trails on a slope that faces north usually retain their snow later in the spring than those on a slope that faces south. Why does this occur? [1]

26 Why are equatorial areas equal in size to Earth's polar regions heated much more intensely by the sun? [1]

27 How does the way that noontime shadows are cast in New York State change with the approach of the summer solstice? [1]

28 In late summer 1991, Mt. Pinatubo, a volcano in the Philippines, exploded and sent thousands of tons of volcanic dust into the atmosphere. According to scientists, what effects did this event have on Earth's average temperatures in the months that followed? [1]

Part C

Using information from the following paragraph and your knowledge of earth science, answer questions 29 through 33.

Recent data from the study of tree rings and gases trapped in Greenland ice indicate that much of the Northern Hemisphere experienced a warm period—the Medieval Warm Period—from approximately 1000 A.D. to 1350 A.D. The data also indicate a much colder period—the Little Ice Age—which lasted from 1350 A.D. to approximately 1850 A.D. Thermometer readings from 1850 to the present indicate an overall temperature rise, often called global warming.

29 What human activities could have caused the overall change in temperature after 1850 and how could these activities cause the temperature change? [2]

Name of Gas	Symbol	Concentration in Troposphere (parts per billion)	Relative Greenhouse Effect per Kilogram of Gas (in equal concentrations)	Decay Time (years)
Carbon dioxide	CO_2	353,000	1	120
Methane	CH_4	1700	70	10
Ozone	O_3	10–50	1800	0.1
Chlorofluorocarbon	CFC-11	0.28	4000	6.5
Chlorofluorocarbon	CFC-12	0.48	6000	120

30 Propose two methods of slowing down or reversing the changes in temperature that have occurred since 1850 and explain how these methods might accomplish the goal. [2]

31 At the end of the Medieval Warm Period, Vikings abandoned their settlements in North America and Greenland. What are two possible natural climate-related causes and their effects that might explain this action by the Vikings? [2]

32 Some scientists propose that the Little Ice Age was in part the result of a few exceptionally cold winters increasing the ice and snow coverage in the Northern Hemisphere. How is it possible that more ice and snow would make it colder for such an extended number of years? [1]

33 Some scientists have suggested that an increase in solid aerosols—produced by burning wood and coal—deposited on Earth's surface from the atmosphere, at least in part, resulted in the end of the Little Ice Age. Explain how the deposited aerosols might produce the end of the Little Ice Age. [1]

Base your answers to questions 34 through 36 on the diagram below, which represents Earth at a specific position in its orbit as viewed from space. The shaded area represents nighttime. Points *A* and *B* are locations on Earth's surface.

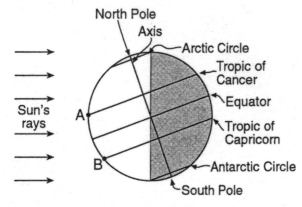

34a State the month in which Earth is at the position shown in the diagram. [1]

34b State the latitude that receives the most intense radiation from the Sun when Earth is at this position in its orbit. [1]

35 Describe the length of daylight at point A compared to the length of daylight at point B on the day represented by the diagram. [1]

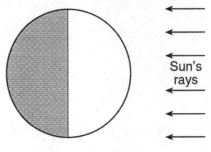

Earth's position in its orbit 6 months later

36 The model of Earth provided *above* represents Earth in its orbit *6 months later*. On the model provided above:
- draw the position of Earth's axis and label the axis [1]
- label the North Pole [1]
- draw the position of Earth's Equator and label the Equator [1]

37 The diagram below shows a view of the ground from directly above a flagpole in New York State at solar noon on a particular day of the year. The flagpole's shadow at solar noon is shown. Draw the position and relative length of the shadow that would be cast by this flagpole three hours later. [2]

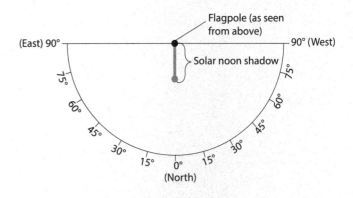

Weather

How Scientists Study Weather

? Did the Wicked Witch of the East not follow the right advice? ?

What should you do if there is a tornado warning? Many people think that the first thing they should do is open all the windows and doors to equalize the air pressure if a tornado arrives. Is that a good idea?

Chances are you have a higher risk of a house falling on you like the Wicked Witch of the East than you do of being sucked out of a window or door by a tornado. In truth, almost all of the injuries and deaths from tornadoes result from flying objects and collapsing buildings, and not from being sucked into the low pressure of the tornado. In any case, time should not be wasted opening windows and doors. You should immediately find the safest location in the building you are in and cover yourself with a heavy coat or blanket.

Vocabulary

air mass	dew point	psychrometer
air pressure gradient	front	radar
anemometer	humidity	relative humidity
atmospheric, barometric, or air pressure	isobar	stationary front
atmospheric transparency	jet stream	station model
barometer	monsoon	troposphere
cloud cover	occluded front	visibility
cold front	planetary wind belt	warm front
cyclone	polar front	water vapor
cyclonic storm	precipitation	weather variables
	probability	

Topic Overview

Are you going to have a picnic or tennis match today? Will the airplane be able to take off for Florida before the approaching ice storm arrives? Will there be a snow day and no school? So much of what you do and how you feel depends on the weather. These conditions affect such things as purchases, your health, how crops grow, the costs of heating and cooling, and the clothing you wear.

Weather is the state or condition of the variables of the atmosphere at any given location for a short period of time. **Weather variables** include temperature, air pressure, wind, moisture conditions, cloud cover, precipitation, and storms. Most of the weather changes occur in the **troposphere,** the part of the atmosphere immediately above Earth's surface. (See Selected Properties of Earth's Atmosphere in the *Earth Science Reference Tables*.)

Variations in insolation cause heat energy to be unevenly distributed in the atmosphere. This heat energy tends to move toward a condition of more uniform distribution. That movement of heat energy results in the constant changes in the atmosphere that are a major cause of weather.

Atmospheric Temperature

Most of the world uses the Celsius scale to measure temperatures, but in the United States people still use the Fahrenheit scale. However, people who work in medical fields and other areas of science often use either the Celsius or Kelvin scales. You should be able to convert between the Fahrenheit, Celsius, and Kelvin scales using the Temperature section of the *Earth Science Reference Tables*.

Air <u>temperature</u> is usually measured using a liquid-filled glass tube called a thermometer. As the temperature of the liquid in the thermometer rises, the liquid expands and moves up the scale. Often temperature is modeled on maps and charts by the use of isolines called <u>isotherms</u>.

Heating of the Atmosphere

The sun is the original source of almost all the heat in the atmosphere. Generally, the more <u>insolation</u> at a location, the warmer Earth's surface and the atmosphere will be. The atmosphere acquires much of its heat directly by contact with Earth's surfaces, but it also gains energy in other ways. The many ways in which the atmosphere is heated include the following:

- Conduction moves heat from Earth into the atmosphere as air touches Earth's surface.
- Direct absorption of insolation from the sun by gases and aerosols moves heat into the atmosphere. (An aerosol is any liquid or solid particle, such as solid smoke particles or liquid cloud droplets, suspended or floating within a gas.)
- Absorption of long-wave infrared radiations from Earth's surface move heat into the atmosphere. Much of the infrared absorption by the atmosphere is due to the presence of water vapor, methane, and carbon dioxide; the larger the amounts of these greenhouse gases, the more heat is absorbed by the atmosphere.
- <u>Condensation</u> (change of water vapor to liquid water) and sublimation/deposition (change of water vapor directly to ice) release large amounts of stored heat, directly heating the atmosphere. Condensation and sublimation release this energy when clouds, fog, dew, and frost form.
- The <u>Coriolis effect</u>, which results from the rotation of Earth and wind—causes friction where the atmosphere and Earth's surface meet. This friction produces heat, some of which is absorbed by the atmosphere.

Convectional Transfer of Heat in the Atmosphere Heat energy is transferred within the atmosphere by convection. Differences in air density cause differences in air pressure. The air pressure differences in turn cause air to move in circular patterns—<u>convection currents,</u> or cells. These air convectional movements transfer heat energy within the atmosphere, especially the troposphere. Winds are the parts of convection currents that are parallel to Earth's surface.

Heating and Cooling of Air by Expansion and Compression When a gas expands, its temperature decreases; when a gas is compressed—or contracted—its temperature increases. Thus when air rises in the atmosphere, it expands and its temperature decreases; similarly, when it descends, it is compressed and its temperature increases. Under average conditions air temperature in the troposphere decreases with increasing altitude because as air rises there is less air above it and less air pressure and thus the air expands and cools. (See Selected Properties of Earth's Atmosphere in the *Earth Science Reference Tables.*) ®

Memory Jogger

Recall that <u>temperature</u> is the measure of the average kinetic energy of particles of a body of matter. Therefore, the greater the average kinetic energy of the particles in the air, the higher the atmospheric temperature.

You may also recall that <u>insolation</u> (INcoming SOLar radiATION) is the portion of the sun's radiation that reaches the top of Earth's atmosphere.

Review Questions

1. Where does the greatest amount of daily weather change take place?

   (1) tropopause
   (2) stratopause
   (3) troposphere
   (4) stratosphere

2. The highest air temperature ever recorded in Albany, New York, is 104°F, which occurred on July 4, 1911. This temperature is equal to

   (1) 35°C
   (2) 40°C
   (3) 45°C
   (4) 50°C

3. Which source provides the most energy for atmospheric weather changes?

   (1) radiation from the sun
   (2) radioactivity from Earth's interior
   (3) heat stored in ocean water
   (4) heat stored in polar ice caps

4. The transfer of heat energy within the troposphere occurs primarily by

   (1) insolation
   (2) conduction
   (3) radiation
   (4) convection

5. As a mass of air rises in the troposphere its temperature will usually

   (1) decrease due to expansion
   (2) decrease due to compression
   (3) increase due to expansion
   (4) increase due to compression

6. Which graph best represents what most likely happens to the temperature of Earth's atmosphere as the amount of carbon dioxide in the atmosphere increases over a period of many years?

7. The diagram below shows the direction of movement of air over a mountain. As the air moves down the leeward side of the mountain, the air will

   (1) warm due to compression
   (2) warm due to expansion
   (3) cool due to compression
   (4) cool due to expansion

Atmospheric Pressure and Density

Air pressure and density are directly related. The denser the atmosphere, the greater the weight of a given volume of air, and therefore the greater the air pressure it exerts. **Atmospheric pressure**—also called **barometric pressure** and **air pressure**—is the pressure due to the weight of the overlying atmosphere pushing down on any given area.

Measurement of and Changes in Air Pressure

Instruments called **barometers** are used to measure air pressure. Two types of barometers are used—the mercury barometer and the aneroid barometer. In a mercury barometer, a tube with a closed top is placed in a container of mercury. When a column of air from above pushes down on

Figure 7-1. Aneroid Barometer

the mercury in the container, the mercury rises in the tube. The air pressure is read in inches of mercury. In an aneroid barometer (Figure 7-1), a metal can contains a partial vacuum that expands and contracts with changes in air pressure, and a series of mechanical parts display a reading on a dial.

The mercury barometer is the standard reference instrument, but it is difficult to transport, and there is the danger of mercury vapor. Standard air pressure (one atmosphere) at sea level is 14.7 pounds per square inch, 29.92 inches of mercury, or 1013.2 millibars. Barometric pressure in millibars can be converted to inches of mercury using the Pressure chart in the *Earth Science Reference Tables*. (See Figure 7-2.) The barometric trend—shown on weather maps—is how the magnitude of the air pressure has changed over the past three hours. Air pressure is often shown on weather maps by the use of isolines called **isobars,** as shown in Figures 7-6, 7-18 and 7-22A.

Effect of Temperature on Air Pressure Changes in the temperature of the air cause changes in air pressure. As the temperature of air increases, the air expands and its density and pressure decrease. Decreasing temperature has the reverse effect.

Effect of Water Vapor on Air Pressure The greater the amount of water vapor in the air (called moisture content, absolute humidity, and humidity), the lower the air density and pressure. Each water molecule in the atmosphere replaces another molecule of air, usually oxygen or nitrogen. Since a water molecule weighs less than either an oxygen or a nitrogen molecule, the greater the amount of water vapor in the air, the less dense the air as a whole becomes. (See Figure 7-3.)

Effect of Altitude on Atmospheric Pressure As altitude or elevation increases, atmospheric density and pressure decrease. As you go up higher in the atmosphere, the less gas there is above you. If you have ever climbed a high mountain, the lower air pressure, and thus less oxygen, was the reason you were "short of breath." (See Atmospheric Pressure with Selected Properties of Earth's Atmosphere in the *Earth Science Reference Tables*.)

To summarize, as either altitude, temperature, or moisture content in the atmosphere increases, air density and air pressure decrease.

Figure 7-2. Method of converting from millibars to inches of mercury in air pressure readings: This is part of the chart from the *Earth Science Reference Tables*. The millibar part of the table has divisions for each whole millibar. You should be able to estimate to the nearest tenth of a millibar within three tenths. The inch part of the scale's big divisions is for each tenth of an inch, and smaller divisions are for hundredths of an inch. Because of the smallness of these divisions, a measurement to the nearest hundredth of an inch is a reasonable answer. Some conversions are 1013.2 millibars (mb) = 29.92 inches, 1022.8 mb = 30.20 inches, 30.53 inches = 1034.0 mb, 29.81 inches = 1009.5 mb.

Type of Gas	Relative Molecular Weight
N = N_2, nitrogen molecules	28
O = O_2, oxygen molecules	32
W = H_2O, water molecules	18

Figure 7-3. Effect of water vapor on air pressure: When water vapor is "added" to volume of air, it is not really added. A molecule of water vapor replaces a molecule of nitrogen or oxygen in that volume of air—resulting in the same number of molecules as there were before the water vapor was added. Since each molecule of water has less weight and mass than nitrogen and oxygen, the more water vapor in a given volume of air, the less the air's weight, density, and pressure. The effect shown in the diagram is greatly exaggerated.

Review Questions

8. A balloon carrying weather instruments is released at Earth's surface and rises through the troposphere. As the balloon rises, what will the instruments generally indicate?

   (1) a decrease in both air temperature and air pressure
   (2) an increase in both air temperature and air pressure
   (3) an increase in air temperature and a decrease in air pressure
   (4) a decrease in air temperature and an increase in air pressure

9. An air pressure of 1023 millibars is equal to how many inches of mercury?

   (1) 30.10   (2) 30.15   (3) 30.19   (4) 30.21

10. An air pressure of 30.15 inches of mercury is equal to

    (1) 1017 mb   (3) 1021 mb
    (2) 1019 mb   (4) 1023 mb

11. Which weather variable is the following instrument designed to measure?

    (1) visibility   (3) dew point
    (2) relative humidity   (4) air pressure

12. A barometer indicates a pressure of 30 inches of mercury at sea level; at $3\frac{1}{2}$ miles above sea level, it indicates a pressure of 15 inches. What is the best conclusion you can draw from these data?
    (1) humidity affects the pressure
    (2) temperature affects the pressure
    (3) of the total mass of air, about 99 percent is within $3\frac{1}{2}$ miles of sea level
    (4) of the total mass of air, about 50 percent is less than $3\frac{1}{2}$ miles above sea level

13. At sea level, as the temperature of the atmosphere decreases, the air pressure usually

    (1) decreases
    (2) increases
    (3) remains the same

14. Which graph best represents the relationship between air temperature and air density in the atmosphere?

    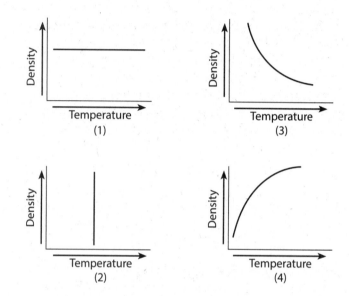

15. If the air humidity increases and the temperature remains the same, the air pressure will

    (1) decrease
    (2) remain the same
    (3) increase
    (4) first increase, then decrease

16. What is the approximate elevation above sea level at which atmospheric pressure is 0.2 atmosphere?

    (1) 7.0 km   (3) 27 km
    (2) 17 km   (4) 37 km

17. As a parcel of air increases in altitude, its pressure will

    (1) decrease
    (2) increase
    (3) remain the same

Figure 7-4. Cause of wind illustrated by land and sea breezes: In diagram A, a sea breeze develops because the land heats up faster than the water during the day—resulting in warm, less dense, low-pressure air that rises. Over the ocean cooler, denser, higher-pressure air forms. The cooler, denser, higher-pressure air from the sea replaces the rising warmer air over land—resulting in a sea breeze. In diagram B, at night, reverse conditions result in a land breeze. Note that land and sea breezes can be part of a convection cell.

Wind

Horizontal movement of air parallel to Earth's surface is called <u>wind</u>. Wind is a type of field called vector because it requires a magnitude and direction to totally describe it.

Wind Speed

Winds are caused by differences in air pressure, which are often caused by changing atmospheric conditions of temperature and water vapor content. Figure 7-4 illustrates the cause of wind using local land and sea breezes as an example. The difference in air pressure for a specific distance is called the **air pressure gradient.** The closer together the isobars on a weather map are, the greater (steeper) the pressure gradient. The greater the pressure gradient, the faster the wind speed. (See Figure 7-6.) An instrument called an **anemometer** (Figure 7-5) is used to measure wind speed. Wind speed is measured in miles per hour and <u>knots</u>—nautical miles per hour. One knot equals 1.15 miles per hour (mph); thus, 5 knots equals about 5.75 miles per hour.

Wind Direction

Air (wind) moves from areas of high pressure to areas of low pressure. However, the <u>Coriolis effect</u> (caused by Earth's rotation) modifies that

Figure 7-5. Anemometer: An Anemometer is an instrument for measuring wind speed. It usually consists of 3 or 4 cups to "catch" the wind attached to rods that are connected to a shaft that can spin. The faster the wind is blowing the greater the spinning of the anemometer. The spinning of the shaft is connected to a dial by mechanical or electronic means which can be read in units of wind speed.

Figure 7-6. Pressure gradient as indicated by closeness of isobars on a weather map: The closer together the isobars, the greater the air pressure gradient. The greater the pressure gradient, the greater the wind speed.

Memory Jogger

You may recall seeing a wind vane or a picture of one. The arrowhead of a wind vane points into the wind—that is, it points in the direction that the wind is blowing from.

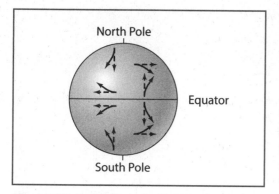

Figure 7-7. Deflection of winds by the Coriolis effect: The dashed arrow in each case shows the direction the wind would blow if there were no Coriolis effect. The solid arrow shows the actual path of the wind. If you face toward the direction the wind is blowing toward, it is always deflected to the right in the Northern Hemisphere and to the left in the Southern Hemisphere.

pattern of movement, deflecting winds to the right in the Northern Hemisphere and to the left in the Southern Hemisphere. Figure 7-7 illustrates how wind directions are modified by Earth's rotation.

A wind is named for the direction from which it comes; for example, a wind blowing from the south toward the north is a south wind. A wind blowing towards the southeast is a northwest wind—the direction the wind is coming from. An instrument called a wind vane, or weather vane, is often used to determine wind direction. The arrowhead of a wind vane points into the wind—that is, it points in the direction that the wind is blowing from.

Formation of Waves on Surface Water

Wind blowing over bodies of water creates friction where the air and liquid water meet. The friction transfers energy from the wind to the body of water and produces waves. The stronger the wind, the higher the waves. These energy waves move out from the area where they are produced and toward land where the energy results in wave erosion at shorelines.

Review Questions

18. As the pressure gradient increases, wind velocity

(1) decreases
(2) increases
(3) remains the same

19. The following map represents a portion of an air-pressure field at Earth's surface. At which position is wind speed lowest?

(1) A   (2) B   (3) C   (4) D

20. In the Northern Hemisphere, a wind blowing from the south will be deflected towards the

(1) northwest
(2) northeast
(3) southwest
(4) southeast

21. Which cross-section best shows the normal movement of the air over Oswego, New York, on a very hot summer afternoon?

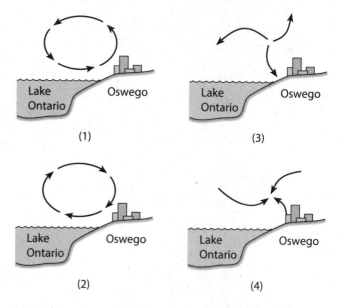

22. The weather element determined by an anemometer is

(1) pressure
(2) humidity
(3) visibility
(4) wind velocity

23. Winds blow from regions of
(1) high temperature to regions of low air temperature
(2) high air pressure to regions of low air pressure
(3) low temperature to regions of high temperature
(4) low air pressure to regions of high air pressure

24. Which is NOT true about wind?
(1) Wind direction is named for the direction toward which the wind blows.
(2) Wind moves from regions of higher pressure to lower pressure.
(3) The steeper the gradient, the greater the wind speed.
(4) Wind is horizontal movement of air.

General Circulation of the Air in the Troposphere

Differences in air temperature and pressure in various portions of the troposphere cause air to be in constant motion. This circulation of air produces convection cells throughout the troposphere.

Convection Cells

The unequal distribution of insolation on Earth results in unequal heating and differences in air pressure. Cooler air, being denser, sinks toward Earth under the influence of gravity, causing the less dense, warmer air to rise. The result is a series of convection cells around Earth at various latitudes, as shown in Figure 7-8. As indicated by the solid arrows, there are upward currents in the vicinity of 0° latitude (the equator) and 60° North and South latitudes. Downward currents exist near 30° and 90° North and South latitudes. Regions where air comes together to form vertical currents are regions of convergence. Regions where air spreads out from the vertical currents are regions of divergence.

As part of these tropospheric convection cells, there are bands of easterly moving air at the top of the troposphere, called **jet streams.** The winds of the jet stream can blow 200 miles an hour or more. Commercial airplanes flying with the jet stream can save a half hour of flight time traveling from the west to east coasts of the contiguous United States, or lose an hour going in the other direction, if the jet stream is not avoided. The jet streams have an important influence on the formation and direction of weather pattern movement in mid-latitude regions such as the United States. The jet streams help steer the air masses and low pressure centers. The locations of the jet streams are shown on Figure 7-8 and on the Planetary Wind and Moisture Belts in the Troposphere in the *Earth Science Reference Tables.*

Planetary Wind and Pressure Belts

At Earth's surface, winds blow horizontally away from regions of divergence and high air pressure, and toward regions of convergence and low air pressure. Figure 7-8 shows the pressure belts of Earth with generally consistent high or low air pressure. Because of the Coriolis effect, winds moving away from high air pressure are deflected to the right in the Northern

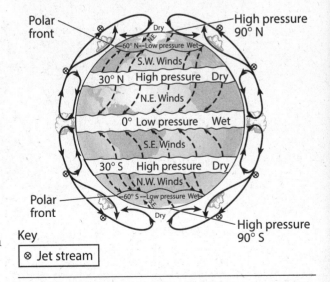

Figure 7-8. Planetary wind, pressure, and moisture belts in the troposphere: The drawing shows the locations of the belts near the time of an equinox. The locations shift somewhat with the changing latitude of the sun's vertical rays.

Hemisphere and to the left in the Southern Hemisphere, as indicated by the dashed arrows in Figure 7-7. The result is a series of **planetary wind belts** within which the winds move generally in a specific direction much of the time—thus they are <u>prevailing</u> <u>winds</u>.

Seasonal Shifting of the Wind and Pressure Belts Because the vertical rays of the sun shift north and south with the seasons, the pressure belts and the resulting wind belts generally follow the vertical rays of the sun. This results in many parts of Earth being under the influence of different wind and/or pressure belts in different seasons. Difference in air pressure and prevailing winds can often mean quite different weather conditions. As an example, in the winter the northern portions of the contiguous United States often get cold weather conditions from Canada caused by northerly prevailing winds. These same regions in summer usually get more southerly winds of the prevailing southwesterlies and warmer weather conditions.

In some regions of Earth, there are regular and extreme weather changes caused by the shifting wind and pressure belts. These extreme weather changes are called the **monsoons.** Figure 7-9 shows the changing monsoon conditions of part of Asia around India. Note that the wind that brings the rain blows from the high pressure area over the ocean to the low pressure area over the land.

Weather Movement in the Contiguous United States Much of the contiguous United States is affected by planetary winds that blow from the southwest to the northeast—called the prevailing southwesterly winds. Therefore, weather changes in the United States move generally from a southwesterly direction to a northeasterly direction.

Figure 7-9. Monsoon conditions of Southeast Asia: (A) In the summer, the wet, low pressure belt that is normally over the equator (see Figure 7-8) moves northward and brings high amounts of rain to much of Southeast Asia, including India. (B) In the winter, the high pressure area is over the land, and this brings dry air from Central Asia over Southeast Asia towards the low pressure belt.

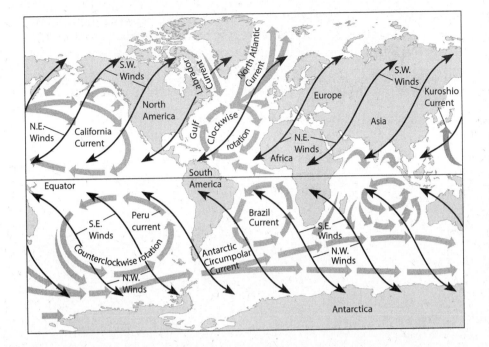

Key

→ Prevailing winds

⇒ Surface ocean currents

Figure 7-10. Cause of surface ocean currents: When you observe a comparison of the directions of Earth's prevailing winds and the location of the surface ocean currents, it is obvious that they are related. Prevailing winds transmit kinetic energy and "drive" the surface ocean currents. The Coriolis effect twists the direction of the currents to the right in the Northern Hemisphere creating a clockwise rotation of the currents there. In the Southern Hemisphere, the Coriolis effect shifts currents to the left (west), creating a counterclockwise rotation of the surface ocean currents.

Formation of Surface Ocean Currents Surface ocean currents are caused by wind blowing over the oceans and transferring energy to the water. The direction of these currents is affected by the direction of the planetary winds. Compare the map Surface Ocean Currents with the diagram Planetary Winds and Moisture Belts in the Troposphere in the *Earth Science Reference Tables* as well as with Figure 7-10. The directions of the surface ocean currents are also affected by blocking by landmasses and the rotation of Earth through the Coriolis effect. Note that the maps of the surface ocean currents show that they are often part of a circular pattern that spins clockwise in the Northern Hemisphere and counterclockwise in the Southern Hemisphere. This difference in spinning direction is caused by the Coriolis effect's deflection to the right in the Northern Hemisphere and to the left in the Southern Hemisphere.

Since the surface ocean currents are a direct result of the transfer of energy from the movement of the prevailing winds, they can seasonally shift their positions. Some of the surface ocean currents shift position north and south as the winds of the prevailing wind belt do—following the motions of the vertical rays of the sun.

Review Questions

25. Planetary winds do not blow directly north or south because of
    (1) the Coriolis effect
    (2) gravitational force
    (3) magnetic force
    (4) Earth's revolution

26. On a certain day in Syracuse, New York, there is a high-pressure center directly north and a low-pressure center directly south. Because of the effect of Earth's rotation, the air in Syracuse will
    (1) blow directly to the south
    (2) blow directly to the north
    (3) be deflected toward the southwest
    (4) be deflected toward the northeast

To answer questions 27 through 31, refer to the following diagram, which shows movement of air in the lower part of the atmosphere around the time of an equinox.

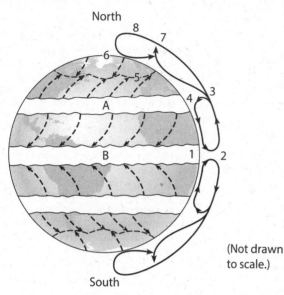

(Not drawn to scale.)

27. The movement of air from 1 to 2 to 3 to 4 to 1 would be called a

(1) high-pressure cell
(2) contiguous cell
(3) convection cell
(4) Coriolis cell

28. What is the basic underlying reason for the movement of air shown?

(1) differences in gravity
(2) differences in air density
(3) differences in pressure gradient
(4) differences in magnetism

29. What would be the most likely cause of the movement of air at position 1?

(1) low moisture content and low temperature
(2) high moisture content and high temperature
(3) low moisture content and high temperature
(4) high moisture content and low temperature

30. The air moves at the surface of Earth, from position A to position B, because

(1) positions A and B have low pressure
(2) positions A and B have high pressure
(3) position A has low pressure, and position B has high pressure
(4) position A has high pressure, and position B has low pressure

31. Condensation would most likely occur at position

(1) 3   (2) 4   (3) 6   (4) 7

32. Pilots flying from the west coast of the United States to New York may sometimes shorten their flight time by using a high-speed tailwind. They are most likely using the

(1) prevailing northwesterlies
(2) jet stream
(3) convection cells
(4) prevailing southeasterlies

33. Which diagram shows the usual path of low-pressure storm centers as they pass across the United States?

(1)   (3)

(2)   (4)

34. What is the primary source of energy for ocean currents and waves?

(1) the moon
(2) the atmosphere
(3) the continents
(4) the sun

35. What is the most direct cause of major surface ocean currents?

(1) prevailing winds
(2) gravity
(3) tides
(4) salinity differences

Atmospheric Moisture

Atmospheric moisture—water—exists in three states of matter: liquid, solid, and gas. Gaseous water in the atmosphere is called **water vapor.** The oceans, which cover about 70 percent of Earth's surface, are the source of most atmospheric moisture.

Moisture in the form of water vapor enters the atmosphere by evaporation, sublimation to a gas, and transpiration. Evaporation is the process by which a liquid changes to a gas; transpiration is the process by which plants release water vapor as part of their life functions. Collectively, evaporation and transpiration are called evapotranspiration. Sublimation to a gas is the process by which ice changes directly to water vapor without forming any liquid water.

Energy of Evaporation and Transpiration of Water

Large amounts of energy (approximately 2260 joules/gram) are required to change liquid water into water vapor during the processes of evaporation and transpiration. Almost all of this energy comes from insolation. The solar energy is converted into a type of potential or stored energy in the water vapor. When evaporation or transpiration occurs, the more energetic water molecules leave the liquid and form water vapor. Since the molecules leaving the liquid are the more energetic ones, the average kinetic energy of the molecules remaining in the liquid decreases. As a result, the temperature of an evaporating liquid is somewhat lower than its surroundings. You have noticed this effect of evaporation when you step out of the shower and you feel chilled.

Process of Evaporation

Figure 7-11 helps to explain what happens when water—or any other liquid—evaporates. Diagram A shows a closed container of air into which some water has just been added. We assume there are no water vapor molecules in the air at this moment. However, as soon as water is placed in the container, some of its more energetic molecules begin to escape into the air above and mingle with the other gas molecules that are present. Diagram B shows the situation a short time later. There are water molecules in the air. We see two more molecules in the process of leaving the water. However, one molecule in the air is about to enter the water, so that there will be five molecules in the air. Diagram C shows the situation some time later. There are now eight water molecules in the air. Again, two more water molecules are about to leave the water, but now two molecules in the air are about to return to the water. The net result will be eight molecules in the air—the same number as before. We have a condition of dynamic equilibrium in which the rate at which water is entering the gaseous state (evaporation) equals the rate at which water vapor is returning to the liquid state (condensation).

o Air molecules • Water molecules

Figure 7-11. The saturation of the air with water vapor and evaporating liquid water: In diagram A, no evaporation has occurred. In diagram B, evaporation is proceeding faster than condensation. In diagram C, a dynamic equilibrium between evaporation and condensation has been reached, and the air is saturated with water vapor.

Factors Affecting Evaporation Rates of Water

The net evaporation rate of water at a location is determined by

- amount of energy available: the more energy available, and thus the higher the temperature, the faster the evaporation of available water
- surface area of the water: the more spread out the water, the greater the air-water interface and the faster the evaporation
- degree of saturation of the air with water vapor: the higher the water vapor content of the air, the closer the air is to being saturated with water vapor and the slower the net evaporation rate
- wind speed: wind often moves air at the water-air interface that is high in water vapor and replaces it with air that is less saturated and thus speeds up evaporation rates. The greater the speed of the wind, the more air replacement occurs.

Humidity, Temperature, and Dew Point

Like moisture, **humidity** is a general term that refers to the water vapor content of the atmosphere. The amount (mass) of water vapor in each unit volume of air is called the <u>absolute</u> <u>humidity</u>. Absolute humidity is often measured in grams of water vapor per cubic meter of air. The maximum absolute humidity, or moisture capacity, increases rapidly with an increase in air temperature, as shown in the graph in Figure 7-12. This means that the total amount of water vapor the air can hold—its capacity—increases with an increase in temperature, or in other words, hotter air can hold more water vapor than colder air.

The ratio of the amount of water vapor in the air (absolute humidity) to the maximum amount it can hold (its moisture capacity) is **relative humidity.** It is usually expressed as a percent. In simpler terms, relative humidity is the amount of water vapor in the air compared to the amount of water vapor the air can hold at a specific temperature. The closer the absolute humidity is to the maximum absolute humidity (capacity) the higher the relative humidity. Note that relative humidity is a percentage of saturation, or capacity, NOT how much water vapor there is in a volume of air.

Relative Humidity and Temperature At any given time and place, the air has a certain amount of water vapor (humidity), with a corresponding absolute humidity. If the temperature of the air changes but the amount of water vapor remains the same, the relative humidity will change. For example, if the temperature increases, the relative humidity will decrease. This occurs because the capacity increases with the increase in temperature, while the absolute humidity remains the same. On the other hand, if the temperature decreases while the absolute humidity remains the same, the relative humidity will increase.

If the temperature of the air remains constant, but more water vapor is added to the air by evaporation or transpiration, both the absolute

Figure 7-12. Relationship between air's capacity for water vapor and temperature: Note that air with a temperature of 35°C can hold about four times more water vapor than air at 10°C can. Note that when the air at 10°C has 50 percent relative humidity, it has only about 1/4 as much water vapor as air at 35°C with 50 percent relative humidity.

humidity and the relative humidity will increase. The relative humidity increases because the air becomes closer to its capacity, or saturation point, when more water vapor is added.

Dew Point If the temperature of the air decreases while the absolute humidity remains the same, the temperature will eventually reach a point at which the absolute humidity equals capacity. At this temperature, the relative humidity will be 100 percent. This temperature is called the **dew point**—the temperature at which air is filled with water vapor. If the air temperature drops below the dew point, water vapor in the air will condense to liquid water or sublimate to a solid.

The dew point depends on the absolute humidity and not on the relative humidity. As the amount of water vapor in the air increases, the dew point also rises because the more water vapor in the air, the closer the air is to its saturation point—the dew point.

Measuring Relative Humidity Relative humidity is measured by indirect methods. Two similar instruments are commonly used to help measure relative humidity—a sling **psychrometer** and a hygrometer. Figure 7-13 shows these two instruments. Both use two thermometers. The instruments contain an ordinary thermometer called a <u>dry-bulb thermometer,</u> and another thermometer with a wick around its bulb, called the <u>wet-bulb thermometer</u>. With a sling psychrometer, when the wick is moistened and the thermometers are whirled in the air, the temperature of the wet bulb drops because of the cooling effect of the evaporation of the water. The amount of cooling depends on the rate of evaporation, and is therefore related to the relative humidity.

A
A hygrometer

18°C
Dry bulb

10°C
Wet bulb

Wet Cloth wick

Reservoir of water

B Sling psychrometer

Sock or wick

Wet bulb

Dry bulb

Handle

Figure 7-13. Hygrometer and Sling Psychrometer: Both the hygrometer (A) and sling psychrometer (B) use the difference in the dry and wet-bulb temperature readings to help determine relative humidity and dew point. Note that the dry-bulb reading on the sling psychrometer at 20°C is the same as a regular temperature reading at 20°C.

To determine percent relative humidity, use the Relative Humidity (%) tables in the *Earth Science Reference Tables* and the following procedure. Ⓡ

- Locate the dry-bulb reading on the left-hand side of the Relative Humidity (%) chart in the *Earth Science Reference Tables*.
- Subtract the wet-bulb reading from the dry-bulb reading.
- Locate the difference between the wet-bulb and dry-bulb readings across the top of the chart.
- Follow the horizontal row for the dry-bulb reading to the right until it meets the vertical column running down from the top. This number is the relative humidity.

See Figure 7-14 for an example for determining relative humidity.

Determining Dew Point To determine the dew point, you need the dry-bulb and wet-bulb readings from a sling psychrometer or hygrometer and the

Dry-bulb Temperature (°C)	Difference Between Wet-Bulb and Dry-Bulb Temperatures (°C)									
	1	2	3	4	5	6	7	8	9	10
−20	28									
−18	40									
−16	48	0								
−14	55	11								
−12	61	23								
−10	66	33	0							
−8	71	41	13							
−6	73	48	20	0						
−4	77	54	32	11						
−2	79	58	37	20	1					
0	81	63	45	28	11					
2	83	67	51	36	20	6				
4	85	70	56	42	27	14	= 14% Relative humidity			
6	86	72	59	46	35	22	10	0		
8	87	74	62	51	39	28	17	6		
10	88	76	65	54	43	33	24	13	4	

Figure 7-14. Determining relative humidity: Suppose the dry-bulb reading is 4°C and the wet-bulb reading is −2°C. The difference is 6°C. Reading across from 4°C and down from 6°C, you find a relative humidity of 14%.

Dewpoint Temperatures chart in the *Earth Science Reference Tables*. Use the following procedure which is very similar to the procedure used to determine the relative humidity:

- Locate the dry-bulb reading on the left-hand side of the chart.
- Subtract the wet-bulb reading from the dry-bulb reading.
- Locate the difference between the wet-bulb and dry-bulb readings across the top of the chart.
- Follow the horizontal row for the dry-bulb reading to the right until it meets the vertical column running down from the difference between the wet-bulb and dry-bulb readings. This number is the dew point temperature.

For example, suppose the dry-bulb reading is 8°C, and the wet-bulb reading is 6°C. The difference is 2°C. Reading across from 8°C and down from 2°C, you find a dew point temperature of 3°C.

Cloud Formation

If the temperature of the air cools (often by expanding) below the dew point, the water vapor will usually condense to a liquid or sublimate to a solid (deposition), changing to microscopic liquid water droplets or ice crystals, respectively. At Earth's surface, condensation produces liquid dew, and sublimation produces the solid frost. If the temperature in the atmosphere is above 0°C, condensation produces water droplets, which appear as a cloud when grouped. Some clouds are composed of ice crystals, which form when water vapor sublimates to a solid. A cloud is therefore a collection of liquid water droplets and/or ice crystals suspended in the atmosphere and dense enough to be visible. If there is only a low density of water droplets or ice crystals, a condition called haze may result. **Cloud cover**—found on some weather maps—is the fraction or percent of the total sky at a location that is covered by clouds. If a cloud is on, or just above, Earth's surface, it is called fog. The condensation or sublimation that forms clouds and fog releases tremendous amounts of energy into the troposphere. This is the potential energy that was imparted to water molecules during evaporation and sublimation to a gas.

Besides needing saturated air, condensation usually requires a surface upon which the vapor can condense. This is called the condensation surface. In the formation of clouds and fog, the condensation surfaces are aerosols such as dust, bacteria, and volcanic ash. In the formation of dew, the condensation surfaces are the features of Earth's surface like grass and leaves.

Since air temperature and dew point temperature both decrease with altitude in the troposphere, the altitude where temperature and dew point are the same is the level where clouds form by condensation or sublimation. This level is often seen as the flat bottoms on some clouds.

Figure 7-15. Rain/Precipitation gauge: This instrument collects the precipitation and allows it to be measured in units such as inches or centimeters using a ruler.

— ruler

— collecting tube

Precipitation

The falling of liquid or solid water from clouds toward the surface of Earth is **precipitation.** For precipitation to occur, the ice crystals or water droplets in clouds must come together to become big enough so that they will fall under the influence of gravity. The forms in which precipitation occur are rain, drizzle, snow, sleet, freezing rain, and hail. The conditions that result in the formations of these different types of precipitation are shown in Figure 7-16.

A rain gauge, a type of precipitation gauge, is used to measure liquid precipitation. (See Figure 7-15.) It is measured in depth—usually inches or centimeters. Snow depth is often measured with a ruler, or it is gently warmed and the depth of liquid is measured and reported as precipitation. A rain shower is brief, rapidly forming, rapidly ending, and often heavy rain associated with thunderstorm-type clouds. A snow shower is a brief, heavy snowfall.

To review, precipitation usually occurs when rising air cools portions of the troposphere. This action reduces the differences between air temperature

Rain Falling liquid droplets larger than 0.2 mm in diameter; may be melted snow

Drizzle Falling liquid droplets from 0.2 to 0.5 mm in diameter

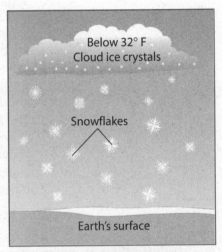

Snow Falling ice crystals formed by combining cloud ice crystals

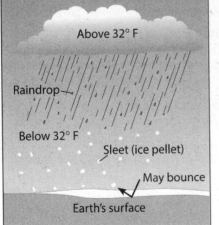

Sleet Solid pellets of ice that form by freezing of rain drops as they fall

Freezing rain Rain or drizzle that freezes on contact with features of Earth's surface

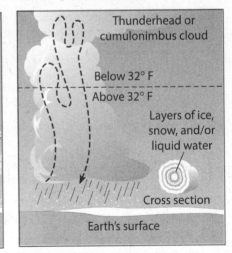

Hail Layers of ice, snow, and water formed by many up-and-down movements in a thunderstorm cloud; may be grapefruit-sized

Figure 7-16. Forms of precipitation

and the dew point temperature until the water content of the air equals the air's capacity to hold water vapor. If the air continues to cool below the dew point, liquid water droplets (by condensation) or tiny ice crystals (by sublimation/deposition) form—usually producing clouds. When these liquid or solid water cloud particles collide or otherwise combine, they become heavy enough to fall, producing precipitation. The factors that cause the rising air, and thus cooling, are upward movement of air at fronts, air blowing against a mountain, or portions of air that are selectively heated at Earth's surface, such as over a dark road.

Atmospheric Transparency and Precipitation

The more pollutants added to the atmosphere by the activities of people and nature, the more aerosols are present. The more aerosols in the air, the less transparent the atmosphere is to insolation. How transparent the atmosphere is to insolation is called **atmospheric transparency.** When the atmosphere is less transparent, it means that more energy from the sun is absorbed or reflected by the atmosphere, resulting in less insolation reaching Earth's surface.

When the atmosphere has an aerosol content so high that distant images are blurred, and a cloudless sky does not appear blue, the condition is called haze. A <u>haze</u> or fog, usually brownish, which is highly polluted is <u>smog</u>. Condensation in cloud formation incorporates some of the aerosols, and these aerosols are removed from the atmosphere during precipitation. The falling liquid or solid water also collects other aerosols on the way down, thus lowering air pollution levels and cleaning the atmosphere. **Visibility**—sometimes found on weather maps—is how far you can see along Earth's surface expressed in miles. The poorer the atmospheric transparency, the lower the visibility.

Review Questions

36. As altitude within the troposphere increases, the amount of water vapor generally

(1) decreases, only
(2) increases, only
(3) remains the same
(4) decreases, then increases

37. By which process does moisture leave green plants?

(1) convection
(2) condensation
(3) transpiration
(4) radiation

38. Most moisture enters the atmosphere by the processes of

(1) convection and conduction
(2) condensation and radiation
(3) reflection and absorption
(4) transpiration and evaporation

39. The primary source of most of the moisture in Earth's atmosphere is

(1) soil-moisture storage
(2) rivers and lakes
(3) melting glaciers
(4) oceans

40. As the exposed area of a moist object decreases, the rate of evaporation of the liquid from that object

(1) decreases
(2) increases
(3) remains the same

41. As the amount of light energy striking a moist object increases, the rate of evaporation of the liquid from that object

(1) decreases
(2) increases
(3) remains the same

42. As the amount of water vapor in a given volume of air increases, the rate of evaporation from a moist object

(1) decreases
(2) increases
(3) remains the same

43. There will most likely be an increase in the rate at which water evaporates from a lake if there is

(1) a decrease in the temperature of the air
(2) a decrease in the altitude of the sun
(3) an increase in the moisture content of the air
(4) an increase in the wind velocity

44. In the following diagram, at which location would the amount of water vapor in the air most likely be greater?

(1) A   (3) C
(2) B   (4) D

45. In the closed aquarium shown in the following diagram, the amount of water evaporating is equal to the amount of water vapor condensing.

Which statement best explains why these amounts are equal?

(1) The glass sides of the aquarium are warmer than the water.
(2) The air in the aquarium is 50 percent saturated.
(3) The relative humidity outside the aquarium is 100 percent.
(4) The air in the aquarium is saturated.

46. Which graph best represents the relationship between the moisture-holding capacity of the atmosphere and atmospheric temperature?

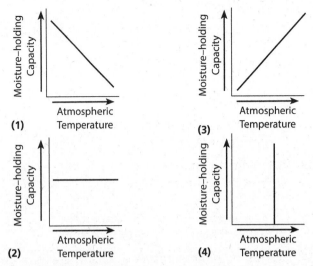

47. To say that the relative humidity on a given day is 70 percent means that the air

(1) is composed of 70 percent water vapor
(2) holds 70 percent of its water vapor capacity
(3) contains 70 parts of water to 100 parts of dry air
(4) contains the same amount of water that it would contain at 70°F

48. If the amount of water vapor in the air increases, then the dew point of the air will

(1) decrease
(2) increase
(3) remain the same

49. During which part of the day is the relative humidity usually lowest?

(1) morning
(2) midafternoon
(3) evening
(4) late night

50. As the air temperature rises, the relative humidity

(1) increases
(2) decreases
(3) remains the same

51. Air with a temperature of 60°F and a relative humidity of 51 percent was warmed to a temperature of 70°F, but the relative humidity remained at 51 percent. How did the moisture content change?

(1) The moisture content decreased.
(2) The moisture content increased.
(3) The moisture content remained the same.

52. Which statement best explains why the wet-bulb thermometer of a sling psychrometer usually shows a lower temperature than the dry-bulb thermometer?

(1) Water evaporates from the wet-bulb thermometer.
(2) Water vapor condenses on the wet-bulb thermometer.
(3) The air around the wet-bulb prevents absorption of heat.
(4) The air around the dry bulb prevents absorption of heat.

53. When the dry-bulb temperature is 20°C, and the wet-bulb temperature is 16°C, the relative humidity is

(1) 42 percent   (3) 66 percent
(2) 62 percent   (4) 69 percent

54. The dry-bulb temperature is 20°C. The wet-bulb temperature is 17°C. What is the dew point?

(1) 12°C   (2) 13°C   (3) 14°C   (4) 15°C

Base your answers to questions 55 and 56 on the weather instrument shown in the following diagram.

Wet bulb

Dry bulb

55. What are the equivalent Celsius temperature readings for the Fahrenheit readings shown?

(1) wet 21°C, dry 27°C   (3) wet 70°C, dry 80°C
(2) wet 26°C, dry 37°C   (4) wet 158°C, dry 176°C

56. Which weather variables are most easily determined by using this weather instrument and the *Earth Science Reference Tables*?

(1) air temperature and wind speed
(2) visibility and wind direction
(3) relative humidity and dew point
(4) air pressure and cloud type

57. Which process most directly results in cloud formation?

(1) condensation   (3) precipitation
(2) transpiration   (4) radiation

58. At which temperature could water vapor in the atmosphere change directly into solid ice crystals?

(1) 20°F   (2) 40°F   (3) 10°C   (4) 100°C

59. Which statement best explains how atmospheric dust particles influence the water cycle?

(1) Dust particles are the main source of dissolved salts in the sea.
(2) Dust particles increase the capacity of the atmosphere to hold water vapor.
(3) Dust particles increase the amount of evaporation that takes place.
(4) Dust particles provide surfaces on which water vapor can condense.

60. Atmospheric transparency is most likely to increase after

(1) volcanic eruption
(2) forest fires
(3) industrial activity
(4) precipitation

Air Masses and Fronts

Much of the weather of the contiguous United States is the result of the invasion of air masses and their interactions at their boundaries. An **air mass** is a large body of air in the troposphere with similar characteristics of pressure, moisture, and temperature.

Characteristics of Air Masses

An air mass forms when a large mass of air remains stationary over a part of Earth's surface for a period of time and thus acquires some of the characteristics of that surface. The geographic regions in which air masses are formed are called source regions. The source regions for the air masses that affect weather in the United States are shown in Figure 7-17.

If the source region is at a high latitude, the air mass will have a low temperature; if it is at a low latitude, the air mass will have a high temperature. If the source region is land, the air mass will be dry; if it is water, the air mass will be moist. The symbols used for the various air masses are shown in the key of Figure 7-17 and in the *Earth Science Reference Tables.* The arrows in Figure 7-17 indicate the path or tracks of air masses that affect weather across the contiguous United States.

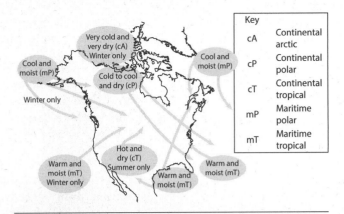

Figure 7-17. Source regions and tracks of air masses that affect weather of the continental United States

Lows and Highs

The troposphere is divided into two portions according to air pressure and direction of circulation of winds. <u>Lows</u> [L], also called **cyclones,** have low pressure. Lows include the cyclonic storms to be discussed later in the topic. The pressure in a low is lowest at its center, and thus winds blow toward the center. The Coriolis effect deflects the winds, so that in the Northern Hemisphere a counterclockwise circulation occurs within lows, as shown in Figure 7-18. <u>Highs</u> [H], or <u>anticyclones</u>, have high pressure. Air mass centers are usually regions of high air pressure. The pressure in a high is greatest at its center, and thus winds blow out from the center. The general circulation around highs is clockwise in the Northern Hemisphere. Lows are usually associated with stormy weather with high cloud cover, much precipitation, and high winds. Highs are usually associated with relatively clear skies and little or no precipitation.

Fronts

Where two air masses of different characteristics meet, an interface, or boundary, called a **front** develops. (See Figure 7-20.) Most of the storms and severe weather of the mid-latitude United States, except for hurricanes, are usually formed in association with fronts.

Types of Fronts A **cold front** is the boundary of an advancing cold air mass and a warmer air mass, where the underlying cold air pushes forward like a wedge. A **warm front** is the boundary of an advancing warm air mass and a retreating wedge of a cooler air mass. Because the cooler air is denser, the warm air mass is forced to rise as it advances. An **occluded front** is the boundary of opposing wedges of cold air masses formed when a cold front overtakes a warm front, lifting the warm air mass off the ground. Occluded fronts are important because they are associated with the formation of mid-latitude cyclones (lows), as shown in Figure 7-18. When two adjacent air masses of different characteristics remain in the same positions, they form a **stationary front**. The **polar front** (see Figure 7-8) is an ever-changing boundary in the

Figure 7-18. Circulation of winds and interaction of high- and low-pressure areas in the Northern Hemisphere: Air circulates clockwise in a high and counterclockwise in a low. Winds blow out from a high and blow into a low.

Figure 7-19. Direction of surface wind circulation around lows and highs in Northern and Southern Hemispheres: Wind directions around lows [L] (cyclones) and highs [H] (anticyclones) are the result of contributing agents that include pressure gradient, Coriolis effect, and friction with surface features.

middle latitudes between the colder air masses toward the poles and the warmer air masses toward the equator.

Fronts and Weather Maps On weather maps, half circles and/or triangles are used on the lines representing fronts to indicate the type of front. See Figure 7-18 or the Front Symbol section of Weather Map Information in the (R) *Earth Science Reference Tables* for specific front symbols. The triangles and half circles point in the direction the fronts and associated air masses are moving.

Tracks of Air Masses and Fronts In the United States, the tracks (paths) and rate of movement of air masses and fronts can be predicted on the basis of past observations. Thus, the succession of weather changes that accompanies such movements can be reasonably forecasted. The arrows in Figure 7-17 indicate the direction of some of these tracks. Most of the tracks follow a southwest to northeast or westerly to easterly route in the contiguous United States because of our location in the prevailing southwest winds belt.

Figure 7-20. Cross-sectional view of the (A- - - -B) line in Figure 7-18: The conditions of the cold front at left are: steep slope, cumulus-type, or puffy thunderstorm type clouds, and precipitation just before and after the point at which the front meets Earth's surface. The conditions of the warm front at right are gentle frontal surface, stratus-type or layered clouds, and a broad band of precipitation preceding the point at which the front meets Earth's surface.

Review Questions

61. In order for a large mass of air to acquire uniform characteristics, it must

(1) stagnate over a large land or water surface
(2) descend from the upper troposphere
(3) move rapidly with the prevailing westerlies
(4) move in the general planetary circulation

62. During the summer a warm, moist air mass moved over Texas. This air mass probably originated over

(1) northern Canada
(2) the Pacific Ocean
(3) southern Arizona
(4) the Gulf of Mexico

63. On a weather map, an airmass that is very warm and dry would be labeled

(1) mP   (2) mT   (3) cP   (4) cT

64. The movement of air in a low-pressure cyclonic system in the Northern Hemisphere is best described as

(1) toward the center and clockwise
(2) toward the center and counterclockwise
(3) away from the center and clockwise
(4) away from the center and counterclockwise

65. Why do clouds usually form at the leading edge of a cold air mass?

(1) Cold air contains more water vapor than warm air does.
(2) Cold air contains more dust particles than warm air does.
(3) Cold air flows over warm air, causing warm air to descend and cool.
(4) Cool air flows under warm air, causing the warm air to rise and cool.

66. The original characteristics of an air mass are determined by the

(1) surface over which it is formed
(2) pressure of the air mass
(3) insolation it receives
(4) rotation of Earth

Base your answers to questions 67 and 68 on the following diagram, which shows the frontal boundary between mT and cP air masses.

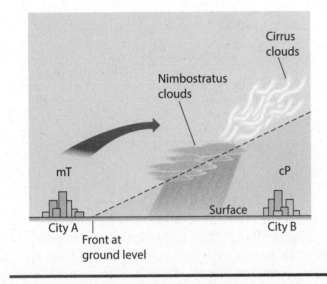

67. If the front at ground level is moving toward city B, which type of weather front is shown?

(1) cold front
(2) warm front
(3) occluded front
(4) stationary front

68. Why do clouds and precipitation usually occur along the frontal surface?

(1) The warm air rises, expands, and cools.
(2) The warm air sinks, expands, and warms.
(3) The cool air rises, compresses, and cools.
(4) The cool air sinks, compresses, and warms.

69. A storm system centered over Elmira, New York, will most often track toward

(1) Albany
(2) Jamestown
(3) Rochester
(4) New York City

Storms and Severe Weather

A storm is violent or severe disturbance of the atmosphere that usually creates dangerous, destructive, or unpleasant conditions on Earth's surface. Most storms are associated with high winds, heavy precipitation, fronts, and the low air pressure of cyclonic conditions. Types of storms include mid-latitude cyclones, hurricanes, thunderstorms, tornadoes, hail, and blizzards. People need to be aware that storms can cause loss of life, injuries, and loss of property.

Mid-latitude or Cyclonic Storms

Movements of air masses along the polar fronts of the middle latitudes can result in the formation of low-pressure storm systems called mid-latitude cyclones, wave cyclones, or just **cyclonic storms.** These storms bring much of the precipitation of the middle latitudes, including the contiguous United States. These storms form as a result of a variety of conditions associated with polar fronts that eventually result in an occluded front— the lifting of a warm air mass as it develops into a low-pressure cyclone. The rotation is the result of the Coriolis effect caused by Earth's rotation. Mid-latitude cyclones are often associated with many thunderstorms and associated hail and tornadoes.

Hurricanes

Usually in late summer or early fall, low pressure centers form over tropical ocean waters. These low pressure centers gain their energy from the condensation of millions of gallons of water vapor that acquired its

Figure 7-21. Hurricanes around the world and their more common paths or tracks: The insert shows the more accurate view of tracks that affect the eastern United States, including New York State. Typhoons and cyclones are local names for hurricanes.

Figure 7-22. A Simple weather map and satellite image of Atlantic hurricanes: (A) Note the location of the hurricane's eye and that the wind direction symbols illustrate the surface counterclockwise rotation of hurricanes in the northern hemisphere. (B) Note the bands of heavy precipitation and the clear hurricane eye. Satellite views of northern hemisphere hurricanes, taken from above, illustrate the clockwise movement of the air at the top of this hurricane.

energy from solar evaporation of ocean water. When a tropical low pressure center gains enough energy and a large enough pressure gradient to sustain winds of 74 miles an hour or more, it is called a hurricane. Hurricanes have different names in different parts of the world as shown in Figure 7-21. They are all characterized by rotating bands of precipitating clouds, a cloudless eye in the center that has the lowest air pressure, and high winds often over 150 miles an hour. (See Figure 7-22.) When a hurricane passes over land or cold ocean water, it loses its energy source of evaporating water and slowly dissipates. Moving over land hurricanes lose energy due to friction with ground.

Hurricanes are a threat to people on ships from high winds and ocean waves, but the most significant danger is when a hurricane strikes land. The biggest danger in the United States is often in areas along the southern and eastern coasts as shown in Figure 7-21. Hurricanes sometimes bring high winds that can blow down all but the strongest buildings and trees, and in doing so, cause injury and death from falling or flying debris. Hurricanes also bring a danger to humans due to flooding. When a hurricane travels over land, the heavy rains can overwhelm streams and the ground's ability for infiltration and runoff. Flooding along coastlines can also be caused by a storm surge, which is a wall of ocean water that invades low coastal areas due to the low pressure and high winds of the hurricane. If you are near the ocean coast, when a hurricane is predicted, the best tactic is usually to evacuate using the emergency plans and routes developed by government agencies.

Thunderstorms

At any one time over 2000 thunderstorms are happening on Earth. Thunderstorms are heavy rainstorms accompanied by thunder and lightning from thunderstorm-type clouds. Only thunderstorm clouds have enough up-and-down air movement to produce the type of precipitation called hail. Thunderstorms often form from the uplifting of warm air associated with fronts, but they also form as part of hurricanes and within air masses when local heating causes much convective rising of warm, moist air. Figure 7-23 is a model for the formation of a thunderstorm.

Thunderstorms can create many hazards including flooding, hail, high winds, and lightning. In many years, more people get killed from lightning than from any other weather-related cause. To protect yourself from lightning, don't be the highest object in an area or stand under a tree, as lightning tends to strike the highest object in an area. Cars are usually safe because a car's metal shell directs the electrical charge around the outside of the car to the ground. If you are inside during a thunderstorm, don't touch electrical devices or anything attached to the building's plumbing.

Digging Deeper

Hurricanes are the largest of storms—typically over 350 miles in diameter. They are also the longest lasting storms—usually a week or more.

Tornadoes

The most violent of all storms is the tornado. A <u>tornado</u> is a rapidly rotating, extremely low-pressure funnel that hangs down from thunderstorm clouds towards Earth's surface. Some scientists say that the funnel must touch Earth's surface to be a true tornado. Tornadoes are usually quite narrow—about 100 feet or so in diameter—but they may exceed a half-mile. Most tornadoes only last a few minutes, but some can

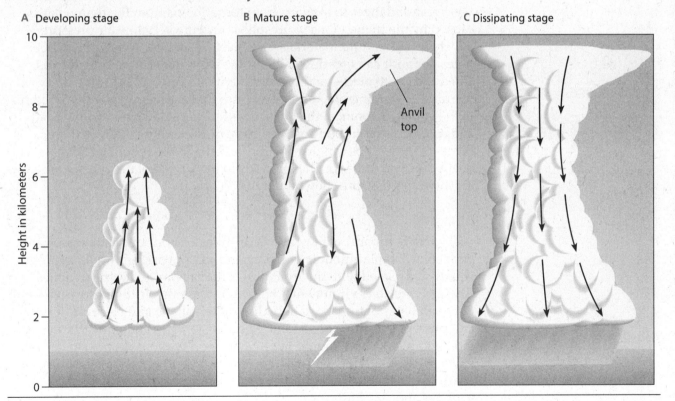

A Developing stage B Mature stage C Dissipating stage

Height in kilometers

Anvil top

Figure 7-23. Formation of a thunderstorm cloud: This cloud, often called a thunderhead or cumulonimbus, and associated storm often follow a series of stages. In stage A, the towering puffy cloud indicates rising air. There is occasional lightning and usually little rain falls. In stage B, most likely hail, heavy rain, frequent lightning, strong winds, and tornadoes occur. The storm occasionally has a black or dark green appearance. It lasts an average of 10 to 20 minutes, but may last longer. In stage C, rainfall decreases in intensity. Some thunderstorms produce a burst of strong winds during this stage; lightning remains a danger. The cloud eventually changes to water vapor—usually after a few hours.

Figure 7-24. Tornado incidence: The map shows the average tornado incidence per 26,000 sq km (10,000 sq mi). New York State averages between 0.5 and 1.0 tornadoes per year.

last over an hour. Radar has calculated the wind speed in a tornado at 318 miles an hour—the record for measured surface wind speed—but it is believed that wind speeds over 350 miles an hour are possible. The actual formation of tornadoes is still not completely understood, but we do know that they form at fronts between air masses with big differences in temperature from thunderstorm-type clouds, usually in later afternoon when the atmosphere is the warmest.

The greatest danger to humans from tornadoes is from the flying debris caused by the tremendous wind speeds and the very low air pressure, which "vacuums" up materials from Earth's surface. Winds of 200–300 miles per hour can tear down all but the strongest structures and trees, shred them into pieces, and convert them into projectiles. At the first warning or sighting of a tornado, go into the strongest available structure, in the strongest room, at the lowest possible level, and cover your head and as much of your body as possible with something like a coat or blanket. These steps can provide the best chance of avoiding injury or death during a tornado. The locations in the United States where tornadoes are most common are shown in Figure 7-24.

Blizzards

A <u>blizzard</u> is a storm with winds of 35 miles an hour or greater associated with considerable amounts of falling and/or blowing snow. Blizzards are usually associated with the frontal conditions of mid-latitude cyclones. Blizzards are an environmental hazard because the drifting snows can shut down all types of transportation, disrupt telephone and electrical service, and prevent people from obtaining needed services and products such as food and fuel. People caught out in a blizzard without proper shelter can suffer many conditions including frostbite, hypothermia, and freezing to death. To prepare for a blizzard, people should have food and other supplies and stay indoors.

Emergency Preparedness for Storms

With accurate weather predictions and the knowledge of how to react to the different types of storms, we can greatly reduce the chances of loss of life, personal injury, and loss of property. This emergency preparedness often includes prior planning by individuals, families, communities, and government agencies to design evacuation routes out of the area or to safer areas within a building. The preparedness also includes having emergency supplies such as food, fresh water, lighting, heat, and backup electric power available before a severe storm approaches.

Review Questions

Base your answers to questions 70 through 72 on the data table below. The data table shows a classification system for hurricanes. A storm surge is a dome of water 65 to 80 kilometers wide that sweeps ashore at the coast near the point where the storm center (eye) reaches land.

Safir-Simpson Hurricane Scale				
Hurricane Category	Central Air Pressure (mb)	Wind Speed (km/hr)	Expected Storm Surge Height (m)	Expected Damage
1	Over 979	119-153	1.2-1.5	Minimal
2	965-979	154-177	1.6-2.4	Moderate
3	945-964	178-209	2.5-3.6	Extensive
4	920-944	210-250	3.7-5.4	Extreme
5	Below 920	Over 250	Over 5.4	Catastrophic

70. Which characteristic must a tropical storm have to be classified as a hurricane on the Safir-Simpson scale?

   (1) enough strength to cause catastrophic damage
   (2) a storm surge of at least 2.0 m
   (3) central air pressure over 980 mb
   (4) a wind speed of at least 119 km/hr

71. A hurricane with a central air pressure recorded at 28.70 inches has an expected storm surge of

   (1) 1.3 m   (3) 3.3 m
   (2) 2.0 m   (4) 4.0 m

72. The difference between the wind speed of a category-1 hurricane and the wind speed of a category-5 hurricane is primarily caused by the differences in

   (1) types of clouds
   (2) amounts of precipitation
   (3) air-pressure gradients
   (4) air-temperature gradients

73. Most storms are associated with high winds, heavy precipitation, and

   (1) high air pressure
   (2) slowly rising air pressure
   (3) low air pressure or cyclonic conditions
   (4) rapidly rising air pressure

74. The characteristic of a blizzard that makes it an environmental hazard is

   (1) heavy rainfall
   (2) drifting snow
   (3) freezing rain
   (4) flying debris

75. Along the coast, the most dangerous aspect of hurricanes is the

   (1) lightning and hail
   (2) flooding by high waves
   (3) large central eye
   (4) suction effect of the funnel

76. The funnel of a tornado can "vacuum" up materials from Earth because of its extremely

   (1) high pressure
   (2) high temperature
   (3) low pressure
   (4) low wind speed

77. The most dangerous place to be during a thunderstorm is

   (1) in a car
   (2) under a high tree
   (3) in a ditch
   (4) in your bed

Weather Prediction and Probability

Accurate forecasts are important in giving people time to prepare for severe weather. Given accurate forecasts, people can shore up buildings, move to higher ground, move to safer parts of a building, go to stronger buildings, evacuate, or take other measures—all of which can potentially save them from death, injury, and loss of property.

Computers and Probability Prediction

Many weather predictions, or forecasts, are based on the **probability**—chance—of occurrence of types of weather based on relationships between weather variables. Computer models that use data collected over many years provide these predictions today. For example, suppose that during a twenty-day period the air pressure drops on ten days, and the air temperature increases on eight of those ten days. What is the probability that air temperature will increase if air pressure is decreasing? Based on the data above, there is an 8 in 10 chance, or 80 percent probability, of increasing temperature. In computing probability of weather events, the Weather Service bases its predictions on large amounts of data collected over many years.

Computer modeling has aided people's ability to work out the probabilities of a vast number of possible relationships between variables. Weather forecasting has become more accurate in recent years because of the ability of computers to rapidly compare present conditions around the world with data from several previous years. After rapidly calculating the probabilities, timely forecasts are produced. The following are some of the simple relationships between weather variables:

- Air pressure is related to temperature changes. As temperature increases pressure decreases, and vice versa.
- The chance of precipitation increases as the air temperature gets closer to the dew point. The smaller the difference between the air temperature and the dew point, the nearer the air is to saturation, condensation, and precipitation.
- The greater the air pressure gradient in an area, the faster the wind speeds.
- Rapidly falling air pressure at a location indicates that a storm system or low pressure center is approaching and that the chances of precipitation are very high in the very near future.

Weather Maps and Station Models

For over a hundred years, weather data has been collected at various locations and sent by electronic means to a central location where it is plotted to produce weather maps. These maps provide a synoptic weather map, which is a summary of weather variables for a short period of time. This information becomes the basis for future forecasts. The National Weather Service has specific sites that collect

Figure 7-25. Weather map.

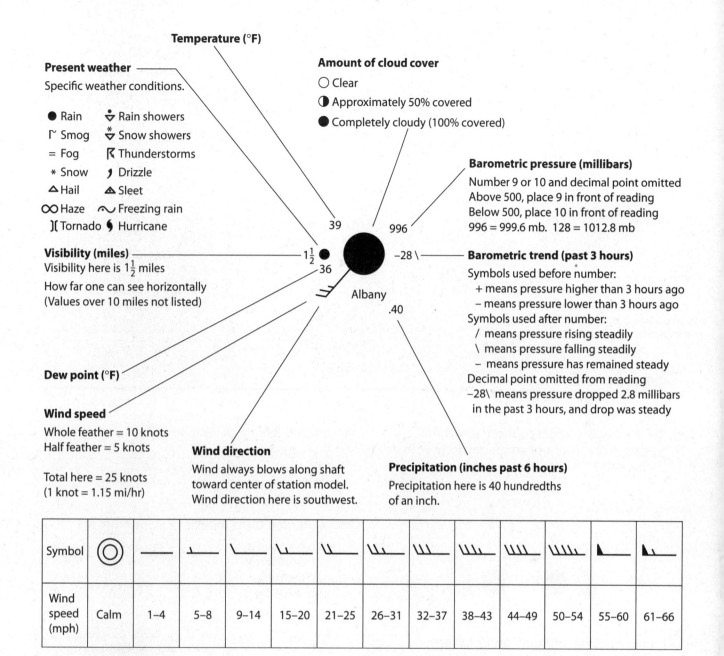

Present weather
Specific weather conditions.

● Rain   ⧨ Rain showers
⌐ Smog   ⧨ Snow showers
= Fog   ⟨ Thunderstorms
∗ Snow   ⟩ Drizzle
△ Hail   ⧩ Sleet
∞ Haze   ∿ Freezing rain
)(Tornado   ⟩ Hurricane

Temperature (°F)

Amount of cloud cover
○ Clear
◑ Approximately 50% covered
● Completely cloudy (100% covered)

Barometric pressure (millibars)
Number 9 or 10 and decimal point omitted
Above 500, place 9 in front of reading
Below 500, place 10 in front of reading
996 = 999.6 mb. 128 = 1012.8 mb

Visibility (miles)
Visibility here is 1½ miles
How far one can see horizontally
(Values over 10 miles not listed)

Barometric trend (past 3 hours)
Symbols used before number:
+ means pressure higher than 3 hours ago
– means pressure lower than 3 hours ago
Symbols used after number:
/ means pressure rising steadily
\ means pressure falling steadily
– means pressure has remained steady
Decimal point omitted from reading
–28\ means pressure dropped 2.8 millibars
in the past 3 hours, and drop was steady

Dew point (°F)

Wind speed
Whole feather = 10 knots
Half feather = 5 knots

Total here = 25 knots
(1 knot = 1.15 mi/hr)

Wind direction
Wind always blows along shaft
toward center of station model.
Wind direction here is southwest.

Precipitation (inches past 6 hours)
Precipitation here is 40 hundredths
of an inch.

Symbol	⊚	—	⌐	⌐	⌐⌐	⌐⌐	⌐⌐⌐	⌐⌐⌐	⌐⌐⌐⌐	⌐⌐⌐⌐	⌐⌐⌐⌐⌐	◤	◤⌐
Wind speed (mph)	Calm	1–4	5–8	9–14	15–20	21–25	26–31	32–37	38–43	44–49	50–54	55–60	61–66

Figure 7-26. Sample station model for weather map: Also see the charts of Weather Map Information in the *Earth Science Reference Tables.*

weather information from different areas. Weather maps often show this information plotted in a circle around these sites. The circle indicates where the collection site—usually a city—is located. Often the weather data is represented by symbols to save space. The symbols and the circle make up a **station model,** which indicates a site's weather variables for a specific time of day. For a sample of a station model see Figure 7-26 and Ⓡ Key to Weather Map Symbols in the *Earth Science Reference Tables.*

Other Aids in Weather Prediction

Weather scientists have many tools available to aid them in preparing their forecasts. Atmospheric cross-sections—such as in Figure 7-20—help give a three-dimensional view of weather conditions. **Radar**—which stands for

RAdio **D**etection **A**nd **R**anging instrument—reflects radio electromagnetic energy off the aerosols of precipitation and clouds. This gives forecasters information about the intensity and distance of approaching storms. Doppler radar picks up the indicator, or "fingerprint" of tornado formation, providing accurate short-range predictions.

Since the 1960s, satellite images have provided weather forecasters with visual and infrared images of storm systems such as mid-latitude cyclones and hurricanes. (See Figures 7-22B and 7-27.) Because satellite images show the locations of advancing hurricanes or blizzards from a winter mid-latitude cyclone, these storms and their movements can be tracked. People of the United States and much of the rest of the world are, therefore, no longer surprised by these storms.

Figure 7-27. Weather Satellite: Modern weather satellites typically have solar cells for power, cameras for visual and infrared images, and a radio antenna for communications with Earth's surface.

Review Questions

78. Which station model correctly shows the weather conditions of a thunderstorm with heavy rain?

(1)   **(3)**

(2)   **(4)**

To answer questions 79 through 87 use the following diagram, which shows four station models, at the same instant in time, identified by letters A–D. The stations are located on a west-east line at fifty-mile intervals in the United States.

79. The strongest wind is reported at station
(1) A   (2) B   (3) C   (4) D

80. Station B has just experienced the passage of a
(1) warm front
(2) cold front
(3) stationary front
(4) hurricane

81. At station D the wind is blowing from the
(1) northeast
(2) northwest
(3) southeast
(4) southwest

82. The temperature at station A is
(1) 6°F   (2) 16°F   (3) 32°F   (4) 38°F

83. The relative humidity at station C is
(1) 10%   (2) 25%   (3) 70%   (4) 100%

84. Heaviest rainfall in the past 6 hours was reported from station
(1) A   (2) B   (3) C   (4) D

85. Clear skies are reported from station
(1) A   (2) B   (3) C   (4) D

86. What is the wind speed at station B in mi/hr?
(1) 3 mi/hr   (3) 34.5 mi/hr
(2) 23 mi/hr   (4) 69 mi/hr

87. What is the wind speed at Station A in knots?
(1) 5 knots   (3) 15 knots
(2) 10 knots   (4) 20 knots

Directions

Review the Test-Taking Strategies section of this book. Then answer the following questions. Read each question carefully and answer with a correct choice or response.

Part A

1 As the temperature of a given volume of saturated air decreases the condensation
   (1) decreases (2) increases (3) remains the same

2 By which process does water vapor leave the atmosphere and form dew?
   (1) condensation   (3) convection
   (2) transpiration   (4) precipitation

3 Clouds and fog differ principally in
   (1) amount of water droplets
   (2) density
   (3) amount of dust
   (4) height above the ground

4 Why does fog disappear after sunrise?
   (1) air pressure rises   (3) air pressure falls
   (2) fog evaporates   (4) fog condenses

5 Which is a form of precipitation?
   (1) frost   (2) snow   (3) dew   (4) fog

6 Rain passing through layers of air below 32°F may form
   (1) dew   (2) frost   (3) sleet   (4) snow

7 Which graph best represents the relationship between water droplet size and the chance of precipitation?

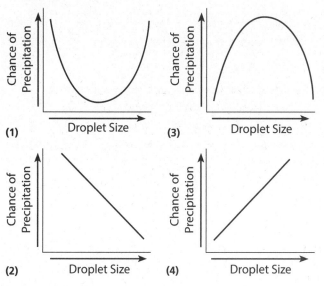

8 Which process is most likely to remove pollutants from the air?
   (1) precipitation   (3) transpiration
   (2) evaporation   (4) runoff

9 Which graph best shows the relationship between atmospheric transparency and the concentration of pollution particles in the air?

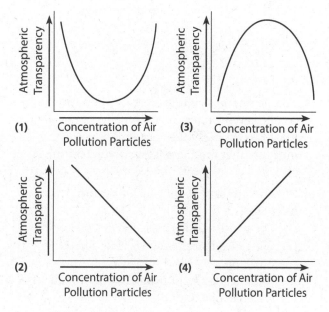

10 Which best describes the movement of air in a high-pressure air mass (anticyclone) in the Northern Hemisphere?
   (1) clockwise and away from the center
   (2) clockwise and toward the center
   (3) counterclockwise and away from the center
   (4) counterclockwise and toward the center

11 In approaching the center of a cyclone on a weather map, the numerical values of the isobars
   (1) increase
   (2) may increase or decrease
   (3) decrease
   (4) remain the same

12 A high-pressure center is generally characterized by
   (1) cool, wet weather   (3) warm, wet weather
   (2) cool, dry weather   (4) warm, dry weather

13 The following diagram shows four points on a map with their positions relative to a low-pressure weather system.

Scale (kilometers)

Which point is most likely having heavy precipitation?
(1) 1 (2) 2 (3) 3 (4) 4

14 A large number of thunderstorms occur in the southeastern United States. Which type of air mass is most likely the main source of the moisture that produces these thunderstorm?
(1) cP (2) mP (3) mT (4) cT

15 Which statement about a major hurricane is an inference?
(1) The wind speed is measured at 200 km/hr.
(2) The central air pressure is recorded at 946.0 mb.
(3) A rain gauge records three inches of rain in less than one hour.
(4) Damage from the storm is expected to be extensive.

16 The highest wind velocities are usually encountered in
(1) monsoons (3) blizzards
(2) hurricanes (4) tornadoes

17 On a July afternoon in New York State, the barometric pressure is 29.85 inches and falling. This reading most likely indicates
(1) an approaching storm
(2) rapidly clearing skies
(3) continuing fair weather
(4) gradually improving conditions

18 The chief reason for plotting a surface weather map is to
(1) locate major wind belts
(2) identify cold fronts
(3) forecast weather conditions
(4) record climatic data

19 Tornadoes are usually associated with
(1) cold fronts
(2) tropical fronts
(3) stationary fronts
(4) warm fronts

Part B

To answer questions 20 through 22 refer to the following graph, which shows the hourly surface air temperature, dew point, and relative humidity for a 24-hour period during the month of May at Washington, D.C.

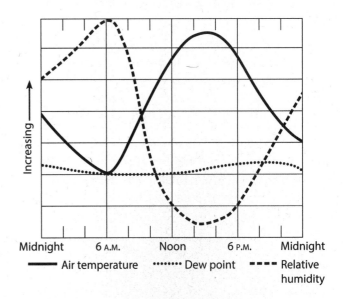

20 The greatest net change in air temperature occurred during what period? [1]

21 What does the graph indicate about the relationship between air temperature and relative humidity? [1]

22 At approximately what time is condensation most likely to occur? [1]

Base your answer to questions 23 through 26 on the following diagram, which represents a vertical cross section of a frontal system moving from west to east in an area of New York State. Temperatures for seven weather stations, A through G, are shown on the diagram.

23 How will the cloud cover change at Station E as the front approaches and how will it change after the front passes? [2]

24 What barometric pressure change will occur as the front passes station E? [1]

25 Will the temperature increase or decrease at station E after the front passes? [1]

26 Describe how the motion of the air masses causes clouds to form along the front. [1]

Base your answers to questions 27 and 28 on the meteorological conditions shown in the following table and partial station model, as reported by the weather bureau in the city of Oswego, New York.

Air temperature: 65°F
Wind direction: from the southeast
Windspeed: 20 knots
Barometeric pressure: 1017.5 mb
Dewpoint: 53°F

27 Using the meteorological conditions given, copy and complete the partial station model by recording the air temperature, dew point, and barometric pressure in the proper format. [2]

28 State the sky conditions, or amount of cloud cover, over Oswego as shown by the station model. [1]

Part C

Use the information in the following paragraph and your knowledge of earth science to answer questions 29 through 32.

A person on the 102nd floor (at an elevation of 1250 feet) of the Empire State Building in New York City observes that it is snowing. At the same time, another person on the 50th floor observes that it is raining. Also at the same time, a third person at street level notices that the sky is completely covered by clouds, but there is no precipitation.

29 Explain the differences regarding precipitation that the three people observed at the three levels of the Empire State Building. [3]

30 During a gentle rain, at a temperature of 25°F, what type of precipitation would strike the sidewalk around the Empire State Building? [1]

31 Comment on the accuracy of the following statement. "The top floor of the Empire State Building is in the stratosphere." [1]

32 State what two weather variables—besides moisture condition—would likely change from the top to the bottom of the Empire State Building. Include in your answer how the magnitude of these two weather variables would be different. [4]

Base your answers to questions 33 and 34 on the cross section provided below, which represents a house at an ocean shoreline at night. Smoke from the chimney is blowing out to sea.

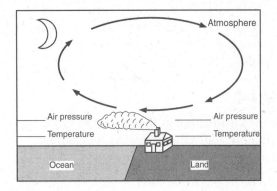

33 Label the *two* lines provided on the cross section above to show where air pressure is relatively "high" and where it is relatively "low." [1]

34 Assume that the wind blowing out to sea on this night is caused by local air-temperature conditions. Label the *two* lines provided on the cross section *above* to show where Earth's surface air temperature is relatively "warm" and where it is relatively "cool." [1]

Base your answers to questions 35 through 39 on the weather satellite photograph of a portion of the United States, Cuba, and Haiti provided below. The photograph shows the clouds of Hurricane Andrew approaching the eastern coastline of Florida. The calm center of the hurricane, the eye, is labeled.

35 State the latitude and longitude of the hurricane's eye. The compass directions must be included in the answer. [1]

36 This hurricane has a pattern of surface winds typical of all low-pressure systems in the Northern Hemisphere. On the satellite photograph provided, draw *three* arrows on the clouds to show the direction of the surface wind movement outside the eye of the hurricane. [1]

37 Cloud droplets form around small particles in the atmosphere. Describe how the hurricane clouds formed from water vapor. Include the terms "dewpoint" and either "condensation" or "condense" in your answer. [1]

38 At the location shown in the photograph, the hurricane had maximum winds recorded at 110 miles per hour. Within a 24-hour period, the hurricane moved 150 miles inland and had maximum winds of only 65 miles per hour. State why the wind velocity of a hurricane usually decreases when the hurricane moves over a land surface. [1]

39 *a* State two dangerous conditions, other than hurricane winds, that could cause human fatalities as the hurricane strikes the coast. [2]

   b Describe one emergency preparation humans could take to avoid a problem caused by one of these dangerous conditions. [1]

Base your answers to questions 40 and 41 on the weather map provided, which shows a large white band of clouds moving toward the southeast. The line shown in the middle of the white cloud band is the frontal boundary between a cP air mass and an mT air mass. Two large arrows show the direction the front is moving.

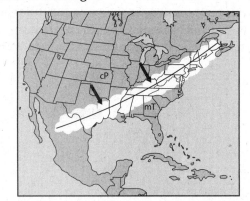

40 On the frontal boundary line on the weather map provided, draw the weather front symbol to represent the front moving toward the southeast. [1]

41 On the same weather map, place an **X** centered on the geographic region that was most likely the source of the warm, moist (mT) air mass. [1]

Water and Climate

How **Scientists** **Study** Climate

? *Where would be the __worst__ place to live if you didn't like the hottest temperatures?* **?**

You might guess the equator, because the equator gets the most incoming solar radiation at the top of the atmosphere. Therefore, you might think that it has the hottest air temperatures all the time. But the equator has a lot of thunderstorm (cumulonimbus) cloud cover that reflects the radiation back into space. Also much of the insolation that does arrive at the surface at the equator does not heat the surface, because it is converted to latent heat in the evaporation of water and in the conversion of solar energy into food in the process of photosynthesis thanks to the vast plant life of the tropical rain forests.

However, at 25° to 30° of latitude, the falling air molecules compress the atmosphere so there isn't as much cloud cover. Therefore, at those latitudes you would experience the hottest surface air temperatures most of the time, especially in the summer season.

TOPIC 8

Water and Climate

Vocabulary

capillarity	porosity	unsorted
climate	prevailing winds	urbanization
ground water	runoff	water cycle
hydrologic cycle	seep	water retention
infiltrate	sorted	water table
permeability	stream discharge	

Topic Overview

While weather is the study of the short-term events of our atmosphere, climate is the study of the conditions of the atmosphere over long periods of time—tens, hundreds, thousands of years.

Climate greatly affects the kind of natural vegetation, the type of landscape features, and the crops and animals that are native to a region. Water is one of Earth's most important natural resources—one that people need to sustain their lives, help grow crops, and provide transportation. Water also has an effect on weather and climate and erodes Earth's surface. Since liquid water covers about 70 percent of Earth's surface, it creates environments for a large percentage of the life forms on our planet in streams, ponds, lakes, seas, and oceans.

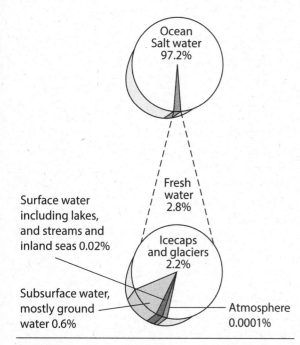

Figure 8-1. Graph of distribution of Earth's water by volume: Most of Earth's water is located in the ocean and is too salty for most human uses. Most fresh water is in the ice of glaciers or frozen on top of the oceans. Ground water is the biggest readily available supply of the natural resource fresh water.

The Water Cycle

Earth has been recycling its water supply for approximately 4 billion years—ever since the outgassing of water vapor (from Earth's solid surface) and its cooling to form liquid water. Many scientists believe that most of Earth's water supply was created when Earth formed and that large amounts have not been gained or lost since. Figure 8-1 illustrates the locations of Earth's water. This figure shows that the oceans contain most of the water, while the majority of the water people can drink—fresh water—is in glacier ice and floating on ocean tops in cold regions.

One model used to illustrate the movement and the phase changes of water at and near Earth's surface is the **water cycle**—also called the **hydrologic cycle**. (See Figure 8-2.) The water cycle is "fueled" by solar energy—insolation—which changes liquid or solid water to water vapor, and by gravity pulling water down in the atmosphere, hydrosphere, and upper parts of the lithosphere. The ultimate source of most water on land is the evaporation of the oceans' water. The moisture gets to the land from the oceans by way of the atmosphere. When precipitation falls on the land, four things can happen to it.

- Precipitation can be stored or retained on the land surface as ice or snow—**water retention.** Water can also be retained on the leaves of trees and other plants.
- Precipitation can **infiltrate,** or **seep** (sink) into the upper parts of Earth's lithosphere under the influence of gravity. All the water beneath Earth's surface is called subsurface water.
- Precipitation can flow over Earth's surface as **runoff.** About one third of the precipitation falling on land is returned to the water cycle through runoff.
- The combination of <u>evaporation</u> and <u>transpiration</u> is evapotranspiration. It usually includes the sublimation of ice and snow directly into water vapor. Approximately two thirds of the precipitation that falls on land is evaporated or transpired back into the atmosphere.

Recall that evaporation is the change in phase from liquid to a gas, such as liquid water into water vapor. Remember too that transpiration is the process by which a plant releases water vapor into the atmosphere as part of its life function.

Factors Affecting Infiltration

Most infiltration occurs in the loose material (including soil) that directly covers much of Earth's solid surface or is beneath a thin vegetation zone. Some infiltration can also occur into rock exposed at or near Earth's solid surface. The amount of water that can infiltrate when precipitation occurs depends on several variables.

Slope of the Land The steeper the slope (gradient) of Earth's solid surface, the less the infiltration or seepage.

Degree of Saturation The more saturated the materials at Earth's surface, the less the infiltration. Figure 8-2 shows that Earth's surface is divided into the zone of saturation, where the pores between particles are filled with water and the zone of aeration, where the pores are filled with air and water. Surface water infiltrates down, under the influence of gravity, until it meets the **water table** interface between the zone of saturation and zone of aeration. The subsurface water below the water table is called **ground water.** The depth of the water table varies with amounts of infiltration; the greater the infiltration the higher the water table and the closer it is to Earth's surface. It is ground water—through wells and springs—that supplies a large portion of human water requirements. Withdrawing water from wells faster than it can be replenished lowers the water table.

Porosity The percentage of open space (pores and cracks) in a material compared to its total volume is its **porosity.** Generally, the greater the porosity of the loose materials at Earth's surface and the rocks, the greater the amount of infiltration that

Figure 8-2. The water cycle—a model of the movement and phase changes of water at and near Earth's surface: The water table is an interface of changing position between the zone of saturation, where the pores of Earth's loose materials are filled with water (ground water), and the zone of aeration, where the pores are only partly filled with water (capillary water). Withdrawal of water from wells causes the water table to be lower.

Figure 8-3. Effect of particle or sediment shape, packing, and sorting on the porosity of loose materials on Earth's surface: White regions are areas of porosity. (A) Well-rounded particles have more porosity than particles with angular shapes. (B) Loosely packed particles have more porosity than closely packed particles. (C) Sorted particles have more porosity than unsorted particles.

can occur. The shape, packing, and sorting of the particles composing a material determine its porosity. (See Figure 8-3.)

Shape Well-rounded particles have greater porosity than angular or plate-shaped particles because round shapes do not fit together as tightly as the other shapes do.

Packing The more closely packed the particles, the lower the porosity. The constant passage of people, animals, or vehicles in the same place or path will pack the soil, lowering the rate of infiltration.

Sorting If all the particles in a material are about the same size, they are said to be **sorted;** if the particles are of mixed sizes, they are said to be **unsorted.** The more unsorted the particles, the lower the porosity because the small particles can fit into the spaces between the larger particles. It should be noted that particle size by itself does not affect porosity. For example, a material with large particles may have about the same porosity as one with smaller particles if the shape, packing, and sorting of both particle sizes are about equal. If there were two rooms of equal size, one filled with marbles and the other filled with basketballs, the total volume of pore space would be about the same for both rooms.

Permeability The ability of a material to allow fluids such as water to pass through it is **permeability.** The permeability rate is the speed at which fluids will flow through a material. A material can be porous and yet impermeable—not permeable. It is often how well connected the pores or openings in rock and loose materials are that will determine the degree of permeability, not just the volume of openings. Impermeability may be due to tight packing or cementing of particles, which seals off the pores from one another so that water cannot enter them. In the winter the cementing is often due to ice. Ground water can deposit some of its dissolved minerals, adding cement to loose materials and rocks, and thus reducing porosity and permeability. In loose particles, the larger the particle size, the faster the permeability rate and infiltration because the size of the pores increases.

Capillarity During infiltration, some water is stopped from moving downward by the attractive force between water molecules and the surrounding Earth materials. This attractive force is **capillarity.** The water that is stored in small openings in the zone of aeration is capillary water. Capillarity also causes water to move up from the water table, against gravity, toward Earth's surface in the zone of aeration. This upward movement is capillary migration (capillary action). Capillary migration is extremely important in supplying water to plants when the soil is not saturated with water, which is the usual situation. When the particle size of loose particles become smaller, the capillarity and capillary migration become greater. (See Figure 8-4.) When the size of the particles increases the size of pores increases, and the effects of capillarity are reduced.

Vegetation The amount and type of vegetation in an area influences the amount of water that infiltrates the ground. Grasses, trees, and other plant types intercept falling precipitation, reducing its velocity and temporarily storing some of the water above Earth's surface. The reduced speed of the precipitation gives the ground more time to absorb the water. Plant litter—dead and partly decayed vegetation—serves the same function. Some of the water stored on vegetation and plant litter falls to the ground after

Figure 8-4. Capillary action, or migration, as a result of pore size: Capillarity causes water to move up against gravity in these glass tubes in the same way it moves up in Earth's loose materials and rocks by capillary action. The smaller the grain or sediment sizes are, the smaller the pores. The smaller the pores are, the higher the capillary action.

precipitation has stopped, and this can increase infiltration and reduce runoff. Ground without vegetation usually has high runoff and low infiltration rates.

Land Use How land is used by people can greatly influence the amount of water seeping into the ground. Roads, parking lots, and buildings cover otherwise permeable ground and create impermeable surfaces. These impermeable surfaces often channel runoff directly to streams or drainage pipes, reducing the chances of water seeping into the ground. Farming, cutting down trees, and the grazing of domesticated animals often either reduce the amount of plant life in an area or compact the soil, making it less permeable.

Factors Affecting Runoff and Stream Discharge

Surface runoff can occur when

- the rate of precipitation exceeds the permeability rate (or infiltration rate) of Earth's solid surface
- the pore space of loose material or rock is saturated with water
- the slope of the surface is too great to allow infiltration to occur
- the water on the surface has not evaporated or sublimated to a gas

Most runoff gets to streams, which often carry the water back to the oceans—completing a major part of the water cycle. The greater the runoff, the greater the amount of stream discharge in local streams. There is a time lag between times of highest precipitation and greatest stream runoff due to the time it takes the water to get to the streams. **Stream discharge** is the volume of water flowing past a certain spot in a stream in a specific amount of time, and is expressed in units such as cubic meters/second or liters/minute.

Flooding Flooding occurs when a stream overflows its normal channel. Flooding also happens when precipitation exceeds the ability of the ground to infiltrate the water, and evapotranspiration is not rapid enough, and when water is not able to move to the streams quickly enough. Flooding can also be the result of a hurricane's storm surge, coastal storms, the rising of sea level, sinking land, or tides moving water onto the land.

The first rule of safety in dealing with a flood, or the possibility of a flood, is to move to higher ground. Accurate predictions and measurements of snow or rain might give people sufficient time to evacuate an area before the flooding. Many communities have planned escape routes determined through the study of topographic maps and other elevation models.

Digging Deeper

Ground water is retained, or kept, in soil or sediment because of the capillary attraction of water to soil or sediment particles. The smaller the particles of soil or sediment the greater the amount of water retained after ground water has drained or has been withdrawn such as by infiltration or seepage.

Digging Deeper

Clay's small size (less than 0.0004 cm) affects its permeability. The combined adhesive properties of water and clay keep water from easily passing through clay sediments. Thus, even though it is porous, clay is impermeable to water movement because the pores are so small.

Review Questions

1. On Earth as a whole, what happens to most of the precipitation?

   (1) It recharges the soil moisture deficit.
   (2) It becomes runoff and moves to the oceans.
   (3) It is stored in the soil as capillary water.
   (4) It is returned to the atmosphere through evaporation and transpiration.

2. The primary source of moisture for the local water supplies is

   (1) potential evaporation and transpiration
   (2) actual evaporation and transpiration
   (3) ground water storage
   (4) precipitation

Base your answers to questions 3 through 5 on the following diagrams. The diagrams show two soil cross sections from adjacent fields in New York State. Both soils are the same except that human activities have removed the vegetation from the surface of field B. Each field has been receiving rain for several hours.

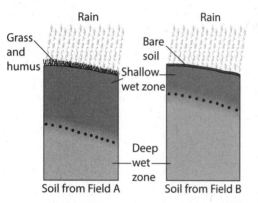

Soil from Field A   Soil from Field B

3. The soils in field B would have a higher rate of permeability if the soils

   (1) had lower porosity
   (2) had steeper surface slope
   (3) were composed of larger rock particles
   (4) were compacted by machinery traveling over the field

4. How would water infiltration be affected by replanting vegetation in field B?

5. If the skies remain clear for the week following this rain, the water in the shallow wet zone in field B will

   (1) mostly become surface runoff
   (2) partially evaporate into the air
   (3) all remain as stored water along the surface
   (4) mostly transpire into the ground

6. The following diagram is a cross-sectional view of rain falling on a farm field and then moving to the water table.

   Which word best describes the movement of the rainwater through zone A?

   (1) runoff   (3) infiltration
   (2) saturation   (4) precipitation

7. Which event is a direct result of evaporation and transpiration?

   (1) The atmosphere warms.
   (2) Cloud cover decreases.
   (3) Moisture enters the atmosphere.
   (4) Moisture leaves the atmosphere.

8. What is the largest source of the moisture for the atmosphere?

9. Which graph best illustrates the relationship between the slope of the land and the amount of surface runoff?

10. A rock with a high porosity will probably

    (1) be resistant to weathering
    (2) be composed of large grains
    (3) have a large percentage of space between particles
    (4) have a small percentage of rounded particles

11. Soil with the greatest porosity has particles that are

    (1) poorly sorted and densely packed
    (2) poorly sorted and loosely packed
    (3) well-sorted and densely packed
    (4) well-sorted and loosely packed

12. Which graph best represents the relationship between soil permeability rate and infiltration when all other conditions are the same?

13. Which Earth material covering the surface of a landfill would permit the least rainwater to infiltrate the surface?

    (1) silt   (2) clay   (3) sand   (4) pebbles

14. As the temperature of soil decreases from 10°C to −5°C, what will most likely happen to the infiltration rate of water through it?

15. Water moves upward through the soil because of

    (1) capillary action   (3) porosity
    (2) permeability   (4) infiltration

16. In which tube will capillary action be the greatest?

Pebbles   Fine sand

Water   Water

(1)   (3)

Coarse sand   Coarse sand and pebbles

Water   Water

(2)   (4)

17. The rate of flow of water through rock is determined by the
(1) types of minerals that make up the rock
(2) total amount of space between mineral grains
(3) number of connected pore spaces and their sizes
(4) position of the rock with respect to the water table

18. As the amount of precipitation on the land increases, what happens to the distance from the surface of Earth to the water table?

19. Which diagram best illustrates the condition of the soil below the water table?

(1)   (3)

(2)   (4)

Key
□ Soil particles
■ Water
□ Pore space (air)

20. Surface runoff of precipitation occurs when
(1) porosity is exceeded by permeability
(2) the infiltration rate is greater than the precipitation rate
(3) the precipitation rate is greater than the infiltration rate
(4) the evaporation rate is increased

21. Surface runoff will be greatest when the
(1) rainfall is light and the ground is permeable
(2) infiltration rate is greater than the rainfall rate
(3) slope of the land is too great to permit infiltration
(4) ground is permeable and unsaturated

22. Why do most streams in New York State have a greater stream discharge runoff in spring than in summer?
(1) Potential evaporation and transpiration is greater in spring than in summer.
(2) More transpiration occurs in spring than in summer.
(3) Most areas of New York State get their maximum solar energy in spring.
(4) Melting snow increases runoff in spring.

23. Water will infiltrate surface material that is
(1) impermeable and unsaturated
(2) impermeable and saturated
(3) permeable and unsaturated
(4) permeable and saturated

24. In which area will surface runoff most likely be greater during a heavy rainfall?
(1) sandy desert   (3) level grassy field
(2) wooded forest   (4) paved city street

25. When rain falls on a soil surface, flooding at that location would most likely occur if the
(1) soil surface is permeable
(2) soil surface is covered with vegetation
(3) soil pore spaces are filled to capacity
(4) infiltration rate exceeds the precipitation rate

Climate

The overall view of a region's weather conditions over a long period of time—tens to thousands of years—is its **climate.** Climate is not just average weather; it includes extremes like the number of hurricanes and the number of days of damaging hail. The two major aspects of climate are temperature and moisture or water conditions.

Temperature and Moisture

In terms of climate, two characteristics of the temperatures of a region are most important: (1) the average temperature over the year, and (2) the range of average monthly temperatures—often called annual

| Less than 500 | 500 to 1500 | 1500 to 2000 | 2000 and over |

Figure 8-5. World map of insolation at Earth's surface in thousands of calories/cm²/year: Note how yearly insolation generally increases with decreasing latitude. Due to many factors, however, especially differences in cloud coverage, it is not a perfect correlation. (Darkest areas have very high elevation.)

| Less than 500 | 500 to 1500 | 1500 to 2000 | 2000 and over |

Figure 8-6. World map of potential for evaporation and transpiration in centimeters per year: Note the similarities to the yearly insolation map above. It is not a perfect correlation, because local heat values are affected by many other factors such as surface ocean currents and tropospheric convection currents.

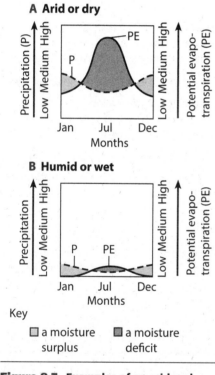

A Arid or dry

B Humid or wet

Key

☐ a moisture surplus   ■ a moisture deficit

Figure 8-7. Examples of an arid and a humid climate: Graph A shows the relationship between precipitation (P) and potential evapotranspiration (PE) for a region of moderate amounts of rainfall but high potential evapotranspiration. Since the yearly totals of P are less than the yearly PE values for the year—there is a yearly moisture deficit—the region has an arid climate. Graph B represents a climate with low yearly amounts of P, but even smaller yearly amounts of PE. Since there is more P than PE for the year—there is a yearly moisture surplus—the climate is humid, or wet.

temperature range. This is the average difference between the average temperature of the hottest month and the coldest month, calculated using data from many years.

An area's climate is called arid, or dry, if the average total precipitation during the year is less than the average yearly potential evapotranspiration. Potential evapotranspiration is the amount of water vapor that would evapotranspirate from an area if the water were available. Potential evapotranspiration is largely determined by an area's amount of energy available for evapotranspiration thus temperature. An area's average temperature is often determined by the solar energy or insolation it receives. An analysis of Figures 8-5 and 8-6 will show the direct relationship between insolation received at Earth's surface and potential evapotranspiration.

An area's climate is humid, or wet, if the average precipitation for the year is greater than the average potential evapotranspiration. Thus, whether a climate is said to be arid or humid depends not on the amount of precipitation, but on the difference between the amount of moisture available from precipitation and the potential need for water as determined largely by temperature. As illustrated in Figure 8-7, a region can have very little precipitation and still have a humid climate. Regions where the potential evapotranspiration is much greater than what an area receives as precipitation are called deserts. If an area has somewhat equal amounts of precipitation and potential evapotranspiration, the term semi-arid or sub-humid can be used to describe the climate.

Factors Affecting Climate

The factors that determine climate include

- latitude
- planetary wind and pressure belts
- oceans and other large bodies of water
- ocean currents

- mountains
- elevation
- amount of cloud cover
- vegetation

Descriptions of these factors that determine the type of climate of an area follow. Often, many factors interact to determine an area's type of climate.

Latitude and Temperature Latitude is a major factor in determining climates because of its influence on both temperature and moisture conditions. Temperature characteristics vary with latitude because of the relationships between angle, intensity, and duration of <u>insolation</u> and latitude. At low latitudes, where the maximum angle of insolation is always high, average temperatures are high throughout the year. Because the duration of insolation is fairly constant at about 12 hours per day, there is little temperature variation during the year. At high latitudes, where the maximum angle of insolation is never large and in some months remains zero, average temperatures are low. Since the duration of insolation varies from zero to 24 hours a day, and is longest at the times of greatest angle of insolation, temperatures vary over a wide range from winter lows to summer highs. Figure 8-8 is an example of how Earth can be divided into temperature zones largely based on latitude.

Latitude and Moisture Moisture conditions vary with latitude because of the location of the planetary wind and pressure belts. Where there is low pressure at Earth's surface, such as near the equator and in mid-latitudes, the air rises. The cooling of the rising air results in many clouds, much precipitation, and humid climates. When air falls toward Earth's surface, it creates high pressure, warming of the air, and often arid or desert climates. These conditions result in the belts of arid climates around 30° latitude and around the geographic poles.

Memory Jogger

Recall that insolation (**IN**coming **SO**Lar radi**ATION**) is the part of the sun's radiation that is received by Earth.

Figure 8-8. Earth's latitudinal climate zones based on temperature: The lines on the map are isotherms—isolines of equal temperature. This is a very basic climate classification based entirely on temperature. In the tropical climate zone, the average monthly temperatures at sea level never drop below 18°C. In the polar climate zones, the average monthly temperatures never rise above 10°C. Effects of altitude have been omitted.

The map Planetary Wind and Moisture Belts in the Troposphere in the *Earth Science Reference Tables* shows the locations of these dry belts and the wet belts.

Latitudinal Climatic Patterns The combination of the temperature and the moisture effects of latitude results in a basic distribution of climate types around the world—latitudinal climate patterns—shown in Figure 8-9. Note that with increasing distance from the equator (increasing latitude) the annual temperature range increases. This is largely because higher latitudes have a greater amount of change in duration of insolation during the year than areas of lower latitude nearer the equator.

Large Bodies of Water Large bodies of water—oceans, seas, and large lakes—serve to modify the latitudinal climate patterns. If a land mass is near a large body of water, its temperatures will be moderated by the slow heating up and cooling off of the water body. This is especially true if the prevailing winds blow toward the landmass much of the year.

An area with temperatures moderated by proximity to a body of water is said to have a marine climate. Marine climates have cooler summers and warmer winters than inland areas, and thus a small annual range of temperatures compared to inland areas at the same latitude. Inland areas away from the effects of large bodies of water have cooler winters and warmer summers and a wider annual range of temperatures. Such areas are said to have a continental climate. The larger a landmass is, and the farther it is from the effects of large bodies of water, the wider the annual temperature range. This is why central Eurasia has a more pronounced continental climate than North America. Figure 8-9 illustrates the differences in the temperatures of regions with continental versus marine climates.

Prevailing Winds Movements of air over Earth's surface that blow in the same direction most of the time are **prevailing winds.** The Planetary Wind and Moisture Belts in the Troposphere in the *Earth Science Reference Tables* show the latitudinal locations of the prevailing winds— planetary winds—on Earth. These belts of prevailing winds are caused by the air pressure differences (from unequal heating of Earth by the sun) and the effects of Earth's rotation (the Coriolis effect).

Most of the contiguous United States is located in the prevailing southwesterly wind belt for much of the year, which means that most weather conditions move from southwest to northeast—more generally west to east. The west coast of the contiguous United States has much more of a marine climate than the east coast because the west coast's prevailing winds are from the ocean. Since the east coast has its prevailing winds blow from

Figure 8-9. Latitudinal climatic zones and continental and marine climates based on temperature and moisture conditions of an imaginary continent on a planet similar to Earth: Compare the zones here to the more simplified pattern in Figure 8-8. Note that as the latitude increases, the annual range of temperatures increases. Also note that marine climates—with ocean influences—have a much narrower annual temperature range than continental regions at similar latitudes. Notice the opposite temperature patterns in northern and southern hemispheres, which are the result of opposite seasons in the two hemispheres.

the center of the North American continent, it has continental climates almost to the shore of the Atlantic Ocean. Long Island, New York, has some marine moderation of climate compared to the rest of the state, as do some western parts of New York State downwind of Lake Erie and Lake Ontario.

The prevailing southwesterly winds also have an important large climatic effect by moving the air masses and frontal low pressure storms across the contiguous United States generally from west to east. The paths of these air masses and storm movements are often called "tracks," as shown in Figure 8-10. Much of the precipitation in the mid-latitudes is the result of these tracks and associated weather. Western New York State is noted for the lake effect snows caused by winds and storms blowing over the Great Lakes, picking up moisture, and then dropping the moisture as deep snows.

Figure 8-10. Tracks or paths of air masses and low-pressure storms across the contiguous United States: The weather systems are pushed across the United States by the prevailing southwest winds. These air masses and storms tend to follow similar tracks. Certain tracks are associated with specific parts of the year or seasonal shifting winds and pressure belts.

Monsoons are the weather changes caused by the seasonal shifts in the direction of prevailing winds. Though monsoons are usually associated with the wet summers and dry winters of southeast Asia—especially India—other areas experience a monsoon effect. Portions of southern Europe, northern Australia, and even the southeastern United States experience shifting prevailing winds and changing seasonal precipitation associated with the north and south seasonal movements of the vertical rays of the sun.

Besides the prevailing southwesterly wind belt, other wind belts also cause similar climatic effects in their associated latitudinal zones. The effects of the prevailing winds and their shiftings compared to the simple latitudinal climatic pattern of Figure 8-9 result in the more realistic climate zones illustrated in Figure 8-11.

Surface Ocean Currents Coastal climates are often modified by surface ocean currents. Currents flowing away from the equator carry warm water to higher latitudes, while currents flowing toward the equator carry cool water to lower latitudes. A cool ocean current will cause a coastal area to have cooler temperatures and less precipitation. One reason there is less precipitation is that cool water results in cool air, which cannot hold much water vapor. A warm ocean current will cause a coastal area's climate to be warmer and have more precipitation. The greater amounts of precipitation are due to the fact that warmer air can hold more water vapor and that warmer air—because it is less dense—will tend to rise and then cool, so that condensation can produce the clouds that bring precipitation. One of the best examples of an ocean current's climatic effects is illustrated in the warm, humid climates of Iceland, England, and Ireland, which result from the effects of the Gulf Stream and North Atlantic warm surface ocean currents. The locations of

Figure 8-11. Climate zone of an imaginary continent modified from Figure 8-9 by addition of prevailing winds and their shifting latitudes during the year: Seasonal winds and their associated weather are often called monsoons. The summer winds shown on the diagram would bring humid weather with much precipitation into areas that would be much drier without the monsoons.

Figure 8-12. Isolines of average annual precipitation in New York State: Even though southeastern New York is on the ocean, this region doesn't have the highest amount of precipitation, because the prevailing southwest winds blow towards the ocean, not away from it. The prevailing winds cause air masses to deposit the most precipitation in the three highest regions of the state—the Catskills, Tug Hill Plateau, and the Adirondack Mountains. Areas downwind from these high elevation regions—such as the Hudson Valley and Champlain Lowlands—receive lower amounts of precipitation.

the warm and cool ocean currents are shown on the Surface Ocean Currents map in the *Earth Science Reference Tables*. Ⓡ

Elevation The elevation of an area above sea level modifies the latitudinal climate pattern because as air rises, it expands and cools. Thus, the higher the altitude at any given latitude, the cooler the climate. Another reason higher elevations are cooler is the lower amounts of the greenhouse gases (carbon dioxide, water, and methane) at higher altitudes, and this means less absorption of long-wave radiation from the sun and Earth's surface.

Elevation also affects precipitation. As the elevation increases, the temperature and water vapor capacity decrease; the air thus approaches the dew point, condensation forms clouds, and precipitation often occurs.

Therefore, areas at higher altitudes generally have more precipitation than lower areas. In New York State, the Catskills and the Adirondack Mountains are generally cooler and have more precipitation than most surrounding areas. (See Figure 8-12 and Landscape Regions of New York State and Their Characteristics in the Appendix.)

Mountains Mountains that intersect prevailing winds, such as those associated with the planetary wind belts, can modify the latitudinal climate pattern. Figure 8-13 shows a cross section of a mountain against which the prevailing winds blow from the left. This side is the windward side. As the wind strikes the windward side of the mountain, the air is forced to rise. As it does so, it expands and cools. When rising air cools to the dew point, condensation releases stored heat energy, which lowers the rate of cooling with increasing elevation. At elevations above the place the dew point is reached, condensation results in clouds and then precipitation on the windward side. On the opposite side of the mountain—the leeward side—the air begins to descend. As the air descends, it is compressed and warmed. The warming of the air raises the temperature above the dew point, and condensation and precipitation stop. As a result, the leeward side is warmer than the windward side at any given altitude. The leeward side also has much less precipitation because the air has lost much of its moisture, and its water vapor capacity rises as its temperature increases. A good example of this mountain effect is the fact that the Champlain Lowlands get the least amount of precipitation in New York State. The Champlain Lowlands are on the leeward side of the Adirondack Mountains.

Figure 8-13. Climate effect when mountains intersect prevailing moist winds: The windward side of mountains has much precipitation while the leeward side is dry.

Another way that mountains modify climate is by acting as barriers to moving air masses, preventing cold air or warm air from crossing the mountain to the other side. As a result, opposite sides of a mountain can have different temperature patterns. In southeastern New York, the Hudson Highlands often keep warmer air south and colder air north. Therefore, sometimes during winter when it rains in New York City, there is either snow or no precipitation in the Hudson Valley north of the Hudson Highlands.

Vegetation An area's natural vegetation amounts and types are largely determined by the climate. Thus, an arid area has desert vegetation and a hot, humid climate has tropical rainforest vegetation. On the other hand, the vegetation of an area can help determine the climate of an area. When rainforests are cut down and converted into farms or grazing land, the climate often becomes hotter and less humid. Part of the reason for this is that there is more runoff and less transpiration to add humidity. Also, without all the trees to absorb solar energy and convert it into potential food energy, the solar energy heats the land instead, which then heats the atmosphere it touches. Have you ever noticed how much cooler it is under just one shade tree than it is when you are out in the open? Cutting down or <u>deforestation</u> of whole sections of forest would just multiply the effect of moving out from under a tree. Building cities—**urbanization**—also causes a decrease in forests and grasslands and causes changes in climate and weather.

Cloud Cover If an area has a high percentage of cloudy days, this will have a major climatic effect. Without clouds, the atmosphere is much more transparent to insolation, and more of the sun's energy can reach and heat Earth's surface. The high angle of incidence and thus high intensity of the sun's rays near the equator would make you think that areas at or near the equator would be the hottest on Earth, but this is not true. Thunderstorm clouds often cover the area around the equator, and these clouds absorb a large percentage of the insolation or reflect it back into space. On the other hand, the desert regions that exist around or at 30 degrees of latitude seldom have clouds. These dry latitudes without much cloud cover are often hotter than regions closer to the equator. See the dry and wet latitude belts on the Planetary Wind and Moisture Belts in the Troposphere in the *Earth Science* Ⓡ *Reference Tables*.

Climatic Change

A study of Figure 8-14 will indicate that Earth has gone through many times of overall increasing or decreasing temperatures. During the times of cooling, glaciers have advanced from the polar regions into the mid-latitudes and maybe even into the regions that are now considered warm or tropical. These times of advancing glaciers into the mid-latitudes were the <u>ice ages</u>. Global warming, El Niño, the greenhouse effect, the ozone "hole" problem, the effects of volcanic ash and other aspects of climatic change cause changes in Earth's climates over time.

Figure 8-14. Graph of climatic changes on Earth: The graph shows a comparison of the generalized sea levels and climatic conditions over the past 600 million years. Periods of warmer climate generally correspond with times of higher sea levels and periods of colder climates, with ice ages, generally correspond to the times of lower sea levels.

26. Which would cause the potential evaporation and transpiration to increase in a given month?

    (1) below-normal precipitation
    (2) a major flood
    (3) a month-long cold spell
    (4) higher amount of solar energy

27. Although New York City is at approximately the same latitude as Omaha, Nebraska, New York City's winter months are warmer and summer months are cooler. Which statement best explains why this is so?

    (1) The sun's rays shine more directly on New York City in the winter.
    (2) Nebraska is nearer to the Rocky Mountains.
    (3) The water around New York City has a moderating effect on the temperature
    (4) The prevailing westerlies have a greater effect on Omaha than on New York City.

28. Which would cause the potential evaporation and transpiration to decrease in a given month?

    (1) below-normal precipitation
    (2) drilling of a large well
    (3) a month-long cold spell
    (4) a high rainfall

29. Which generally has the greatest effect in determining the climate of an area?

    (1) degrees of longitude
    (2) extent of vegetation
    (3) distance from equator
    (4) month of the year

30. Two locations, one in northern Canada and one in the southwestern United States, receive the same amount of precipitation each year. The location in Canada is classified as a humid climate. Why would the location in the United States be classified as an arid climate?

31. The planetary wind and moisture belts indicate that large amounts of rainfall occur at Earth's equator because air at Earth's surface is

    (1) converging and rising
    (2) converging and sinking
    (3) diverging and rising
    (4) diverging and sinking

32. Describe the temperature differences between a coastal city and an interior city, at the same latitude, during summer and winter.

33. Which climate conditions are typical of regions near the North Pole and the South Pole?

    (1) low temperature and low precipitation
    (2) low temperature and high precipitation
    (3) high temperature and low precipitation
    (4) high temperature and high precipitation

34. As the degrees of latitude from the equator increases, what generally happens to the yearly average temperature?

35. On one of the Hawaiian Islands, the annual rainfall is 200 inches per year on one side of the island and less than 20 inches per year on the opposite side of the same island. This difference is most likely caused by

    (1) jet streams
    (2) hurricanes or typhoons
    (3) monsoons
    (4) prevailing winds and mountains

36. Which two climate factors are most directly responsible for the amount of snowfall normally received in Buffalo, New York?

    (1) ocean currents and storm tracks
    (2) mountain barriers and average temperatures
    (3) elevation and potential evaporation and transpiration
    (4) prevailing wind direction and proximity to a large body of water

37. Which planetary wind pattern is present in many areas of little rainfall?

    (1) Air sinks and winds converge.
    (2) Air rises and winds converge.
    (3) Air sinks and winds diverge.
    (4) Air rises and winds diverge.

38. Which area of New York State would probably have the lowest annual temperature range?

    (1) Long Island
    (2) the Catskills
    (3) the Adirondack peaks
    (4) the Mohawk Valley

39. Bodies of water have a moderating effect on climate primarily because

    (1) Water gains heat more rapidly than land does.
    (2) Water surfaces are flatter than land surfaces.
    (3) Water temperatures are always lower than land temperatures.
    (4) Water temperatures change more slowly than land temperatures do.

40. Which is a characteristic of water that helps the oceans to moderate the climates of Earth?

(1) Water is a fluid with a high specific heat.
(2) Water can exist as a high-density solid.
(3) Water can dissolve and transport minerals.
(4) Water can flow into loose sediments to deposit mineral cements.

41. If Lake Michigan were to vanish, the winters in Chicago would probably

(1) remain the same in temperature and humidity
(2) remain the same in temperature but become drier
(3) become colder and drier
(4) become warmer and drier

42. Which locality has the greatest annual range of temperature?

(1) Seattle, Washington
(2) Bismarck, North Dakota
(3) New York City
(4) Miami, Florida

43. Compared to an inland location of the same elevation and latitude, a coastal location is likely to have

(1) warmer summers and cooler winters
(2) warmer summers and warmer winters
(3) cooler summers and cooler winters
(4) cooler summers and warmer winters

44. A low-pressure storm center located over New York State will most likely move toward the

(1) southeast   (3) east
(2) southwest   (4) northwest

45. As a parcel of air rises, its temperature will

(1) decrease due to expansion
(2) decrease due to compression
(3) increase due to expansion
(4) increase due to compression

46. Which statement best explains why a cloud is forming in the following diagram?

(1) Water vapor is condensing.
(2) Moisture is evaporating.
(3) Cold air rises and compresses.
(4) Warm air sinks and expands.

47. Arrows on the map represent ocean currents.

These ocean currents affect the climate pattern of city X by

(1) decreasing the average annual cloud cover
(2) decreasing the average annual evaporation and transpiration
(3) increasing the average annual temperature
(4) increasing the average annual air pressure

48. Two coastal cities have the same latitude and elevation, but are located near different oceans. Which statement best explains why the two cities have different climates?

(1) They have different longitudes.
(2) They are near different ocean currents.
(3) They have different angles of insolation.
(4) They have different numbers of daylight hours.

49. The following diagram shows the locations of the cities of Seattle and Spokane, Washington. Both cities are located at approximately 48°N latitude, and the Cascade Mountains separate them.

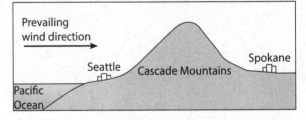

How does the climate of Seattle compare with the climate of Spokane?

(1) Seattle—hot, dry; Spokane—cool, humid
(2) Seattle—hot, humid; Spokane—cool, dry
(3) Seattle—cool, humid; Spokane—warm, dry
(4) Seattle—cool, dry; Spokane—warm, humid

Refer to the following diagram to answer questions 50 through 53.

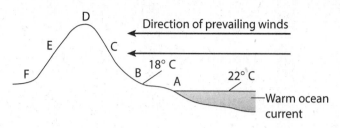

50. Which location would have the coolest average temperature?

51. Which location would have the most condensation in its atmosphere during the year?

(1) B   (3) E
(2) C   (4) F

52. Which location would most likely be driest?

53. How is the potential evaporation and transpiration of area A-B affected by the ocean current?

Base your answers to questions 54 through 57 on your knowledge of earth science and on the following diagram. The diagram represents an imaginary continent on Earth surrounded by water. The arrows indicate the direction of the prevailing winds. Two large mountain regions are also indicated. Points A, B, E, and H are located at sea level; C, D, and F are in the foothills of the mountains; G is high in the mountains.

54. Which physical characteristic would cause location G to have a colder yearly climate than any other location?

(1) the nearness of location G to a large ocean
(2) the location of G with respect to the prevailing winds
(3) the elevation of location G above sea level
(4) the distance of location G from the equator

55. Which location probably has the greatest annual rainfall?

(1) A   (2) F   (3) C   (4) D

56. Which location probably has the widest range in temperature during the year?

(1) A   (2) B   (3) H   (4) D

57. Which location will probably record its highest potential evaporation and transpiration values for the year during January?

(1) A   (2) F   (3) C   (4) D

58. Which New York State location is most likely to experience the heaviest winter snowfall when the surface winds are blowing from the west or north-west?

(1) New York City   (3) Oswego
(2) Binghamton   (4) Plattsburgh

59. Which ocean current transports warm water away from Earth's equatorial region?

(1) Brazil Current
(2) West Australia Current
(3) Falkland Current
(4) California Current

60. Once the surface of Lake Erie completely freezes over with ice, the amount of snow from each snowstorm is usually reduced. Explain why a covering of ice on Lake Erie may cause the amount of snow from snowstorms to be reduced.

61. Earth's entire equatorial climate zone is generally a belt around Earth that has

(1) high air pressure and wet weather
(2) high air pressure and dry weather
(3) low air pressure and wet weather
(4) low air pressure and dry weather

Directions

Review the Test-Taking Strategies section of this book. Then answer the following questions. Read each question carefully and answer with a correct choice or response.

Part A

1 The following flowchart shows one process by which moisture enters the atmosphere.

The last step of this process is known as
(1) condensation   (3) radiation
(2) convection   (4) transpiration

2 Replanting forests usually results in an increase in
(1) floods   (3) run-off
(2) ground water   (4) soil erosion

3 Which graph best represents the relationship between porosity and particle size for soil samples of uniform size, shape, and packing?

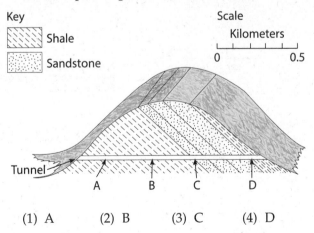

4 The following diagram represents a cross-sectional view of a tunnel cut through a mountain. The area where the mountain is located receives heavy rainfall. If the shale layers are impermeable, at which point would the most water seep through the roof of the tunnel?

(1) A   (2) B   (3) C   (4) D

5 Which statement best explains why Plattsburgh has a low average annual precipitation compared to most of New York State?
(1) Ocean currents bring warm, moist air to Plattsburgh.
(2) A planetary low-pressure belt is located over Plattsburgh.
(3) High latitudes cause a warm, dry climate near Plattsburgh.
(4) Prevailing winds travel over the Adirondack Mountains before they reach Plattsburgh.

6 Under which condition would a climate be classified as humid?
(1) When the soil moisture is being used all year long.
(2) When the annual precipitation equals the annual potenital evapotranspiration.
(3) When the annual precipitation is much greater than the annual evapotranspiration.
(4) When the annual precipitation is much less than the annual potential evapotranspiration.

Base your answers to questions 7 through 11 on the following diagram. The diagram represents two identical barrels, each filled to the same level, one with steel pellets and the other with marbles.

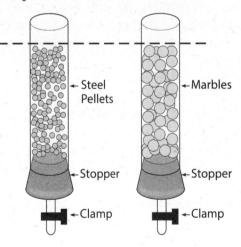

7 If water were added to each barrel to the height of the dashed line and then the clamps opened, which graph best illustrates how fast the water would run through each barrel?

8 After the water has been allowed to pass freely through the barrels, which graph best illustrates the amount of water retained by each barrel?

9 If the barrels and their contents were dried of all water and then arranged in such a way as to show capillary action, which graph best illustrates the height to which water would rise in each barrel?

10 How does the total amount of pore space in the barrel with the steel pellets compare with the total amount of pore space in the barrel with the marbles?
(1) It is much more.
(2) It is much less.
(3) It is approximately the same.

11 If an identical third barrel were filled with a mixture of steel pellets and marbles to the same level as the other two barrels, how would the size of the pore spaces in this barrel compare with the size of the pore spaces in the barrel of marbles?
(1) It would be less.
(2) It would be greater.
(3) It would be the same.

12 As the heat and pressure applied to buried sediments is increased, the porosity of the sediments will probably
(1) decrease
(2) increase
(3) remain the same

Base your answers to questions 13 through 15 on the following map. The map shows the climate classifications of some countries in eastern Africa.

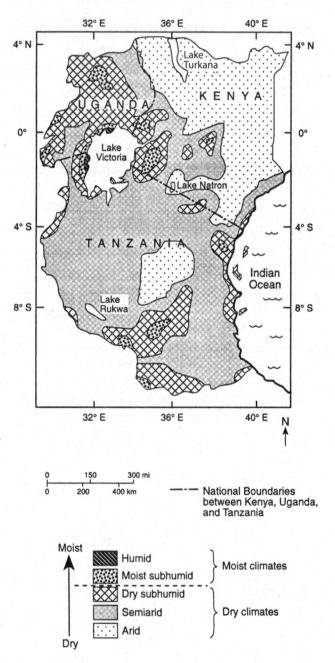

13 Which inference best explains the cause of the climate of the northeastern section of Kenya?

(1) The air reaching this section comes from a dry landmass region.

(2) Warm ocean currents bring moisture to this coastal section.

(3) Mountains force air to rise over this section.

(4) Cloud cover reflects most insolation in this section.

14 Which body of water appears to produce the greatest increase in the climate humidity of the adjacent land area?

(1) Indian Ocean

(2) Lake Turkana

(3) Lake Rukwa

(4) Lake Victoria

15 Which pattern represents the general surface planetary winds during March in this region?

16 The following graphs show some climate data for four cities: A, B, C, and D.

Which city would have the driest climate?

(1) A

(2) B

(3) C

(4) D

17 What is the best explanation for the following two statements?

- Some mountains located near Earth's equator have snow-covered peaks.
- Ice exists at Earth's poles.

(1) High elevation and high latitude have a similar effect on climate.

(2) Both mountain and polar regions have arid climates.

(3) Mountain and polar regions receive more energy from the sun than other regions do.

(4) An increase in snowfall and an increase in temperature have a similar effect on climate.

18 Diagram I shows the planetary wind belts of Earth. Diagram II is a graph of the average yearly precipitation for locations between 90° N latitude and 90° S latitude.

Which statement about Earth's average annual yearly precipitation is best supported by the diagrams?

(1) Precipitation is lowest at latitudes where planetary winds converge (meet).

(2) Precipitation is highest at latitudes where planetary winds converge (meet).

(3) Precipitation is highest at latitudes where planetary winds diverge (move apart).

(4) Precipitation is unrelated to planetary wind belts.

19 There are greater extremes of temperature at the South Pole than at the North Pole because the

(1) continent of Antarctica is primarily a landmass

(2) Gulf Stream flows around the continent of Antarctica

(3) North Pole is inclined toward the sun

(4) South Pole is inclined toward the sun

Part B

Base your answers to questions 20 through 22 on the data table below. The table shows the elevation and average annual precipitation at ten weather stations, A through J, located along a highway that passes over a mountain.

Data Table

Weather Station	Elevation (m)	Average Annual Precipitation (cm)
A	1,350	20
B	1,400	24
C	1,500	50
D	1,740	90
E	2,200	170
F	1,500	140
G	800	122
H	420	60
I	300	40
J	0	65

Symbol Chart

Key for Average Annual Precipitation

0–25 cm	△•
26–75 cm	▪
76–127 cm	◉
128–170 cm	✕

20 On the grid above, graph the data shown on the data table by following the directions below.

  a Mark the grid with a point showing the elevation of *each* weather station. [1]

  b Surround *each* point with the proper symbol from the symbol chart to show the amount of average annual precipitation for the weather station. [1]

21 State the relationship between the elevation of weather stations *A* through *E* and the average annual precipitation at these weather stations. [1]

22 Although stations *C* and *F* are at the same elevation, they have very different amounts of average annual precipitation. Explain how the prevailing wind direction might cause this difference. [1]

Base your answers to questions 23 through 34 on the map below. The map represents an imaginary continent and an island on Earth, which are surrounded by oceans. Locations E and H are on a coast at sea level, locations B, D, F, I, and J are about 500 meters in elevation, locations A and C are at the base of mountains at about 500 meters elevation, and Location G is at the top of a mountain at an elevation of 3000 meters. The arrows represent the direction of the prevailing winds. Some of these arrows have been omitted. Three mountain ranges with elevations over 1,000 meters are indicated.

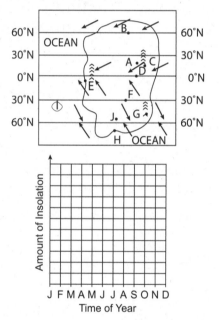

23 On the grid above draw a line that best represents the relationship between time of year and the amount of insolation at location *F*. [1]

24 What is the main reason why location *B* is colder in January than in July? [1]

25 Which location, with an elevation below 600 meters, most likely has the lowest average yearly temperature? [1]

26 Which non-polar location has the most arid (dry) climate due to falling air from the upper troposphere? [1]

27 Why would location *F* have cooler winters and warmer summers than location *I*? [1]

28 On the map draw three arrows to indicate the prevailing wind direction between 35°N and 50°N. [1]

29 Draw a big **W** in the ocean just off the west coast of the imaginary continent where there is most likely the location of a cold water ocean current just off the coast. [1]

30 How would a warm water ocean current just off of location *C* affect the amount of precipitation at this location? [1]

31 Which location on the map has the combination of highest yearly temperatures and high yearly amounts of precipitation? [1]

32 Why is location A much more arid (drier) than location C? [1]

33 What physical aspect of location *G* would cause it to be much colder than location *J*? [1]

34 Which location has higher than normal amounts of precipitation for its latitude because moist air is forced to rise, expand, cool, producing large volumes of clouds? [1]

Base your answers to questions 35 through 37 on the graph below, which shows the average monthly temperatures for a year for city *X* and city *Y*. Both cities are located at the same latitude.

Time (months)

35 What was the range in the average monthly temperatures for city *Y* during the year? [1]

36 Explain why city *X* has a greater difference between summer and winter temperatures than city *Y*. [1]

37 What evidence shown on the graph indicates that both cities, *X* and *Y*, are located in the Northern Hemisphere? [1]

Part C

38 Many astronomers believe that between 3 billion and 4 billion years ago, the sun radiated only 70 percent of the energy radiated today. This would suggest that at that time Earth would not have been hot enough to have liquid water at its surface. However, geologists cite evidence of sedimentary rocks and fossils that formed in liquid water during this time. Suggest a way in which Earth's surface could have been warm enough to have liquid water and life forms with much less energy coming from the sun. [1]

39 In a region of flat landscape, one family is obtaining drinking water from a well drilled 150 feet below the surface and 50 feet below the water table—all in sediment. Another family, in the same landscape area 2 miles away, has the same type of well drilled to the same depth, but this well produced almost no water. Describe a sediment condition that could account for the differences in water production from the two wells. [1]

40 You are at an ocean beach where it hasn't rained in weeks. You observe that for miles along the beach the sand is saturated with water about 5 feet inland and about 2 feet higher than any recent ocean levels. Describe a common condition that would account for the water-saturated sand above ocean levels. (Don't consider splashing of waves.) [1]

41 In the last few years drought in the southwestern United States has been associated with sinking land and development of cracks in Earth's surface. Some of the mile-long cracks are over 12 feet deep and over 20 feet in width. Soil scientists have suggested that the cracks and sinking land are due to the lowering of the water table and changes in the sediments between the new and old water-table levels. Describe how sediments above and below the water table have changed and how the changes could account for the sinking land and the formation of surface cracks. [2]

Base your answers to questions 42 through 47 on the article and diagram that follow.

New York Lake-Effect Snows

In much of western and central New York State winter snows called lake-effect snows are a major part of daily life, often closing roads with drifting snows. These snows usually account for a large portion of the total yearly precipitation.

What creates this lake-effect snow that is so common in areas around Buffalo, Rochester, Syracuse, and Oswego among other locations in an area of New York State commonly called the "snow belt"? The diagram that follows will aid in answering this question.

In late fall and for most of an average winter, the water temperature of Lake Ontario (as well as Lake Erie) is warmer than the surrounding land in the USA and Canada. When the prevailing westerly winds blow over Lake Ontario, the air is warmed and this warmer air evaporates large amounts of water vapor from the lake. The greater the difference between the cooler air from the land and the warmer lake temperatures, the more water evaporates into the air as it moves over the lake. The amount of evaporation is aided by the long east–west orientation of Lake Ontario and Lake Erie combined with the westerly winds.

When the warmer moist air blows over the eastern end of the lakes and over the land, orographic lifting, the effect of the air being forced to rise, cools the air to the dewpoint. The resulting condensation creates the clouds and often heavy snows characteristic of this snow belt. The air continues to rise from the Erie-Ontario Lowlands to the Tug Hill and Allegheny Plateaus and even over the higher Adirondack Mountains.

42 State the relationship that must exist between water temperature and air temperature for lake-effect snow to develop. [1]

43 State why locations east and southeast of Lake Ontario are more likely to receive lake-effect snow than are locations west of the lake. [1]

44 State where on the diagram above the annual precipitation would most likely be the lowest. [1]

45 State why very heavy snowfall occurs in the Tug Hill Plateau region. [1]

46 State where it would be the safest location to plant crops that would be killed by large extremes of temperature. [1]

47 State two reasons why the land around location *A* is cooler in the summers compared to areas fifty miles directly east of location *A*. [1]

Base your answers to questions 48 through 50 on the field map below, which shows an area of a state park where an underground gasoline tank leaked and contaminated the groundwater. Groundwater-monitoring wells were installed to determine the extent of the contamination. The concentration of contaminants in parts per million (ppm) in each of the wells is indicated on the map.

48 On the field map, draw the 50-ppm, 100-ppm, and 150-ppm isolines. The 0-ppm isoline has been drawn for you. [1]

49 State the relationship between the distance from the gasoline tank and the concentration of contaminants in the groundwater. [1]

50 Park officials do not want to see another incident of groundwater contamination from gasoline tanks. State *one* action that park officials could take to prevent gasoline from contaminating the groundwater in the future. [1]

Weathering and Erosion

How Scientists Study Erosion

? *Which activity do you think is the dominant agent of erosion on Earth—running water, human activity, glaciers, waves and ocean currents, landslides, or wind?* **?**

Although running water is the main contributor to natural erosion, surprisingly, human activities have moved more sediment in recent years than running water. These activities include road-building, livestock overgrazing, deforestation, construction projects, mining and urbanization, and poor farming methods.

Many scientists now believe that the significant human activity on earth has created a new part of geologic time called the Anthropocene (*anthropo* meaning "human"). One of the reasons for this is that humans have likely altered over 75% of Earth's land surface. Another reason for the Anthropocene is the present rapid extinction of species of life due, in part, to human activities.

Learn more about erosion in this topic. Brainstorm with your classmates about the kinds of things you can do to make a difference in reducing the human contribution to erosion.

Weathering and Erosion

Vocabulary

abrasion	glacial parallel scratches	stream
breaking wave	glacier	stream abrasion
chemical weathering	mass movement	stream channel shape
delta	meander	tributary
erosion	physical weathering	U-shaped valley
finger lake	sandbar	V-shaped valley
flood plain	sandblasting	watershed
glacial groove	sediment	weathering

Topic Overview

Weather conditions, such as temperature changes and precipitation, play an important role in the rock cycle. Weather conditions, the actions of living things, and other factors can make Earth's surface rocks break down into smaller particles. Moving water or wind can then carry the rock particles away as **sediments**. Eventually, sediments are deposited in environments such as the ocean floor, where they become part of sedimentary rocks.

Weathering

The chemical and physical breakdown of rocks at or near Earth's surface is called **weathering**. Weathering occurs when rocks are exposed to air, water, pressure changes, and the actions of living things. The origins of most of Earth's landscape features and soils can be traced to the weathering of exposed rocks. Weathering processes also affect structures such as buildings and roads.

Types of Weathering

Like other types of matter, rocks can undergo physical or chemical changes. Weathering processes are classified into two types—those that cause chemical changes in rock and those that cause physical changes.

Chemical Weathering The breakdown of rock through a change in mineral or chemical composition is called **chemical weathering**. One form of chemical weathering is oxidation—such as when iron combines with oxygen to make iron oxide, or rust.

Another form of chemical weathering is the effect of water on minerals. Water is often called the universal solvent because, over time, water can dissolve most rock materials. Acids from decaying organic matter mix with

Recall that oxidation is the chemical combining of oxygen from the air with other elements. You have probably seen rust (iron oxide) on old nails and other iron objects. The iron in rocks and soil can also oxidize, combining with oxygen to form red, brown, and yellow pigments.

Sink hole Cave   Limestone icicles

Limestone rock

Underground stream

Figure 9-1. Landscape features of limestone bedrock that has been chemically weathered: When carbonic acid in underground water dissolves limestone, the dissolved limestone erodes, producing features such as sink holes and caves. Some of the limestone reforms by chemical precipitation into cave features, such as limestone icicles.

groundwater and aid in dissolving rocks. Water can also combine with carbon dioxide from air to form carbonic acid. Carbonic acid in surface water and ground water easily dissolves some rocks—especially limestone and marble.

This dissolving of limestone and marble often results in unique features that include sink holes and caves, and indirectly, in the formation of limestone terraces and limestone "icicles." (See Figure 9-1.)

Physical Weathering The breakdown of rock into smaller pieces without chemical change is called **physical weathering.** Physical weathering occurs when frost action, plant root growth, pressure changes, or abrupt temperature changes cause rocks to crack apart.

Frost action breaks up rocks in a way similar to the formation of road potholes, as shown in Figure 9-2. When water freezes, its volume expands nearly ten percent. At temperatures below 0°C, water trapped in cracks freezes and expands, enlarging the cracks. After many cycles of freezing and thawing, the rock crumbles.

Another type of physical weathering occurs when the confining pressure on rocks is decreased when rock is removed by humans in mining or quarrying or by natural processes such as in erosion or when glaciers melt. When the rock (including ice) is removed, the pressure is reduced on the remaining rocks and these rocks expand and crack.

Physical weathering also occurs when rock particles grind against rock in a process called **abrasion.** Abrasion occurs as sediments moved by ice, gravity, running water, or air come into contact with other rocks. The characteristic rounded shape of rocks from river beds and beaches is caused by abrasion.

A Precipitation

Crack

Pavement
Sub-base
Seepage
Soil

B Freezing

Angular
pieces   Ice

C Thawing

Hole

D Break-in

Erosion
by tire

Figure 9-2. Formation of a road pothole by frost action: (A) Water seeps into cracks in the pavement. (B) Freezing water expands and pushes upward through the path of least resistance. (C) Thawed water seeps into the ground and leaves a hole. (D) The pavement breaks down further.

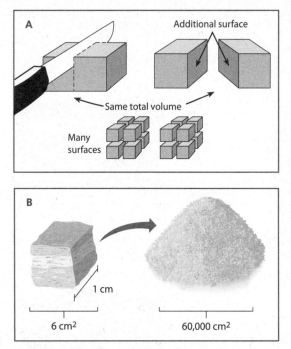

Factors Affecting the Rate and Type of Weathering

Many factors determine the rate and type of weathering that will occur in a given location on Earth's surface. These factors include variations in the location, composition, and size of rocks, as well as in local climate conditions.

Exposure Both the rate and type of weathering are dependent on the exposure of rocks to air, water, and the actions of living things. Generally, the closer a rock is to Earth's surface, the faster it will weather. The difference in the amount of solar energy on the north and south sides of mountains affects the temperature and amount of moisture available for weathering. This often results in different soil characteristics on opposite sides of mountains.

Particle Size Weathering results in the formation of rock particles of different sizes. As shown in Figure 9-3 when the rock particles are smaller, the total surface area per unit volume exposed to weathering is greater. Therefore, the rate of weathering is faster. To understand the effect of increased surface area, consider what happens when you add sugar to a drink. Granulated sugar dissolves more quickly than an equal mass of sugar cubes because the granulated sugar has a greater surface area exposed to the liquid around it.

Figure 9-3. Surface area increases as particle size decreases: (A) When a block is divided into smaller and smaller pieces, the total surface area will increase rapidly, although the total mass of material will remain the same. (B) When a rock is broken up, the surface area of the material that forms it increases.

Mineral Composition A rock's mineral composition affects the rate of weathering because different minerals have different physical and chemical properties. Some minerals, such as calcite in limestone and marble, weather rapidly because they dissolve in slightly acidic water. In contrast, the mineral quartz does not react chemically with most substances in the environment. Thus, quartz is largely unaffected by chemical weathering and is commonly found as sand in many environments.

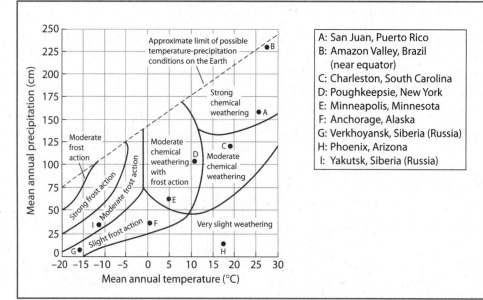

Figure 9-4. Dominant type of weathering for various climatic conditions: The upper left region of the graph represents extreme conditions that almost never occur on Earth.

Climate As shown in Figure 9-4, the rate and type of weathering in a given location are greatly influenced by climate. Chemical weathering is most pronounced in warm, moist climates. Generally, the higher the average temperature and precipitation, the more rapid the chemical weathering. In cold climates, frost action is the most common form of weathering. Frost action is especially intense in moist climates with temperature variations that lead to repeated cycles of freezing and thawing.

Soil Formation

Physical and chemical weathering processes are important in the formation of soil. Soil is the mixture of rock particles and organic matter on Earth's surface that supports rooted plants. Living things play a significant role in soil formation. For example, the activities of ants and burrowing animals expose rock surfaces to weathering. Plant roots widen cracks in rocks. Plants also drop leaves, which decay on the ground, releasing acids that dissolve rock. Dead leaves and remains of other living things form humus—a part of soil that serves as a source of plant nutrients.

Soils can form in place from a parent material, such as bedrock. Over time, soils develop horizontal layers with a distinctive profile, as shown in Figure 9-5. Soils formed in place have some characteristics of the parent material from which they formed. However, the most important factor in determining the type of soil that forms in a particular place is the area's climate.

Soils can also be transported into an area from another place—usually by wind, by moving water, or by the moving ice of a glacier. Already-formed soils are often directly transported while in other cases sediments are transported by erosion, which upon deposition becomes the parent material for soil development. The soils covering most of New York State formed from sediments deposited by glaciers during the most recent ice age, or by water melted from these glaciers. In the last 10,000–15,000 years, soil-forming processes have worked on these transported sediments to produce the present-day soils. Most of these soils have a soil profile similar to the immature soil shown in Figure 9-5B. New York does have some true transported soils deposited by the flooding of rivers and streams.

A **Very immature soil**   B **Immature soil**   C **Mature soil**

Figure 9-5. Soil development from bedrock: (A) Originally, there is unweathered bedrock at the surface. (B) Soil development, by way of weathering, starts at Earth's surface and gradually progresses downward over time to produce soil layers. (C) The formation of mature soil often takes many thousands of years.

1. What is the main difference between chemical and physical weathering?

   (1) Chemical weathering alters the composition of minerals, and physical weathering does not.
   (2) Chemical weathering increases the surface area of minerals, and physical weathering does not.
   (3) Physical weathering alters the composition of minerals, and chemical weathering does not.
   (4) Physical weathering increases the surface area of minerals, and chemical weathering does not.

2. Which is the best example of physical weathering?

   (1) the cracking of rock caused by the freezing and thawing of water
   (2) the transportation of sediment in a stream
   (3) the reaction of limestone with acid rainwater
   (4) the formation of a sandbar along the side of a stream

3. Water is a major agent of chemical weathering because water

   (1) cools the surroundings when it evaporates
   (2) dissolves many of the minerals that make up rocks
   (3) has a density of about one gram per cubic centimeter
   (4) has the highest specific heat of all common earth materials

4. In which climate would the chemical weathering of limestone occur most rapidly?

   (1) cold and dry
   (2) cold and humid
   (3) warm and dry
   (4) warm and humid

5. What is the general relationship between the depth of a soil formed from underlying bedrock and the length of the weathering period responsible for its formation?

6. A variety of soil types are found in New York State primarily because areas of the state differ in their

   (1) amounts of insolation
   (2) distances from the ocean
   (3) underlying bedrock and sediments
   (4) amounts of human activities

7. Describe the specific temperature and moisture characteristics of a climate in which frost action is dominant in the winter season.

8. The chemical composition of a soil formed in a certain area from the bedrock beneath it is determined by the

   (1) method by which the soil was transported to the area
   (2) slope of the land and the particle size of the soil
   (3) length of time since the last crustal movement in the area occurred
   (4) minerals in the bedrock beneath the soil and the climate of the area

9. Which type of climate has the greatest amount of rock weathering caused by frost action?

   (1) a wet climate in which temperatures remain below freezing
   (2) a wet climate in which temperatures alternate between below freezing and above freezing
   (3) a dry climate in which temperatures remain below freezing
   (4) a dry climate in which temperatures alternate between below freezing and above freezing

10. New York State soils are most likely composed of rock particles that have been

    (1) weathered from the underlying bedrock
    (2) weathered from the bedrock of northern Pennsylvania
    (3) transported by glaciers or water
    (4) transported by wind

Erosion

Weathering of rock produces particles that are transported as sediments through the process of **erosion.** Over time, erosion shapes and lowers Earth's surface. Sediments displaced from their source are evidence of erosion. Such sediments can be seen in muddy streams, on beaches, in rock fields near glaciers, along riverbanks, and in soils.

Transporting Systems of Erosion

Erosion involves a transporting system with several components:

- an agent of erosion, such as a stream, glacier, surface ocean wave, surface ocean current, turbidity current, or human activity
- the sediments being moved
- a driving force

The driving force for most types of erosion comes from gravity. Rocks and sediments at higher elevations have gravitational potential energy, part of which changes into kinetic energy when gravity pulls them downward. The process is ongoing because heat energy input from Earth's interior raises landmasses upward.

Energy from the sun plays an important indirect role in erosion. The sun's energy drives the water cycle, producing precipitation that results in running water and glaciers. Insolation also "fuels" wind patterns that create ocean currents and waves.

Gravity Erosion As explained previously, gravity is the driving force behind erosion. It causes sediments to move downslope by way of running water, glaciers, and underwater currents. However, gravity can also act largely on its own by pulling rocks and sediments downhill in **mass movements.** The term landslide is commonly used to refer to most types of mass movements.

Mass movement—sometimes called direct gravity erosion—involves two major opposing forces. One force is the constant downward pull of gravity. The other force is friction, which attempts to keep objects in place. Rocks and other loose materials on Earth's surface slide downward when the forces holding them in place become weaker than the downward pull of gravity. For example, when a heavy rainstorm saturates the ground, frictional forces are greatly lowered. Under these conditions, mass

Process	Soil Creep	Debris Flow	Mud Flow (debris flow)	Rock Fall, or Debris Fall
Illustration				
Description	Gradual downhill movement of soil	Rapid downslope plastic flow of a mass of debris	Downward flow of fine particles (mud) and large amounts of water	Rapid falling of pieces of rock from a cliff or steep slope
Velocity	Less than 1 cm/year	1 mm/day to 1 km/hr	1 to 5 km/hr	Greater than 4 km/hr
Slowest		Increasing Velocities		Fastest

Table 9-1. Types of Mass Movement

movements often occur. Other conditions leading to mass movements include earthquakes, wave erosion, side cutting by streams, and road-building activities.

As shown in Table 9-1, great variation exists among the types and speeds of mass movements from the slow downward movement of soil (soil creep) to the rapid fall of rock from a cliff. The rock piles found at the base of many steep slopes result from frost action and rock fall mass movements over time.

Running Water Erosion and Streams Running water is often considered the most common natural agent of erosion on Earth's solid surface. Running water erosion often begins with the splashing of raindrops, which may move silt and clay a few centimeters. During rainstorms, thin sheets of water often flow over the land, also causing running water erosion. These sheets of water often become confined to a channel of a temporary stream valley called a rill, or gully.

When running water erosion is confined to a channel, a **stream** exists. In this book, water flowing through a channel—whether a large river or a narrow creek—is referred to as a stream. A smaller stream that flows into a larger stream is called a **tributary.** If water flows through a particular channel for the major part of the year, the stream is considered permanent.

Streams carry sediments in different ways. Dissolved minerals are carried in solution. Solid sediments of small size—including clay-sized sediments—are carried suspended in the water. Larger solid sediments are usually carried by rolling, sliding, or bouncing along the stream bottom, resulting in rounding of sediments by **stream abrasion.** The way in which a particular type of solid sediment moves varies with how fast the stream flows.

Figure 9-6. Formation of a stream's V-shaped valley: The action of stream downcutting alone would produce a very narrow vertical channel. However, mass movements and run-off erode the sides of a stream valley, creating the characteristic V-shape.

Over time, streams carve deeper channels. As shown in Figure 9-6, a **V-shaped valley** forms. The V-shape results from the combined actions of stream downcutting, runoff, and mass movement, which causes the sides of the valley to "cave in." The area of land drained by any one stream is called its **watershed,** or drainage area. An example is shown in Figure 9-7. As streams vary in size, watersheds do also. A watershed can be as small as the size of this book or can cover a large portion of a continent—such as the area drained by the Mississippi River and all its tributaries. A region of higher land that separates one watershed from another is called a divide. In the United States, the Continental Divide follows the crest of the Rocky Mountains. Watersheds on the eastern side of the continental divide drain toward the Atlantic Ocean, while watersheds on the western side drain toward the Pacific Ocean.

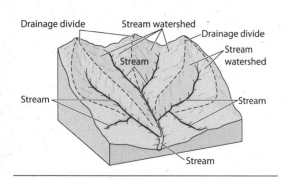

Figure 9-7. Stream watersheds or drainage basins: The portion of Earth's surface drained by one stream is a watershed.

Stream Velocity Three factors are most important in determining the average velocity of a stream. One factor is the <u>gradient</u>, or slope of the stream. Another factor is the <u>discharge</u>, or volume of water in the stream. Generally, as either the slope or the discharge of a stream increases, the velocity increases. The third factor involved is the **stream channel shape**—the shape of the bed of rock or loose materials that confine the stream.

Figure 9-8 shows how stream channel shape affects stream velocity. Notice that a wide, flat stream channel has a large surface in contact with moving water—and therefore, a large amount of friction is present to slow down the stream. In contrast, a semicircular stream channel shape results in less friction and greater stream velocity.

Water does not move at equal velocities throughout a stream, as shown in Figure 9-9. The region of maximum velocity shifts when the stream changes direction. When the stream channel is straight, maximum velocity occurs at the center of the stream. When the stream channel curves, the region of maximum velocity shifts to the outside of the curve. Velocity also varies with depth. It is greatest just below the surface and least near the stream bed, or stream channel bottom. At the air-water interface and at the stream bed, velocity is reduced by friction.

Generally, the solid sediments being transported by a stream move much more slowly than the stream itself. The greater the velocity of a stream, the larger the sediment particles it can carry, and the greater the velocity, the more total sediments it can carry. (See Figure 9-10.) Also see Relationship of Transported Particle Size to Water Velocity in the *Earth Science Reference Tables*.

A stream with greater velocity can carry larger sediment particles, as shown in Figure 9-10. For example, a stream moving faster than 800 cm per second can transport large boulders. In addition,

A

Cross-sectional area = 10 square units
Perimeter = 12 units
Wide and shallow stream channel

B

Cross-sectional area = 10 square units
Perimeter = 12 units
Deep and narrow stream channel

C

Cross-sectional area = 10 square units
Perimeter = about 8 units
Semicircular stream channel

Figure 9-8. Effect of channel shape on stream velocity: Although the cross-sectional area of the three streams is the same, the semicircular shape in diagram C has less water in contact with the material of the stream channel. If all other factors for the stream system are the same, less contact means less friction and higher stream velocity.

Key
X = Region of maximum velocity
Arrow length proportional to stream velocity

Figure 9-9. Variations in stream velocity: (A) Where the stream course is straight the maximum velocity is at the center of the cross section. **(B)** and **(C)** Where the stream course changes direction, the location of maximum velocity moves toward the outside of the curve, or meander. Low velocity at the inside of curves results in deposition of the larger and denser sediments there.

Figure 9-10. Relationship between stream velocity and particle size: Point A on the graph would be particle diameter 0.3 cm, and stream velocity 20cm/s (second). Calculate the coordinates for points B, C, and D on the graph. [B = 0.02 cm × 1 cm/s, C = 20 cm × 200 cm/s, D = 0.0007 cm × 0.04 cm/s]

streams with greater velocities can also move a greater total amount of sediments.

Evolution of a Stream Streams slowly change their characteristics over time in response to changes in elevation, gradient, volume of water, and available sediments. Figure 9-11 shows a typical stream in various stages of its evolution. In its uppermost part, this stream starts at a **finger lake.** Finger lakes are bodies of water in U-shaped valleys carved by glaciers and often partly dammed at one end by a pile of glacially deposited sediments.

In the early stages of the stream, most of its energy is used to downcut a narrow V-shaped valley. There usually is a steep slope and many abrupt changes in elevation resulting in waterfalls and rapids. Farther downstream, more water from tributaries and from ground water increases the size of the stream.

As the stream grows larger, it begins to shift its course in a series of bends or turns called **meanders.** In shifting from side to side, the stream carves a wider valley. During times of flooding, the stream may flow out onto this wider valley and deposit sediments—forming a **flood plain.**

Near the end or mouth of a stream, the discharge of water is often great, but there is little slope to the stream channel. At this stage the stream cuts a very wide valley and an equally wide flood plain. Deposition of sediments along the banks of a stream commonly accompanies frequent flooding—in some cases forming sediment mounds, called levees. Sediments are also deposited on the flood plain. At the very end of a stream, there is often a fan-shaped **delta.** A delta forms from sediments deposited over time from the ever-shifting channel at the stream's mouth.

Wind Erosion Another agent of erosion is wind. When loose sediments the size of sand or smaller are present, nearby solid surfaces are susceptible to erosion by wind. Arid regions, such as deserts, and lake or ocean coastlines are the most common places where loose sediments are available for wind erosion. There are two main aspects to wind erosion—deflation and sandblasting, or abrasion. Examples of each are illustrated in Figure 9-12. Deflation takes place in areas with small, loose sediments exposed to the atmosphere. Winds readily blow away the loose sediments, lowering the land surface. The lowering of the land surface can continue until there are no longer any small solid sediments exposed to the winds.

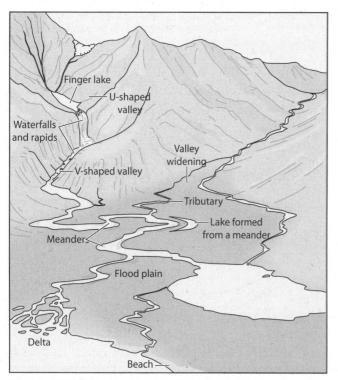

Figure 9-11. Features of an evolving stream

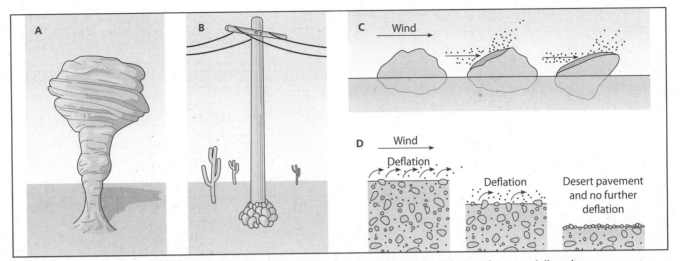

Figure 9-12. Features of wind erosion: (A) Abrasion by wind blown sand often sandblasts rocks—especially at lower levels—leaving a "mushroom rock." (B) The base of a utility pole has to be protected from sand blasting so it will not be "sawed" off. (C) Prevailing winds can abrade rocks into sediments with flat sides. (D) Wind erosion can lower an area's landscape by removing sand and smaller sediments.

Sandblasting occurs when winds blow sand or silt grains against rocks and other objects. The pelting by the grains can erode, or abrade, rocks in a manner similar to the process used to clean brick and stone buildings. Since wind can usually lift sand grains only about one meter into the air, the lower portions of exposed rocks become more eroded than the upper portions, as shown in diagram A in Figure 9-12. When sand grains collide, sandblasting also results in abrasion, and the frosted, or pitted, appearance of the sand grains themselves.

Glacial Erosion A **glacier** is a naturally formed mass of ice and snow that moves downhill on land under the influence of gravity. Mountain glaciers are found in high mountain valleys around the world. Ice-sheet, or continental, glaciers cover huge landmass regions. The area covered by a glacier has an ever-changing boundary determined by the accumulation of snow and ice and the wasting away of the glacier by melting, iceberg formation, and sublimation. If more snow and ice accumulates than wastes away, the glacier will advance. If the opposite occurs, the glacier will retreat. It should be noted that ice within a glacier is always moving in a particular direction, even if the glacier retreats as its overall boundaries shrink.

Glacial movement often is by plastic flow. The glacial ice acts like a fluid, and many of its motions are like those of a stream. As a result, glaciers are often called "rivers of ice." Figure 9-13C shows that a valley glacier moves fastest in the middle and slowest at the sides. This is true because there is more friction at the sides of the valley than in the middle. In the cross-section, glaciers usually flow fastest near the top and slowest at the bottom because the greatest friction is at the bottom.

At times, glacial motion is caused by sliding at the base of the glacier when liquid water helps to overcome friction.

Types and Features of Glacial Erosion When a glacier moves over the land, loose rocks and other materials beneath it freeze into the ice and are dragged along. The rocks and loose sediments frozen to the bottom of the glacier act like gougers and sandpaper on rock surfaces beneath them.

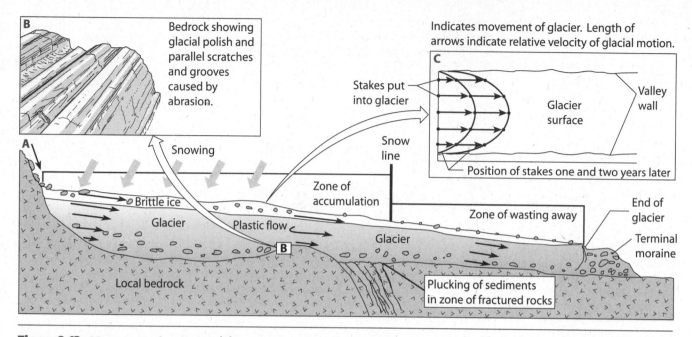

Figure 9-13. Movement of a glacier: **(A)** A glacier constantly flows forward. As a glacier moves forward, it transports sediments and abrades and plucks the bedrock beneath. The length of the arrows on the glacier shows comparative velocity of glacial motion. The greatest velocity is near the top of the glacier, and the slowest velocity is near the bottom. **(B)** Abrasion forms polished, scratched, and grooved bedrock. **(C)** As seen from above, glacial movement is fastest near the middle of the glacier and slowest at the interface with valley walls.

Figure 9-14. Some landscape features of glacial erosion: The sharp and angular features shown here are characteristic of mountain glaciers. The fan-shaped deposits (land deltas) are features of stream deposition. These mountain features can be seen in higher regions of New York State, such as the Adirondack Mountains, the Catskills, and the Hudson Highlands.

These gouging and sanding actions produce **glacial grooves** and **glacial parallel scratches,** along with more loose sediments. The direction of exposed glacial grooves and scratches on bedrock shows the direction of former glacial movement.

Many of the sediments carried by a glacier are carried on or near its surface. These sediments are generally rock fragments broken off from valley walls by frost action and deposited onto the glacier by mass movements. Often the rock fragments are very large—up to the size of a small house. Glacial sediments can be carried hundreds of miles. When deposited, they may differ greatly from the bedrock in their new location. Such contrasting sediments, called erratics, are found in much of the northern United States and most of New York State.

The wide, thick ice of a glacier erodes its confining valley walls as much as it does the rock beneath it. The result is a characteristic glacial **U-shaped valley.** The Finger Lakes of western New York occupy former V-shaped stream valleys that were altered to a U-shape by ice sheets during the last ice age. New York State also has other erosional features associated with continental and mountain glaciers from the last ice age, as shown in Figure 9-14.

Wave and Current Erosion Where lake or ocean waters meet land, waves and currents act as agents of erosion—creating unique landscape features. Winds transfer energy to the surface of lakes and oceans, creating waves.

Beach   Returning water   Zone of breaking waves (surf)   Note the ripple marks at the sediment-water boundary caused by the water moving up and down the beach.

Sediment

Shallow water   Wave first touches bottom   Deep water   Bottom of wave motion

Bedrock

Figure 9-15. Motion of waves in deep and shallow water: When ocean waves move in deep water, there is no forward movement of the water—only circular movements that diminish rapidly with depth. When a wave comes near shore, the shallower water depth causes the wave to drag on the bottom. This dragging causes the water in the waves to actually fall forward as the waves bunch together, rise up, and break against the shore. Ripple marks are not drawn to scale.

Notice in Figure 9-15 how waves passing through deep water cause brief circular water movements. However, when waves enter shallow water near the shore, they drag against the bottom. The waves then become unstable and water rushes toward the shore as **breaking waves,** or surf.

Breaking waves continually pound against the shoreline, unleashing a great amount of energy. Usually, waves arrive at an angle to the shore. Arriving waves often become refracted or bent, concentrating energy on parts of the shore that extend out into the water. Over time, these parts of the shore erode away. If the coastline is straight, the wave energy is more evenly spread out, and the waves pound the entire shoreline. If the shore has no depositional features to protect it, such as a beach or barrier island, wave action may carve a sea cliff with the aid of mass movement.

Because waves usually strike the shore at an angle, the waters near shore are often pushed in one direction along the shore. This causes a flow of water, sometimes called a longshore current, that can carry large amounts of sediments parallel to

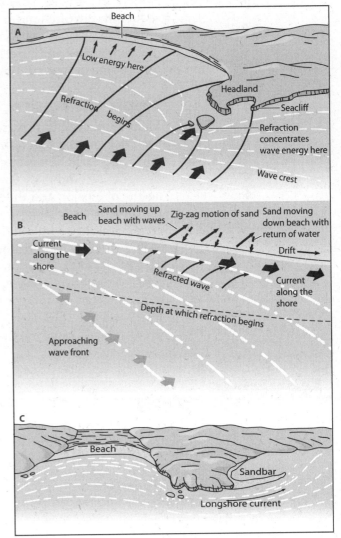

Figure 9-16. Erosional and depositional features of a shoreline: (A) Most waves strike a coastline at an angle and when the bottom of the wave drags, they are refracted, or bent. This refraction concentrates the energy of erosion on the areas of the coast that extend into the water. (B) The bent waves result in sand moving in a zig-zag pattern as they strike the coast. The angled water movement also results in a longshore current flowing along the shore in one direction. (C) When the current slows, sediments are deposited, creating such depositional features as beaches and sandbars.

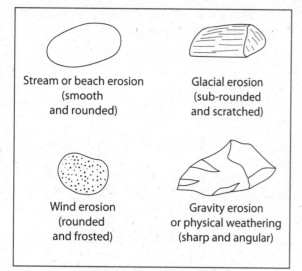

Figure 9-17. Sediment features reflect the erosional or weathering agents that produced or transported them.

the shore. Over time, sediments on shore tend to move in a zig-zag pattern along the same direction as the longshore current. This movement occurs because breaking waves, bearing sediments, strike the beach at an angle. However, as water from the breaking waves washes back into the lake or ocean, it flows straight downhill.

In the zone of breaking waves, deposited sediments can create a series of mounds called a **sandbar.** Figure 9-16 shows an example of a sandbar and other erosional and depositional features formed at the shoreline by ocean waves and currents. Over time, the constant movement and abrasion of the sediments at a shoreline causes the sediments to become more rounded, smoother, and smaller.

Sediment Features and Erosional Agents

Each agent of erosion produces distinctive characteristics in the sediment it transports, as illustrated in Figure 9-17. A solid sediment in wind, beach, or stream erosion will become smooth, rounded, and smaller. The longer the time the sediment is eroded, the smaller, smoother, and rounder it becomes. Wind-blown sediments are often more frosted (pitted) than stream sediments. Glacial sediments are only partly rounded (sub-rounded), and often have scratches of various sizes and directions on them. Sediments produced by physical weathering or moved directly by gravity are often very angular in shape.

People and Erosion

Many human activities greatly increase the erosion of land. Recently it has been determined that humans have become the major agent of erosion on Earth. Construction projects, road-building, mining, deforestation, overgrazing, and poor farming methods expose soil and loose materials to agents of erosion and thereby increase erosion rates. Many types of mass movements/landslides are major natural hazards in the United States, creating almost 4 billion dollars in damage annually. It is possible for people to make decisions to restore past damage and discontinue activities that increase erosion. For example, people can choose to replant logged forests, restore coastal vegetation, and set limits on grazing. Farming techniques such as no-till farming and contour plowing can be used to minimize erosion. Highways can be designed to create gentler slopes that are less likely to produce mass movements.

Review Questions

11. By which processes are rocks broken up and moved to different locations?
    (1) evaporation and condensation
    (2) weathering and erosion
    (3) burial and cementation
    (4) compaction and transportation

12. The best evidence that erosion has taken place would be provided by
    (1) deep soil formed in place on a hillside
    (2) sediment observed at the bottom of a cliff
    (3) folded rock layers observed on a mountain
    (4) faulted rock layers observed on a plateau

13. The primary force responsible for most of the transportation of rock material on the surface of Earth is

(1) gravity
(2) wind
(3) running water
(4) glaciers

14. The composition of sediments on Earth's surface usually is quite different from the composition of the underlying bedrock. This observation suggests that most

(1) bedrock is formed from sediments
(2) bedrock is reduced by weathering
(3) sediments are formed from local bedrock
(4) sediments are transported

15. Describe the relationship between mass movement and gravity.

16. Which agent probably contributes most to the general wearing down of Earth's surface?

(1) wind
(2) glaciers
(3) running water
(4) ocean waves and currents

17. The area drained by a river and its tributaries is called its

(1) watershed
(2) mouth
(3) source
(4) divide

18. The increase of dissolved materials in the ocean is primarily the result of the

(1) abrasion of the ocean floor
(2) transporting of material by rivers
(3) melting of continental glaciers
(4) deposition of materials by ground water

19. The velocity of a stream at a particular location is controlled mainly by the

(1) elevation of the stream at the location
(2) distance of the location from the source
(3) slope of the stream channel at the location
(4) amount of sediments carried at the location

20. A pebble is being transported in a stream by rolling. How does the velocity of the pebble compare to the velocity of the stream?

(1) The pebble is moving more slowly than the stream.
(2) The pebble is moving more quickly than the stream.
(3) The pebble is moving at the same velocity as the stream.

21. Which is the largest sediment type that could be carried by a steam flowing at a velocity of 75 centimeters per second?

22. Which statement best describes a stream with a steep gradient?

(1) It flows slowly, producing a V-shaped valley.
(2) It flows slowly, producing a U-shaped valley.
(3) It flows rapidly, producing a V-shaped valley.
(4) It flows rapidly, producing a U-shaped valley.

23. Which is the slowest stream velocity needed to maintain 1 cm particles moving downstream?

(1) 50 cm/sec
(2) 75 cm/sec
(3) 100 cm/sec
(4) 125 cm/sec

24. Much of the erosion by wind is caused by

(1) pushing sediments over cliffs
(2) abrasion by blowing sand
(3) deposition of silt and clay in dunes
(4) scraping and gouging deep depressions in Earth's surface.

25. Wind erosion is most active in regions that have

(1) a hot climate
(2) much loose sediment
(3) weak or non-resistant bedrock
(4) bedrock exposed to the atmosphere.

26. Which agent of erosion formed the long U-shaped valleys now occupied by the Finger Lakes in central New York State?

(1) running water
(2) ocean currents
(3) wind
(4) glacial ice

27. The mushroom rock illustrated in Figure 9-12A shows sign of sandblasting. Explain why the rock has been eroded more at the base than at the top.

28. Ocean waves do most of their erosion

(1) at the bottom of deep ocean water
(2) at and near the zone of breaking waves
(3) at the highest parts of beaches
(4) at the bottom of Sandbars where sand is most dense

29. What is the most important reason that sediments at beaches are usually rounded and smooth?

(1) The water dissolves the edges of the sediments.
(2) The high heat at beaches partly melts the sediments.
(3) The moving water causes sediments to abrade against each other.
(4) The coastal storms move rounded sediments toward the beach from deep ocean areas.

Directions

Review the Test-Taking Strategies section of this book. Then answer the following questions. Read each question carefully and answer with a correct choice or response.

Part A

1 In addition to its effects on living organisms, acid rain may cause changes in the landscape by
   (1) decreasing chemical weathering due to an increase in destruction of vegetation
   (2) decreasing physical weathering due to a decrease in frost action
   (3) increasing the breakdown of rock material due to an increase in chemical weathering
   (4) increasing physical weathering of rock material due to an increase in the circulation of ground water

2 Chemical weathering will occur most rapidly when rocks are exposed to the
   (1) hydrosphere and lithosphere
   (2) mesosphere and thermosphere
   (3) hydrosphere and atmosphere
   (4) lithosphere and atmosphere

3 Which factor has the most influence on the development of soil?
   (1) climate
   (2) longitude
   (3) amount of rounded sediment
   (4) age of the bedrock

4 The following diagram represents a geologic cross section.

Key
▦ Conglomerate
▤ Limestone
▦ Sandstone
▤ Shale

Which statement best explains why the conglomerate appears to be the most weathered bedrock?
   (1) The conglomerate particles are large.
   (2) The conglomerate is composed of quartz cobbles and pebbles.
   (3) The conglomerate underlies a steeper-sloped surface.
   (4) The conglomerate has been exposed to weathering the longest.

5 Which change would cause the topsoil in New York State to increase in thickness?
   (1) an increase in slope
   (2) an increase in biologic activity
   (3) a decrease in rainfall
   (4) a decrease in air temperature

6 The following diagram shows soil layers formed in an area of granite bedrock. Four different soil layers—A, B, C, and D—are shown.

Which soil layer contains the greatest amount of material formed by biological activity?
   (1) A   (2) B   (3) C   (4) D

7 Which is the best evidence that erosion has occurred?
   (1) a soil rich in lime on top of a limestone bedrock
   (2) a layer of basalt found on the floor of the ocean
   (3) sediments found in a sandbar of a river
   (4) a large number of fossils embedded in limestone

8 Which erosional force acts alone to produce avalanches and landslides?
   (1) gravity   (2) running water
   (3) winds   (4) sea waves

9 How are dissolved particles of sediment carried in a river?
   (1) by bouncing and rolling
   (2) by precipitation
   (3) in solution
   (4) in suspension

10 Which material would most easily be carried in suspension by a slow-moving stream?
(1) clay   (2) sand   (3) silt   (4) gravel

11 In summer, a small stream has a depth of 3 meters and a velocity of 0.5 meter per second. In spring, the same stream has a depth of 5 meters. The velocity of the stream in spring is more likely closest to
(1) 0.1 m/sec   (2) 0.5 m/sec
(3) 0.2 m/sec   (4) 0.8 m/sec

12 Two streams, A and B, carry the same volume of water, but stream A has a greater velocity. The most likely cause of this greater velocity would be that stream A
(1) has more tributaries
(2) has a wider streambed
(3) flows down a steeper slope
(4) travels over less resistant bedrock

13 Which graph best represents the relationship between the maximum particle size that can be carried by a stream and the velocity of the stream?

(1)   **(2)**   **(3)**   **(4)**

14 The following diagram is a map view of a stream flowing through an area of loose sediments. Arrows show the location of the strongest current.

Which stream profile represents the cross section from **A** to **A'**?

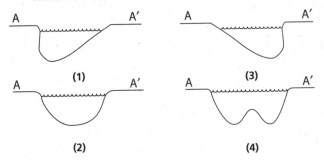

(1)   **(3)**

(2)   **(4)**

15 Which evidence best supports the inference that the movement of the ice sheet was generally from north to south over New York State during the Pleistocene glaciation?
(1) pieces of anorthositic rock from the Adirondacks found near Albany
(2) scratches aligned east to west on bedrock near Utica
(3) rocks of Devonian age found near Elmira
(4) the direction of flow of the Niagara River at Niagara Falls

16 In the following diagram of a straight-flowing stream, the lengths of the arrows represent differences in relative stream velocity on the stream's surface.

Which diagram best represents the relative stream velocity from the surface to the bottom of the stream for the cross section from **A** to **A'**?

17 In the following diagrams, which rock fragment shows the least evidence of erosion?

(1)   (2)   (3)   (4)

Part B

Base your answers to questions 18 through 21 on the following diagrams. Diagram A shows the paths of two streams over Earth's surface. Diagram B shows the longitudinal profile of the major stream.

Diagram A

Diagram B

18 The following diagram shows the cross section of the stream at **C-C'**. At which position in the stream channel would the velocity of the water be greatest?

19 What is the approximate average gradient of this stream between points **A** and **F**? [1]

20 The greatest volume of water would most likely be moving past which location? [1]

21 Which cross-section best represents the shape of the stream at **D-D'**?

Base your answers to questions 22 through 27 on the following data table. Samples of three different rock materials, A, B, and C, were placed in different containers of water and shaken vigorously for 20 minutes. At 5-minute intervals, the contents of each container were strained through a sieve screening. The mass of the material remaining in the sieve was measured and recorded as shown in the data table.

Data Table: Mass of Material Remaining in Sieve			
Shaking Time (minutes)	Rock Material A (grams)	Rock Material B (grams)	Rock Material C (grams)
0	25.0	25.0	25.0
5	24.5	20.0	17.5
10	24.0	18.5	12.5
15	23.5	17.0	7.5
20	23.5	12.5	5.0

Following the directions in questions 22 through 24, use the information in the data table to construct a line graph on a grid such as the one shown.

Mass of Rock Versus Shaking Time

- ◉ Rock Sample A
- ▲ Rock Sample B
- ▣ Rock Sample C

22 Plot the data for rock sample A for the 20 minutes of the investigation. Surround each point with a small circle and connect the points. [1]

Example:

23 Plot the data for rock sample B for the 20 minutes of the investigation. Surround each point with a small triangle and connect the points. [1]

Example:

24 Plot the data for rock sample C for the 20 minutes of the investigation. Surround each point with a small square and connect the points. [1]

Example:

25 State the most likely reason for the differences in the weathering rate of the three rock materials. [1]

26 Describe the most likely appearance of the corners and edges of rock material C at the end of the 20 minutes. [1]

27 Calculate the rate of change in the mass of rock material C at the end of the 20 minutes. [1]

Part C

Use data from the paragraph below about sediment and your knowledge of earth science to answer questions 28 through 36.

A cobble-sized sediment is naturally broken off the steep sides of a valley in a mountainous region. The sediment falls onto a glacier that occupies much of the valley. Over several years, the sediment "falls through" the glacier and is then dragged along the glacier's bottom. Next, the sediment is deposited in a pile of debris at the end of the glacier. A few years later, the sediment becomes part of a sand dune many miles from the glacier. The sediment is then transported to a stream from which, after a few months, it is deposited in a delta out in the ocean. Finally, the sediment becomes part of a child's sand castle on a beach tens of miles from the delta.

28 What natural cause broke the sediment off the side of the valley? [1]

29 What is the most likely shape of the sediment just after it fell onto the glacier? Explain the reason for your answer. [2]

30 Explain how the sediment can be considered a "tool" or aid to erosion while it is in the glacier and describe a landscape feature the sediment could help create. [2]

31 Tell how the sediment would most likely end up in a sand dune due to natural processes. [1]

32 Provide three reasons to explain why the stream would transport the sediment at varying speeds. [3]

33 Explain how the sediment could have naturally moved from the delta to the beach. [2]

34 What evidence in the paragraph suggests that a human was an agent of erosion for the sediment? [1]

35 Based on your reading of the paragraph, list five natural agents of erosion that could have been responsible for moving the sediment. [2]

36 Describe three likely changes in the appearance of sediment as it was transported from the valley wall to the beach, and indicate the cause or causes of the changes. [3]

Base your answers to questions 37 through 39 on the data table below and on your knowledge of Earth science. The data table shows the average monthly discharge, in cubic feet per second, for a stream in New York State.

Data Table												
Month	Jan	Feb	Mar	Apr	May	Jun	Jul	Aug	Sept	Oct	Nov	Dec
Discharge (ft³/sec)	48	52	59	66	62	70	72	59	55	42	47	53

37 On the following grid, plot with an **X** the average stream discharge for *each* month shown in the data table. Connect the **X**s with a line. [1]

38 State the relationship between this stream's discharge and the amount of suspended sediment that can be carried by this stream. [1]

39 Explain *one* possible reason why this stream's discharge in April is usually greater than this stream's discharge in January. [1]

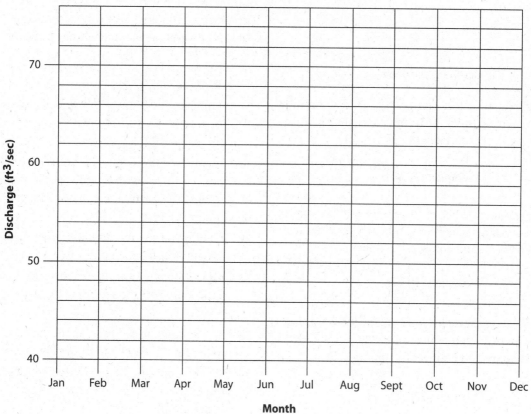

Average Monthly Stream Discharge

Deposition

How Scientists Study Deposition

? How can a "mountain" of sand be created? **?**

If you've ever been to the beach, you might have seen large piles of sand that resemble small mountains. These piles are called sand dunes, and they have a gentle slope on one side and a steeper slope on the opposite side.

You might think that water is the agent of erosion that forms sand dunes since you're at the beach. But water has little to do with it. Read the section in this topic called "Characteristic Features of the Chief Depositional Agents" to find out which agent of erosion is involved.

Vocabulary

barrier island	kettle lake	sand dune
deposition	moraine	sorted sediments
drumlin	outwash plain	unsorted sediments

Topic Overview

The process by which sediments are released, settled from, or dropped from an erosional system is **deposition,** or sedimentation. Deposition includes the releasing of solid sediments and the process of <u>precipitation</u>— the releasing of dissolved minerals, hardness, or salts from a water solution to form chemical sedimentary rocks.

The deposition of sediments has many effects on people. For example, you might play on a beach or marvel at the formations in caves (which are the product of precipitation of rocks). People mine sand and gravel from wave, glacier, and stream deposits. They also mine chemical sedimentary rocks, such as rock salt, rock gypsum, and dolostone. Most people spend a large part of their lives on sediment depositional features such as beaches, flood plains, deltas, marine coastal plains, and glacial deposits, or on the sedimentary rocks formed from deposition of sediments.

Deposition is part of a series of processes that start with the formation and movement of sediments by weathering and erosion. In deposition the sediments are placed in locations where they may form beds, or layers, of sedimentary rocks. Most final deposition occurs in large water bodies (such as lakes and oceans) because running water is the most important natural erosional system. Before sediments reach the large water bodies, many of them are temporarily deposited in different environments by running water, wind, glaciers, or other such means. Many of these depositional environments are shown in Figure 10-1.

Factors Causing Deposition

Deposition usually occurs when the velocity, or speed, of the stream, wind, or other erosional system decreases or just stops moving. Think of a piece of paper that has been picked up by a gust of wind. The piece of paper may blow all over, but when the wind slows down or stops blowing the paper will settle or be deposited. The time it takes for sediments to be deposited—the rate of deposition—varies. The faster the rate of deposition, the less time deposition takes; and the slower the rate of deposition, the more time deposition takes. Two types of factors—the velocity of the erosional system and characteristics of the sediments themselves—affect the rate of deposition.

Memory Jogger

Recall the types of solid sediments—such as sand, silt, and clay—from the Scheme for Sedimentary Rock Identification in the *Earth Science Reference Tables.*

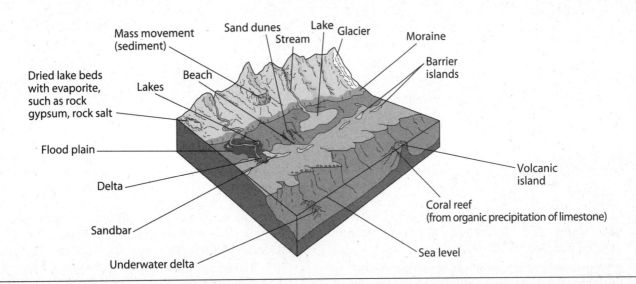

Figure 10-1. Types of depositional environments: The delta is formed from streams and the moraines from glaciers. Beaches, sandbars, and barrier islands are formed by ocean waves and longshore ocean currents. Sand dunes are formed by wind. Some sloped deposits are formed by mass movement (rock falls). Underwater deltas are formed by sediment-laden density currents.

Velocity of an Erosional System and Rate of Deposition

The faster a stream flows, the larger size sediments it can carry. Refer to the Relationship of Transported Particle Size to Water Velocity in the *Earth Science Reference Tables*. If the stream flows below a certain velocity, it will (R) deposit the sediments it can no longer carry. As an example, if a fast moving stream flowing at 350 cm/sec (7.8 miles per hour) slows down to 10 cm/sec (0.2 miles per hour) it will deposit all the pebbles, cobbles, and boulders it may be transporting. At 10 cm/sec the stream can continue to transport sand, silt, and clay-sized sediments of average density and shape. Similar relationships exist for other erosional systems.

Characteristics of Sediments and Rate of Deposition

Many aspects of the sediments themselves affect how fast they will be deposited in air or water environments. These factors include size, shape, and density, and saturation of dissolved minerals.

Size All other factors being equal, the larger sediments settle out first when wind or running water slows down. This occurs because the larger sediment particles are heavier and therefore sink faster. Very small particles, such as clay-sized particles (less than 0.0004 cm in diameter), may remain suspended in water almost indefinitely. Clay suspended in water is the "mud" of muddy or cloudy water.

Shape The shape of a particle helps determine how fast it will be deposited from wind or running water. All other factors being equal, the more rounded a sediment, the faster it will settle out. The more flattened it is, the greater its resistance—caused by friction—to deposition.

Density All other factors being the same, the higher the density of a sediment, the faster it will settle out of air or water. If two particles have the same size and shape, the denser one will be heavier.

Figure 10-2. Settling rates of sediments of various shapes: As sediments of equal volume and density become less rounded and more flattened, it takes more time for them to settle, so the settling rate decreases.

Saturation of Dissolved Minerals Evaporation, temperature changes, or increases in amount of dissolved minerals in a water body such as a lake, sea, or ocean may result in a saturated condition. When this happens, the dissolved mineral or minerals will settle or precipitate out of the dissolved condition and crystallize. As a result, rocks composed of one mineral, such as rock salt and dolostone, may form.

Review Questions

1. Which evidence best supports the idea that a vast inland sea once covered the Great Plains area of the United States?
   (1) considerable erosion has occurred there
   (2) extensive igneous intrusions are presently exposed there
   (3) extensive sedimentary rock layers have been formed there
   (4) numerous earthquakes occur there

2. When a river enters the ocean, sediment is deposited. Describe the change in kinetic energy of the river that leads up to this event.

3. A stream is carrying sediment particles ranging from 0.0004 to 25.6 centimeters. When the stream's velocity decreases from 300 to 100 centimeters per second, the stream will most probably deposit
   (1) silt and clay   (3) pebbles and sand
   (2) sand and silt   (4) cobbles and pebbles

4. The rate at which particles are deposited by a stream is least affected by the
   (1) size and shape of the particles
   (2) velocity of the stream
   (3) stream's elevation above sea level
   (4) density of the particles

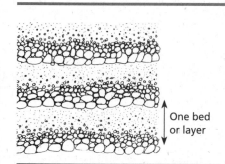

One bed or layer

Figure 10-3. Layers of sediment with graded bedding: In each bed or layer, sediment sizes decrease from bottom to top. Graded bedding results from rapid deposition in an erosional system, such as by a flooding stream. Each bed is the result of a single flood by a stream.

Sorting of Sediments and Deposition

During deposition, sediments of similar size, shape, or density get separated or sorted by types. At any one time the majority of sediments being moved are similar in density and shape, and thus sediment size is the most common type of sorting performed by most agents of deposition. If a deposit or layer of sediment has particles that are similar in size (or density, or shape), they are considered **sorted sediments.** The greater the similarity of size, the more sorted the sediments are said to be. If sediments are very mixed in size (or density, or shape), they are considered **unsorted sediments.**

When a mixture of sediment sizes in water settles out rapidly, a horizontal bed, or layer, develops with the sediment size decreasing from the bottom to the top. Such an arrangement in a sediment layer is called "graded bedding." (See Figure 10-3.) Graded bedding is most often associated with sediment-laden density currents. These currents are most common on the sloped ocean bottoms off the coasts of continents, and on lake bottoms where flooding streams rapidly decrease in velocity when they enter.

When the velocity of a wind or water erosional system gradually decreases, such as when a stream flows into the ocean at a delta, the larger, denser, and more rounded sediments settle out first. This results in layers with horizontal sorting, in which the sediment size, roundness, and density generally decrease in the direction toward which the erosional system was moving. (See Figure 10-4.) Horizontal sorting is a major reason why most sediment deposits are sorted.

Unsorted Glacial and Mass Movement Deposits

In a solid erosional system such as a glacier, sediments of all sizes, shapes, and densities are deposited together when the glacier melts. This deposition results in the unsorted and unlayered characteristic of direct glacial deposits that cover much of New York State. (See Figure 10-5.)

When there is mass movement, such as a rock fall, landslide, or avalanche, the sediments are usually dumped together in a random deposit that is unsorted and unlayered, similar to glacial deposits. Remember the jumbled masses of ice, rock, snow, and trees that you have observed in avalanches on television. You may have observed another example—a pile of sediments at the base of a cliff along a highway.

Figure 10-4. Horizontal sorting where a stream enters the ocean or lake forming a delta: The larger sediments settle first (nearer the shore). Sediments become smaller as distance from the shore increases. Precipitation nearer the shore may provide the cement for the formation of the types of sedimentary rocks indicated.

A Model of an Erosional-Depositional System

Figure 10-6 shows a side view and a top view of an imaginary stream used as a model of an erosional-depositional system. In this simple model it is assumed that the volume of discharge—water flow—is the same throughout the length of the stream.

Energy Transformations in the Model System

At the source, or beginning, of the stream the system has a maximum of potential energy. (See A in Figure 10-6.) As the stream flows toward its mouth, or end, potential energy is continuously being transformed into kinetic energy. (See D in Figure 10-6.) The kinetic energy is at the same time being lost to the environment in the form of heat produced by friction. Where the slope of the stream is steep, the transformation of energy occurs most rapidly, the stream has its greatest velocity, and the system has its greatest kinetic energy. Where the slope is small, the rate of energy transformation decreases, the stream slows down, and the kinetic energy of the system decreases. At the mouth of the stream, the velocity drops to zero, and the system has zero kinetic energy. Since the system has less potential energy because of its lower elevation, there has been a net loss of energy between the source and the mouth.

Erosion and Deposition in Relation to Energy Changes Wherever the kinetic energy of the system is large, erosion is the dominant process. Where the kinetic energy is small, deposition is the dominant process. Thus, erosion occurs in regions of steep slope or high discharge, and deposition occurs in regions of gentle slope or low discharge. Deposition is particularly rapid at the mouth of the stream, where the kinetic energy becomes zero. Stream velocity is faster at the outside of curves, or meanders, and slower at the inside. Therefore, erosion usually occurs at the outside of meanders, and deposition occurs at the inside.

Figure 10-5. Unsorted glacial deposits: In direct glacial deposition, there is no fluid medium in which sediments can become sorted. Thus, direct glacial deposits are characterized by a random distribution of sediment sizes (unsorted) and no bedding, or layering.

Side view

Top view

Figure 10-6. Model of a stream representing an erosional-depositional system: O indicates the outside of a curve or meander and I indicates the inside. Some deposition may occur at C, where the slope and velocity decrease. Erosional-depositional interfaces will then exist between B and C, between C and D, and between each pair of O's and I's.

If one or more tributaries were to enter a stream, this would increase the mass or discharge of water, thus increasing the potential energy of the stream. The velocity of the stream would increase, causing erosion to increase and deposition of solid sediments to decrease.

Erosional-Depositional Interfaces Since there are regions of erosion and regions of deposition along the length of the stream, an interface between an erosional and a depositional state can often be located in the system. Interfaces between erosion and deposition exist at the meanders in the model stream, and between the source and the mouth of the stream. They may also be found where changes in slope occur, as between points B and C in Figure 10-6.

Dynamic Equilibrium of an Erosional System Since all sediments picked up by the stream during erosion must eventually be deposited, the system is in a state of <u>dynamic equilibrium</u>. Although erosion and deposition are occurring continuously, the rate of erosion equals the rate of deposition by the system as a whole. If a flood occurs, a stream will erode—pick up and transport—more sediment, but it will also deposit an equally increased volume of sediment, thus establishing a new balance of equilibrium.

Review Questions

5. Small spheres that are identical in shape and size are composed of one of four different kinds of substances: A, B, C, or D. The spheres are mixed together and poured into a clear plastic tube filled with water. Which property of the spheres caused them to settle in the tube as shown in the diagram below?

   (1) their size   (3) their density
   (2) their shape   (4) their hardness

6. The following diagram represents a cross section of sedimentary deposits. Where would this type of deposition most likely occur?

   (1) at the base of the shifting sand dune
   (2) at the rapids in a stream
   (3) beneath a large glacier
   (4) in a lake fed by a stream that often floods

7. Much of the sediment that covers New York State was deposited by glaciers. Describe a depositional characteristic that these sediments should have in common.

Base your answers to questions 8 and 9 on the following diagram. The diagram shows points A, B, C, and D on a meandering stream.

8. Which material is most likely to be transported in suspension during periods of slower stream velocity?

(1) gravel (2) sand (3) silt (4) clay

9. At which point is the amount of deposition more than the amount of erosion?

(1) A (2) B (3) C (4) D

10. More deposition than erosion will take place in a streambed when the

(1) density of the rock particles carried by the stream decreases
(2) slope of the stream increases
(3) discharge of the stream increases
(4) velocity of the stream decreases

11. Which is the most probable description of the energy of a particle in an erosional-depositional system?

(1) Particles gain kinetic energy during erosion and lose kinetic energy during deposition.
(2) Particles lose kinetic energy during erosion and lose kinetic energy during deposition.
(3) Particles gain potential energy during erosion and gain potential energy during deposition.
(4) Particles lose potential energy during erosion and gain potential energy during deposition.

Base your answers to questions 12 through 14 on the diagram below. The diagram represents the landscape features associated with a meandering stream. An arrow shows the direction the stream is flowing.

12. At which location is stream erosion greatest?

(1) W
(2) X
(3) Y
(4) Z

13. The lake most likely formed when a

(1) stream changed its path
(2) crater flooded
(3) cavern roof collapsed
(4) fault block subsided

14. The greatest width of the flood plain is located at

(1) A to B
(2) E to F
(3) X to Y
(4) C to D

Characteristic Features of the Chief Depositional Agents

Deposition occurs mainly by streams, glaciers, water waves and currents, wind, and mass movements. Each of these depositional agents has its own characteristic features.

Deposition by Streams

Streams make their deposits in different locations. In the stream course itself sediments are deposited on the inside of the meanders where stream

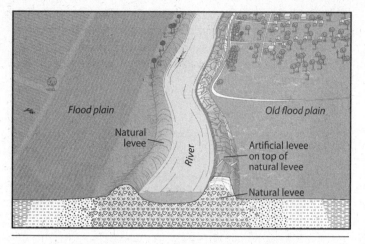

Figure 10-7A. A levee is a mound of sediment at the boundaries of a river created by deposition during flooding. Artificial levees are built to heighten their level to protect human property from flooding.

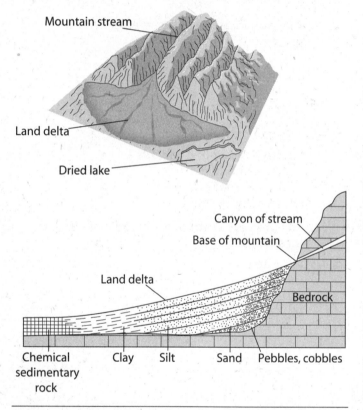

Figure 10-7B. A land delta: In arid to semi-arid climates, streams flow off mountains—usually from flash floods—onto more level land and deposit most, if not all, of their sediment load. This fan-shaped deposition forms a land delta. Note the horizontal sorting of the sediment which is very similar to a regular delta, such as that in Figure 10-4.

velocity is slow. When a stream floods and overflows its banks, some of the sediment forms a mound at the edge of the river called a levee, but most of the sediment is spread over a relatively flat region to the sides of a stream forming a <u>flood plain</u>. Often the high velocity of a flooding stream will cut a straighter path through a meander. Depositions at the side of a stream will then separate the former meander from the main stream—forming a curved lake. The sediment that makes it to a lake or ocean will be deposited. This deposition at the end of a stream, with characteristic horizontal sorting as shown in Figure 10-4, is a <u>delta</u>. If there are strong ocean or lake currents, a delta may not form because the velocity of the water is not reduced enough at this location. Figure 10-7B shows the formation of a delta in arid regions.

Deposition by Glaciers

At the end of a glacier where there is a balance between melting and forward movement, the sediments it carries are just dropped in unsorted sheets or piles called a **moraine**. Figure 10-8 illustrates this unsorted, unlayered nature of direct glacial deposits. If the moraine is a thin sheet deposited from the bottom of the glacier, it is called a ground moraine. Ground moraines cover much of the northern United States including much of New York State. If the end or terminus of a glacier stays in one location for some time, the glacier builds up a pile of sediments called a terminal moraine. Parts of central Long Island, New York are the terminal moraine of the last stage of the last ice age. Moraines can also be formed at the sides of a glacier. If a glacier mounds up the ground moraine into a streamlined oval shape that feature is a **drumlin**. The drumlins indicate the direction a glacier came from by being oriented with direction of former glacial movement. Drumlins have steeper slopes pointing to the direction the glaciers came from. (See Figure 10-8.) Sometimes as a glacier melts back, it leaves blocks of ice in the terminal or ground moraine. When these blocks of ice melt, they leave behind circular depressions called kettle holes or kettles. If these kettles intersect the water tables, they will become filled with water and are then called **kettle lakes**.

Wherever glaciers melt, running water will carry sediments from the glaciers to produce layered and sorted sediment deposits when the water slows down or stops. One such feature is an **outwash plain**—a broad delta-like feature.

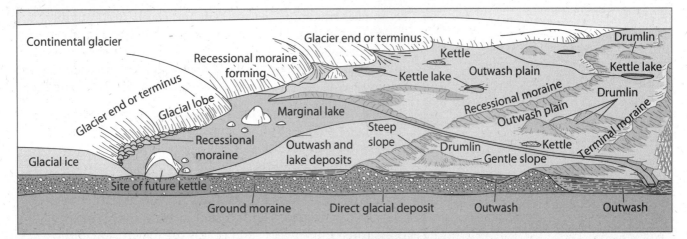

Figure 10-8. Depositional features associated with glaciers: When glaciers melt, some of the sediments are directly deposited into a single layer or small hills.

Much of southern Long Island, New York, is an outwash plain formed by running water when the last sheets of the ice age left this region.

Deposition on Coastlines by Water Waves and Currents

When wind-generated ocean or lake waves slow down as they drag bottom approaching the shore, they tend to move sediment towards shore. This wave movement towards the shore often builds up a strip of sediment at the coastline called a <u>beach</u>. Beaches are composed of whatever sediments are available, but most beaches are composed of sand. When a shoreline has a natural or human-made projection out into the ocean—such as a peninsula or pier—sand is deposited on the side of the projection facing an oncoming longshore current. This deposition occurs because

Figure 10-9. Beaches and barrier islands: Two features formed by deposition of sediments by waves and longshore currents are the beach and barrier islands. Barrier islands often protect the shore from direct pounding by storm waves.

the water slows down when it reaches the projection, and the sand settles out. The side of the projection facing away from the longshore current usually gets eroded because it is not protected by the sand deposits. When the waves are more powerful, such as during storms, the beach tends to erode more and the sand is carried back into the ocean. There it is usually deposited as underwater bars parallel to the shoreline. Sand is added to these features by the longshore currents. These longshore currents transport sediment—sand—and when the velocity of the water slows, deposition creates various types of depositional features such as <u>sandbars</u>. If this sandbar rises above average sea level, winds will help to pile up the sediments. Then vegetation can stabilize this offshore sediment pile, creating a **barrier island**. Barrier islands are common along the east and southeast coast of the United States. (See Figure 10-9.)

(A5)

Deposition by Wind

When wind slows down or stops, the sediments it is carrying are dropped. Because air has such a low density compared to liquid water, it usually transports and deposits only sand and smaller sized sediments. The

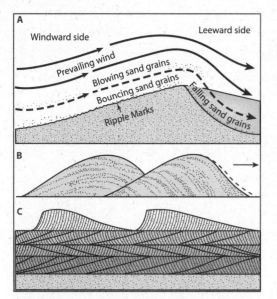

Figure 10-10. Features and movement of sand dunes: When there is loose sand, wind will bounce it along the surface and carry some a few feet into the air. When the wind slows down, it may deposit the sand in a mound called a sand dune. **(A)** Shows that sand dunes have a gentle slope facing into the wind—windward side—and have a steep slope on the opposite side—leeward side. Note the ripple marks on top of the sand dune. **(B)** Shows that dunes migrate up to a few feet a day. **(C)** If the winds change direction, beds of sand will cross one another at various angles producing a feature called crossbedding. Most sand in dunes is well sorted in sloping layers, and the sand grains are well rounded and have a frosted appearance.

sediments smaller than sand (silt and clay) are commonly called dust. Much of the dust picked up by wind or given to the air in volcanic eruptions—as volcanic ash—is deposited over large expanses of the land and water environments, adding to the general sediment layer of Earth's solid surface.

Sand is deposited in mounds called **sand dunes.** Sand dunes have many shapes, but all have a gentle slope facing into the wind and a steeper slope on the opposite side as shown in Figure 10-10. Sand dunes migrate as a body downwind—in the direction the wind is blowing to—creating layers of sloping sorted sediment. The sand within sand dunes is usually very rounded and frosted in appearance due to numerous collisions of sand grains during erosion and weathering.

Deposition by Mass Movement

When an avalanche or other type of mass movement hits the ground and stops moving, the sediments it was transporting are deposited as a landform feature of Earth's surface. These features are usually composed of unsorted and unlayered sediments. Depending on the history of the sediments, many will not be very rounded in shape but will often have sharp sides. This is especially true if the sediments have been recently produced by frost action. The most recognizable depositional feature of mass movement is a pile of sediments that is the result of falling sediments often found at the base of cliffs.

Review Questions

15. Deltas form where

(1) a ground moraine is deposited
(2) stream velocity is reduced
(3) small streams empty into larger streams
(4) extensive ground water action has occurred

Base your answers to questions 16 through 19 on the following diagram. The diagram represents a glacier moving out of a mountain valley. Water from the melting glacier is flowing into a lake. Letters A through F identify points within the erosional-depositional system.

16. Deposits of unsorted sediments would probably be found at location

(1) E
(2) F
(3) C
(4) D

17. An interface between erosion and deposition by the ice is most likely located between points

(1) A and B
(2) B and C
(3) C and D
(4) D and F

18. The clay-sized sediment particles carried by water are most probably being deposited at point

(1) F
(2) B
(3) C
(4) D

19. Which graph best represents the speed of a sediment particle as it moves from point D to point F?

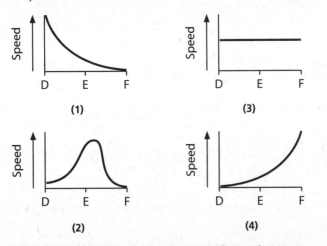

(1)

(2)

(3)

(4)

Base your answers to questions 20 through 25 on the following diagrams. Diagram I shows melting ice lobes of a continental glacier during the Pleistocene Epoch. Diagram II represents the landscape features of the same region at present, after the retreat of the continental ice sheet. Letters A through G indicate surface features in this region.

Diagram I

Diagram II

20. Which features in Diagram II are composed of sediment directly deposited by the glacial ice?

(1) A and C
(2) B and D
(3) C and E
(4) E and F

21. Kettle lakes are located nearest to

(1) A
(2) B
(3) F
(4) G

22. Drumlins that formed under a lobe of ice are located at

(1) A
(2) B
(3) C
(4) D

23. An outwash plain of sorted layered sediment is located at

(1) A
(2) B
(3) C
(4) D

24. A moraine deposit formed at a former interface of a glacier and no glacier is located at location

(1) A
(2) C
(3) F
(4) G

25. Which arrow best represents the directions of movement that formed the deposits shown in Diagram II?

Directions

Review the Test-Taking Strategies section of this book. Then answer the following questions. Read each question carefully and answer with a correct choice or response.

Part A

To answer questions 1 through 9 refer to the following diagram, which shows the top and side views of a stream. Consider the volume of water in the stream to be everywhere the same.

1 At which place in the stream would there be the clearest interface between erosion and deposition?
   (1) 1   (2) 2-3   (3) 3-4   (4) 7

2 What happens to the total amount of energy of this stream as it flows from 1 to 10?
   (1) It steadily increases.
   (2) It steadily decreases.
   (3) It increases and decreases.
   (4) It remains the same.

3 Between what two points would the most potential energy be converted to kinetic energy?
   (1) 1-2   (2) 2-5   (3) 5-8   (4) 8-10

4 At which location would the most deposition occur because of loss of energy?
   (1) 4   (2) 6   (3) 9   (4) 10

5 At which location would the stream be doing the most eroding of its side and banks?
   (1) 1   (2) 3   (3) 5   (4) 8

6 If the stream is eroding as much as it is depositing between 8 and 10, the stream at this location can be said to
   (1) be an interface
   (2) have dynamic equilibrium
   (3) be sorted
   (4) have equal amounts of kinetic and potential energy

7 Which characteristic would usually decrease the most between locations 10 and 11?
   (1) the amount of salt solution
   (2) the size of the sediments
   (3) the density of the water
   (4) the depth of the water

8 As the water of the stream flows from 1 to 10, the total potential energy of the stream will
   (1) increase
   (2) decrease
   (3) remain the same

9 An observer looks downstream from a location just above location 8-9 and draws a cross section of the streambed at location 8-9. Which diagram would probably best represent this cross section?

10 The following graph shows the relationship between particle shape and settling rate.

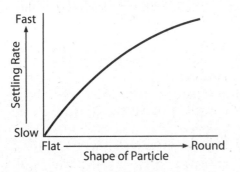

Which statement best describes the relationship shown?
(1) flatter particles settle more slowly than rounder particles
(2) flatter particles settle at the same speed
(3) all particles settle at the same speed
(4) particle shape does not affect settling rate

11 A mixture of sand, pebbles, clay, and silt, of uniform shape and density, is dropped from a boat into a calm lake. Which material most likely would reach the bottom of the lake first?
(1) sand   (3) clay
(2) pebbles   (4) silt

Part B

Match each of the deposition or erosional features in Column 1 with the phrase in Column 2 that best applies to that feature. Briefly describe HOW each feature forms and WHERE it forms. A CHOICE MAY BE USED MORE THAN ONCE AND SOME CHOICES MAY NOT BE USED.

Column 1	Column 2
12 outwash plain [3]	(a) deposited by glaciers
13 sand dune [3]	(b) deposited mostly by water from melting glaciers
14 offshore bar [3]	
15 moraine [3]	(c) formed by glacial erosion
	(d) not related to glaciation

Match each feature in Column 1 with the erosional-depositional agent in Column 2 that is chiefly responsible for producing that feature. Briefly describe how each land feature is produced. A CHOICE MAY BE USED MORE THAN ONCE AND SOME CHOICES MAY NOT BE USED.

Column 1	Column 2
16 drumlin [2]	(a) glaciers
17 barrier island [2]	(b) gravity
18 sand dune [2]	(c) streams
19 flood plain [2]	(d) waves and shore currents
	(e) wind

Base your answers to questions 20 through 25 on the diagram below, which shows ocean waves approaching a shoreline. A short wall of rocks perpendicular to the shoreline and an offshore structure have been recently constructed along the beach. Letters A, B, C, D, and E represent locations in the area.

20 What is the most common cause of the approaching waves?
(1) underwater earthquakes
(2) variations in ocean-water density
(3) the gravitational effect of the moon
(4) winds at the ocean surface

21 At which location will the beach first begin to widen due to sand deposition?
(1) A   (2) B   (3) C   (4) E

22 The size of the bulge in the beach at position D will
   (1) decrease
   (2) increase
   (3) remain the same

23 How was this beach directly formed?
   (1) uplifting from an earthquake
   (2) sinking of land during a landslide
   (3) deposition of sediments by ocean waves and currents
   (4) erosion of bedrock by ocean waves and currents

24 If sand dunes were located on the beach, they would have been formed by
   (1) deposition by strong winter ocean waves
   (2) erosion by mild summer ocean waves
   (3) deposition by wind
   (4) erosion by surf and ocean shore currents

25 Which statement best describes the ocean current that is modifying this coastline?
   (1) the current is flowing northward at a right angle to the shoreline
   (2) the current is flowing southward at a right angle away from the shoreline
   (3) the current is flowing eastward parallel to the shoreline
   (4) the current is flowing westward parallel to the shoreline

Base your answers to questions 26 through 28 on the map below, which shows the drainage basin of the Mississippi River system. Several rivers that flow into the Mississippi River are labeled. The arrow at location X shows where the Mississippi River enters the Gulf of Mexico.

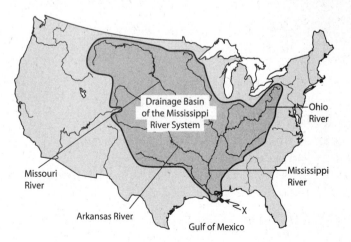

26 The entire land area drained by the Mississippi River system is referred to as a
   (1) levee   (3) meander belt
   (2) watershed   (4) floodplain

27 Sediments deposited at location X by the Mississippi River most likely have which characteristics?
   (1) angular fragments arranged as mixtures
   (2) rock particles arranged in sorted beds
   (3) rocks with parallel scratches and grooves
   (4) high-density minerals with hexagonal crystals

28 The structure formed by the deposition of sediments at location X is best described as a
   (1) moraine
   (2) tributary
   (3) delta
   (4) drumlin

Base your answers to questions 29 and 30 on the diagram below, which shows a clear plastic tube containing water and a beaker containing a mixture of rounded quartz grains of different sizes.

(Not drawn to scale)

29 When the rounded quartz grains are poured all at once into the tube, the grains will settle to the bottom of the tube. On the cross section provided below, draw the approximate grain sizes and pattern of arrangement of the rounded quartz grains at the bottom of the tube. [1]

Cross Section of the Bottom of the Tube

Key
Approximate size
○ 2-mm diameter
○ 3-mm diameter
○ 4-mm diameter

30 The side-view diagram below shows the same mixture and amount of rounded quartz grains being poured all at once into a moving stream with a depth of 3 meters.

Side View of Stream

Describe the general location of the 2-mm-diameter rounded quartz grains compared to the 4-mm-diameter rounded quartz grains as they are transported and deposited downstream. [1]

Base your answers to questions 31 and 32 on the cross section below, which represents part of the Atlantic Ocean seafloor. An earthquake occurred on November 18, 1929, triggering an underwater sediment flow. The location of the epicenter is labeled. Letters A through D indicate locations on the seafloor. Time, in hours, at each lettered location represents the arrival of the sediment flow after the earthquake.

31 Calculate the gradient of the ocean floor between locations *A* and *D* and label your answer with the correct units. [2]

32 Explain why the velocity of the sediment flow created by the earthquake *decreased* as the sediment moved from location *B* to location *C*. [1]

33 The cross section below illustrates the normal pattern of sediments deposited where a stream enters a lake. Letter *X* represents a particular type of sediment.

(Not drawn to scale)

(a) Briefly explain why deposition of sediment usually occurs where a stream enters a lake. [1]

(b) Name the type of sediment most likely represented by letter *X*. [1]

Base your answers to questions 34 through 36 on the map of Long Island, New York. *AB*, *CD*, *EF*, and *GH* are reference lines on the map.

Map

34 Which agent of erosion transported the sediments that formed the moraines shown on the map?
(1) water   (3) ice
(2) wind   (4) mass movement

35 The cross section below represents the sediments beneath the land surface along one of the reference lines shown on the map.

Along which reference line was the cross section taken?
(1) *AB*   (2) *CD*   (3) *EF*   (4) *GH*

36 A major difference between sediments in the outwash and sediments in the moraines is that the sediments deposited in the outwash are
(1) larger   (3) more angular
(2) sorted   (4) older

Part C

37 A person finds gold nuggets near a meander, or curve, of a stream in California. Explain where in the meander area the gold nuggets were most likely found. Why is gold (density 19.3 g/cm^3) deposited at this location and not minerals such as halite (density 2.2 g/cm^3) and gypsum (density 2.3 g/cm^3)? [2]

38 You are investigating a dry stream bed at the point it once entered a lake. As you walk out into the lake bed from the mouth of the stream, you notice that the sediments below your feet become smaller. You also notice that as you dig vertically in the same location, the uncovered sediments gradually increase in size. Using your knowledge of erosion and deposition, state a hypothesis to explain both observations. [2]

39 Your friend offers the following description of sediment she observed in a V-shaped canyon on a camping trip in Arizona. "The pebbles were all piled together evenly and they were very uniform in size. They were rounded, and smooth, with almost no markings of any kind. I think that they must have been deposited long ago by a glacier." Do you agree with her inference? Cite four clear pieces of evidence to either support or refute her conclusion. [5]

Base your answers to questions 40 through 45 on the notes below written by a student during field trips to three different locations in New York State.

NOTES
Location A

Good view from this hilltop; chilly and windy. We rested to catch our breath, then collected samples. Rocks are visible everywhere. There are boulders, cobbles, and pebbles of many sizes and shapes mixed together. These surface rock fragments are composed of metamorphic rock sitting on the limestone bedrock. The teacher showed us parallel scratches in the bedrock. I saw almost no soil.

Location B

It is rocky and the stream bank is steep. Where we are standing, we can see a waterfall and rapids. It is cool by the water. From the streambed we collected pebbles and cobbles—some red, some white, others a mixture of many colors. The streambed is full of rocks of all sizes. The teacher warned us to be careful of the strong stream current.

Location C

It is cool in the shade, and the rock cliff above us still has some ice on it from winter. The rocks we are sitting on have sharp edges. Rock fragments at the bottom of the cliff are the same color as the cliff. Our teacher warned us to watch out for falling rocks.

40 *a* State the agent of erosion that deposited most of the sediment found at location *A*. [1]

41 *b* State *one* observation recorded by the student that supports this conclusion. [1]

42 Some samples of sediment collected from the streambed at location *B* are shown below.

Explain why these samples are smooth and have rounded shapes. [1]

43 Explain how ice in cracks on the cliff at location *C* may have helped cause weathering of the bedrock on the face of the cliff. [1]

44 What agent of erosion resulted in the deposition of the rocks with the sharp edges at location *C*?

45 What is one feature of wind deposited sediments that would differ from rocks (sediments) deposited at locations A and B?

Base your answers to questions 46 and 47 on the illustration below, which shows a mountainous region cut by a large valley in its center.

46 What characteristic of this large valley supports the inference that glacial ice formed the valley? [1]

47 Describe additional geologic evidence that might be found on the valley floor that would support the idea that glacial ice formed this valley. [1]

Earth Materials— Minerals, Rocks, and Mineral Resources

How Scientists Study Minerals

? *Do you think every mineral has a unique chemical composition?* **?**

It is the crystal structure that is unique to each mineral and not the chemical composition. Just consider the minerals graphite and diamond, which are both composed of only carbon. It is hard to believe that two minerals with the same chemical composition could be so different: Graphite is one of the softest minerals and diamond is the hardest of the somewhat common minerals. Diamond has a brilliant luster and graphite is greasy to metallic. Graphite is used as a lubricant, while diamond is used as an abrasive. And graphite is an electrical conductor, while diamond is an insulator.

Graphite and diamond are not the only example. Calcite and aragonite are two minerals that are composed of calcium carbonate ($CaCO_3$). There are at least five minerals with the formula SiO_2, with quartz being the most common.

Earth Materials—Minerals, Rocks, and Mineral Resources

Vocabulary

bioclastic sedimentary rocks	fracture	mineral crystal
chemical sedimentary rocks	hardness	mineral resources
clastic sedimentary rock	igneous rock	organic
cleavage	inorganic	precipitation (of minerals)
contact metamorphism	intrusive igneous rock	regional metamorphism
crystal shape	luster	rock cycle
crystal structure	magma	sedimentary rocks
extrusive igneous rock	metamorphic rocks	streak
foliation	metamorphism	texture
fossil	mineral	

Topic Overview

Rocks and minerals are the source of much of the material and energy that people want or need. If you make a list of about one hundred objects you used or wanted to use today, most likely 95 to 100 percent of them come from rocks and minerals. Earth materials—minerals, rocks, and mineral resources—are of value to people in many ways. Earth materials fuel our industrial society as extracted fossil fuels. They provide the raw materials for the building of homes and other construction projects. Rocks and minerals make up Earth's solid surface—the lithosphere— that you live on. When Earth's solid surface is weathered and eroded, the end results are the landscape features that people live, work, and play on.

A X-ray diffraction pattern

X-ray tube
Photographic film
Diffracted rays
Halite Crystal
Crystal carrier
Lead shields
Unique Pattern

B Atomic model of crystal structure

Chlorine atoms   Sodium atoms

C Crystal shape

D Cubic cleavage

Figure 11-1. Crystal structure and properties of the mineral halite: Halite is the mineral with the formula NaCl (sodium chloride). It is the one mineral of rock salt and common table salt.

Minerals

Minerals have characteristic physical and chemical properties. Some of these properties are color, streak, luster, hardness, density, cleavage and crystal structure.

What a Mineral Is

A **mineral** is a naturally occurring, inorganic, crystalline solid having a definite chemical composition. A mineral is considered to be naturally occurring because it is formed in nature and not made by people. It is **inorganic** because it has not been made by or composed of life forms. Thus fossil fuels or a pearl from an oyster are NOT minerals.

A mineral is crystalline because its atoms have a specific arrangement. This arrangement of atoms is called **crystal structure**. Each mineral has its own distinctive crystal structure that can lead to very accurate identifications through the use of X-rays. Figure 11-1 illustrates the crystal structure of a mineral.

All minerals are solids that are composed of one or more chemical elements. The chemical composition of a mineral describes the types and ratios of elements that make up the mineral. Some minerals contain only one element and others are compounds of two or more elements. You can find the characteristics of some minerals ® in the Properties of Common Minerals in the *Earth Science Reference Tables*.

Relation of Minerals to Rocks

All minerals are rocks, but not all rocks are minerals nor are they all composed of minerals. A rock is any naturally formed solid that is part of Earth or any other celestial body. Though a large percentage of rocks is composed of minerals, many rocks are composed of organic or glassy materials that are not minerals. Glasses are not minerals because their atoms are not arranged in a specific pattern. The majority of rocks are made of two or more minerals—multiple-mineral rocks. Some rocks are composed of only one mineral—single-mineral rocks.

A review of the three schemes for rock identification—sedimentary, ® metamorphic, and igneous—in the *Earth Science Reference Tables* and Figure 11-2 indicates that only a small number of minerals are commonly found in rocks. These 20 to 30 very common minerals, found in rocks, are called the rock-forming minerals. Many of these rock-forming minerals are listed in ® the Properties of Common Minerals in the *Earth Science Reference Tables*.

Element Composition of Earth's Crust

The chemical element composition of Earth's crust is shown in Figure 11-3.

- The graph indicates that over 99 percent of Earth's crust and its minerals are, by volume and mass, composed of only 8 of the 90 naturally occurring elements found on Earth.
- Silicon is the second most abundant element by mass, but the element potassium is number two in crustal abundance by volume because of its lower density and higher volume.

Mineral Crystal Structure

The crystal structure, or atomic arrangement of the atoms, that comprise minerals is responsible for many of their chemical and physical properties, such as crystal form, breaking pattern, and hardness. Most rock-forming minerals are silicates. Silicate minerals have a structure that results from various arrangements of a tetrahedron-shaped (4-sided) unit of oxygen and silicon called the silicon-oxygen tetrahedron. Figure 11-4 shows how each tetrahedron is composed of one atom of silicon and four atoms of oxygen. It also shows different ways the silicon-oxygen tetrahedron can be arranged resulting in different breaking patterns (cleavage and fracture).

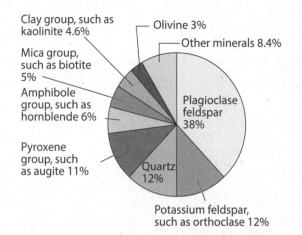

Figure 11-2. Circle graph of the most common minerals of Earth's crust: 90 percent of Earth's crust by weight is composed of eight minerals or groups of minerals—all silicates. These common minerals are called rock-forming minerals.

Relative amounts by mass

Relative amounts by volume

Figure 11-3. Percentages of the chief elements in Earth's crust by mass and by volume: Volume is the amount of space occupied by the atoms of each element in the solid substances of the crust. Also see Average Chemical Composition of Earth's Crust, Hydrosphere, and Troposphere in the *Earth Science Reference Tables*.

Silicate structure	Key: ✦ Silicon, ● Shared oxygen, ○ Unshared oxygen			
Silicate structure	Single tetrahedron	Chains of tetrahedra	Sheets of tetrahedra	A network of tetrahedra in three dimensions
Mineral example	Olivine— peridot is gem variety	Pyroxene, such as augite	Mica, such as biotite	Quartz
Cleavage or fracture type	Curved or conchoidal fracture	Two directions of cleavage into blocky or splinter shapes and fracture	One direction of cleavage into sheets and fracture	Curved or conchoidal fracture
Drawing		Cleavage / Fracture	Cleavage / Fracture	

Figure 11-4. Various arrangements of the silicon-oxygen tetrahedron in silicate minerals: The tetrahedra combine with themselves and other elements in different atomic structures. The different combinations affect the physical properties of the minerals—including cleavage and fracture patterns shown in the illustration.

Mineral Formation

Since all minerals are rocks, they form by one of two processes. Minerals form as the result of inorganic crystallization—a process of organizing atoms to form crystalline solids. Minerals also form by recrystallization of atoms from the solids, liquids, and gases associated with various rock- forming environments.

Mineral Properties and Identification

Each mineral has a characteristic set of physical and chemical properties that can be used to help identify it. The crystal structure and the chemical composition of minerals largely determine these properties. Some properties, such as color, are often caused by impurities. The mineral corundum, when pure, is colorless. However, with slight chemical impurities, corundum becomes the blue sapphire or red ruby.

The most accurate method for identifying minerals is by the use of X-ray diffraction instruments (see Figure 11-1) and other machines not available to most individuals. Therefore, simple tests and mineral identification charts are relied on. An example of a mineral identification key, or chart, ® is found in Properties of Common Minerals in the *Earth Science Reference Tables*.

Color The color of a mineral is one of its most obvious properties. However, in most cases color is not useful because many minerals have the same color. In addition, the color of many minerals varies due to impurities, and many minerals are clear or colorless when pure. In a few cases however, such as in the yellow of sulfur, the gray of graphite (pencil lead) and galena, or the brassy yellow of pyrite (fool's gold), the mineral's color is usually consistent.

Streak The color of finely crushed residue or powder of a mineral is its **streak**. When you write on a chalkboard, you observe the streak of the rock chalk. The streak of a mineral is usually quite consistent; thus streak color is much more useful than mineral color. For example, the iron ore mineral, hematite, can be various shades of silver-gray to red in color, but the streak is a consistent red.

Luster The shine from an unweathered mineral's surface, or the way a mineral looks in reflected light, is **luster**. There are two broad groups of luster—metallic and nonmetallic. Minerals with a metallic luster, such as pyrite and galena, shine like the surface of a clean stainless steel pot. Most minerals have a nonmetallic luster. There are many types of nonmetallic luster, such as the glassy luster of black hornblende and clear quartz "rhinestone," or the pearly luster of muscovite mica.

Hardness The resistance a mineral offers to being scratched is its **hardness**—the scratchability of a mineral, not how easily the mineral breaks. Diamond is the hardest mineral (see Digging Deeper on page 220), but drop an unmounted diamond on a tile floor and it will likely shatter. On the other hand, if the very soft mineral graphite is dropped, only a small amount will chip off, or cleave.

Figure 11-5 shows the Mohs hardness scale and some other common materials that are often used to determine hardness. Mohs hardness scale is arranged from the softest #1 (talc) to the hardest #10 (diamond). A quick way to determine relative hardness is to use a piece of window glass. If a mineral scratches the glass, the mineral is hard, and if it doesn't, it is soft.

Figure 11-5. Mohs and absolute hardness scale: The differences in the hardnesses on the Mohs scale vary, as shown by the comparison to an absolute scale of hardness. Note that on the absolute scale, the difference of hardness between diamond and corundum—ruby or sapphire—is more than all the way from talc to corundum.

Density Each mineral has a specific <u>density</u> or a small range of densities—for those minerals that vary in mineral composition. Often in mineral studies, density is stated as specific gravity, a value without units. Specific gravity is the density of a mineral compared to the density of water. Specific gravity is a good test to distinguish gemstones, because it doesn't harm the samples like hardness or cleavage tests do. In mining and refining processes, differences in the densities of various minerals allow them to be separated. A common example is the panning of high-density gold.

Cleavage The tendency of a mineral to break along the zones of weakness and form smooth to semi-smooth parallel sides, or surfaces, is called **cleavage**. Cleavage surfaces can often be distinguished from sides without cleavage by having a shinier or more brilliant luster (smooth surfaces reflect better). If a mineral lacks preferred zones of weakness in the crystal structure, then it will demonstrate uneven breaking surfaces called **fracture.** For example, some types of fracture are irregular (earthy), fibrous (splintery), and curved (conchoidal). The curved surfaces in a type of quartz called flint make this

Recall that <u>density</u> is the ratio of the mass of an object to its volume. Therefore, an element that has a lower density than another element has a smaller mass per volume than an element with higher density.

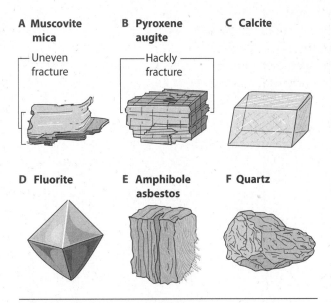

A Muscovite mica
— Uneven fracture

B Pyroxene augite
— Hackly fracture

C Calcite

D Fluorite

E Amphibole asbestos

F Quartz

Figure 11-6. Types of cleavage and fracture: (A) shows one direction of cleavage and some uneven fracture. (B) shows two directions of cleavage and a hackly (bumpy) fracture. (C) shows three directions of cleavage. (D) shows four directions of cleavage. (E) shows fibrous fracture. (F) shows curved fracture.

Digging Deeper

A few minerals have very fine lines—called striations—on cleavage surfaces and on the faces of their crystal form. These striations can be used to distinguish the mineral plagioclase feldspar from the potassium feldspars such as orthoclase. Striations are an outward expression of the internal arrangement of the atoms within a mineral.

material very useful in making knives and arrowheads. Often a mineral will have both cleavage and fracture on different sides, such as the silicates hornblende and the feldspars. (See Figures 11-4 and 11-6)

Crystal Structure The outward geometric shape of a mineral, the crystal form, or **crystal shape,** reflects the crystal structure—orderly arrangement of the atoms in the mineral. It is only when individual mineral grains have the room to freely grow that this crystal shape, with its smooth sides or faces, can take shape. This is the reason most mineral samples found in nature don't illustrate the crystal forms; the use of crystal form in mineral identification is limited. Another problem is that even though the internal crystal structure of minerals is unique, the outward crystal shape, such as the cubic shape of halite, galena, and fluorite, isn't unique. Also, any mineral can have many different crystal shapes.

Other Mineral Properties Besides physical properties, some chemical properties of minerals are also used for identification. One of these chemical properties is the reaction of a mineral with acid. When a small amount of dilute hydrochloric acid is placed on a mineral or rock containing calcite ($CaCO_3$), the mineral or rock will bubble (effervesce)—giving off carbon dioxide. The mineral dolomite can be distinguished from calcite, because dolomite will bubble in acid only after the mineral is powdered.

Many other chemical and physical properties are used to identify minerals. Many of the properties only apply to a few minerals and will often be the key to a mineral's identification. For example, some minerals such as thin pieces of muscovite and biotite micas are flexible. This means that they can be bent and will snap back to their original shape. Other properties used for identification are found in Properties of Common Minerals in the *Earth Science Reference Tables*. ®

Review Questions

1. A mineral CANNOT be

(1) organic
(2) crystalline
(3) a solid
(4) formed in nature

2. Which rock is usually composed of several different minerals?

(1) rock gypsum
(2) limestone
(3) quartzite
(4) gneiss

3. Only a small number of Earth's minerals are commonly found in rocks. This fact indicates that most

(1) minerals weather before they can be identified
(2) minerals have properties that are difficult to identify
(3) rocks have a number of minerals in common
(4) exposed surface rocks are mostly igneous

4. The data table shows the composition of six common rock-forming minerals.

Mineral	Composition
Muscovite Mica	$KAl_3Si_3O_{10}$
Olivine	$(FeMg)_2SiO_4$
Orthoclase	$KAlSi_3O_8$
Plagioclase	$NaAlSi_3O_8$
Pyroxene	$CaMgSi_2O_6$
Quartz	SiO_2

The data table provides evidence that

(1) the same elements are found in all minerals
(2) a few elements are found in many minerals
(3) all elements are found in only a few minerals
(4) all elements are found in all minerals

5. What are the four most abundant elements, by volume, in Earth's crust?

(1) oxygen, potassium, sodium, and calcium
(2) hydrogen, oxygen, nitrogen, and potassium
(3) aluminum, iron, silicon, and magnesium
(4) aluminum, calcium, hydrogen, and iron

6. Diamonds and graphite are both minerals that are composed of the element carbon. Diamond has a hardness of 10, while graphite has a hardness of 1. Based on your knowledge of earth science, what is the most probable cause of this difference in hardness?

7. Minerals are composed of

(1) one or more rocks
(2) only one rock
(3) one or more chemical elements
(4) only one metal

8. The cubic shape of a mineral crystal is most likely the result of that crystal's

(1) hardness
(2) density distribution
(3) internal arrangement of atoms
(4) intensity of radioactive decay

9. The following diagrams represent four different mineral samples.

Which mineral property is best represented by the samples?

(1) density   (3) hardness
(2) cleavage   (4) streak

10. Minerals are identified on the basis of

(1) the method by which they were formed
(2) the type of rock in which they are found
(3) the size of their crystals
(4) their physical and chemical properties

11. A six-sided mineral crystal is a very hard mineral called

(1) hornblende   (3) quartz
(2) orthoclase feldspar   (4) biotite mica

12. The relative hardness of a mineral can best be tested by

(1) scratching the mineral across a glass plate
(2) squeezing the mineral with calibrated pliers
(3) determining the density of the mineral
(4) breaking the mineral with a hammer

13. What property would a mineral have if it appears like a new quarter in reflected light?

(1) a metallic luster
(2) metallic element composition
(3) magnetic
(4) a high density

14. Which property of the mineral diamond allows diamond powder to be used to shape gems for jewelry?

(1) crystal shape   (3) luster
(2) cleavage   (4) hardness

15. What information about a mineral is needed to determine its density?

(1) shape and volume
(2) shape and mass
(3) volume and mass
(4) volume and hardness

Rocks

A rock is any naturally formed solid on Earth or in any part of the universe. The definitions for rock and the individual rock types are not nearly as specific as those for a mineral. The reason is that rocks, except for the single-mineral ones, are mixtures of minerals, organic materials, glasses, and fragments of other rocks. A single-mineral rock is both a rock and a mineral and has a mineral's definite composition and properties.

In your study of rocks you will often have to refer to parts of the *Earth Science Reference Tables*. The Generalized Landscape Regions of New York State and the Generalized Bedrock Geology of New York State will allow you to see in which portions of New York State different rock types are found and the geologic ages (periods) of the rocks. The Rock Cycle in Earth's Crust diagram will allow you to quickly understand the relationships among the three major rock types and the processes that form them. The Scheme for Igneous Rock Identification, Scheme for Sedimentary Rock Identification, and Scheme for Metamorphic Rock Identification will provide you with the basic individual rock properties and how to identify most of the important rock types.

Rock Types

Rocks are classified into three categories—sedimentary, igneous, and metamorphic—based on the three methods of rock formation. Sometimes metamorphic and igneous rocks are grouped together as nonsedimentary rocks. As a group, rocks are distinguished and identified based on their composition and the texture. The **texture** of a rock is not how rough it feels, but the size, shape, and arrangement of the materials the rock is composed of. The majority of rocks are composed of individual grains of minerals called **mineral crystals**. Rocks that are made of intergrown or interconnecting mineral crystals are called crystalline.

Sedimentary Rocks

Rocks that form from an accumulation of sediments derived from preexisting rocks and/or organic materials are **sedimentary rocks**. These rocks form by various processes that occur on or within the top few kilometers of Earth's crust.

Formation of Sedimentary Rocks Most sedimentary rocks are made up of solid fragments or sediments, often called "clasts," that have been weathered or eroded from older rocks. After formation, erosional agents, such as running water, glaciers, wind, ocean waves, currents, and gravity transport sediments to new locations under water or on land. Most sedimentary rocks form under large bodies of water, such as lakes, seas, and oceans, where the sediments are usually deposited in horizontal layers. Some methods of formation of sedimentary rocks are cementation, compaction, chemical action, and organic processes.

Cementation Often the clasts, such as sand, silt, and pebbles, are cemented together in a process called <u>cementation</u>. This happens as the sediments lose water and the dissolved minerals in the pores of sediments precipitate out, forming crystalline mineral material. Minerals, such as calcite, quartz, and hematite, are the common cements that glue the solid sediments together. Cementation can happen alone or in combination with other processes to form the clastic sedimentary rocks, such as siltstone and conglomerate. A **clastic sedimentary rock** is one that is largely composed of solid sediments, such as the sand in sandstone, or the tiny pieces of clay in shale.

Digging Deeper

Most precipitation of minerals occurs at the bottoms of lakes, seas, and oceans; but it also happens in soil, in caves—forming rock "icicles"— around mineral springs, and in homes— forming a rock film on water glasses and shower stalls.

Compaction Crustal movements and the weight of overlying water and sediments compress, or compact, sediments. This causes a reduction in volume due to the loss of pore space and water. The process is called compaction. While some sedimentary rocks, such as shale and bituminous coal, may form only by compaction, most of the clastic or fragmental rocks form due to compaction and cementation.

Chemical Action All natural liquid water on Earth contains dissolved minerals. In water, these dissolved minerals are called by various names— hardness in drinking water and salts in the sea—but they are all minerals that have been dissolved by chemical weathering. When these dissolved minerals precipitate, or drop out from the water, they often form a crystalline mass of intergrown or interconnected mineral crystals called a **chemical sedimentary rock or evaporites**. This **precipitation** of minerals is the result of evaporation, saturation with dissolved minerals, or changes in temperature. Chemical sedimentary rocks or evaporites, are composed of interconnected crystals of just one mineral.

Organic Processes When dissolved minerals are withdrawn from water by life forms, it is termed chemical—not mineral—precipitation. **Organic** means anything related to living organisms or to things that were alive. Any rock made by living organisms or mostly composed of materials from life forms is an organic, or **bioclastic sedimentary rock.** When a clam makes a shell, a coral makes a skeleton, or you make bones and teeth, chemicals are precipitated from water. Some organic sedimentary rocks, such as the limestone of a coral reef, are formed directly by chemical precipitation.

Characteristics of Sedimentary Rocks Some features that distinguish sedimentary rocks from igneous and metamorphic rocks include the following:

- Most sedimentary rocks are clastic—composed of fragments called sediments, or clasts.
- The clasts or sediments are usually rounded particles because they have been moved by running water, wind, waves, or ocean currents.
- The clasts or sediments are often sorted into a small range of sizes because of horizontal sorting.
- Some sedimentary rocks are organic and thus contain fossils. A **fossil** is any evidence of former life.
- One of the most distinguishing characteristics of sedimentary rocks is the beds or strata—parallel layers of the sediments in the rock. These beds are often seen in hand specimens, but are even more obvious outside where sedimentary rocks are exposed at Earth's surface in places such as road cuts or stream valleys.
- Sedimentary rocks often contain features that indicate they formed at Earth's solid surface. Some features might be mud cracks, rain drop impressions, or ripple marks that formed on the top of a sand dune or at the bottom of the ocean. Other features might be fossils that indicate an earlier Earth's surface.
- The chemical sedimentary rocks are not composed of sediments or clasts, but are composed of interconnected mineral crystals of one mineral variety.

A Conglomerate

B Breccia

C Sandstone

Clastic

D Shale

E Coquina fossil limestone

Bioclastic

F Rock salt

Crystalline

Figure 11-7. Some characteristics of sedimentary rocks: In diagrams A, B, and C the dark shading is sediment and the light color is the cement. (A) has unsorted sediments, mostly larger than sand, cemented together. (B) has sediments similar to conglomerate that are angular, not rounded. (C) has sorted sand-size sediments cemented together. (D) has compacted and sometimes cemented clay-sized sediments. (E) is an organic rock composed of shells cemented together. (F) is a chemical sedimentary rock of intergrown mineral crystals of the mineral halite.

Figure 11-8. Layers in a sedimentary rock: Layers—called beds or strata—result from changes, often minor, in the types of sediment deposited at different times.

Identifying Sedimentary Rocks The more common clastic, or fragmental, sedimentary rocks are distinguished largely on the basis of their sediments—clay, silt, sand, or larger sediment sizes. If the sediments of a conglomerate are mostly rounded, the rock is regular conglomerate. If the sediments are mostly angular the rock is breccia. In basic rock identification, it makes no difference what type of mineral or rock fragments are in a clastic rock—texture is the main factor used for classification and identification. For example, if a rock is composed of sand-sized sediments, the rock is sandstone. Refer to the chart Scheme for Sedimentary Rock Identification in the *Earth Science Reference Tables*. Ⓡ

This chart also shows that nonclastic rocks are predominantly composed of one mineral. Therefore, you treat most of them as if they are minerals. Bioclastic limestone is composed of $CaCO_3$, so it will easily fizz in dilute hydrochloric acid. If the rock only fizzes after some of it is powdered, then the rock is likely dolostone. Other examples of nonclastic rocks are rock salt, composed of the mineral halite, and rock gypsum, composed of the mineral gypsum.

Igneous Rocks

Rocks that form when natural, molten (liquid) rock-forming material cools and turns into a solid are **igneous rocks.** Liquid rock material beneath Earth's solid surface is called **magma.** When magma comes out onto or above Earth's solid surface, it becomes lava. If Earth was largely molten in its earliest stages of formation, then igneous rocks were the first rocks to form on Earth.

When magma solidifies beneath Earth's solid surface, it forms rocks called **intrusive** (plutonic) **igneous rocks.** The bodies, or masses, of these rocks can range from finger size up to the size of one or more of our states, such as Vermont. These bodies are called intrusions. Figure 11-9 illustrates many of the types of intrusions from the thin dikes and sills, common as light and

Digging Deeper

To measure sand or larger sediments in a rock, a ruler can be placed on or next to the rock. If you can't easily see the sediments, but the rock feels gritty to a fingernail, then it is most likely siltstone. You can use a magnifying glass or microscope to see silt-sized sediments. If you can't see the sediments under a normal microscope, or if the rock does not feel gritty, it is likely shale.

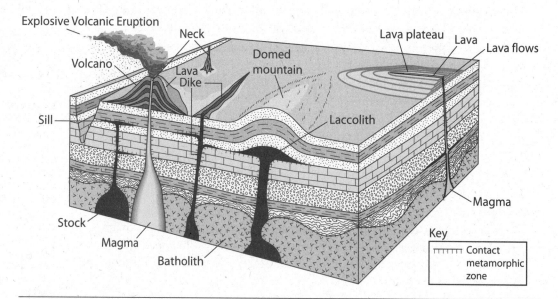

Figure 11-9. Examples of igneous intrusions and extrusions: The types of intrusions are batholith, stock, laccolith, sill, and dike. (Except for sill, you need not know the names of the various types of intrusions.) Note that both the volcano and the laccolith intrusion have formed mountains.

dark streaks in eastern New York State road cuts, to massive batholiths. It is believed that most intrusions form, within Earth's solid outer layer—the lithosphere.

When lava solidifies on or above Earth's solid surface, the result is **extrusive igneous rock.** Extrusive, or volcanic rocks, form landscape features called <u>extrusions</u>. The two most common extrusions are lava flows and volcanoes. (See Figure 11-9.)

Formation of Igneous Rocks All igneous rocks are the result of <u>solidification</u>—the change from a liquid to a solid. Most igneous rocks are produced as a result of the type of solidification called <u>crystallization.</u> Crystallization results when molten lava or magma cools and forms a solid composed of intergrown mineral crystals—a crystalline rock. Some igneous rocks that form at or above Earth's surface cool so fast that mineral crystals don't have a chance to form. The result is a type of solid called glass. In glass there is no pattern or arrangement of the atoms, therefore the substance is non-crystalline.

Crystal Sizes and Glasses The size of the crystals in an igneous rock depends on the conditions in which the rock formed. The immediate cause of the difference in the size of the crystals, or lack of crystals, is the time in which the cooling takes place. Generally, the longer the time of cooling, the larger the crystals become. However, the cooling time itself depends on the temperature and pressure of the environment, and the composition of the magma or lava. Generally, molten rock low in silica (SiO_2) content or high in water content will take longer to cool. The pressure and temperature deep within the lithosphere are very high, and therefore magma cools slowly—over many thousands of years. The result is rocks with large or coarse crystals easily visible to the human eye.

The temperature and pressure at or near Earth's surface are much lower, and the lava there cools much more quickly, forming fine-grained rocks with small crystals, not easily seen with the unaided human eye. If the cooling is very fast (usually seconds to hours), a glassy rock with no or few mineral crystals forms. Most lava flows and volcanoes are composed of rocks with small mineral crystals or no crystals in them.

Textures of Igneous Rocks Texture in igneous rocks depends on the size of mineral crystals, the presence of glass and rounded pores (vesicles). These features are related to the cooling time of magma or lava and the rock-forming environment. (See Figure 11-10). Rocks with crystals easily seen by the unaided eye are coarse-textured intrusive rocks like granite and gabbro, and almost always form within the lithosphere. Medium textured rocks like diabase have barely visible crystals. Pegmatite intrusive rocks have a very coarse texture and can have meter sized crystals.

Associated with lava flows and volcanoes, most of the extrusive igneous rocks have a fine texture of crystals smaller than one millimeter in size. To clearly see mineral crystals in fine-textured rocks, such as basalt and rhyolite, magnification is required. Many of the extrusive igneous rocks of lava flows and volcanoes have rounded openings in them caused by lava solidifying around trapped expanding gases. The rocks with these openings are said to have a vesicular texture. These openings or pockets are like the pores in the foam produced when you shake up a carbonated

A Coarse texture in granite
Crystals

B Fine texture in rhyolite
Magnified section

C Glassy texture in obsidian

D Porous texture in scoria

Figure 11-10. Textures of igneous rocks: (A) Slow cooling of magma results in coarse-sized crystals easily visible to the unaided eye. (B) Fast cooling of lava at Earth's surface results in fine-sized crystals not easily visible without magnification. A magnified section resembles the texture in (A). (C) If lava cools very rapidly, a rock with a glassy texture of no minerals will form. (D) In fine—or glassy—textured rocks or extrusive igneous rocks, there is often a mixed, porous vesicular texture. The pores are due to expanding gas forming bubbles in the lava as it solidified.

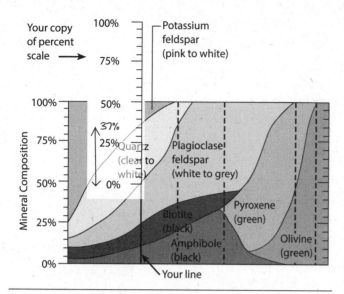

Figure 11-11. How to use the Scheme for Igneous Rock Identification in the *Earth Science Reference Tables* to measure the percent of mineral composition: Refer to the identification scheme in the *Earth Science Reference Tables* as you proceed. To obtain a percent for a particular part of the chart, do the following: **(1)** Copy the scale from the left side of the chart. **(2)** Draw a vertical line on the chart in pencil through the "t" in the word "quartz," as shown. **(3)** To compute the mineral composition of quartz, place your copy of the percent scale on the chart along your drawn line, as shown. **(4)** Align the 0% of your copy of the scale with the bottom of the quartz portion of the chart and read the percent at the top part of the mineral. The art shows quartz at about 37%. **(5)** Repeat this procedure for each of the other minerals. The values for the other minerals are: amphibole 10%, biotite 13%, plagioclase feldspar 24%, and potassium feldspar 14%. Usually you can obtain answers within 2–3 percent of the actual value.

soft drink. Basalt with many pores is called vesicular basalt. Volcanic glass with many pores is called pumice or scoria depending upon color and composition. In pumice the vesicular texture is often due to gases expanding in lava during an explosive volcanic eruption.

Identification of Igneous Rocks Igneous rocks are identified largely on the basis of texture (very coarse, coarse, medium, fine, glassy, or vesicular) and percent mineral composition. In the coarse-grained rocks you can often identify the minerals easily because they are visible to the unaided eye. You match the percents of what you observe in the rock with the chart of percent by volume of the surface of a rock. With a strong enough microscope the same thing can be done with the fine-textured rocks. For aid in using the percent mineral composition chart see Figure 11-11.

When microscopes are not available, both rock density and rock color can be a guide to the mineral composition. Refer to the Scheme for Igneous Rock Identification in the *Earth Science Reference Tables*. This scheme shows a method of classifying and identifying igneous rocks. The color of an igneous rock is more like shade, or tone—it is the overall lightness or darkness of the total rock—not the actual color. Light-colored rocks are on the left side of the scheme and dark-colored rocks are on the right. Nonvesicular igneous rocks range from 2.7 g/cm³ for low-density rocks (on the left side) to approximately 3.4 g/cm³ for high-density rocks (on the right side). Thus both density and color hint at mineral composition when the minerals can't be seen, or if identification of the minerals is uncertain.

The percent mineral composition divides igneous rocks on the diagram into vertical columns of igneous rock families usually named for the coarse-grained member. An example would be the granite family, which includes granite, pegmatite, rhyolite, vesicular rhyolite, pumice, and some obsidian. The left, or granite side, of the chart is also the felsic side, which indicates a high aluminum (Al) and silicon (Si) content compared to the peridotite and dunite side on the right, which is mafic. Mafic rocks are higher in iron (Fe) and magnesium (Mg) and lower in silicon and aluminum. Note that all the minerals listed on this chart are silicates, with the oxygen-silicon tetrahedron as the basic component of the minerals' atomic structure.

Metamorphic Rocks

Rocks that form from changes in previously existing rocks due to heat, pressure, and/or mineral fluids without weathering or melting are **metamorphic rocks**. The previously existing rocks can be sedimentary, igneous, or other metamorphic rocks. The process of forming metamorphic rocks is called **metamorphism.** The changes that produce metamorphic rocks occur within the lithosphere, usually many kilometers deep. The changed rocks resulting from metamorphism are often less porous and more dense than the original rocks. They also have larger mineral crystals, and often have a layering of mineral crystals called **foliation.**

Formation of Metamorphic Rocks When metamorphism occurs the previously existing rocks, called parent rocks, are usually recrystallized. (See Figure 11-12.) Recrystallization is the process of increasing the size of the mineral crystals or rock clasts and/or changing the mineral composition without melting. Under high heat and pressure conditions deep within the lithosphere, atoms can move small distances and become rearranged with changes in mineral composition without true melting, resulting in recrystallization. The various types of metamorphism are described in the sections that follow.

Contact Metamorphism When older rocks come in contact with the magma of an intrusion or lava of an extrusion, the heat and mineral fluids of the liquid rock alter the older rock in a process called **contact metamorphism.** Figure 11-13 shows the details of contact metamorphism. In a contact metamorphic zone there is a progression from igneous rocks, to metamorphic rocks, to the parent rocks, often without clear separations. At contact metamorphic zones, metamorphic rocks, such as hornfel, some marbles, and some quartzites are formed. Because there is mostly heat and not much directional pressure, the rocks formed by contact metamorphism usually don't have foliation.

Regional Metamorphism Sections of the lithosphere called plates may be hundreds of kilometers in width and tens of kilometers in depth. During the convergence (collision) of these plates, rocks are subjected to the high temperatures and pressures associated with a great thickness of overlying rocks and sediments and the pressures resulting from the collisions. These colliding plates often result in mountain building. The closer an area is to the boundary of colliding plates, the greater the increase in temperature and pressure. This increase in temperature and pressure transforms older rocks to a series of metamorphic rocks in a process called **regional metamorphism.** The rocks formed by regional metamorphism are often highly folded (bent) and faulted. The Taconic Mountains and the Hudson Highlands show features of regional metamorphism. Figure 11-14 illustrates the rock types and features formed by regional metamorphism.

Textures of Metamorphic Rocks Metamorphic rocks have two major types of textures—foliated and nonfoliated. Foliated rocks have layers of mineral crystals that have formed by recrystallization under directional pressures associated with regional metamorphism. These rocks are composed of two or more minerals and are made of interconnected mineral crystals. The three types of foliations are shown in Figure 11-15.

Parent Sedimentary Rock — Rounded sediments, Pores, Cement

Metamorphic Rock — Mineral crystals formed by recrystallization with no pores

Figure 11-12. Metamorphic rock formed from sedimentary rock by recrystallization: Under the influence of heat and pressure, minerals in this clastic sedimentary rock combine by recrystallization to form mineral crystals of a coarse-texture (banded) crystalline rock. Recrystallization increases the rock's density by reducing the pore spaces.

A — Intrusion, Extrusion (lava flow)

B — Igneous rock, Metamorphic rock, Transition zone

Figure 11-13. Transition of rock types in contact metamorphic zones: (A) Molten rock flows up through a crack in sedimentary rock to the surface, forming an intrusion below the surface and an extrusion (lava flow) on the surface. **(B)** At the contact zone, between the original local rock and the intrusion or extrusion, there is a blending of rock type from sedimentary, through metamorphic to igneous.

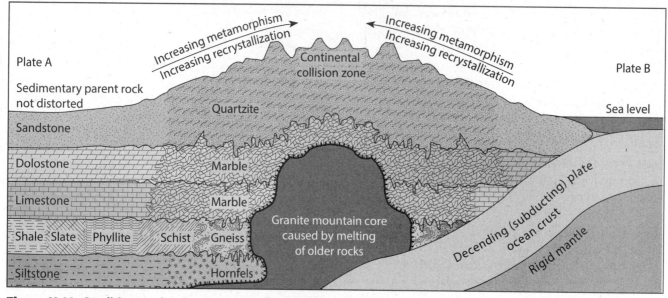

Figure 11-14. Conditions and rocks of regional metamorphism: This extremely ideal view shows two continents that have collided producing a young mountain range. The rocks become increasingly more deformed towards the center of the continents' zone of collision. As heat and pressure increase towards the collision zones, older sedimentary rocks progressively recrystallize into metamorphic rocks. With shale as the parent rock, a series of metamorphic rocks are formed as heat and pressure increases—shale → slate → phyllite → schist → gneiss. In the center of the mountain range, the heat and pressure have become so great that the rocks melted to form a granite intrusion of igneous rock.

A   **Fine-grained mineral crystals in slate**

B   **Medium-grained mineral crystals in schist**

C   **Coarse-grained mineral crystals in gneiss**

Figure 11-15. Foliation in metamorphic rocks: There are three types of foliations. Metamorphic foliations are very thin in the variety shown in diagram A. The slightly thicker foliations have mineral crystals that are reasonably visible with various minerals blending together in one foliation as in diagram B. Extreme recrystallization in diagram C has resulted in a separation (segregation) of minerals into broad bands of different color-sometimes called banding.

Nonfoliated metamorphic rocks are not layered because the minerals are not flat, or sheet-like, and/or the rocks were not subjected to a directional pressure. These rocks are composed of interconnected mineral crystals. Two single-mineral, crystalline rocks are quartzite, whose parent rock was pure quartz sandstone, and marble, whose parent rock is either limestone or dolostone.

Identification of Metamorphic Rocks Similar to sedimentary and igneous rocks, metamorphic rocks are classified and identified based on composition and texture. If the rock has foliations that are thin, if it breaks into smooth layers, and if the mineral crystals are not easily visible, the rock is slate, or phyllite (if the surface is shiny). If the rock is foliated, the mineral crystals are just clearly visible, and the rock has a high-mica mineral content, then the rock is schist. If the rock has coarse foliations—banded—and the mineral crystals are easy to see and distinguish, then the rock is gneiss. Refer to the Scheme for Metamorphic Rock Identification in the *Earth Science Reference Tables*. Ⓡ

In the nonfoliated metamorphic rocks the composition of the rock is usually the key to identification and classification.

- A rock that looks something like sedimentary conglomerate, but whose crystallized pebbles are stretched out and broken through, is probably a meta-conglomerate.
- A grainy single-mineral rock that easily scratches glass—because the quartz mineral content is much harder than glass—is quartzite.
- Grainy single-mineral metamorphic rocks that don't scratch glass are likely marble.
- Marble will fizz in dilute hydrochloric acid either directly or after powdering depending on if the parent rock is limestone or dolostone.

- Hornfels are very difficult to identify unless you know the specimen was collected next to an intrusion or under an extrusion.
- Anthracite coal is usually shiny black with a curved/conchoidal fracture.

Environment of Rock Formation

The type of environment in which a rock formed is inferred from its composition, structure, and texture. Four examples follow:

Large thick areas of rock salt in western New York State led to the inference that there was a large area of salty water in the past that has evaporated. This in turn suggests that the same could happen today in isolated seas of salt water exposed to a hot dry climate, such as the Mediterranean Sea.

The bent and twisted rock structure of surface metamorphic rocks in the Adirondack Mountains of northern New York State suggests that this region once experienced one or more mountain-building periods. See Landscape Regions of New York State and Their Characteristics in the Appendix. The rock structure also suggests that much uplift and erosion has occurred to expose rocks that formed deep beneath the surface.

If the sediments in a clastic sedimentary rock are sharp and angular, such as those in breccia, it can be inferred that the rock was formed near where weathering produced the sediments. This is because any long-distance transporting would have rounded the sediments.

A piece of igneous rock from a lava flow that has many large mineral crystals mixed with fine-grained crystals may indicate that solidification of magma had begun below the surface to produce the larger crystals. Then the lava with the large crystals erupted onto Earth's surface where the rest of the liquid solidified into rock.

The Rock Cycle

The **rock cycle** is a model used to show how the rock types— sedimentary, igneous, and metamorphic— are interrelated. It also shows the process that produces each rock type. Two examples of the rock cycle are Figure 11-16 and the Rock Cycle in Earth's Ⓡ Crust in the *Earth Science Reference Tables*. Some of the major concepts about the rock cycle are described in the following paragraphs.

Rocks Change Types Any rock type can change into any other rock type. Thus a specimen of any rock type can have materials in it that were once part of any other rock type. Examples include the solid sediments in sedimentary rocks, inclusions of older rocks in igneous rocks, or distorted fossils and sediments in metamorphic rocks.

No Preferred Direction of Movement There is no preferred direction of movement of material in the rock cycle for any one mass of chemical elements. Any one piece of mass can stay in one place for any

Figure 11-16. The rock cycle: Some of the processes by which one type of rock can be changed to another.

length of time, or it can follow any one of the paths of the rock cycle. As an example, there are sedimentary rocks over 3 billion years old that have remained largely unaltered. On the other hand a newly formed rock from a volcano can be eroded off by a hiker's boot, blown into evaporating water of a mineral spring, and become a sediment in a sandstone.

No Exact Point of Separation There is often no exact point of separation between the rock types. One example is the progression from igneous rock, to contact metamorphic rock, to the older intruded rock associated with contact metamorphism. (See Figure 11-13.) In areas of regional metamorphism there are zones many miles wide where identification of the rock type is debatable. Whether the rock is sedimentary shale or metamorphic slate, slate or schist, schist or gneiss, and even metamorphic gneiss or igneous granite is questionable.

Driving Forces The input of energy from Earth's interior, insolation from the sun, impacting meteorites, and gravity are the driving forces of the rock cycle. These forces create the processes of uplift, erosion and weathering, pressure, and melting.

Review Questions

16. When dilute hydrochloric acid is placed on the sedimentary rock limestone and the metamorphic rock marble, a bubbling reaction occurs with both. What would this indicate?

(1) The minerals of these rocks are similar.
(2) Heat and pressure have changed the molecular structure of these two rocks.
(3) The physical properties of these two rocks are identical.
(4) The two rocks originated at the same location.

17. What do most igneous, sedimentary, and metamorphic rocks have in common?

(1) They are formed from molten material.
(2) They are produced by heat and pressure.
(3) They are composed mostly of minerals.
(4) They are found mostly in distinct layers.

18. Which pair of rocks could each be composed of only one mineral?

(1) dunite and rock salt
(2) peridotite and rock gypsum
(3) dolomite and obsidian
(4) marble and schist

19. Which sedimentary rocks are formed from mostly organic matter?

(1) rock salt and shale
(2) bituminous coal and limestone
(3) dolostone and rock gypsum
(4) sandstone and conglomerate

Base your answers to questions 20 and 21 on the following diagram which represents the formation of a sedimentary rock (sediments are drawn actual size).

Sediments   Sedimentary Rock

20. The formation of which sedimentary rock is shown in the diagram?

21. Which two processes formed this rock?

(1) folding and faulting
(2) melting and solidification
(3) compaction and cementation
(4) heating and application of pressure

22. Which would most likely occur during the formation of igneous rocks?

(1) compression and cementation of sediments
(2) recrystallization of unmelted material
(3) solidification of molten materials
(4) evaporation and precipitation of dissolved sediments

23. Which graph best shows the relationship between the size of the crystals in an igneous rock and the length of time it has taken the rock to solidify?

(1)   (2)   (3)   (4)

24. Which diagram below shows an area in which fine-grained igneous rocks are most likely to be found?

(1)   (3)

(2)   (4)

25. The green sand found on the shores of the Hawaiian Island volcanoes most probably consists of the mineral

(1) quartz   (3) biotite mica
(2) olivine   (4) potassium feldspar

26. Generally as the percentage of felsic minerals in a rock increases, the rock's color will become

(1) darker and its density will decrease
(2) lighter and its density will increase
(3) darker and its density will increase
(4) lighter and its density will decrease

27. The diagram below represents a cross section of a coarse-grained igneous rock (drawn to true scale). This rock is most likely

(1) rhyolite   (3) basalt
(2) scoria   (4) granite

Plagioclase Feldspar

Biotite

Amphibole

Potassium Feldspar

Quartz

28. After collecting samples of igneous rocks, a student wishes to classify them as either intrusive or extrusive. Which characteristic of the samples might be the most useful to use?

29. A fine-grained rock has the following mineral composition: 50 percent potassium feldspar (orthoclase), 26 percent quartz, 13 percent plagioclase feldspar, 8 percent biotite mica, and 3 percent of the amphibole hornblende. The rock would most likely be

(1) granite   (3) gabbro
(2) rhyolite   (4) basalt

30. Metamorphic rocks form as the direct result of

(1) precipitation from evaporating water
(2) melting and solidification of magma
(3) erosion and deposition of soil particles
(4) heat and pressure causing changes in existing rock

31. What is the main difference between metamorphic rocks and most other rocks?

(1) Most metamorphic rocks contain only one mineral.
(2) Many metamorphic rocks have an organic composition.
(3) Many metamorphic rocks exhibit foliation and distortion of structure.
(4) Most metamorphic rocks contain a high amount of oxygen and silicon.

32. The regional metamorphism of a sandstone rock will cause the rock

(1) to be melted
(2) to recrystallize into smaller rock fragments
(3) to become denser
(4) to occupy a greater volume

33. Slate is formed by the

(1) deposition of feldspars and micas
(2) foliation of schist
(3) metamorphism of shale
(4) folding and faulting of gneiss

34. Which rock is composed of materials that show the greatest variety of rock origins?

(1) a limestone composed of coral fragments cemented together by calcium carbonate
(2) a conglomerate composed of pebbles of granite, siltstone, and gneiss
(3) a very fine-grained basalt with sharp edges
(4) a sandstone composed of rounded grains of quartz and feldspars

35. What ancient environment is the most likely inferred by the large rock salt deposits in the Syracuse, New York area?

36. Which statement about a large bedrock exposure of granite and gneiss is most likely correct?

(1) a number of volcanoes is nearby
(2) the granite and gneiss are the result of lava flows
(3) the rocks were never under water
(4) a great deal of erosion has taken place at this location

37. Which statement about inorganic rocks is true?

(1) all inorganic rocks are formed from other rocks
(2) all inorganic rocks except igneous rocks are formed from other rocks
(3) all inorganic rocks except metamorphic rocks are formed from other rocks
(4) all inorganic rocks except igneous and metamorphic rocks are formed from other rocks

Mineral Resources

Except for energy from the sun and the few things people might use from meteorites and similar objects, all things that people need come from Earth. These things, such as water to drink, air to breathe, plants to eat and use for lumber, and animals to provide clothing and milk products, are types of natural resources.

Earth materials—including minerals, rocks, and fossils fuels—are grouped together as **mineral resources.** In a lifetime, each person in the United States, on the average, is responsible for the consumption of some $3\frac{1}{2}$ million pounds of minerals, rocks, and mineral fuels that are extracted from the crust of Earth.

New York State has over 2,200 active mines that produce approximately 1.1 billion dollars of non-fuel resources. Of this, about 98% is from cement (made from limestone, gypsum, and shale), construction sand and gravel, crushed stone, salt, and the mineral wollastonite.

Mineral Resources Are Nonrenewable

Some types of natural resources are renewable—which means they are replaced, or can be replaced, by Earth or sun processes at rates similar to the rates at which humans use them. Renewable natural resources include drinking water, trees, soil, oxygen, fish, and electromagnetic energy from the sun. Mineral resources are nonrenewable natural resources. This means that once the minerals are extracted—by mining or drilling—they are gone and will not be replaced at rates comparable to human life spans. Thus, there is a limited supply of the mineral resources, such as oil, gold, copper ore, sulfur, pure white marble, and other similar resources.

Rock Properties and Humans

Humans often use rocks because of the characteristics of the whole rock. Some examples include the following:

- Slate is impermeable and cleaves along foliations to produce thin flat pieces that can be used for roofing and chalkboards.
- Basalt and diabase resist crushing, so they are used as a base under roads and railroad tracks.
- Coal can burn releasing much heat energy.
- The natural pore space and low density of pumice make it useful for building insulation.
- Granite and quartzite are very resistant to weathering because of their nonporous composition, thus they are used as building stone.

Memory Jogger

You may know that an _ore_ is a rock or mineral deposit that can supply enough of a needed material to make it worthwhile to mine or drill for it from Earth's crust. Most minerals are mined to obtain one or more of the chemical elements the mineral contains.

Rock Properties and Land Usage

The type of rock that underlies the landscape of an area has many effects on how people use the land. Some examples follow:

- Limestones and dolostones often weather to produce nonacidic soils which are useful for certain crops; but often, underground water can dissolve these rocks producing caves that collapse forming dangerous depressions called sinkholes.

- Regions having much shale are often low in topography with a rolling landscape of gentle slopes. These topographic features are the result of the fact that shales usually weather and erode easily. This low rolling topography makes it easy to build homes and other human constructions such as roads. The high populations and many transportation facilities of the Hudson-Mohawk Lowlands of eastern New York State are often built on shale.

- Certain rock types withstand tremendous weight without crumbling or flowing under pressure. These types of rocks, such as gneiss and granite, occurring near Earth's surface allow for the safe construction of high-rise buildings, such as in New York City.

Mineral Properties and Humans

The physical properties of a mineral often determine how people use the mineral. Some examples of minerals and their useful properties are listed below:

- Quartz, when put under even minor amounts of pressure, will vibrate in a very regular fashion, which makes it ideal to use in the inexpensive yet very accurate quartz watches.

- Many minerals with a high hardness are used in jewelry and as abrasives in sandpapers and drilling operations. Diamond, corundum (ruby when red and sapphire when blue), the garnets, and quartz (amethyst when purple and citrine when golden yellow) are used in great volumes in the jewelry and abrasive industries. Mines in the Adirondack Mountains of New York State are one of the largest producers of garnet in the world.

- Graphite is soft and has a black streak that makes it very useful as a main ingredient of pencil "lead." The lead is largely graphite, not the element lead.

- Talc is very soft and has one direction of cleavage, which makes it feel smooth or greasy. For these reasons it is used in cosmetics and many baby and foot powders. Portions of the Adirondack Mountains have talc mines.

- Hematite's red color has proven to be useful to humans for many thousands of years. It is the red color of cave paintings, many cosmetics, and most red paints.

- The use(s) of many minerals is listed in the chart "Properties of Common Minerals" in the *Earth Science Reference Tables*. (R)

Global Distribution of Mineral Deposits

Many of the more important elements required by our society are found in ores located outside of the United States. As the population of the United States and the rest of the world continues to grow, demand for the limited

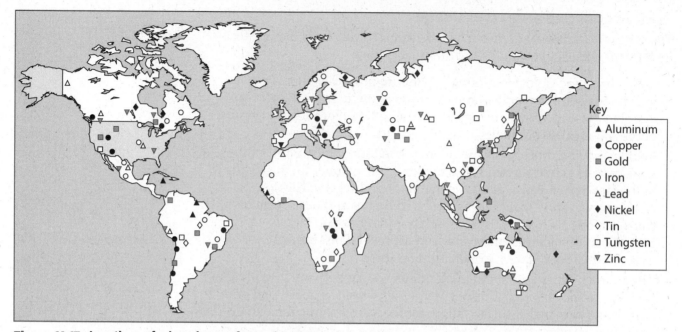

Figure 11-17. Locations of mineral ores of some important chemical elements used in the United States: The map shows that the United States must import much of the rock and mineral sources of aluminum, nickel, tin, tungsten, and zinc.

rock and mineral resources becomes more and more competitive. At present the United States has to import almost 100 percent of the ores for aluminum, tungsten, cobalt, manganese, and graphite—plus over 50 percent of the ores for tin, zinc, nickel, and chromium. These materials are crucial for the production of much of our advanced industrial and military equipment. (See Figure 11-17.)

Fossil Fuels

Fossil fuels—which include oil (or petroleum), natural gas, coal, and oil shale—are the result of compaction and organic chemical changes in large deposits of organic sediments. These sediments are the remains of dead plants and animals.

Figure 11-18A indicates that at present three nonrenewable fossil fuels provide 90 percent of our energy needs. At present the United States can

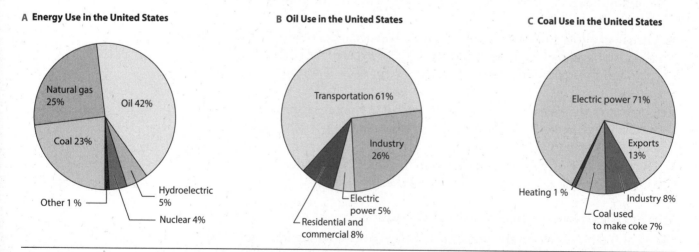

Figure 11-18. Circle graphs of sources of energy and uses of two fossil fuels in the United States.

provide a large proportion of our coal and natural gas demands, though our reserves are dwindling fast. Almost 60 percent of the oil used in the United States is imported. New York State produces small amounts of oil and natural gas, but has no commercial coal deposits. In recent years over 54 million cubic feet of natural gas and 300,000 barrels of oil were produced from 13,000 wells in New York State.

Review Questions

38. Which geological resource in New York State resulted from glaciation?

(1) oil shale and anthracite coal
(2) sand and gravel deposits
(3) gold and silver ores
(4) calcite and gypsum crystals

39. Rocks and minerals are natural resources that are mined in New York State. State *one* negative impact that should be considered before mining these natural resources.

Base your answers to questions 40 through 43 on the following chart. The chart shows information about selected mineral and energy resources.

Group	Mineral Resource	Uses
Elements	Gold	coins, jewelry, investment, electrical conductors, dental fillings
	Copper	electrical wiring, plumbing, coins
	Graphite	lubricants, pencil "lead"
Mineral Compounds	Hematite (ore of iron)	construction, motor vehicles, machinery parts
	Halite	food additive, melting of ice, water softeners, chemicals
	Feldspar	abrasives (sandpaper), jewelry
Fuels	Coal	heating, electric generation plants, plastics and other synthetic chemicals
	Petroleum	automobile fuel, lubricants, plastics and other synthetic chemicals, medicines, heating

40. Name two resources that would last longer if people used public transportation.

41. What is the primary source of all the resources listed in the chart?

(1) recycled and discarded waste materials
(2) deposits within Earth's crust
(3) substances extracted from ocean water
(4) meteorites that came from outer space

42. Which of the minerals listed in the chart does NOT have a metallic luster?

(1) gold   (3) graphite
(2) copper   (4) halite

43. Which of the materials from the chart is NOT a mineral or NOT made of minerals?

(1) copper   (3) halite
(2) hematite   (4) coal

44. Which home-building material is made mostly from the mineral gypsum?

(1) plastic pipes   (3) drywall panels
(2) window glass   (4) iron nails

45. Which statement about the minerals plagioclase feldspar, gypsum, biotite mica, and talc can best be inferred?

(1) These minerals have the same chemical and physical properties.
(2) These minerals have different chemical properties, but they have similar physical properties.
(3) These minerals have different physical and chemical properties, but they have identical uses.
(4) The physical and chemical properties of these minerals determine how humans use them.

46. Which of the minerals listed below contain only one element?

(1) graphite   (3) halite
(2) hematite   (4) garnet

47. Wood and coal are both organic natural resources. Explain why coal is considered a fossil fuel, while wood is not.

Directions

Review the Test-Taking Strategies section of this book. Then answer the following questions. Read each question carefully and answer with a correct choice or response.

Part A

1 Which of the following pairs of rocks usually contains only one mineral?
(1) rock gypsum and marble
(2) sandstone and conglomerate
(3) quartzite and schist
(4) dunite and gabbro

2 Which of the following properties is most useful in mineral identification?
(1) hardness
(2) color
(3) size
(4) texture

3 Which property of minerals is illustrated by the peeling of biotite mica into thin flat sheets?
(1) fracture
(2) cleavage
(3) a low hardness
(4) a weak streak

4 The main difference between sedimentary, metamorphic, and igneous rocks is the
(1) means by which they are located
(2) conditions under which they are formed
(3) minerals of which they are composed
(4) location in which they are found

5 Which rock was formed by the compaction and cementation of particles 0.07 centimeters in diameter?
(1) conglomerate
(2) sandstone
(3) shale
(4) siltstone

6 Dolostone and rock gypsum are formed by the processes of
(1) melting and solidification
(2) evaporation and precipitation
(3) erosion and deposition of clastic fragments
(4) weathering and metamorphism

7 Which would most likely cause molten rock material to become glassy igneous rock?
(1) cooling over a long period of time
(2) cooling under high pressure
(3) cooling on Earth's surface
(4) cooling at great depth within the crust

8 An igneous rock, which has crystallized deep below Earth's surface, has the following approximate composition: 70 percent pyroxene (augite), 15 percent plagioclase feldspar, and 15 percent olivine. What is the name of this igneous rock?
(1) granite
(2) rhyolite
(3) gabbro
(4) basalt

Use the following diagram to answer questions 9 and 10. The diagram shows an igneous rock intrusion in sedimentary rock layers.

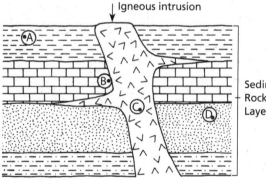

9 At which point would there most likely be contact metamorphic rock?
(1) A
(2) B
(3) C
(4) D

10 Which rock type would most likely be located at the contact between rocks C and D?
(1) metaconglomerate
(2) gneiss
(3) marble
(4) quartzite

11 In which parts of New York State would you most likely find large amounts of bedrock formed by regional metamorphism?
(1) Atlantic Coastal Plain and Newark Lowlands
(2) Hudson Highlands and Adirondack Mountains
(3) Tug Hill Plateau and Allegheny Plateau
(4) Erie-Ontario Lowlands and the Catskills

12 Which actual-size diagram best represents a sample of the metamorphic rock gneiss?

(1)   (3)

(2)   (4)

13 Which type(s) of rock can be the source of deposited sediments?
(1) igneous and metamorphic rocks, only
(2) metamorphic and sedimentary rocks, only
(3) sedimentary rocks, only
(4) igneous, metamorphic, and sedimentary rocks

14 A certain igneous rock is composed of large mineral grains. This suggests that the rock formed
(1) on the surface, under high pressure, and at a rapid rate of cooling
(2) on the surface at high temperature, and at a slow rate of cooling
(3) deep underground under high pressure, at high temperature, and at a rapid rate of cooling
(4) deep underground under high pressure, at high temperature, and at a slow rate of cooling

15 Which characteristic would indicate that a rock was formed from sediments deposited in shallow water near shore rather than in deep water?
(1) hardness
(2) dark color
(3) a large grain size
(4) a large amount of cement

Part B

Base your answers to questions 16 and 17 on the diagram below and the *Earth Science Reference Tables*. The diagram shows the elements found in four minerals.

	O	Si	Al	Fe	Ca	Na	C
Quartz	■	■					
Feldspar	■	■	■		■	■	
Olivine	■	■		■			
Diamond							■

■ = element present

16 Which of the minerals in the diagram has the greatest variety of elements in it? [1]

17 Which of the elements listed in the diagram is second in abundance, by mass, in Earth's crust? [1]

Follow these directions for questions 18 through 23. The following numbered diagrams represent mineral specimens. Using these diagrams, write the name of the mineral which is best described by each of the statements. (If a mineral has cleavage, the diagram illustrates it.)

1 Colorless   2 Colorless   3 Colorless to white

4 Red   5 Black   6 Gray

18 Diagram 1 is a mineral that easily bubbles when exposed to dilute acids. [1]

19 Diagram 2 is a very hard mineral that has a curved fracture. [1]

20 Diagram 3 shows intergrown crystals of this salty tasting mineral. [1]

21 Diagram 4 is an ore of iron with a red streak. [1]

22 Diagram 5 is a soft mineral with cleavage that forms thin flexible sheets. [1]

23 Diagram 6 is an ore of lead that is soft and has a metallic luster. [1]

Base your answers to questions 24 through 28 on the following diagram. The diagram represents a profile view of exposed rock layers. The layers are labeled A through H.

Key

Limestone

Shale

Sandstone

Conglomerate

24 State the range of particle sizes of the sediments that formed rock layer C. [1]

25 State two ways in which the composition of rock layer A differs from the composition of rock layer B. [2]

26 State a method by which rock layer A could have formed. [1]

27 Based on information in the diagram, state a reason why you would choose to use rock from layer A instead of rock from layers C or D for a tombstone or statue. [1]

28 State the name of the sediment that was compacted to form rock unit B. [1]

29 Describe two conditions that can result in the metamorphosis of a rock. [2]

30 If an igneous rock layer is composed of vesicular andesite, identify three types of minerals that could be found in sand weathered from the rock layer. [1]

Part C

The following paragraph provides information about a meteorite impact in New York State. Use data from the paragraph and your knowledge of earth science to answer questions 31 through 34.

Recently a New York State Geological Survey geologist has produced much evidence indicating a large meteorite impact crater in the Catskills of New York State. This supposed crater that formed approximately 375,000,000 years ago is now buried by hundreds of feet of horizontal sedimentary rock. By drilling beneath the surface sedimentary rock, samples of various rock types have been brought up from in and around the crater.

31 Suppose that the meteorite impact produced enough heat to melt much of the meteorite and parts of Earth's surface at the impact site. Describe the type of rock and its texture that would form from the melted meteorite and Earth rocks. [2]

32 Further out from the center of the crater, the meteorite impact caused high temperatures and very high pressure, but the temperatures were not high enough to melt the rocks. What type of rock would form in this environment? [1]

33 At the time of the impact, solid angular rock fragments, mostly larger than sand grains, were hurled far out from the crater. Describe how these fragments could form a sedimentary rock and suggest the most likely name of this sedimentary rock. [2]

34 State the geologic eon, era, and period when this supposed impact crater was formed. [2]

35 You observe that a sample of mineral has many smooth sides or surfaces. The sample has not been cut, sanded, or otherwise smoothed by people. Describe two ways in which the parallel smooth sides of the mineral specimen were most likely formed. Then describe an experiment that could help you determine which of the two ways formed the smooth sides on this mineral specimen. [3]

36 Two students were given nearly identical samples of the same mineral and were asked to identify the mineral. Student A said the mineral was graphite because it had a silver color and had a low hardness. Student B said the mineral was hematite because of its silver color and low hardness. Describe two mineral tests that could be used to determine the correct identification of the mineral. [2]

Base your answers to questions 37 and 38 on the rock cycle diagram below.

37 State the specific names of rocks A, B, and C in the diagram. Do *not* write the terms "sedimentary," "igneous," and "metamorphic." [3]

38 State *one* condition or process that would cause the high-grade metamorphism of rock A. [1]

39 A family wants to use rock materials as flooring in the entrance of their new house. They have narrowed their choice to granite or marble. Which of these rocks is more resistant to the physical wear of foot traffic and explain why this rock is more resistant. [2]

40 The mineral wollastonite forms during the intense metamorphism of a sandy limestone. The expression below shows part of the process that results in the formation of wollastonite.

Metamorphism

$$CaCO_3 + SiO_2 \rightarrow CaSiO_2 + CO_2$$

Mineral 1 Mineral 2 Wollastonite Carbon dioxide

a Name the *two* minerals involved in the formation of wollastonite. [1]

b What *two* conditions normally cause intense metamorphism? [1]

Base your answers to questions 41 through 43 on the cross-section below which represents a portion of the Earth's crust. Letters A, B, C, and D are rock units.

Key
Igneous rock
Contact metamorphism (transition zone)

41 Igneous rock *B* was formed after rock layer *D* was deposited but before rock layer *A* was deposited. Using the contact metamorphism symbol shown in the key, draw that symbol in the proper locations on the cross section above to indicate those rocks that underwent contact metamorphism when igneous rock *B* was molten. [1]

42 In relation to rock units *A* and *B* in the cross section, when was igneous rock *C* formed? [1]

43 Describe one observable characteristic of rock *A* that indicates that rock *A* is sedimentary. [1]

Base your answers to questions 44 through 46 on the passage below.

Carbon

Carbon may be the most important element on our planet because it is the chemical building block of all living things. The element carbon is formed in dying stars and scattered when the stars explode. Our solar system formed from such star remnants. Pure carbon comes in several forms, which include the minerals graphite and diamond (hardness = 10), and the fossil fuels bituminous coal and anthracite coal. Almost all diamonds are mined from igneous rocks that originate at an approximate depth of 150 kilometers under immense pressure. Most graphite is formed through the metamorphism of organic material in rocks closer to Earth's surface.

44 Identify two uses for the mineral graphite. [1]

45 Explain why graphite and diamond have different properties. [1]

46 Complete the table below to show the properties of the minerals diamond and graphite. [1]

Property	Diamond	Graphite
color	variable	
luster	nonmetallic	
hardness		

Earth's Dynamic Crust and Interior

How Scientists Study Earth's Dynamic Crust and Interior

? *Is there continental drift?* **?**

Well, yes and no. During the early 1900s, some geologists believed in an idea called continental drift, which Alfred Wegener developed into a fleshed-out hypothesis that described evidence to show that continents have changed locations over time. But he could not figure out how this happened. In the mid-1900s, scientists began studying the ocean floor, finding new data that led to the modern theory of plate tectonics. This theory describes how continents move, but as part of larger plates. Hence, there is "plate drift," not continental drift.

Earth's Dynamic Crust and Interior

Vocabulary

asthenosphere	lithosphere	P-waves
continental crust	lithospheric plate	seismic wave
convergent plate boundary	mantle	subduction
crust	mid-ocean ridge	S-waves
divergent plate boundary	Moho	tectonic plate
earthquake	oceanic crust	transform plate boundary
epicenter	ocean trench	tsunami
faulted	original horizontality	uplifted
folded	outer core	volcanic eruption
hot spot	plate	volcano
inner core	plate tectonic theory	young mountains
island arc		

Topic Overview

Much evidence, such as volcanoes and earthquakes, indicates that Earth's crust is constantly undergoing change. You know that the crust moves because you have witnessed or read about earthquakes and the eruption of volcanoes. You also may have heard about measurements that indicate that mountains are "growing" and that the landmasses are changing their positions on Earth's surface.

Evidence of past movements of the crust is more indirect. Scientists must "read" the characteristics of rocks to learn about these past events. Thus, scientists have learned to understand Earth's lithosphere, surface features, and plate movements as well as the properties of Earth's interior. The **lithosphere** is the layer of rock that forms the outer shell at the top of Earth's interior. Earth's **crust** is the upper portion of the lithosphere. Note that whatever is stated in this chapter about the crust usually applies to the lithosphere as well.

Small Scale Crustal Changes

Much of the evidence for past movements of the crust is based on the concept of **original horizontality.** This concept assumes that sedimentary rocks and some extrusive igneous rocks, such as lava flows, form in horizontal layers parallel to Earth's surface. The layers of sedimentary rocks and extrusive igneous rocks are called <u>strata</u> or beds. Therefore, most strata found in positions other than horizontal are thought to have been deformed by crustal movement. (See Figure 12-1.)

Rock layers (strata) that no longer show their original horizontality are called deformed layers. Some of the types of deformed layers are folded, tilted, and faulted. **Folded** rock layers are bent or curved. Tilted rock layers are slanted or tipped. **Faulted** rock layers are offset or displaced along a type of crack called a <u>fault</u>. A fault is a crack in a mass of rock or soil along which there has been displacement, shifting, or movement of the rock or soil layers on each side of the crack.

Displaced marine (ocean) rocks as well as rocks with fossils are often found in sedimentary rock hundreds or thousands of meters above sea level. A <u>fossil</u> is any evidence of former life. These displaced rocks and fossils indicate that the land has been raised up, or **uplifted,** to its present position. A lowering of sea level could not have changed the location of the fossils because it is believed that sea level has only ever varied a few hundred meters. On the other hand, fossils from shallow water and from land have been found many hundreds of meters below sea level, which indicates a sinking or lowering of part of Earth's crust.

Figure 12-1. Strata, illustrating original horizontality and three types of deformed strata: The numbers in diagram D indicate strata that were originally continuous. The arrows show the direction of relative movement along the fault.

Review Questions

1. Draw a diagram of folded strata. Explain a geological event that might account for this deformation.

2. While hiking with a friend in New York State, you discover marine fossils in sedimentary strata at high elevations. What is the most logical explanation for their presence?

3. A line of former beaches along a coast, all 50 meters above sea level, is evidence of
   (1) present erosion
   (2) the present melting of polar ice caps
   (3) land uplift
   (4) a decrease in the deposition of marine fossils

4. The following diagram represents a vertical cross section of sedimentary rock layers that have not been overturned. Which principle best supports the conclusion that these layers have undergone extensive movement since deposition?

(1) Sediments are deposited with the youngest layers on top.
(2) Sediments are deposited in horizontal layers.
(3) Rock layers are older than igneous intrusions.
(4) Sediments containing the remains of marine fossils are deposited above sea level.

5. The following diagrams show cross sections of exposed bedrock. Which cross section shows the least evidence of crustal movement?

(1)

(3)

(2)

(4)

6. The following diagram represents a cross section of a portion of Earth's crust. What do these tilted rock layers suggest?

(1) This area remained fairly stable since the sediments were deposited.
(2) The sediments were deposited at steep angles and then became rock.
(3) Metamorphism followed the deposition of the sediments.
(4) Crustal movement occurred sometime after the sediments were deposited.

7. Recent measurements of elevation in New York State indicate that the land is slowly rising in the Adirondack Mountain region. Which statement best explains this change?

(1) The Adirondack Mountains are in a region of crustal uplift.
(2) The Adirondack Mountains are in a zone of few earthquakes.
(3) The rocks in the Adirondack Mountains are younger than those in other regions of New York.
(4) The gravitational attraction of the moon is greater in the higher Adirondack region.

8. Shallow-water fossils are found in rock layers deep beneath the ocean floor. This suggests that

(1) shallow-water organisms always migrate to deeper water to die
(2) parts of the ocean floor have been uplifted
(3) parts of the ocean floor have sunk
(4) the surface water cooled off, killing the organisms

Earthquakes and Igneous Activity, Including Volcanoes

An **earthquake** is a natural rapid shaking of the lithosphere caused by the release of energy stored in rocks. Most earthquakes are caused by the movement along faults, or <u>faulting</u>. Some earthquakes are associated with the movements of magma within the lithosphere and with volcanic eruptions. During an earthquake the potential energy stored in the rocks is given off as **seismic waves,** or earthquake waves. As shown in Figure 12-2, the earthquake starts at the <u>focus,</u> from which the waves are emitted. The location on Earth's land or water surface directly above the focus is called the **epicenter.** You often see epicenters plotted on maps of Earth's surface.

Scientists measure and record earthquake waves by using a seismograph—an instrument that shows how Earth shakes from the seismic waves. A seismograph records (on paper or another medium) "wiggles"— amplitudes of the wave—that represent Earth's shakings. The recording is called a seismogram. (See Figure 12-3.)

Earthquake Waves

Seismic waves can be grouped into three categories— P-waves, S-waves, and surface waves. **P-waves,** also called <u>primary</u> <u>waves,</u> cause the particles they travel through to vibrate in the direction the waves are moving. The slower **S-waves,** also called <u>secondary</u> <u>waves,</u> cause the particles they travel through to vibrate at right angles to the direction the waves are moving.

The surface waves are produced when a P-wave or S-wave comes to Earth's surface. These waves only travel around Earth's solid surface and cause much of the surface shaking and damage of an earthquake.

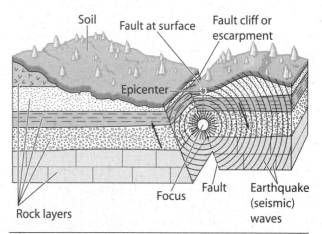

Figure 12-2. Terminology of an earthquake: Note the displacement of the rock layers along the fault. Also note that the epicenter is on Earth's surface directly above the focus.

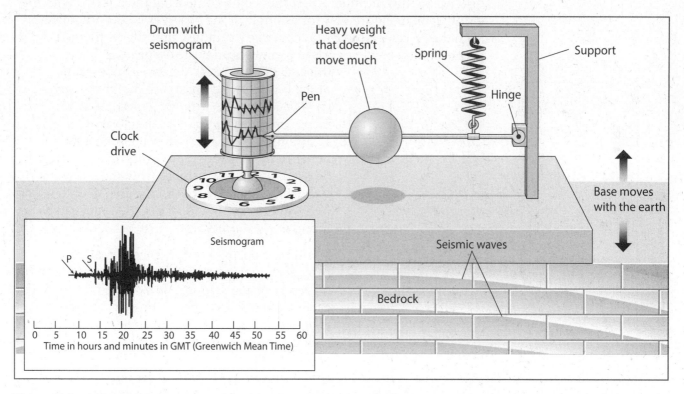

Figure 12-3. A simple seismograph and a seismogram: As Earth shakes during an earthquake, most of the seismograph moves up and down. Since the heavy weight resists movement because of momentum, the attached pen "writes" wiggles on a seismogram (shown in the insert). This seismogram has the record of the arrival times of P-waves (P) and S-waves (S) from an earthquake. P-waves arrive first because they are fastest.

Properties of Earthquake Waves The different types of seismic waves have different properties depending on the materials they pass through:

- In any one material, P-waves travel faster than all other types of seismic waves. S-waves are the second fastest. When an earthquake occurs, the P-waves will reach a seismograph before the S-waves do. (See Figures 12-3 and 12-4.)

- The velocity of seismic waves in Earth depends on the properties of the materials they are passing through. Generally, the more dense and rigid a material is, the greater the velocity of the waves. As seismic waves pass from a material of one density to a material of higher or lower density, the waves are refracted, or bent.

- Within the same material, an increase in pressure increases the velocity of the seismic waves.

- P-waves will pass through solids, liquids, and gases. S-waves will only pass through solids.

- Some P-waves and S-waves are reflected by, or bounce off, dense rock layers within Earth. This property is often used to locate valuable rock and mineral resources within Earth.

Location of an Epicenter Epicenters are located by using the velocity differences between the P-waves and S-waves. Since P-waves move faster than S-waves, the farther an observer is from an epicenter, the larger the time interval between the arrival of the P-waves and S-waves. The distance to the epicenter is determined by comparing the interval with the graph data. In Figure 12-4 for example, if the observer is 1000 kilometers from the epicenter, the P-waves arrive 2 minutes after the earthquake occurs and the S-waves arrive 4 minutes after the occurrence. There is thus a 2-minute interval between observation of the P-waves and observation of the S-waves. At 4000 kilometers from the epicenter, it takes 7 minutes for the P-waves to arrive and $12\frac{1}{2}$ minutes for the S-waves; the time interval between them is thus $5\frac{1}{2}$ minutes. The graph can be used to find the distance from the epicenter if the time interval between the arrival of the two waves is known. A similar diagram can be found in the *Earth Science Reference Tables*. Ⓡ

To find the position of the epicenter, at least three seismograph locations must be used, and the epicenter distance must be calculated for each. For each of the three locations, the epicenter distance is then used as a radius, and circles are drawn on a globe or a map, as shown for locations A, B, and C in Figure 12-5. The place where all three circles intersect is the epicenter of the earthquake. Observations at one seismograph location provides only the distance to the epicenter, not the location or direction.

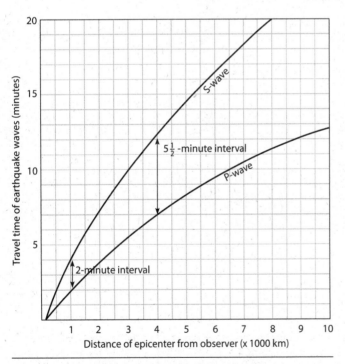

Figure 12-4. Travel times of P-waves and S-waves: The two curves in this graph show the time required for P-waves and S-waves to travel a given distance from the epicenter of an earthquake. Since the S-waves travel more slowly than the P-waves, the S-waves take longer to reach an observer.

Finding the Origin Time of Earthquakes The time an earthquake originated can be determined from the epicenter distance and seismic-wave travel time.

The farther an observer is from the epicenter, the longer it takes the seismic waves to travel to the observation point. For example, suppose the observer is 4000 kilometers from the epicenter. Figure 12-4 shows that it took the P-wave 7 minutes to arrive; thus the earthquake occurred 7 minutes earlier than the time at which the P-waves were observed on the seismograph. Try this example: If the S-wave first arrived at a station at 10 hr:12 min:30 sec and the seismograph is 5500 kilometers away from the epicenter, when did the earthquake occur?

Magnitude of Earthquakes The strength of an earthquake can be measured in various ways. An earthquake intensity scale can be used to measure the various effects of an earthquake on humans and the types of damage the event causes. Generally, the closer to the epicenter, the greater the damage; that is, the intensity for an earthquake varies with distance.

Scientists most often use an <u>earthquake</u> <u>magnitude</u> <u>scale</u> to measure the strength of earthquakes. Magnitude scales use the height of the wiggles on seismograms to help us infer the total amount of energy released by an earthquake.

The lowest value of magnitude is determined by the sensitivity of seismographs (less than 1), and the highest value (approximately 9.5) is determined by how much stress rocks can withstand before breaking. Figure 12-6 shows an example of one magnitude scale and the number of earthquakes that occur each year.

Epicenter
(the one point that is on all 3 circles)

Figure 12-5. Locating the epicenter of an earthquake: Seismograph observations at three locations that are widely spaced are used. The distance to the epicenter is determined for each station, and a circle with this radius is then drawn around the station. The one point that lies on all three circles must be the epicenter.

Earthquakes as a Natural Hazard

Earthquakes can cause great damage, injury, and death. What causes all the damage, death, and injuries during an earthquake? Earth doesn't

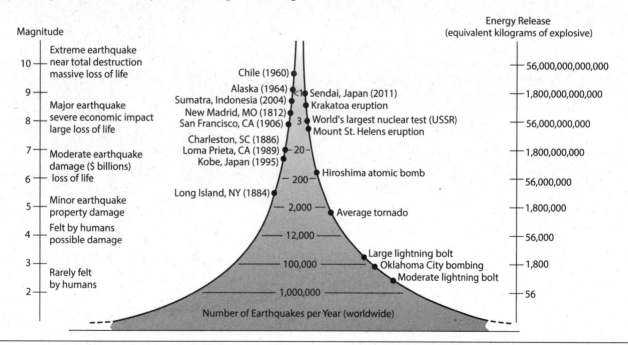

Figure 12-6. Earthquake magnitude scale: This scale provides one value for each earthquake that is an estimate of the total energy the event emits. Each whole-number value equals between 31 and 32 times more energy than the next lower number.

Digging Deeper

For many years, the Richter Scale was used, but the scale—named in 1935 after Charles F. Richter of the California Institute of Technology—was really only designed for small-to moderate-strength earthquakes in California and would not provide meaningful data for the strongest earthquakes. Most scientists now use a magnitude scale, which not only uses the height of the wiggles on the seismograms but also considers the length of the movement of the earthquake.

open up and "swallow" buildings and people; the shaking ground causes a series of events.

For example, shaking ground can cause a break in a railroad track, which in turn can cause a train wreck. If the train is carrying hazardous chemicals, they might spill, perhaps causing an explosion and a fire. Most injuries and fatalities are caused by parts of buildings falling on people and by the other related events.

Earthquake Prediction Scientists have been trying to successfully predict earthquakes for many years without a favorable outcome, except for long-term predictions. If we could predict earthquakes by a few weeks or even days, the population could then be evacuated. At present, the only reasonably good predictions have been general and long-term for a certain area. This type of prediction is possible because most earthquakes occur in specific zones. (See Figure 12-9.) Therefore, if enough earthquake history is known for a specific zone, then a reasonable prediction can be made.

Emergency Planning for Earthquakes Even though current methods of earthquake prediction are not of much value, the amount of damage, death, and injury from earthquakes can be greatly reduced with proper planning.

On an individual level, try to remember "drop, cover, and hold." Upon the first signs of shaking from what you believe to be an earthquake, don't go far, but drop down under a strong object (a strong desk or table, for example). Turn away from windows, and use one hand to cover your eyes. With the other hand, hold onto the strong object you are under. Do not try to run out of a building until the shaking is over. Most earthquakes last only 10 to 30 seconds, and it takes most of that time just to react.

Earthquake drills in the home, at work, and at school can help people to protect themselves, as can having emergency supplies at home, at work, in cars, and at school.

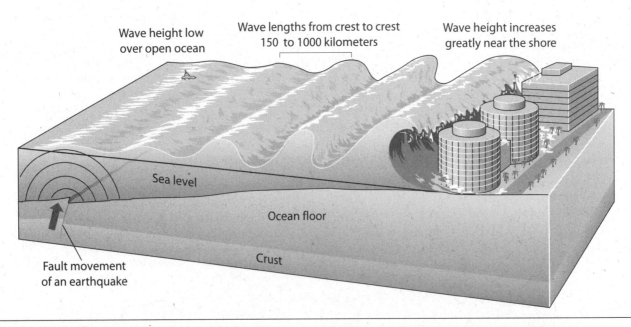

Figure 12-7. Tsunamis: These sometimes giant ocean waves can cause destruction similar to hurricane waves on shorelines. Tsunamis usually come as a series of waves from 10 to 60 minutes apart and may be over 30 meters high at shorelines.

On a community level, proper planning of building sites and proper building construction techniques can greatly reduce the chance of death and injury during an earthquake. An example of important planning includes inspecting the soil and bedrock to ensure that new buildings are constructed on solid ground. Another example of proper planning is retrofitting older buildings to make them safer, such as bolting buildings to their foundations and cross-bracing walls.

Tsunami

A special condition associated with strong earthquakes on the ocean floor is the production of seismic sea waves. **Tsunami**—the Japanese word for "wave in the harbor"—is a large wavelength ocean wave produced by disruption of the ocean floor. This disruption can be caused by the faulting associated with an earthquake (as shown in Figure 12-7), volcanic eruptions, meteorite impact or rapid landslide type of mass movement. The shoreline damage from a tsunami is much the same as that created by hurricane waves. In rare cases a tsunami can produce destructive coastal waves of more than 30 meters. If a tsunami warning is announced for your area, quickly move to higher ground, further inland, or to a high level of a tall strong structure.

Igneous Activity and Volcanoes

Recall that igneous rocks and the features formed from them are of two types—intrusive and extrusive. Intrusions composed of intrusive (plutonic) igneous rock form when magma stays within the lithosphere. When magma reaches the surface, it becomes lava and forms masses—extrusions—composed of extrusive (volcanic) igneous rock. If the lava flows out of cracks and is very fluid, a feature called a "lava flow" forms. Successive lava flows can form large features like the Columbia Lava Plateau, which covers much of Oregon, Washington, and Idaho. (See Figure 12-8, diagram D.) If the lava forms a significant mound with a slope of at least a few degrees, then the mass is a volcano. A **volcano** is a mountain composed of extrusive igneous rocks. A **volcanic eruption** is the giving off of gases, lava, and/or lava rock onto Earth's surface or into the atmosphere through the opening or vent of a volcano. Volcanic eruptions range from a flow of lava down the side of a volcano to a massive explosion of gas, solid particles, and/or lava into the atmosphere similar to the Mount St. Helens eruption in Washington in 1980.

Volcanoes as a Natural Hazard Similar to earthquakes, volcanic eruptions can result in a multitude of events that damage, injure, and kill. People can be injured and killed by flowing lava, falling rock, and gases of over 1000°C. Farmland and buildings are often buried or burned by lava flows and volcanic ash during eruptions. The secondary events of a volcano are often more destructive. Volcanic ash often mixes with water from melted glaciers, causing massive mudslides and flooding. The gases emitted by a volcano,

Cinder cone–common in much of western USA and has mostly explosive eruptions

Composite volcano, such as Mount St. Helens in Cascades of western USA and has both explosive and quiet lava flow eruptions

Key

Loose igneous rock fragments, such as ash from explosive eruptions

Lava rock from lava flows or quiet eruptions

Shield cone, such as the Hawaiian Islands and has mostly quiet lava flow eruptions

Lava plateaus

Figure 12-8. Volcanic mountains and plateaus: Volcanic mountains are composed of two types of igneous materials. One is lava rock formed from flows of liquid lava. The other is loose rock fragments—from ash to boulder size—formed by the exploding of lava and rock fragments into the air and their eventual settling to form a mountain. A volcanic plateau is relatively high landscape composed of horizontal layers of lava rock formed by many lava flows emitted from fissures (cracks) in the crust.

Figure 12-9. Zones of current crustal activity and Earth's major plates: Note that the borders of the plates are the locations of most current crustal activity, which includes volcanic eruptions and earthquakes. Most of the world's active volcanoes are located where mid-ocean ridges or young mountains are indicated on the map.

such as sulfur and chlorine compounds and carbon dioxide, can cause immediate death or long-term lung damage. In massive eruptions, volcanic ash is ejected into the stratosphere, where it has been known to cool Earth by blocking insolation reaching Earth's surface.

Prediction of Volcanic Eruptions There has been some success in predicting volcanic eruptions in sufficient time for people to escape from an area. Though most eruptions go unpredicted, some of the more dangerous volcanoes in populated regions are monitored by using a series of tools. Satellites measure infrared energy from the upper atmosphere and report on the increasing heat from rising magma. Tilt meters measure increasing slopes as the volcano inflates with magma. Elevation, benchmarks, latitude and longitude measurements, and topographic maps indicate the increases in elevation and width common before eruptions. When magma moves upward before volcanic eruptions, it pushes rock out of the way, causing hundreds of earthquakes. Using the three-seismograph method to determine epicenters, scientists can "watch" magma rise and can provide eruption predictions within an hour of an actual eruption. With predictions such as these, people have enough early warning to develop emergency action plans, including rescue routes.

Zones of Crustal Activity

Zones of frequent crustal activity can be located on Earth's surface. Major areas of uplift, sinking, earthquakes, and volcanic eruptions are often found together and are associated with features like young continental mountains, ocean trenches, island arcs, and mid-ocean ridges (mountain ranges in ocean areas). Note that the regions surrounding the Pacific Ocean contain a majority of these related events and features, and are thus referred to as the "Ring of Fire." Many of these associations are illustrated in Figure 12-9. The fact that these activities and features are clustered hints at their common origins, which will be discussed later in this topic.

Review Questions

9. The landscape shown in the following diagram is an area of frequent earthquakes.

This landscape provides evidence for

(1) converging convection cells within the rocks of the mantle
(2) density differences in the rocks of the mantle
(3) movement and displacement of the rocks of the crust
(4) differential erosion of hard and soft rocks of the crust

10. Which statement about Earth's crust in New York State is best supported by the many faults found in the crust?

(1) The crust has moved in the geologic past.
(2) The crust has been inactive throughout the geologic past.
(3) New faults will probably not develop in the crust.
(4) An earthquake epicenter has not been located in the crust.

11. Recent volcanic activity in different parts of the world supports the inference that volcanoes are located mainly in

(1) the centers of landscape regions
(2) the central regions of the continents
(3) zones of crustal activity
(4) zones in late stages of erosion

12. Where do most earthquakes originate?

(1) within Earth's outer core
(2) along specific belts within the crust
(3) randomly across the entire Earth's surface
(4) evenly spaced along the Moho interface

13. Earthquakes generate primary waves (P-waves) and secondary waves (S-waves). Compared to the speed of secondary waves in a given Earth material, the speed of primary waves is

(1) always slower
(2) always faster
(3) always the same
(4) sometimes faster and sometimes slower

The following diagram illustrates how the observatories in Pasadena, California; Chicago, Illinois; and Washington, D.C., locate the epicenter of an earthquake. Base your answers to questions 14 through 17 on the diagram.

14. The epicenter of the earthquake is located nearest

(1) A   (2) B   (3) C   (4) F

15. The separation in time between the arrival of primary and secondary waves is

(1) greatest at station G (Pasadena)
(2) greatest at station D (Chicago)
(3) greatest at station E (Washington, D.C.)
(4) the same at all stations

16. If the method illustrated by the diagram is used to locate the epicenter of an earthquake, it appears unlikely for an individual observatory operating independently to determine the

(1) direction to the epicenter
(2) distance to the epicenter
(3) distance to an epicenter under the ocean
(4) interval between the initial and subsequent seismic waves

17. The time lapse between the arrival of the P-waves and S-waves on ONE recording of seismic waves can be used to determine the

(1) magnitude of the earthquake
(2) exact location of the focus
(3) exact location of the epicenter
(4) distance to the epicenter

18. You record evidence of an earthquake on your seismograph. What information about the earthquake's epicenter can be determined from your seismograph alone?

19. A seismic station is 2000 kilometers from an earthquake epicenter. According to the *Earth Science Reference Tables,* how long does it take an S-wave to travel from the epicenter to the station?

(1) 7 min 20 sec   (3) 3 min 20 sec
(2) 5 min 10 sec   (4) 4 min 10 sec

20. The occurrence of earthquakes along a fault in New York State is an example of a

(1) cyclic change that can be predicted
(2) cyclic change that cannot be predicted
(3) noncyclic change that is easy to predict
(4) noncyclic change that is difficult to predict

21. The following diagrams represent seismographic traces of three disturbances—A, B, and C—recorded by the same seismograph.

The traces indicate that the distance from the station to the epicenters of the three disturbances is

(1) least for disturbance A
(2) least for disturbance B
(3) least for disturbance C
(4) the same for all three disturbances

22. The diagram below represents a shoreline in New York State; several general features have been labeled.

Past movements along the fault line most likely caused the formation of

(1) the sandbar
(2) tsunami
(3) ocean currents along the shore
(4) tides

23. Which information would be most useful for predicting the occurrence of an earthquake at a particular location?

(1) elevation
(2) climate
(3) seismic history
(4) number of nearby seismic stations

Base your answers to questions 24 through 28 on the following map. The map shows the time of arrival of seismic sea waves (tsunamis) from locations throughout the Pacific Ocean to the Hawaiian Islands. For example, an earthquake at any location on the line labeled "6 h" could produce a tsunami that would arrive in Honolulu 6 hours later.

Reporting Stations

• Tide stations
△ Seismograph stations

0 500 1000   2000
|___|___|_____|
Distance (miles)

h = hours

24. From which location would a tsunami arrive at Honolulu in the shortest time?

(1) Kodiak   (3) Tahiti
(2) La Jolla   (4) Wake Island

25. Which reporting station is NOT located on the Pacific plate?

(1) Hong Kong   (3) Honolulu
(2) Midway   (4) Tahiti

26. Approximately how fast do seismic sea waves travel from Midway to Honolulu, Hawaii?

(1) 31 to 51 mph   (3) 1500 to 2000 mph
(2) 300 to 500 mph   (4) 3000 to 5000 mph

27. The most likely reason for collecting this Pacific Ocean data is that Honolulu is

(1) the site of frequent major eruptions
(2) an equal distance from many seismic stations
(3) surrounded by earthquake-prone zones
(4) the site of a major tide station

28. Locations in this region where major earthquakes occur are most closely associated with areas of

(1) volcanic eruptions
(2) P-wave absorption
(3) magnetic field reversal
(4) mid-continental folding

A Model of Earth's Interior

Getting information about Earth's interior from direct observation is a difficult task. Therefore, most of its properties have been inferred from the study of earthquake waves.

Methods of Studying Earth's Interior

The deepest mines are little more than 3.5 kilometers deep, and the deepest drill hole (in Russia) is approximately 12 kilometers deep. This 12 kilometers represents less than 0.2 percent of the distance to the center of Earth.

Scientists infer most of the properties of Earth's interior through the study of seismic (earthquake) waves. This is much the same as studying human interiors with methods such as X-rays, ultrasounds, and CAT scans. By comparing thousands of seismograms from hundreds of locations, scientists have determined the times the different types of seismic waves arrive and when they don't arrive at numerous locations around Earth. By comparing these records with tests done using explosives in the oil industry and tests with nuclear bombs, scientists discovered that seismic waves refract, reflect, change velocity, and become absorbed by various parts of Earth's interior. Figures 12-10 and 12-11 show the most common model of Earth's interior that has resulted from these seismic wave studies.

Zones of Earth

Our analysis of seismic waves indicates that Earth is composed of a number of zones, as shown in Figures 12-10 and 12-11. The **crust** is the outermost part of Earth below the atmosphere or hydrosphere. Though mostly solid rock, the crust includes the soil and eroded and weathered rock deposits. Below the crust is the mostly solid part called the **mantle,** Earth's thickest zone that contains approximately 80 percent of Earth's volume. The mantle is separated from the crust by a thin interface called the **Moho.** Below the Moho, the rocks become denser. The whole crust and the very uppermost portion of the mantle (called the rigid mantle) are together called the **lithosphere.** (See Figure 12-11.) The lithosphere is

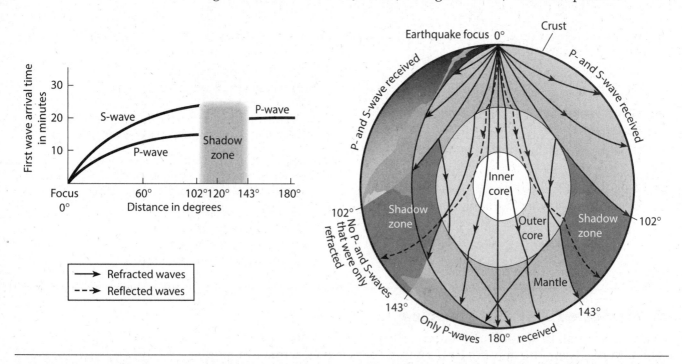

Figure 12-10. **Arrival times and paths of seismic waves moving through Earth's interior:** Analysis of the times seismic waves arrive has resulted in interpretations of reflections and refractions of these waves in Earth's interior. This analysis has resulted in the standard model of the zones of Earth's interior shown here.

divided into sections called "plates," which you will study in the next section.

Below the lithosphere is another portion of the upper mantle called the **asthenosphere.** This zone was discovered because it was found that seismic waves decreased in velocity from approximately 100 to 700 kilometers below Earth's surface. The asthenosphere is believed to be a plastic-like portion of the upper mantle that is at least partly molten. Much of the magma and lava of the crust and lithosphere is thought to originate in this zone. Note on the temperature graph in Figure 12-11 that the melting point and temperature curve intersect, indicating this partial melting. The asthenosphere allows the plates of the lithosphere to move around Earth's surface and to move up and down. Below the asthenosphere is the majority of the mantle, called the stiffer mantle.

Beneath the mantle Earth's core is divided into two parts—the **inner core** and the **outer core.** Figure 12-10 shows the outermost dimension—by area—of the shadow zone of the outer core that, due to refraction, does not receive any refracted seismic waves. The bottom of the outer core is indicated by the waves reflected off the outside edge of the inner core. Figure 12-10 also provides evidence that the outer core is liquid: Because no S-waves pass through the zone, it can't be a solid, and because the zone has too much pressure, it cannot be a gas. The S-waves are absorbed as they enter the outer core. The liquid nature of the outer core is also indicated by the major drop in P-wave velocity, as shown in Figure 12-11. Beneath the outer core is the inner core extending down to Earth's center. Due to the great pressures and the increase in P-wave velocity at the inner core (as shown in Figure 12-11), the inner core is believed to be a solid.

Earth's Crust Earth's crust, or upper lithosphere, is divided into two major divisions. The **continental crust** makes up the continents and larger islands, and the **oceanic crust** makes up most of the crust beneath the oceans. The continental crust is usually much thicker than the oceanic crust. The continental crust is thickest where highest—in mountain regions—and usually thinnest beneath coastal regions.

The two crusts are also distinguished by differences in composition and density.

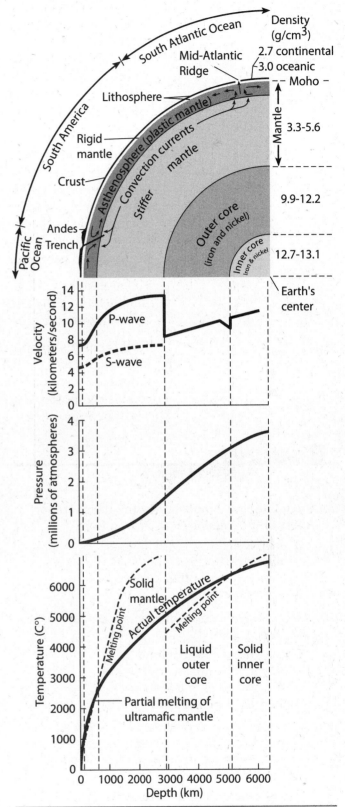

Figure 12-11. Properties and zones of Earth's interior: Analysis of the seismic waves and other studies have resulted in the inference about Earth's interior illustrated here. Note that most of Earth's interior is solid except for the outer core and portions of the asthenosphere, both of which are liquid. (See also the Inferred Properties of Earth's Interior in the *Earth Science Reference Tables.*)

The continental crust is made largely of granitic rocks—rocks with a mineral or chemical composition similar to granite. The oceanic crust is composed mostly of basaltic rocks—rocks similar in mineral or chemical composition to basalt. The granite is less dense than the basalt; thus, the granitic continental crust is less dense than the basaltic oceanic crust. See the average value of the density of the continental crust and oceanic crust Ⓡ on the Inferred Properties of Earth's Interior in the *Earth Science Reference Tables*.

Composition of Earth's Interior Many scientists think Earth's inner and outer core are composed largely of iron and nickel. There is much evidence to support this hypothesis, including the iron and nickel composition of many meteorites and Earth's magnetism—iron and nickel are two of a few magnetic elements. In addition, a combination of iron and nickel at the temperatures and pressures believed to be in Earth's core can account for the observed properties of the seismic waves that pass through the core.

The high-density iron-nickel composition of the core and the low-density composition of the crust indicate that the mantle must have a composition different from the crust and the core and an intermediate density.

Earth's crust is composed mostly of rocks and minerals, as illustrated on Ⓡ the various charts in the *Earth Science Reference Tables* depicting minerals, sedimentary rocks, metamorphic rocks, and igneous rocks. Generally, the crust is composed of low-density rocks with a mixture of granitic and basaltic compositions.

Review Questions

29. In developing a model of Earth's deep interior, most of the evidence was derived from
    (1) deep wells
    (2) mining operations
    (3) observation of other planets
    (4) seismic data

30. Through which zones of Earth do primary waves (P-waves) travel?
    (1) only the crust and mantle
    (2) only the mantle and outer core
    (3) only the outer and inner core
    (4) the crust, mantle, outer core, and inner core

31. According to the *Earth Science Reference Tables*, in which group are the zones of Earth's interior correctly arranged in order of increasing average density?
    (1) crust, mantle, outer core, inner core
    (2) crust, mantle, inner core, outer core
    (3) inner core, outer core, mantle, crust
    (4) outer core, inner core, mantle, crust

32. What evidence has been obtained concerning the existence of the Moho and Earth's mantle?
    (1) satellite images
    (2) well drillings
    (3) exposures in deep canyons like the Grand Canyon
    (4) refraction of earthquake waves

33. What is the relationship among density, temperature, and pressure inside Earth?
    (1) As depth increases, density, temperature, and pressure decrease.
    (2) As depth increases, density and temperature increase, but pressure decreases.
    (3) As depth increases, density increases, but temperature and pressure decrease.
    (4) As depth increases, density, temperature, and pressure increase.

34. In which parts of Earth's interior would melted or partially melted material be found?
    (1) stiffer mantle and inner core
    (2) stiffer mantle and outer core
    (3) crust and inner core
    (4) asthenosphere and outer core

35. An earthquake occurs in city A. Recordings on a seismograph in city B show only the presence of P-waves. City A and B are on opposite sides of Earth—180° apart. What does this information allow you to infer about the structure of Earth's interior?

36. How does the composition of the oceanic crust compare with the composition of the continental crust?

    (1) The oceanic crust is mainly limestone, while the continental crust is mainly sandstone.
    (2) The oceanic crust is mainly limestone, while the continental crust is mainly granitic.
    (3) The oceanic crust is mainly basaltic, while the continental crust is mainly sandstone.
    (4) The oceanic crust is mainly basaltic, while the continental crust is mainly granitic.

37. As one travels from an ocean shore to the interior of a continent, the thickness of Earth's crust generally

    (1) decreases
    (2) increases
    (3) remains the same

38. How does thickness and density of the continental crust compare to that of the oceanic crust?

    (1) The continental crust is thicker and less dense than the oceanic crust.
    (2) The continental crust is thicker and denser than the oceanic crust.
    (3) The continental crust is thinner and less dense than the oceanic crust.
    (4) The continental crust is thinner and denser than the oceanic crust.

39. The overall density of Earth is approximately 5.5 g/cm^3. The average density of Earth's crust is between 2.5 g/cm^3 and 3.0 g/cm^3. What does this suggest about the density of Earth's core?

40. The composition of some meteorites supports the inference that Earth's core is composed of

    (1) aluminum and calcium
    (2) iron and nickel
    (3) silicon and oxygen
    (4) magnesium and potassium

41. The temperature of rock located 1000 kilometers below Earth's surface is approximately

    (1) 1000°C   (3) 3300°C
    (2) 2600°C   (4) 4300°C

Plate Tectonics

People have always wondered about the origin of continents, mountain ranges, volcanoes, earthquakes, and the multitudes of other features and events. In the past, many legends, religious beliefs, and scientific theories have tried to explain Earth's features and events. Some of the older scientific theories include cooling and contraction of Earth, expansion of Earth, and continental drift. None of these earlier theories seems satisfactory for most of the scientific community today. Since the 1960s many new discoveries from the studies of ocean drilling, Earth's magnetism, satellite observations, and detailed analysis of rocks and fossils have led to the plate tectonic theory. This theory has done for the earth sciences what evolution and genetics have done for the biological sciences. It has provided a unifying model to explain most, if not all, major features and events of Earth's lithosphere.

The Plate Tectonic Theory

The basic concept of the **plate tectonic theory** is that Earth's lithosphere is broken up into sections or pieces called **plates**—also called **lithospheric plates** and **tectonic plates**—and their movement and interaction produce major changes in Earth's surface. In this book the term "plates" will mostly be used.

These plates move about Earth's surface at a rate of a few centimeters per year (approximately the rate of fingernail growth). These plates can also move up and down—usually at rates of only millimeters per year—due to uplifting and sinking. The plates can move around and up and down because they are floating on the asthenosphere—a plastic-like layer of the mantle.

Refer to Figure 12-12 and the Tectonic Plates map in the *Earth Science* Ⓡ *Reference Tables* to become familiar with the names and locations of the various plates. You will observe that the plates usually don't follow continent or ocean boundaries. Note that the North American plate includes parts of Asia and North America; the Pacific, Arctic, and the Atlantic Oceans; and Greenland and part of Iceland. Westernmost California and Mexico are part of the Pacific plate. Most plates have continental and oceanic crust at their tops. A small number of plates are oceanic—that is, they have only oceanic crust at their tops, like the Nazca and Philippine plates.

At least three times, if not more, most of the large landmasses (continents and larger islands) have come together, forming supercontinents. Figure 12-12 shows how the supercontinent Rodinia formed approximately 800 million years ago and how the continents have split and formed since then. Note that diagrams G and H indicate the projected positions of landmasses in the future, based on the rates and directions the plates are moving in now.

The Three Types of Plate Boundaries

As the plates move, they interact in three ways—they can separate, collide, and slide by each other. Most of the major events involving Earth's crust—such as mountain building, earthquakes, and volcanic eruptions—occur at the boundaries where the plates interact. Each of the three types of plate boundaries has its own set of unique events and features, which are illustrated in Figure 12-13.

Divergent Plate Boundaries Where two plates separate, or diverge, the boundary is called a **divergent plate boundary.** At these locations the plates move apart and magma rises from below to fill in the separation, resulting in igneous intrusions and extrusions, such as lava flows and volcanoes. (See Figure 12-13B.) This divergence is sometimes called sea-floor spreading.

This magma and resulting lava form igneous rock that creates new crust and lithosphere, which are then split and divided in two by the divergence. The magma that forms in these regions is the result of divergence that lowers the confining pressure and melts rocks of the lower lithosphere and asthenosphere. The divergence also results in many earthquakes, most of which are shallow in depth. If the divergence is within the continental crust, the result is a continental rift valley of mountains created by faulting and much volcanic activity. (See Figure 12-13A.)

When the divergence is within oceanic crust, the faulting and volcanic activity result in a **mid-ocean ridge,** a basaltic mountain range at the bottom of the ocean that is composed mostly of volcanoes and lava flows. The mid-ocean ridges often have a central depression, or rift valley, as shown in Figure 12-13B.

Convergent Plate Boundaries When two plates collide, or converge, the result is a **convergent plate boundary.** Much of the dramatic events and features of Earth's crust are created at these convergent boundaries. There are three varieties of convergent plate boundaries:

- both plates with oceanic crust on top

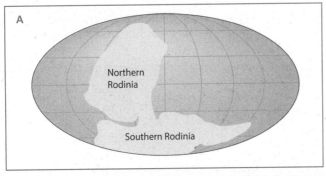

Earth around 700 millions years ago as supercontinent Rodinia is breaking up.

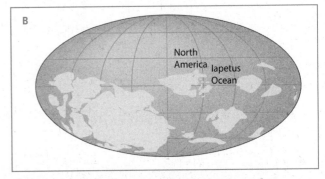

Earth around 550 million years after the break up of a supercontinent.

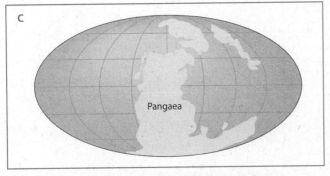

Earth around 250 million years ago when supercontinent Pangaea is just beginning to break up.

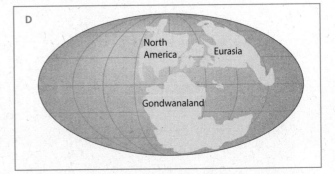

Earth around 135 millions years ago as Pangaea continues to break up.

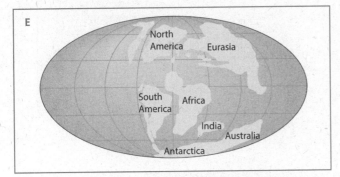

Earth around 100 million years ago with further break up of Pangaea.

Earth at present.

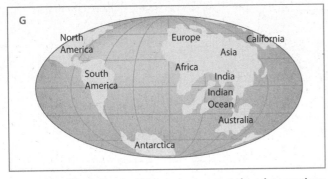

Earth 100 million years in future using present-day plate motions as a guide. Note bigger Atlantic Ocean and how Africa has split and collided with Europe.

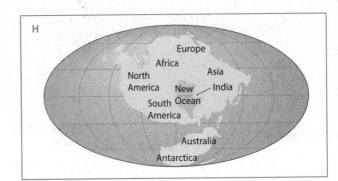

Using present-day plate motions as a guide, in approximately 250 million years, Earth may be close to another supercontinent.

Figure 12-12. **Changes in positions of Earth's landmasses from 700 million years ago to 250 million years into the future because of plate tectonics**

Figure 12-13. Types of plate boundaries: (A) Diverging plate boundaries in the continental crust result in a rift valley. (B) Diverging plate boundaries in the ocean result in a mid-ocean ridge, shallow-depth earthquakes, igneous intrusions, extrusions of lava flows, volcanoes, and passive margin basins in a down-warped part of crust. Plate 1 is moving west and plate 2 is moving east. (C) Converging plate boundaries result in an oceanic trench, volcanic island arcs, igneous intrusions, regional metamorphism, young mountains, and subduction of oceanic plate. Earthquake foci exist at various depths, indicating subductions. Plate 1 is moving east and plate 2 is moving west. (D) Transform plate boundaries result in many shallow-focus earthquakes and little to no igneous activity. Plate 1 is moving north and plate 2 is moving south.

- both plates with continental crust on top
- one plate with oceanic crust and the other with continental crust on top

Where two plates with oceanic crust or oceanic and continental crust at their edges converge, the denser of the two plates sinks under the other plate in a process called **subduction.** As illustrated in Figure 12-13C and the Tectonic Plates map in the *Earth Science Reference Tables*, these regions of ®
subduction of one oceanic plate under another result in ocean trenches and volcanic island arcs. The bending down of the subducting plate warps the crust, producing a long, steep, and narrow depression called an **ocean trench.** Some of these trenches are deeper below sea level than the highest mountains are above sea level. The subducting plate also results in magma bodies. Some of the magma breaks through Earth's solid surface and forms a series of volcanoes and volcanic islands—an **island arc.** The subducting process also results in a large amount of earthquake activity following the slope of the subducting plate into the bottom portions of the lithosphere. Very deep earthquakes only occur within subducting zones. The heat and pressure of the subduction causes large areas of crustal rocks to become metamorphosed in a process called "regional metamorphism."

If there is a continent near the two converging plates with oceanic crust, the crust at the margin of the continent may become bent down producing a down-warped ocean basin that is the site of much deposition of sediments. (See Figure 12-13C.) The sediments come from the eroding island arcs and the edge of the continents. Many of the rocks of eastern New York State formed in this type of down-warped basin before the formation of the supercontinent Pangaea.

Where a plate with oceanic crust on top converges with a plate with continental crust on top, the denser oceanic crust subducts under the continental lithosphere. An ocean trench off the coast of a continent often forms from this event. The magma that forms from the subduction doesn't create an island arc because the continent is above the region of magma formation. What forms instead are relatively new mountain ranges called **young mountains.** Like the Cascades in western Oregon and Washington, these mountain ranges may be mostly volcanic. They may also be a combination of volcanic, faulted, and folded.

When two plates with continents at their edges converge, the two plate edges bunch up together, causing a great thickening of the crust and lithosphere. This bunching up creates the highest of young mountains— such as the Himalayas, where India is colliding with Asia.

Plate convergence that results in the growth of young mountain ranges is called orogeny. The term is also used to indicate the time when mountain building occurs. Refer to Important Geologic Events in New York within Geologic History of New York State in the *Earth Science Reference Tables,* ®
and you will note the four orogenies (Grenville, Taconian, Acadian, and Alleghenian) that have resulted in mountains in New York State and surrounding regions.

Transform Plate Boundaries When two plates collide by sliding past each other, the boundary is called a **transform plate boundary.** The dragging of lithospheric rocks along the edges of the transform boundaries builds up much potential energy in rocks; this energy is eventually released as kinetic

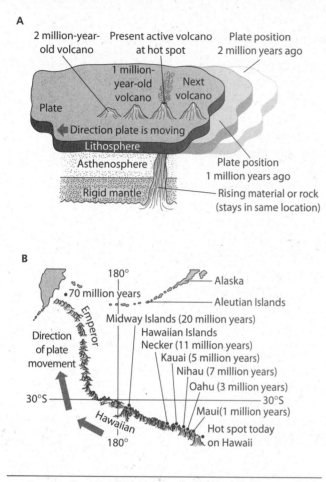

A

2 million-year-old volcano · Present active volcano at hot spot · Plate position 2 million years ago

1 million-year-old volcano · Next volcano

Plate

← Direction plate is moving

Lithosphere

Asthenosphere

Rigid mantle

Plate position 1 million years ago

Rising material or rock (stays in same location)

B

180°

• 70 million years — Alaska

— Aleutian Islands

Emperor

Direction of plate movement

Midway Islands (20 million years)
Hawaiian Islands
Necker (11 million years)
Kauai (5 million years)
Nihau (7 million years)
Oahu (3 million years)

30°S

30°S

Maui (1 million years)

Hawaiian

Hot spot today
on Hawaii

180°

Figure 12-14. Hot spots, rising material, and plate movements: It is believed that rising material (a plume) from the mantle melts through the plates of the lithosphere, forming volcanoes at hot spots. As the plate moves, new hot spots and volcanoes form, as shown in diagram A. The Hawaiian Islands' Emperor Seamount (underwater volcanoes) Trail was created by movements of the Pacific plate over an area of rising material, as shown in diagram B. Note how the Pacific plate may have changed direction some 25 million to 30 million years ago or the rising hot material changed its location.

mechanical energy in the form of earthquakes. The San Andreas fault system in California is an example of a transform plate boundary between the North American and Pacific plates.

Driving Forces of Plate Tectonics

While most scientists accept the major part of the plate tectonic theory, there is still much debate about what makes the plates move. The most accepted theory is that mantle <u>convection</u> <u>currents</u> drag or push the plates apart at places where plates diverge. The exact location of these convection currents is hotly debated. The energy source for these convection currents is the heat of Earth's interior, which causes hotter, less dense parts of the mantle to rise under diverging plates. Gravity pulls down the cooler, more dense regions of the mantle, causing falling convection currents in subduction areas. (See Figures 12-11, 12-13, and 12-15 for illustrations of convection in the mantle.)

Hot Spots

One major aspect of lithosphere and crust that is difficult to explain by the conventional plate tectonic theory concerns major regions of volcanic activity in the interior parts of plates away from plate boundaries. These regions are called **hot spots.** Examples include the big island of Hawaii, the region around Yellowstone National Park in Wyoming and Montana, and maybe even the Adirondack Mountains of New York State. See the hot spots on Tectonic Plates in the *Earth Science Reference Tables*.

Ⓡ

Scientists have proposed that hot spots occur where rising material from the lower mantle remains stationary for millions of years. When a plate moves over the rising materials, it melts its way to or near the surface to form a hot spot. Hot spots become regions of intrusive and extrusive volcanic activity that can build volcanoes and lava flows and push up regions of the crust to form mountains. Because the plate keeps moving over the rising materials, a series of volcanic mountains form for thousands of miles. These trails of hot-spot features can be used to infer past movements of the plates that moved over the hot spots. Hot spots also exist at plate boundaries. See Figure 12-14 to help you understand rising materials and hot spots.

Effects of Plate Tectonics

The movements of the plates for 3 to 4 billion years in the past and for untold millions of years in the future has had and will continue to have many effects on Earth and its inhabitants. Many of these effects are described in the sections that follow.

Appearance of Continents The outlines of the present-day continents appear to fit together like the pieces of a jigsaw puzzle because supercontinent Pangaea split apart starting approximately 225 million years ago, and a few pieces have rejoined one another. This can be seen in Figure 12-12 and in the Inferred Positions of Earth's Landmasses section of the Geologic History of New York in the *Earth Science Reference Tables*. Ⓡ

Figure 12-15. Model of convection currents in Earth's mantle

Features of Landmasses Similarities in minerals, rocks, fossils, age, and structure features of mountain ranges are found at places where the continents and other landmasses may have fitted together in the past. These similar features on different landmasses indicate a commonality in age and origin. Today the continents are separated, and their respective life forms are often greatly different. The variation in life forms on the different land areas is a result of evolution. However, fossil evidence shows that in the past many plants and animals, such as the Glossopteris fossils of Figure 12-16, were the same throughout the world. Such a wide distribution of the same plants and animals probably could not have occurred unless the continents were connected. Figure 12-16 shows some of the now separated locations that have rocks, minerals, fossils, and mountain structures in common. These similarities suggest that the land areas were together when these features were formed, and that these areas have since separated as the plates moved.

As the plates move portions of Earth's surface to new locations, rocks are exposed to different climate conditions. The finding of rocks near the

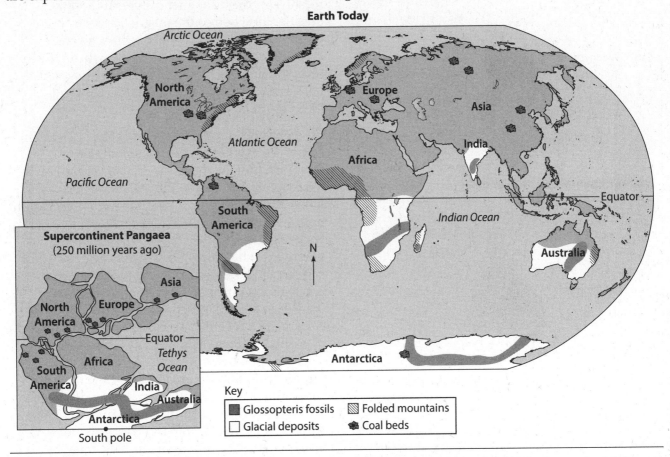

Figure 12-16. Changing features of landmasses due to plate movements: Many features of Earth's landmasses in rocks more than 250 million years old don't make sense unless the landmasses were in different locations approximately 250 million years ago when the supercontinent Pangaea existed.

equator with evidence of glacial erosion and deposition and rocks near the poles with coal deposits of the same ages indicates a climate pattern of hot near the poles and cold near the equator. The probable answer to this dilemma is that plate movements have changed the locations of the landmasses.

Age and Heat Patterns of Oceanic Rocks As the magma rises and forms basaltic igneous rocks at the mid-ocean ridges, it spreads outwards away from the ridges with divergence. This divergence of the plates is illustrated by dating samples of the oceanic basaltic rocks. The farther the sample is from the center of a mid-ocean ridge, the older the igneous rock is. The rocks are dated using the methods of radioactive-decay dating.

Another similar pattern is indicated from heat flow measurements taken from the basaltic ocean crust. Measurements indicate that heat decreases as distances from the mid-ocean ridges increase. This makes sense because the hottest rocks should be closest to the magma and lava from which they formed.

Magnetic Patterns of Oceanic Basaltic Rocks The divergence of the oceanic lithosphere and crust at mid-ocean ridges is shown by patterns in magnetism of the oceanic-basaltic rocks. Earth's magnetic poles flip-flop in polarity (north changes to south and south changes to north) in periods of thousands of years in a process called reversal of Earth's magnetic polarity. The reasons for these magnetic reversals and the question of whether the magnetic reversals are cyclic or non-cyclic have not been answered. What is known is that Earth's magnetic field has reversed hundreds of times since the magnetic field's origin, probably billions of years ago. (See Figure 12-17.)

When basaltic rock crystallizes at the mid-ocean ridges, its magnetic minerals are aligned; therefore, they record the particular polarity when the magma and lava solidify. Normal polarity is when magnetic north is near the north geographic pole and magnetic south is near the south geographic pole—as is true today. Reversed polarity is when magnetic north is near the south geographic pole and magnetic south is near the north geographic pole. It has been found that there is a pattern of corresponding stripes of basaltic rock on either side of the mid-ocean ridges of normal and reversed polarity. This evidence suggests that the corresponding stripes were formed at similar times, and the sea-floor spreading has separated them during divergence. These stripes are illustrated on Figure 12-13 and Appendix 6. Note that these stripes are not a visual feature but a pattern only indicated by magnetic instruments used in airplanes or oceanographic research ships.

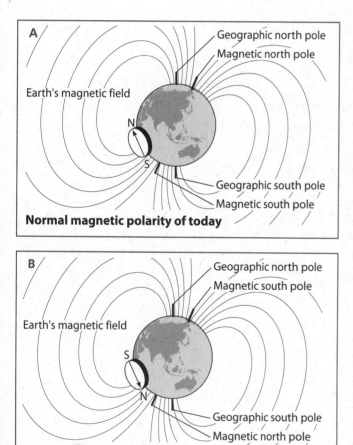

Figure 12-17. **Normal and reversed polarity of Earth's magnetism:** Earth's magnetic field flip-flops from normal polarity to reversed polarity in time spans of thousands of years.

Other Effects of Plate Tectonics The movement of the plates has had and will continue to have other effects on Earth and its inhabitants:

- environmental hazards, such as volcanic eruptions, earthquakes, and tsunamis
- changes in Earth's climate and weather, such as altering the locations of land and ocean areas and creating mountains to change wind patterns
- changes in the factors that cause our day-to-day weather by changing the distribution of land and ocean areas and other features, such as mountains and large continental regions
- the rock cycle
- the major landscape features of Earth—continents, ocean basins, mountains, plains, and plateaus
- exposing rocks to weathering and erosion that carve the details of the solid Earth surface and form sediments

Review Questions

Base your answers to questions 42 through 48 on the following diagram. The diagram is an earlier tectonic-plate model that represents one possible interpretation of the movements of Earth's rock surfaces according to the theory of plate tectonics. According to this interpretation, Earth's lithosphere consists of several large plates that are moving in relationship to one another. The arrows in the diagram show some of this relative motion of the plates. The diagram also shows the age of formation of the igneous rocks that make up the oceanic crust of the northern section of the Pacific plate.

42. According to the *Earth Science Reference Tables*, during which geologic time period were the continents of North America, South America, and Africa closest together?

  (1) Tertiary   (3) Triassic
  (2) Cretaceous   (4) Ordovician

43. According to the theory of plate tectonics, the distance between two continents on opposite sides of a mid-oceanic ridge will generally

  (1) decrease
  (2) increase
  (3) remain the same

44. Which statement is best supported by the relative movement shown by the arrows in the diagram?

  (1) North America and South America are moving toward each other.
  (2) The Indian-Australian plate is moving away from the Eurasian plate.
  (3) The African plate and Eurasian plate are moving away from the North American plate.
  (4) The Antarctic plate is moving away from the North American plate.

45. The boundaries between all of these plates are best described as the sites of

(1) frequent crustal activity
(2) deep ocean depths
(3) continental boundaries
(4) magnetic age pattern

46. Which geologic structure is represented by the double line separating the North American plate from the African and Eurasian plates?

(1) thick continental crust
(2) thick layers of sediment
(3) mid-ocean ridge
(4) granitic igneous rock

47. Which provides the best explanation of the mechanism that causes these plates to move across Earth's surface?

(1) convection currents in the mantle
(2) faulting of the lithosphere
(3) the spin of Earth on its axis
(4) prevailing wind belts of the troposphere

48. The age of formation of the igneous rocks A, B, C, D, and E that make up the oceanic crust of the northern half of the Pacific plate suggests that this section of the Pacific plate is generally moving in which direction?

(1) from north to south   (3) from west to east
(2) from south to north   (4) from east to west

---

49. Scientists theorize that Africa and South America were once part of the same large continent. Cite two pieces of evidence that support this theory.

50. Which statement best supports the concept that continents have shifted position?

(1) Basaltic rock is found to be progressively younger at increasing distances from a mid-ocean ridge.
(2) Marine fossils are often found in deep-well drill cores.
(3) The present continents appear to fit together as pieces of a larger landmass.
(4) Areas of shallow-water seas tend to accumulate sediment, which gradually sinks

51. Describe two expected similarities between rock samples found equal distances from and on opposite sides of the Mid-Atlantic Ridge.

52. Which feature is commonly formed at a plate boundary where oceanic crust converges with continental crust?

(1) a mid-ocean ridge   (3) a transform fault
(2) an oceanic trench   (4) new oceanic crust

53. Evidence of subduction exists at the boundary between the

(1) African and South American plates
(2) Indian-Australian and Antarctic plates
(3) Pacific and Antarctic plates
(4) Nazca and South American plates

54. Which of the following cross-sectional diagrams best represents a model for the movement of rock material below the crust along the mid-Atlantic ridge?

55. The following drawing represents the ocean floor between North America and Africa.

Which graph best represents the age of the bedrock in the ocean floor along line AB?

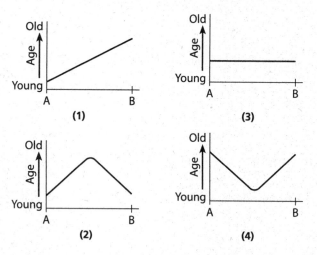

56. Igneous materials found along mid-ocean ridges contain magnetic particles that show reversal of magnetic orientation. This is evidence that

(1) volcanic activity has occurred constantly throughout history
(2) Earth's magnetic poles have exchanged their positions
(3) igneous materials are always formed beneath oceans
(4) Earth's crust does not move

Base your answers to questions 57 through 61 on the following diagram. The diagram shows the magnetic orientation of igneous rock on the sea floor on the east side of a mid-ocean ridge. The pattern on the west (left) side of the ridge has been omitted. The age of the igneous rock and its distance from the ridge center are shown.

 Magnetic minerals in these rocks indicate magnetic north as it is today.

Magnetic minerals in this rock indicate magnetic north to be where magnetic south is today.

57. Which of the following diagrams best represents the pattern of magnetic orientation in the sea floor on the west (left) side of the ocean ridge?

(1)

(3)

(2)

(4)

58. According to the diagram, what is the approximate rate of sea-floor spreading?

(1) 1 km/million years
(2) 2 km/million years
(3) 40 km/million years
(4) 50 km/million years

59. Which inference can best be made from the diagram?

(1) The orientation of Earth's magnetic field has reversed with time.
(2) The size of the continents has changed with time.
(3) The elevation of sea level has changed with time.
(4) The amount of fossil material preserved in the igneous rock has changed with time.

60. The crustal material on both sides of the ridge indicates that the tectonic plates are

(1) diverging
(2) converging
(3) not moving
(4) moving parallel to the ridge

61. As the distance from the center of the ridge increases, the age of the rocks

(1) decreases
(2) increases
(3) remains the same
(4) increases and decreases in a cyclic pattern

Base your answers to questions 62 through 66 on the following diagrams. Diagram I is a map showing the location and bedrock age of some of the Hawaiian Islands. Diagram II is a cross section of an area of Earth that illustrates a stationary magma source (rising magma and hot spot) and the process that could have formed the islands.

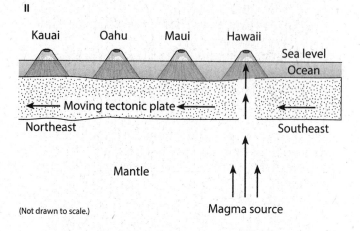

62. If each island formed as the tectonic plate moved over the magma source in the mantle, as shown in diagram II, where would the next volcanic island form?

(1) northwest of Kauai
(2) northeast of Hawaii
(3) southeast of Hawaii
(4) between Hawaii and Maui

63. Compared to the continental crust of North America, the oceanic crust in the area of the Hawaiian Islands is probably

(1) thinner and similar in composition
(2) thinner and different in composition
(3) thicker and similar in composition
(4) thicker and different in composition

64. Volcanic activity like that which produced the Hawaiian Islands is usually closely correlated with

(1) nearness to the center of a large ocean
(2) sudden changes in Earth's magnetic field
(3) frequent major changes in climate
(4) frequent earthquake activity

65. Which of the Hawaiian Islands has the greatest probability of a volcanic eruption?

(1) Kauai (3) Maui
(2) Oahu (4) Hawaii

66. Which of the following graphs best represents the ages of the Hawaiian Islands, comparing them from point A to point B?

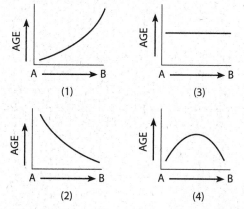

67. What do mid-ocean ridges and hot spots have in common?

(1) They are associated with rising magma.
(2) They are always associated with present-day plate boundaries.
(3) They commonly are associated with earthquakes of great depth.
(4) Neither is associated with plate motions.

68. Which observation provides the strongest evidence for the inference that convection cells exist within Earth's mantle?

(1) Sea level has varied in the past.
(2) Marine fossils are found at elevations high above sea level.
(3) Displaced rock strata are usually accompanied by earthquakes and volcanoes.
(4) Heat-flow readings vary at different locations in Earth's crust.

Directions

Review the Test-Taking Strategies section of this book. Then answer the following questions. Read each question carefully and answer with a correct choice or response.

Part A

1 The following is a record of earthquake waves from a seismic station.

Which information can be determined by using this record?
- (1) the depth of the earthquake's focus
- (2) the direction of the earthquake's focus
- (3) the location of the earthquake's epicenter
- (4) the distance to the earthquake's epicenter

2 Decide which statement best describes the relationship between the travel rates and travel times of earthquake P-waves and S-waves from the focus of an earthquake to a seismic station.
- (1) P-waves travel at a slower rate and take less time.
- (2) P-waves travel at a faster rate and take less time.
- (3) S-waves travel at a slower rate and take less time.
- (4) S-waves travel at a faster rate and take less time.

3 Where is the thickest part of Earth's crust?
- (1) at the edges of the continental shelves
- (2) at mid-ocean ridges
- (3) under continental mountain ranges
- (4) under volcanic islands

4 What is the material between 2900 kilometers and 5200 kilometers below Earth's surface inferred to be?
- (1) an iron-rich solid
- (2) an iron-rich liquid
- (3) a silicate-rich solid
- (4) a silicate-rich liquid

5 An earthquake's P-waves traveled 4800 kilometers and arrived at a seismic station at 5:10 P.M. At approximately what time did the earthquake occur?

6 The theory of plate tectonics suggests that the
- (1) continents moved due to changes in Earth's orbital speed
- (2) continents moved due to the Coriolis effect caused by Earth's rotation
- (3) present-day continents of South America and Africa are moving toward each other
- (4) present-day continents of South America and Africa once fit together like puzzle pieces

7 What is one of the main reasons volcanic eruptions can be predicted in enough time to allow people to escape?
- (1) Many volcanoes emit X-rays before eruptions.
- (2) Most volcanoes form a new crater before major eruptions.
- (3) Most volcanoes swell in volume before major eruptions.
- (4) Most animals escape from an area before most eruptions.

8 What is the best evidence that earthquakes and crustal movements are associated?
- (1) associations of earthquake belts and young mountain ranges
- (2) association of earthquake belts and belts of old metamorphic rocks
- (3) studying faults in lava flows
- (4) samples of rocks and fluids from deep drill holes

Base your answers to questions 9 through 11 on the following map. The map shows a mid-ocean ridge and trenches in the Pacific Ocean.

9 Movement of the plates shown in the diagram is most likely caused by
   (1) the revolution of Earth
   (2) the erosion of Earth's crust
   (3) shifting of Earth's magnetic poles
   (4) convection in Earth's mantle

10 The crust at the mid-ocean ridge is composed mainly of
   (1) granite   (3) shale
   (2) basalt   (4) limestone

11 Mid-ocean ridges such as the East Pacific Ridge are best described as
   (1) mountains containing folded sedimentary rocks
   (2) plateaus containing fossils of present-day marine life
   (3) sections of the ocean floor that contain the youngest oceanic crust
   (4) sections of the ocean floor that are the remains of a submerged continent

12 At which depth below Earth's surface is the density most likely 10.5 grams per cubic centimeter?
   (1) 1500 km   (3) 3500 km
   (2) 2000 km   (4) 6000 km

13 What happens to P-waves and S-waves from a crustal earthquake when the waves reach Earth's core?
   (1) S-waves are transmitted through the outer core, but P-waves are not transmitted.
   (2) P-waves are transmitted through the outer core, but S-waves are not transmitted.
   (3) Both P-waves and S-waves are transmitted through the outer core.
   (4) Neither P-waves nor S-waves are transmitted through the outer core.

14 At a depth of 2000 kilometers, the temperature of the stiffer mantle is inferred to be
   (1) 6500°C   (3) 3500°C
   (2) 4200°C   (4) 1500°C

15 Tsunamis can be directly caused by
   (1) offshore surface ocean currents
   (2) gravitational effects of the moon
   (3) underwater earthquakes
   (4) underwater lava flows at mid-ocean ridges

16 A large earthquake occurred at 45° N, 75° W on September 5, 1994. Which location in New York State was closest to the epicenter of the earthquake?
   (1) Buffalo
   (2) Massena
   (3) Albany
   (4) New York City

17 Oxygen is the most abundant element by volume in Earth's
   (1) inner core
   (2) crust
   (3) hydrosphere
   (4) troposphere

18 Which geologic event occurred most recently?
   (1) initial opening of the Atlantic Ocean
   (2) metamorphism of the rocks of the Hudson Highlands
   (3) formation of the Catskill delta
   (4) collision of North America and Africa

Part B

Base your answers to questions 19 through 21 on the following map. The star symbol represents a volcano located on the mid-Atlantic ridge in Iceland. The isolines represent the thickness, in centimeters, of volcanic ash deposited from an eruption of this volcano. Points A and B represent locations in the area.

19 On the grid below and using the directions below, construct a profile of the ash thickness between point A and point B.

a. Plot the thickness of the volcanic ash along line AB by marking with a dot each point where an isoline is crossed by line AB. [2]

b. Connect the dots to complete the profile of the thickness of the volcanic ash. [1]

20 State one factor that could have produced this pattern of deposition of the ash. [1]

21 State why volcanic eruptions are likely to occur in Iceland. [1]

Base your answers to questions 22 through 24 on the cross section below, which shows the major surface features of Earth along 25° S latitude between 75° W and 15° E longitude. Points A, B, and C represent locations on Earth's crust.

(Not drawn to scale)

22 Identify the crustal feature located at point A. [1]

23 Identify the tectonic plate motion that is causing an increase in the distance between South America and Africa. [1]

24 Bedrock samples were taken at the mid-ocean ridge and points *B* and *C*. On the following grid, draw a line to show the relative age of the bedrock samples between these locations. [1]

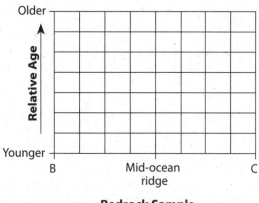

Bedrock Sample Location

Base your answers to questions 25 and 26 on the diagram below, which shows two seismogram tracings, at stations *A* and *B*, for the same earthquake. The arrival times of the *P*-waves and *S*-waves are indicated on each tracing.

Seismogram Tracings

25 Explain how the seismic tracings recorded at station *A* and station *B* indicate that station *A* is farther from the earthquake epicenter than station *B*. [1]

26 Seismic station *A* is located 5,400 kilometers from the epicenter of the earthquake. How much time would it take for the first *S*-wave produced by this earthquake to reach seismic station *A*? [1]

Base your answers to questions 27 through 30 on the map below.

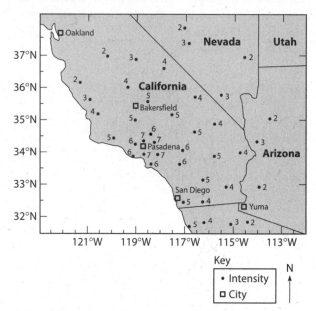

Key

• Intensity

□ City

An earthquake occurred in the southwestern United States. Intensity units were plotted for several locations on a map. (As the numerical value of intensities increases, the damaging effects of the earthquake waves also increases.)

27 Using an interval of 2 units and starting with an isoline representing 2 units, draw an accurate isoline map of earthquake intensity. [4]

28 State the name of the city that is closest to the earthquake epicenter. [1]

29 Identify the most likely cause of earthquakes that occur in the area shown on the map. [1]

30 A newspaper article indicates that a major earthquake is expected in the local area. State three actions individuals could take to increase safety or reduce injury from an earthquake. [3]

Part C

Base your answers to questions 31 through 34 on the map and block diagram below. The block diagram shows a portion of North Island in New Zealand. The Hikurangi Trench is shown forming at the edge of the Pacific Plate. Point X is at the boundary between the lithosphere and the asthenosphere.

Map

Block Diagram

(Not drawn to scale)

31 State the approximate temperature at point X. [1]

32 On what tectonic plate are both North Island and White Island located? [1]

33 Describe the type of tectonic plate motion that formed the Hikurangi Trench. [1]

34 Describe *one* action that people on North Island should take if a tsunami warning is issued. [1]

Use the following information and your knowledge of earth science to answer questions 35 through 39.

Studies of the planet Mars from 1965 to the present have allowed scientists to infer that like Earth, Mars has or had hot spots; but unlike Earth there is no evidence of plates or movement of plates.

35 Describe a landscape feature composed of igneous rocks that you would expect to find on Mars and explain why you would expect to find it there. [2]

36 Identify four large (hundreds of miles in length) types of landscape features that, although common on Earth, would not be expected to be found on Mars. Explain why these features would not likely be found on Mars. [4]

37 Describe two events that are common on Earth that, due to a lack of plate movements, you would not expect to occur on Mars. [2]

38 Explain why folded mountains have not been found, nor are expected to be found, on Mars. [1]

39 Discuss the likelihood of finding metamorphic rocks on Mars, and defend your conclusion. [2]

40 Name one region of the United States that is likely to experience a major damaging earthquake. Explain why an earthquake is likely to occur in that region. [1]

Base your answers to questions 41 through 44 on the information below and on your knowledge of Earth science.

In the 1930s, most scientists believed that Earth's crust and interior were solid and motionless. A small group of scientists were talking about "continental drift," which is the idea that Earth's crust is not stationary, but is constantly shifting and moving.

From seismic data, geophysical evidence, and laboratory experiments, scientists now generally agree that lithospheric plates move at the surface. Both Earth's surface and interior are in motion. Solid rock in the mantle can be softened and shaped when subjected to the heat and pressure within Earth's interior over millions of years.

Subduction processes are believed by many scientists to be the driving force of plate tectonics. At present, this theory cannot be directly observed and confirmed. The lithospheric plates have moved in the past and are still moving today. The details of why and how they move will continue to challenge scientists.

41 Earth's crust is described as "constantly shifting and moving." Give one example of geologic evidence that supports the conclusion that continents have drifted apart. [1]

42 The information given suggests that "subduction processes are the driving force of plate tectonics." Identify a specific location of a subduction zone on Earth. [1]

43 According to the *Earth Science Reference Tables*, at what inferred depth is *mantle* rock partially melted and slowly moving below the lithospheric plates? [1]

44 According to the geologic record, during which geologic time period did the lithospheric plates that made up Pangaea begin to break up? [1]

Base your answers to questions 45 through 48 on the world map shown below and on your knowledge of Earth science. Letters *A* through *H* represent locations on Earth's surface.

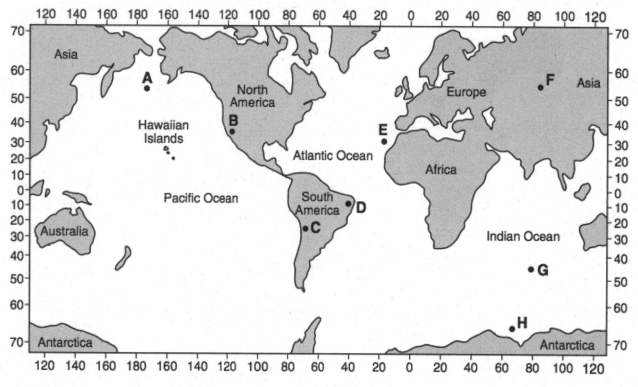

45 Explain why most earthquakes that occur in the crust beneath location *B* are shallower than most earthquakes that occur in the crust beneath location *C*. [1]

46 Explain why location *A* has a greater probability of experiencing a major earthquake than location *D*. [1]

47 Explain why a volcanic eruption is more likely to occur at location *E* than at location *F*. [1]

48 Explain why the geologic age of the oceanic bedrock increases from location *G* to location *H*. [1]

Interpreting Geologic History

How Scientists Study Geologic History

> **How can carbon-14 radioactive decay dating help us know when different organisms lived in the past and whether humans were present at that time?**

Using carbon-14, mastodont bones and evidence of humans found in New York State have been dated at around 10,000 years old, which means they lived at the end of the Pleistocene Ice Age. Carbon-14 was chosen because it can be used for dating organic materials from only 70,000 years ago under the best conditions. This is because the half-life of carbon-14 is only 5,700 years, and there is too little left after 70,000 years for present technology to measure accurately.

Footprints of Coelophysis dinosaurs have been found in southeastern parts of New York in the Newark Lowlands (see index fossils on Geologic History of New York State in the *Earth Science Reference Tables*). The rocks of this area are Late Triassic and Early Jurassic in age, thus they are around 200 million years old. Why couldn't carbon-14 be used to date these rocks? How can 200-million-year-old rocks be dated? Use information on correlations and absolute dating in this topic to answer these questions.

Ⓡ

Interpreting Geologic History

Vocabulary

absolute age	half-life	radioactive dating
bedrock	inclusion	radioactive decay
carbon-14 dating	index fossil	species
correlation	intrusion	unconformity
cross-cutting relationships	isotope	uranium-238
extrusion	organic evolution (theory of)	volcanic ash
fossil	outgassing	
geologic time scale	principle of superposition	

Topic Overview

The composition, structure, position, and fossil content of Earth's rocks provide information about Earth's geologic history. Evidence in Earth's rocks dates back approximately 4.2 billion years. In the *Earth Science Reference Tables*, carefully study the Geologic History of New York State and the Generalized Bedrock Geology of New York State. A bedrock, or geologic, map shows the rock types that underlie an area and their age.

Figure 13-1. The principle of superposition and possible exceptions: (A) Normally, a rock layer is younger than the layers below it. (B) Overturned folds can result in an exception to the principle. Layer 1 at the lower right is actually a continuation of layer 1 at the upper left. (C) and (D) Movement of layers along an overthrust fault can result in an exception to the principle. Layers numbered alike are the same age. The arrow in diagram C shows the direction of overthrusting.

Relative Dating of Rocks and Events

Relative dating is the determination of the age of a rock or event in relation to the age of other rocks or events. The following descriptions explain how methods of relative dating make it possible to determine relative age. Note that relative age differs from **absolute age,** which refers to the actual age of a rock or an event in years.

Principle of Superposition

When observing layers of sedimentary rock, or some extrusive igneous rocks, geologists usually infer that the bottom layer is the oldest. Each overlying layer is then progressively younger, so that the top layer is the youngest, or most recently formed. This inference is called the **principle of superposition,** and it is the basis for methods of relative dating. (See Figure 13-1.) Superposition relates

to the original horizontality of deposited sediments or of volcanic rock layers.

Exceptions to the principle of superposition sometimes occur when changes in Earth's crust cause the deformation of rock layers. Some exceptions are illustrated in Figure 13-1. For example, when there are overturns in folded rock layers, or when movement along faults thrusts older rock layers over younger layers, the principle of superposition no longer holds true.

Dating Intrusions, Extrusions, and Inclusions

When magma squeezes into preexisting rocks and crystallizes, it forms an igneous rock body called an **intrusion,** as shown in Figure 13-2. Intrusions can vary in thickness from centimeters to hundreds of kilometers. An intrusion is younger, in relative age, than any rock it cuts through.

When lava flows on Earth's surface and solidifies, it forms a mass of igneous rock called an **extrusion** as shown in Figure 13-2. Extrusions include lava flows and volcanoes. The extrusion is younger than any rocks beneath it, but will be older than any rocks that may later form on top of it.

An **inclusion** is a body of older rock within igneous rock. Often when magma rises towards Earth's surface, pieces of the rock that the magma is intruding—pushing through—will fall into the magma. Usually these pieces of older rock will melt to become part of the magma. However, if the temperature of the magma is lower, as occurs when the magma is about to solidify, the older body will not melt. The result is the formation of an inclusion as shown in Figure 13-3. Some of Earth's oldest dated rocks have inclusions in them; thus, scientists know that even older rocks exist. However, they may not know how much older these rocks are.

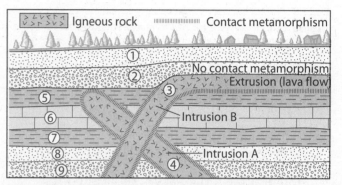

Figure 13-2. Relative ages of intrusions and extrusions: Intrusion A is younger than the layers it intrudes. Intrusion B is younger than intrusion A because it cuts intrusion A. The layers above the extrusion must be younger than the extrusion because of the absence of contact metamorphism along their common boundary. The rocks are numbered in order of increasing age.

Dating Rock Features and Cross-Cutting Relationships

Many of the structural features within rocks provide evidence to use in relative dating. For example, a rock is older than any fault, joint, tilting, or fold that appears in it. The reason is that rocks form without these features, and are folded, tilted, or cracked afterward.

Rock characteristics, as shown in Figure 13-3, can also be used in relative dating. In sedimentary rocks, the sediments are older than the rock itself, while the cement is younger. In igneous rocks, individual mineral crystals vary in age because they form at different temperatures reached by the magma as it cools and hardens over thousands or millions of years. Older mineral crystals are generally larger and show a well-developed crystal shape.

Rocks may also contain mineral deposits called veins. A vein forms when a watery mineral solution fills a crack or permeable zone in the rock. Like an intrusion, a vein is younger than the rock around it. Veins often contain valuable natural resources such as gold, silver, and lead ores.

Intrusions, faults, joints, and veins are types of **cross-cutting relationships.** Because cross-cutting relationships cut across older rock, they are younger.

MemoryJogger

Recall that <u>contact metamorphism</u> occurs when magma or lava comes in contact with older bedrock and alters the minerals and/or sediments by recrystallization. This process results in a younger metamorphic rock with a new texture and/or mineral composition.

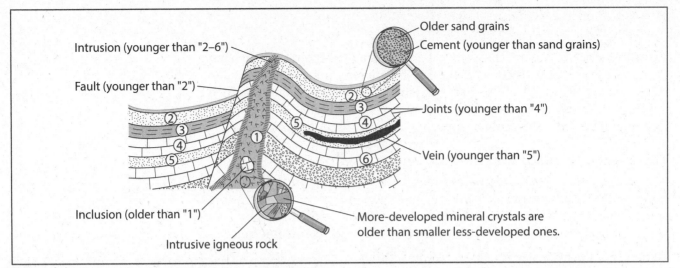

Intrusion (younger than "2–6")

Fault (younger than "2")

Older sand grains

Cement (younger than sand grains)

Joints (younger than "4")

Vein (younger than "5")

Inclusion (older than "1")

Intrusive igneous rock

More-developed mineral crystals are older than smaller less-developed ones.

Figure 13-3. Relative ages of structural and internal features of rocks: Folds, faults, joints, and veins are younger than the rocks in which they occur. Sediments such as sand grains and inclusions in igneous rocks are older than the rocks in which they occur.

Review Questions

1. According to the Generalized Bedrock Geology of New York State in the *Earth Science Reference Tables,* what is the geologic age of the bedrock found at the surface at 43° 30′N latitude by 75° 00′ W longitude?

   (1) Devonian   (3) Early Ordovician
   (3) Cambrian   (4) Middle Proterozoic

2. Which area in New York State is located on rock formations that contain large amounts of salt deposits?

   (1) Syracuse   (3) New York City
   (2) Long Island   (4) Old Forge

3. The following diagram represents a cross-sectional view of a portion of Earth's crust showing sedimentary rock layers that have not been overturned. The letters identify the specific layers.

   Which rock layer is probably the oldest?

   (1) A   (2) B   (3) C   (4) D

4. The following diagram shows a portion of Earth's crust. What is the relative age of the igneous rock?

   (1) It is older than the limestone but younger than the shale.
   (2) It is younger than the limestone but older than the shale.
   (3) It is older than both the limestone and the shale.
   (4) It is younger than both the limestone and the shale.

   Key
   Limestone
   Shale
   Igneous rock formation
   Contact metamorphism

5. Suppose you are examining a section of sedimentary rock. What evidence could you observe that would support the principle of superposition?

6. What is the age of the surface bedrock at Niagara Falls, New York?

   (1) Devonian   (3) Ordovician
   (2) Silurian   (4) Cambrian

7. The following diagram represents exposed bedrock. Which geologic event occurred last?

(1) the intrusion of A
(2) the fault along line B
(3) the fold at C
(4) the deposition of gravel at D

Correlation

The process of **correlation** makes it possible to show that rocks or geologic events from different places are the same or similar in age. Correlation is an important tool in unraveling the sequence of geologic events in an area. Correlation is also useful in finding certain mineral resources, such as fossil fuels, which are found in rocks of a specific age. Some of the methods of correlation are described below.

Correlation by Exposed Bedrock

An area's local rock, or **bedrock**, is usually covered by soil, other loose materials, or human-built structures. Sometimes, however, bedrock is exposed at Earth's surface through natural processes or by human activities such as road-building. Figure 13-4 shows exposed layers of bedrock—outcrops—along both sides of a river valley. Where bedrock is exposed, correlation can be accomplished by directly following the continuity of the rock layers. Direct observation of rock layers is especially easy in arid regions where little soil or vegetation covers the outcrops.

Figure 13-4. Correlation by observations of exposed bedrock and rock similarities: A geologist could follow and correlate bedrock layers in this exposed hillside by walking along the road on the left side of the river valley. The geologist might also be able to correlate layers on opposite sides of the valley by observing similarities in color, texture, and sequence of rock layers.

Correlation by Similarities in Rocks

Where rocks are separated from one another, they may be tentatively correlated by their similarities. These similarities may include overall appearance, color, mineral composition, and rock sequence, as indicated in Figure 13-4. Correlation of rocks by similarity is usually only valid over small areas, and even then may be incorrect. One reason is that similar rocks can form in like environments millions of years apart.

Correlation by Use of Index Fossils

One of the best methods of correlation involves the use of particular fossils or groups of fossils. **Fossils** are the remains or evidence of former living things—such as bones, shells, footprints, or organic compounds (such as DNA). With minor exceptions, fossils are found exclusively in sedimentary rocks. They are rarely found in igneous and metamorphic rocks because fossils are usually destroyed by the melting

Memory Jogger

You may recall that most sedimentary rocks form from compacted and cemented sediments. In contrast, igneous rocks form directly from molten magma or lava, while metamorphic rocks form when rocks are subjected to heat and pressure.

Index Fossils

Mississippian	Devonian	Silurian	Ordovician	Cambrian
Platycrinites symmetricus, crinoid	Cyrtospirifer whitneyi, brachiopod	Pterygotus buffaloensis, eurypterid	Opikina minnesotaenses, brachiopod	Crepicephalus texanus, trilobite

Figure 13-5. Correlation of rock layers by means of index fossils: The layers are in order from younger to older. In diagram **A**, a fossil of an organism known to have lived only during the Devonian Period is found in rock layer 4. This layer was therefore deposited during Devonian times. The layers above it are younger, and those below it are older. In diagram **B**, a similar fossil is found in one of the layers. This is therefore also a Devonian layer. A second index fossil, of the Silurian Period, is found in layer 7. This indicates that layers 5 and 6 are not younger than the Devonian and not older than the Silurian layers.

Memory Jogger

You may recall from the *Earth Science Reference Tables* that sand particles measure between 0.006 cm and 0.2 cm in diameter and that clay particles measure between 0.0001 cm and 0.0004 cm.

of igneous rocks and by the heat and pressure associated with the formation of metamorphic rocks.

The fossils used in correlation are called **index fossils.** As shown in Figure 13-5, the fossil remains of a particular type of life form may become useful as an index fossil if two conditions are met. First, the life form must have lived over a wide geographical area—so that its fossil remains will have a large horizontal distribution throughout rocks formed around the same time. Second, the life form must have existed for a relatively short time, so that its fossil remains have a small vertical distribution in the rock layers in which the fossils occur.

Correlation by Volcanic Ash and Meteorite Deposits

During volcanic eruptions, **volcanic ash** consisting of sand-sized to clay-sized particles of extrusive igneous rock is shot into the air. In large eruptions, volcanic ash scatters over wide areas of Earth's surface. See Figure 13-6. The scattered ash then settles among other sediments in many different environments. Since ash from each volcanic eruption has a unique mineralogical, or chemical, composition, specific ash deposits can be detected in rock layers. Such ash deposits are useful in correlation because they are widely distributed and represent a small interval of time. Deposits of volcanic ash serve as specific age markers in rocks and glacial ice that may be thousands of kilometers apart.

In a similar fashion, rock particles and debris produced by the impact of an asteroid, comet, or meteorite can cover large parts of Earth's surface. For example, at the end of the Mesozoic Era approximately 65 million years ago, a large comet or asteroid hit Mexico's Yucatan peninsula. Debris from the impact scattered over much of Earth's surface and can be found on all continents and in the sediments of most ocean areas. The debris, which included particles of the comet or asteroid, formed identifiable deposits, which can be used in correlation.

Figure 13-6. Volcano eruptions can serve as age markers: An explosive volcano eruption can deposit ash over vast areas and many different rock-forming environments. The deposited ash then serves as a specific age marker in many different rock types.

8. The simplest way to correlate exposed rock layers in the same general vicinity when they contain no fossils is by

   (1) examining intrusions
   (2) radioactive dating
   (3) following the continuity of the layers
   (4) tracing a fault

9. The following diagrams represent the rock layers and fossils found at four widely separated areas of exposed bedrock.

Which fossil appears to be the best index fossil?

   (1)   (2)   (3)   (4)

10. Describe two essential characteristics of an index fossil.

11. In a conglomerate rock sample that is composed of limestone particles cemented together by calcite, what is the oldest part of the rock sample?

Base your answers to questions 12 through 14 on the following diagram.

Key
☐ Soil   ☰ Limestone
☐ Sandstone   ☒ Conglomerate
☐ Shale   ☒ Igneous

12. The disturbed rock structure shown is probably the result of

   (1) warping
   (2) folding
   (3) volcanism
   (4) faulting

13. Which is the oldest sedimentary rock in this diagram?

   (1) conglomerate
   (2) sandstone
   (3) shale
   (4) limestone

14. Rock layer B is the same age as layer

   (1) C   (3) E
   (2) D   (4) F

15. The following diagram of three profile sections show fossil deposits W, X, Y, and Z found at widely separated locations. Which would be the best index fossil?

   (1) W   (3) Y
   (2) X   (4) Z

	Locality A		Locality B		Locality C	
Rock layer 1	W		W		W	Z
Rock layer 2	W	Z		Y		Z
Rock layer 3	W	X	X		X	Z

16. The following diagrams represent cross sections of three areas of exposed bedrock approximately 100 kilometers apart. What would be the best method of correlating the rock layers of each area?

(1) comparing rock types
(2) comparing mineral composition
(3) comparing index fossils
(4) comparing thickness of rock layers

17. Why can layers of volcanic ash found between other rock layers often serve as good geologic time markers?

(1) Volcanic ash usually occurs in narrow bands around volcanoes.
(2) Volcanic ash usually contains index fossils.
(3) Volcanic ash usually contains the radioactive isotope carbon-14.
(4) Volcanic ash usually is rapidly deposited over a large area.

18. According to the *Earth Science Reference Tables*, which rock is most likely the oldest?

(1) conglomerate containing the tusk of a mastodont
(2) shale containing trilobite fossils
(3) sandstone containing fossils of flowering plants
(4) siltstone containing dinosaur footprints

19. The best basis for concluding that a certain layer of shale rock in New York State was deposited at the same time as one in California is that both

(1) are the same distance below the surface
(2) contain similar fossil remains
(3) are sedimentary rocks
(4) have the same chemical composition

20. Why might it be more likely for a fossil to be found in a sedimentary rock than in either an igneous or a metamorphic rock?

Geologic History From the Rock Record

In general, fossils in rock layers serve to establish the relative age of the rock layers. As life forms on Earth constantly evolve, or change over time, some life forms exist or are dominant only during specific intervals of geologic time. Thus, fossils in rocks can be used to order an area's geologic events according to relative age. For example, the rock record shows that dinosaurs and ammonoids existed in a long interval called the Mesozoic Era. However, the rock record also shows that certain types of dinosaurs existed only for shorter time intervals.

Geologic Time Scale

Mainly on the basis of changing fossil evidence, geologists have been able to divide geologic time into divisions. From longest to shortest, these divisions of time are called <u>eons</u>, <u>eras</u>, <u>periods</u>, and <u>epochs</u>. A model of these divisions of geologic time is called the **geologic time scale.** The (R) Geologic History of New York State in the *Earth Science Reference Tables* represents the geologic time scale as a chart, while Figure 13-7 represents it as a timeline. Note that eons, eras, and other divisions of geologic time are not exact units of time such as hours or minutes. For example, in Figure 13-7, which shows the relative lengths of eons and eras, no two eras represent the same amount of time.

The Precambrian is a "super" eon composed of the earliest Archean and Proterozoic eons and represents approximately 88 percent of all geologic time. Precambrian fossils are rare and difficult to identify because the earliest known life forms were small and had no hard parts. Also, most Precambrian rocks have been either buried by more recent rocks, eroded away, or converted to metamorphic rocks or magma. To become familiar with the major divisions of geologic time, review the Geologic History of New York in the *Earth Science Reference Tables*. Also, learn to recognize the names of life forms associated with particular eons, eras, periods, and epochs.

Unconformities

In attempting to read the rock record, geologists often find evidence of buried eroded surfaces called **unconformities.** One example is shown in Figure 13-8. An unconformity in the rock record of an area indicates that at some time in its geologic history, uplift occurred. This uplift exposed the rocks to weathering and erosion, which removed part of the rock record. A later sinking of land or rise in sea level caused the area to be covered by water. New sediments were then deposited on the eroded land surface, producing the unconformity. Most unconformities show a lack of parallelism between the older rock layers beneath the erosion surface and the younger rock layers above. The lack of parallelism occurs because the older rock layers were folded or tilted during uplift.

The presence of an unconformity means that parts of the rock record are missing—like missing pages or chapters in a history book. Although there is a gap in the record of geologic time, an unconformity is still useful in relative dating. The rocks above an unconformity are younger than the unconformity, and the rocks below it considerably older. An unconformity also usually correlates with a time of mountain building, called an orogeny, and the associated plate convergence. In the *Earth Science Reference Tables*, the times of orogenies are listed as Important Geologic Events in New York in the Geologic History of New York State.

Uniformity of Process

One of the basic principles geologists use to interpret geologic history is the uniformity of process, which implies that "the present is the key to the past." This principle assumes that geologic processes happening today also occurred in the past and that much of the rock record can be interpreted by observing present geologic processes. Uniformity of process does not mean that different processes could not have happened or that past geologic processes always occurred at the same rate as they do today.

As an example of uniformity of process, suppose that a geologist in tropical Africa finds a conglomerate sedimentary rock layer. The sediments in the rock are unsorted, have a wide range of sizes, and have some partly rounded shapes with various scratches. Based on glacial processes known today, the geologist can infer that this conglomerate layer was the result of a past glaciation.

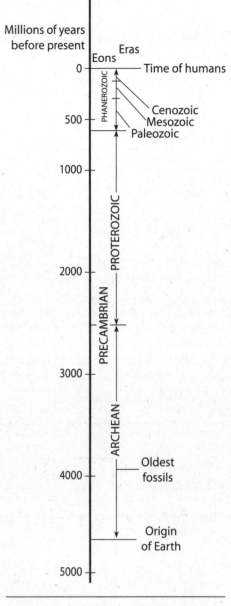

Figure 13-7. Timeline of Earth's geologic time: Life has existed for a large percentage of Earth's history. However, humans have existed for a comparatively short time (only 0.04 percent of Earth's history).

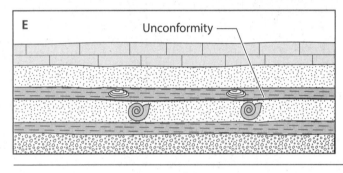

Events producing an unconformity with lack of parallelism: (A) Deposition forms sedimentary rock layers. (B) Crustal deformation and uplift occur. (C) Weathering and erosion remove part of the rock record. (D) Submergence (moved below sea level) and new deposition result in an unconformity along the now buried erosional surface.

An unconformity in parallel layers: (E) Uplift, erosion, and submergence have also occurred here, but without deformation. Evidence of a gap in the rock record may be given by widely different ages of the fossils in the layers above and below the unconformity.

Figure 13-8. Development of an unconformity

Uniformity of process implies that the chemical, physical, geological, and biological characteristics of nature remain the same throughout time. Thus, present observations can not only help geologists interpret Earth's past, but also make certain predictions about its future. By gathering sufficient data, it becomes possible to accurately predict certain natural disasters, such as volcanic eruptions, earthquakes, landslides, storms, and floods. Coupled with appropriate emergency procedures when needed, such predictions can help minimize death, injury, and property loss.

Review Questions

21. You are searching for fossils in the surface bedrock in Elmira, New York. Why are you unlikely to find dinosaur fossils at this location?

22. During which time was the majority of the exposed bedrock in New York State deposited?

(1) Precambrian   (3) Cenozoic
(2) Mesozoic   (4) Paleozoic

23. Rocks containing fossils of the earliest land plants could most likely be found in New York State bedrock near

(1) Syracuse   (3) Ithaca
(2) Oswego   (4) Old Forge

24. Approximately how long ago were the Taconic Mountains uplifted?

(1) 540 million years ago
(2) 470 million years ago
(3) 310 million years ago
(4) 120 million years ago

25. According to the Geologic History of New York State in the *Earth Science Reference Tables,* what is the estimated age of Earth as a planet in millions of years?

(1) 540   (3) 4600
(2) 4000   (4) 5000

26. The geologic time scale has been subdivided into a number of time units largely on the basis of

(1) fossil evidence   (3) rock types
(2) rock thickness   (4) radioactive dating

27. Which line is the best representation of the relative duration of each of the geologic time intervals?

(1) | Precambrian | Paleozoic | Mesozoic | Cenozoic |

(2) | Precam-brian | Paleozoic | Mesozoic | Cenozoic |

(3) | Precambrian | Paleozoic | Mesozoic |

(4) | Precambrian | Paleozoic | Mesozoic | Cenozoic |

Base your answers to questions 28 through 32 on the following diagram.

Shale
Sandstone
Limestone
Basalt
Contact metamorphosed rock
Conglomerate

28. Which is the most recently formed rock?

(1) A   (2) B   (3) C   (4) D

29. An unconformity is located between

(1) A and B   (3) C and D
(2) B and C   (4) F and G

30. The conclusion that the limestone layer D is younger than the basalt layer E is supported by evidence of

(1) faulting
(2) contact metamorphism
(3) igneous intrusion
(4) fossils

31. The last event before faulting occurred was the formation of

(1) C   (2) D   (3) E   (4) J

32. Which must have most recently preceded the formation of layer D?

(1) faulting   (3) intrusion
(2) orogeny   (4) uplift

33. An unconformity between two sedimentary layers is most likely produced by

(1) the deposition of gravel followed by the deposition of sand and silt
(2) continuous sedimentation in a deep basin over a long period
(3) uplift followed by extensive erosion, submergence, and deposition
(4) a period of extrusive vulcanism followed by another period of extrusive vulcanism

34. Because the chemical, physical, geological, and biological characteristics of nature remain the same throughout time, we can interpret the past and

(1) prevent natural disasters
(2) identify unconformities
(3) predict natural hazard events
(4) determine the age of bedrock

35. Fossils are rarely found in Precambrian rocks because, at that time

(1) no life existed
(2) few life forms had hard parts
(3) few sedimentary rocks formed
(4) a meteorite impact destroyed most fossils

36. "The present is the key to the past." Explain what this statement means in the context of geologic history.

Absolute Dating of Rocks Using Radioactive Decay

The principle of superposition and methods of correlation help to determine the relative age of rock layers, but do not give their absolute age. Absolute age is expressed in specific units, such as years before the present. One method of absolute dating is the counting of annual layers of glacial lake sediments, which is similar to tree-ring dating. However, the primary method of absolute dating is described in the text that follows.

Isotopes and Radioactive Decay

An <u>element</u> is a substance consisting of atoms that are chemically alike. Most elements exist in several varieties called **isotopes.** The difference between one isotope of an element and another is in the mass of its atoms. For example, the mass of an atom of the most common isotope of carbon is 12 units. This isotope, carbon-12, is usually just called, "carbon," while another isotope in which the atoms have a mass of 14 units is called carbon-14.

Almost all the mass of an atom is concentrated in a central region called the nucleus (plural, nuclei). The nuclei of the atoms of many isotopes are unstable or radioactive. They emit particles and electromagnetic energy in a process called **radioactive decay,** nuclear decay or nuclear fission thus changing into atoms of other isotopes and elements. The nucleus remaining after radioactive decay may also be unstable and decay further over time. Eventually, a stable isotope—one that is not radioactive or does not undergo radioactive decay—forms.

Uranium-238 One of the most important radioactive isotopes used in dating rocks is **uranium-238,** the isotope of uranium whose atoms have a mass of 238 units. The nuclei of its atoms pass though a series of radioactive decays, eventually producing atoms of lead-206, a stable isotope of the element lead.

Half-life The decay of any individual atomic nucleus is a random event; that is, it may occur at any time. However, among the billions of atoms in any sample of an isotope, a certain definite fraction will decay in a given time. In the next time interval of the same length, the same fraction of the remaining atoms will decay as did in the previous time interval.

The time required for half of the atoms in a given mass of an isotope to decay is called the **half-life** of the isotope. In a given sample of a radioactive isotope, half of the original atoms will have decayed to other isotopes at the end of one half-life period, and half will remain unchanged. At the end of the next half-life period, half of these remaining atoms will have decayed, leaving one-fourth of the original atoms unchanged. This halving of the number of unchanged atoms during successive half-life periods continues indefinitely.

Each radioactive isotope has its own characteristic half-life. The half-life of an isotope is not affected by any environmental factors, such as temperature, pressure, or involvement in chemical reactions. The half-life is also not affected by the amount, mass, or volume of the sample. By the principle of uniformity of process, it can be assumed that the half-life of a given isotope has remained the same throughout Earth's history. Half-lives

Table 13-1. Radioactive Decay Data		
Radioactive Isotope	**Disintegration**	**Half-life** (exponential/ordinal)
Carbon-14	$^{14}C \longrightarrow {}^{14}N$	$5.7 \times 10^3 = 5700$ years
Potassium-40	$_{40}K \Big\langle\begin{smallmatrix} \longrightarrow {}^{40}Ar \\ \longrightarrow {}^{40}Ca \end{smallmatrix}$	$1.3 \times 10^9 = 1{,}300{,}000{,}000$ years
Uranium-238	$^{238}U \longrightarrow {}^{206}Pb$	$4.5 \times 10^9 = 4{,}500{,}000{,}000$ years
Rubidium-87	$^{87}Rb \longrightarrow {}^{87}Sr$	$4.9 \times 10^{10} = 49{,}000{,}000{,}000$ years
Polonium-214	$^{214}Po \longrightarrow {}^{210}Pb$	$1.6 \times 10^{-4} = 0.00016$ seconds

for different isotopes vary widely—from fractions of seconds to billions of years. Table 13-1 shows some examples. For more information, see Physical Constants—Radioactive Decay Data in the *Earth Science Reference Tables*.

Radioactive Dating

The half-life of a radioactive isotope can be used, along with the ratio between the amount of the original isotope and the amount of its decay-product, to estimate the absolute age of a rock sample. This method is called **radioactive dating.** For example, consider a rock formed with uranite mineral grains containing uranium-238 and no lead-206. As time passed, the uranium-238 would slowly change to lead-206—its stable decay product—at its fixed half-life rate. At the end of one half-life period (4.5 billion years for uranium-238), half the uranium-238 atoms would have changed to atoms of lead-206. If a rock is found today with this 1:1 ratio of uranium-238 atoms to lead-206 atoms, it can be concluded that the rock formed 4.5 billion years ago. If the ratio between uranium-238 and lead-206 is higher than 1:1, the rock must have formed less than 4.5 billion years ago.

The age corresponding to any particular ratio of uranium-238 to lead-206 can be calculated mathematically. The curves in Figure 13-9 show how the percentage of uranium-238 decreases and the percentage of lead-206 increases with time in a given rock. The shape of the curves for any other radioactive isotope and its stable decay product would be similar. However, the time intervals would differ due to the different length of the half-life period.

Carbon-14 Dating Radioactive elements with long half-lives, such as uranium-238, are used to date rocks that are hundreds of millions, or even billions, of years old. Over such long periods, any isotope with a short half-life would have decayed to such an extent that the remaining amounts would be immeasurable.

Some radioactive isotopes with short half-lives are useful for dating rocks and organic remains of relatively recent origin. One such useful isotope is carbon-14, with a half-life of 5700 years. **Carbon-14 dating**—also called radiocarbon dating—can be used to date rocks and

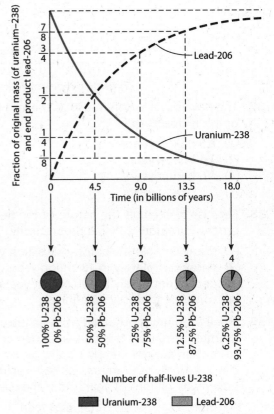

Figure 13-9. Curves showing radioactive decay of uranium-238 and formation of the stable decay product lead-206: After one half-life (4.5 billion years), half, or 50 percent, of the original uranium atoms have become lead atoms. By five half-lives, only 3.125 percent of the uranium atoms are left, and there are 96.875 percent lead atoms.

organic remains, such as the bones of a mastodont, up to approximately 70,000 years in age. See the Geologic History of New York State in the *Earth* ® *Science Reference Tables*.

Review Questions

Base your answers to questions 37 through 39 on the following graph, which shows the radioactive decay of uranium-238.

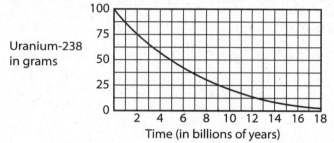
Time (in billions of years)

37. The half-life of uranium-238 as shown on this graph is closest to

(1) 2.5 billion years
(2) 3.5 billion years
(3) 4.5 billion years
(4) 5.5 billion years

38. Because of the half-life nature of the decay process, uranium-238 will theoretically

(1) decay completely before 4.5 billion years
(2) decay completely in 18 billion years
(3) decay completely in 200 billion years
(4) continue to decay indefinitely

39. Some uranium is obtained from an intrusive granite formation. It is then analyzed and found to contain approximately 1 gram of lead-206 to every 3 grams of uranium-238. Approximately how many billions of years old is the granite?

(1) nine   (3) eighteen
(2) two   (4) four

Base your answers to questions 40 and 41 on the following diagrams.

(1)   (2)   (3)   (4)

40. Which curve represents the expected decay rate of uranium-238 if its temperature were raised almost to the melting point?

41. If the decay curve for the element carbon-14 were plotted, which diagram shows the general shape that the curve would be?

42. The half-life of a particular radioactive substance

(1) decreases as pressure on it increases
(2) decreases as its mass decreases
(3) increases as the temperature increases
(4) is independent of mass, temperature, and pressure

43. If a specimen of a given radioactive substance is reduced in size, its half-life

(1) decreases
(2) increases
(3) remains the same

44. Which radioactive substance shown on the following graph has the longest half-life?

(1) A   (2) B   (3) C   (4) D

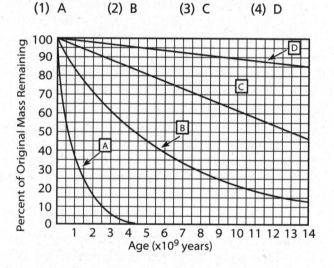
Age (x10⁹ years)

45. Why is carbon-14 usually NOT used to accurately date objects more than 50,000 years old?

(1) Carbon-14 has a relatively short half-life, and too little carbon-14 is left after 50,000 years.
(2) Carbon-14 has a relatively long half-life and not enough carbon-14 has decayed after 50,000 years.
(3) Carbon-14 has been introduced as an impurity in most materials older than 50,000 years.
(4) Carbon-14 has only existed on Earth during the last 50,000 years.

46. Carbon-14 is often used to date fossils from the Holocene Epoch. Why would carbon-14 be less useful in dating an Ordovician fossil?

Evolution of Earth and Life

For a long time, people have wondered about Earth's history and how life on Earth came to be. From the study of fossils and rock layers, scientists have been able to gain much knowledge of Earth's past.

Variations in Fossils and Environments

The fossil record, preserved in sedimentary rocks, shows that a wide variety of life forms have lived in Earth's changing environments over time. Most of these life forms are now extinct. Since the chances of fossilization are low, and the percent of all sedimentary rocks studied for fossils is minuscule, most forms of past life probably have not been identified.

Comparisons of fossils with similar life forms alive today make it possible to infer facts about Earth's past environments, as shown in Figure 13-10. For example, fossils of ancient corals have been found in Devonian period rocks of the Allegheny Plateau in western New York State. As most present-day corals live in shallow, warm ocean waters, it can be inferred that these rocks were formed in a shallow, warm-water ocean environment. The Devonian/Mississippian map, at the far right of the table Geologic History of New York State in the *Earth Science Reference Tables,* shows that ⓡ New York State was much nearer to the equator at that time and thus had a warmer climate.

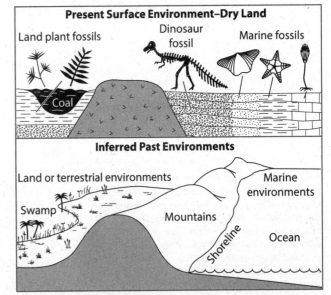

Figure 13-10. Reconstruction of past environments from fossil evidence and rock properties: From the existence of dinosaur fossils, marine fossils, and changes in sedimentary rock type, the location of the former shoreline and ocean can be inferred. From the existence of plant fossils and coal, the location of the former swamp can be inferred.

Environment Evolution and Plate Tectonics A major reason for changes in Earth's environments over geologic time has been the movements of plates and their associated landmasses. In the *Earth Science Reference* ⓡ *Tables* these movements are shown in a series of maps in the column Inferred Positions of Earth's Landmasses in the Geologic History of New York State. As the plates and their landmasses move, their latitude changes. The result is a change in climate. For example, the climate of a landmass which has moved closer to one of Earth's poles will become colder. Similarly, the climate of a landmass which has moved closer to the equator will become warmer.

Plate movements also result in other environmental changes. For example, plate convergence can result in continent-to-continent collisions that form long, high mountain ranges such as the Himalayas. Such mountain ranges can produce local climate changes. Also, rising magma at rapidly diverging plate boundaries can lead to a rise in the ocean floor, pushing ocean water onto the landmasses.

Environmental Evolution and Rock Types As Earth's environments changed over time, specific rocks and minerals formed, as well as deposits of fossil fuels. For example, hot and humid conditions during the Carboniferous Period of the Paleozoic Era and an abundance of land above sea level resulted in widespread swamps. The worldwide coal deposits of today were formed from these swamps. During parts of the Silurian Period of the Paleozoic Era, plate movements in hot and dry environments led to the

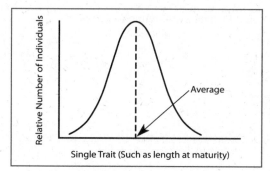

Figure 13-11. Variations in a single trait within a species: In any population of a species, each trait usually has an average value. In most individuals, the trait will be close to the average. In a few, it will be much below average; in a similar number, it will be much above average. If the departure from average in either direction has an advantage for survival and can be inherited, the average will shift in this favorable direction in later generations.

isolation of many ocean areas. Thus isolated, the waters of these ocean areas evaporated— precipitating evaporite rocks and mineral deposits, such as salt and gypsum. Deposits of salt and gypsum are found in western New York State.

Fossils and the Evolution of Life

A **species** of living things is a group of organisms which are similar enough to be able to interbreed and produce fertile young. However, not all members of a species are exactly alike. For example, in humans and in different breeds of dogs one sees that many variations in each species exist. When variations in a species are graphed, a bell-shaped curves often forms, as shown in Figure 13-11.

The theory of **organic evolution** states that life forms change through time. As environmental conditions change, variations within a species give certain individuals a greater chance of surviving and reproducing. Genetic material coding for these variations will be passed on to the offspring, and the favorable variations will be preserved. At the same time, individuals with unfavorable variations will gradually die out or become extinct. After a long period of time, individuals with many accumulated variations can lose the ability to interbreed with earlier varieties of the species. These individuals then become a new species.

The fossil record provides evidence for the theory of organic evolution. Fossils from adjacent intervals of geologic time sometimes show a gradual transition from an older species to a newer one.

Evidence in the fossil record also shows that evolution does not always occur at the same rate. Instead, there are times of rapid extinctions and subsequently rapid evolution of new species (punctuated evolution). Some of these times of rapid extinctions and evolution correspond to major divisions in the geologic time scale.

Rapid Evolution of Life After an Impact Event

An impact event, such as the collision of a comet or asteroid with Earth, may cause catastrophic environmental changes leading to rapid extinctions and evolution. Such an event probably occurred approximately 65 million years ago, at the interface of the Mesozoic and Cenozoic eras. At this time, a mass extinction occurred— about 70 percent of all existing species became extinct, including many species of dinosaurs. This mass extinction ended the Mesozoic Era and the dominance of reptiles on land and in the oceans. The Cenozoic Era began, and mammals became the dominant life forms on land.

Evidence exists that about 65 million years ago, Earth collided with one or more comets or asteroids many kilometers in diameter. This impact event created huge tsunamis, burned much of Earth's vegetation, and hurled millions of tons of dust-sized aerosols into the stratosphere. The aerosols remained in the stratosphere for many years, blocking out much of the insolation from the sun. With the amount of solar energy reaching Earth's surface drastically reduced, surface temperatures cooled. Photosynthesis also declined, reducing the growth of plants and algae which form the basis of the food supply for most living things. These environmental changes led to a mass extinction, and a chance for previously less successful life forms, such as mammals, to thrive and evolve. There is evidence that similar impact events occurred at the ends of the Triassic, Permian, and Devonian Periods of the geologic time scale.

Early Evolution on Earth

You may recall some of the events in the formation of Earth and the solar system. The following paragraphs discuss further inferences about some of the earliest events in Earth's history, based on available evidence. Most events discussed here occurred during the Archean and Proterozoic Eons of the Precambrian. Some of these, along with more recent events in Earth's history, are shown in Figure 13-12.

Find the following events, and other important events in Earth's evolution, on the diagram in Figure 13-12. For further details of Earth's history, see the Geologic History of New York State in the *Earth Science* Ⓡ *Reference Tables.*

- Evidence from the radioactive decay dates of moon rocks and meteorites shows that the planet Earth probably formed approximately 4.6 billion years ago.
- During its early formation, Earth heated up and largely melted due to heat from impact events, radioactive decay of isotopes within Earth's interior, and gravity-induced movement of materials towards Earth's center.
- During early Earth's melting, Earth materials separated into zones according to their density. The densest materials, such as iron and nickel, settled to form Earth's core. The less dense silicates, and other rock and mineral components, became the mantle and perhaps the earliest crust. Gaseous elements and compounds rose above Earth's surface. Most of Earth's earliest atmosphere probably escaped into space.
- After hundreds of million of years, a largely solid crust formed, and plate tectonic activity began. The earliest evidence of a solid crust is approximately 4.2 billion years old. Gases from Earth's interior seeped out of the crust through cracks and volcanic eruptions in a process called **outgassing.** A second atmosphere formed—probably composed of water vapor, carbon dioxide, nitrogen, and other gases.
- When Earth's atmosphere and surface had cooled enough, water precipitated to form the oceans. Sedimentary rocks more than 4 billion years old provide evidence of this early ocean. Approximately 3.8 billion years ago, or earlier, single-celled life forms were present. Ocean salts—dissolved minerals—began to accumulate from chemical weathering of Earth's crust.
- Approximately 3.5 billion years ago, life forms similar to living stromatolites (colonies of bacteria and algae) evolved. These life forms used carbon dioxide and released free oxygen, some of which rose into the atmosphere. Over time, Earth's atmosphere of mostly carbon dioxide changed into one largely of nitrogen and oxygen.
- Most oxygen in the early atmosphere reacted with iron compounds forming iron oxide, or rust. Earth's early landmasses may have looked like the rust-colored surface of Mars. Millions of tons of iron oxide minerals were deposited in the oceans between 3.5 billion and 2.8 billion years ago.

- By approximately 2.8 billion years ago, most of the iron compounds that could react with oxygen had already done so. Thus, the amount of oxygen in the atmosphere began to increase. Some of the oxygen probably formed an early ozone layer in the stratosphere that protected life forms from the sun's deadly ultraviolet radiation.

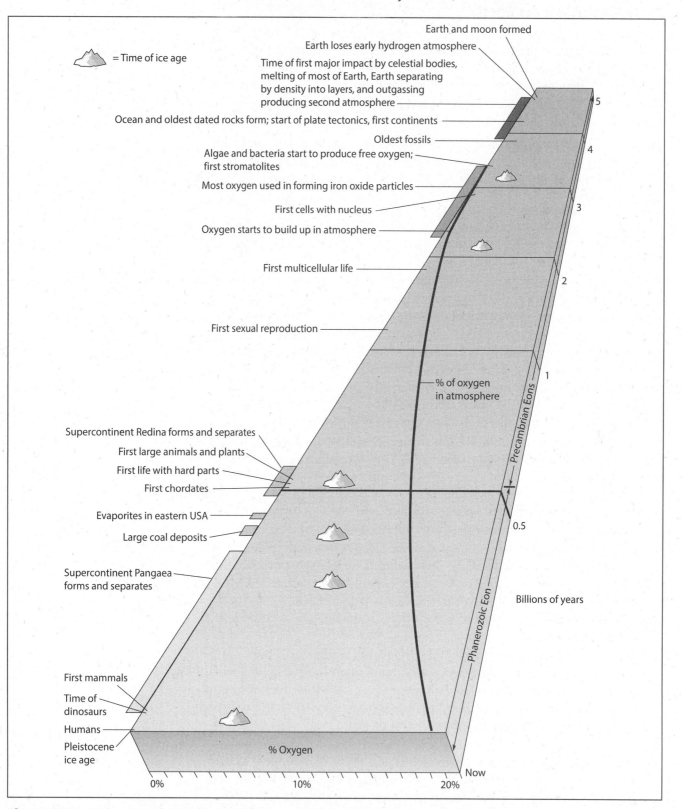

Figure 13-12. History of Earth: The diagram shows some highlights of the evolution of Earth and life.

- During the Precambrian, life forms slowly evolved from single-celled bacteria to multicelled life forms that could reproduce sexually. Most were soft-bodied. In the first part of the Paleozoic Era—the Cambrian Period—life forms evolved hard parts, and extensive evidence of life forms begins to appear in the rock record. Ancestors of most present-day life forms can be found in fossils from the Cambrian Period.

Review Questions

47. The following diagram represents a cross section of Earth's crust. The symbols in the diagram indicate the location on a horizontal surface of certain fossils that formed during the Carboniferous Period. For what purpose would the fossil information on the map be most useful?

    (1) to find the location of the shoreline during the Carboniferous Period
    (2) to measure the age of the bedrock by carbon-14 radioactive dating
    (3) to provide evidence of the evolution of humans
    (4) to indicate the extent of folding that occurred during the Devonian Period

48. Shark and coral fossils are found in the rock record of certain land areas. What does the presence of these fossils indicate about those areas?

    (1) They have undergone glacial deposition.
    (2) They were once covered by thick vegetation.
    (3) They have undergone intense metamorphism.
    (4) They were once covered by shallow seas.

49. Approximately 3.5 billion years ago photosynthetic organisms evolved. What dramatic change in Earth's atmosphere resulted primarily from this event?

50. The changes observed in the fossil record from the Precambrian to the Cenozoic Era best provide evidence of

    (1) sublimation   (3) organic evolution
    (2) radioactive decay   (4) planetary motion

51. Which statement is false?

    (1) Two members of one species must be exactly alike.
    (2) The members of a species can vary in physical features.
    (3) The members of a species can interbreed and produce fertile young.
    (4) A species may exist on Earth for millions of years.

52. The following diagram represents a site in western New York State. The remains of a mastodont were found in sediments from a swamp located above limestone bedrock. Fossils of Paleozoic coral were discovered in the limestone beneath the swamp. Observations made at this site provide evidence that

    (1) the local climate and environment have changed dramatically
    (2) fossil coral provided food for mastodonts
    (3) North America has drifted to the east from Europe and Africa
    (4) mastodonts and coral were alive at the same time

Directions

Review the Test-Taking Strategies section of this book. Then answer the following questions. Read each question carefully and answer with a correct choice or response.

Part A

1   Which of the following landscape features of New York State were most recently formed?
   (1) the Finger Lakes
   (2) the Catskills
   (3) the Palisades sill
   (4) the rocks of the Adirondack Mountains

2   Trilobite fossils from different time periods show small changes in appearance. These observations suggest that the changes may be the result of
   (1) evolutionary development
   (2) a variety of geologic processes
   (3) periods of destruction of the geologic record
   (4) the gradual disintegration of radioactive substances

3   From the study of fossils, what can be inferred about most species of plants and animals that have lived on Earth?
   (1) They are still living today.
   (2) They are unrelated to modern life forms.
   (3) They existed during the Cambrian Period.
   (4) They have become extinct.

4   An igneous rock contains one-half of its original amount of potassium-40. According to the *Earth Science Reference Tables*, the age of the igneous rock is closest to
   (1) 0.7×10^9 years
   (2) 1.3×10^9 years
   (3) 2.1×10^9 years
   (4) 2.6×10^9 years

5   Mesozoic rocks and fossils found in Australia would most likely match Mesozoic rocks and fossils found in
   (1) Europe
   (2) Antarctica
   (3) the Atlantic Ocean
   (4) North America

6   Which two gases were commonly outgassed from Earth's interior into the atmosphere around 4 billion years ago?
   (1) carbon dioxide and nitrogen
   (2) oxygen and hydrogen
   (3) nitrogen and oxygen
   (4) hydrogen and carbon dioxide

7   Geologists can use meteorite fragments to correlate different types of sedimentary rock thousands of kilometers apart because meteorite fragments
   (1) are not changed by erosion
   (2) would be spread over much of Earth's surface
   (3) are all formed from the same minerals
   (4) are often found in layers of sedimentary rock

8   What event in the evolution of life, around 540 million years ago, began an extensive fossil record on Earth?
   (1) flowering plants evolved
   (2) the extinction of armored fish
   (3) animals evolved hard parts
   (4) modern coral groups evolved

9   Trilobite fossils were recently discovered in Himalayan Mountain bedrock. During which geologic period could these organisms have lived?
   (1) Neogene
   (2) Cretaceous
   (3) Triassic
   (4) Cambrian

10   What is the geologic age of the surface bedrock of most of the Allegheny Plateau landscape region in New York State?
   (1) Cambrian
   (2) Devonian
   (3) Silurian
   (4) Ordovician

11   When did the Jurassic Period end?
   (1) 65.5 million years ago
   (2) 146 million years ago
   (3) 163 million years ago
   (4) 200 million years ago

12 According to the *Earth Science Reference Tables*, which geologic event is associated with the Grenville Orogeny?
  (1) the metamorphism of the rocks of the Adirondack Mountains
  (2) the advance and retreat of the last continental ice sheet
  (3) the separation of South America from Africa
  (4) the initial opening of the Atlantic Ocean

13 Present-day corals live in warm, shallow ocean water. Which inference is best supported by the discovery of Ordovician-age corals in the surface bedrock of western New York State?
  (1) Western New York State was covered by a warm, shallow sea during Ordovician time.
  (2) Ordovician-age corals lived in the forest of western New York State.
  (3) Ordovician-age corals were transported to western New York State by cold, freshwater streams.
  (4) Western New York was covered by a continental ice sheet that created coral fossils during the Ordovician period.

14 Unconformities (buried erosional surfaces) provide evidence that
  (1) many life forms have become extinct
  (2) faults are older than the rock in which they are found
  (3) part of the geologic record has been destroyed
  (4) metamorphic rocks have formed from sedimentary rocks

15 Based on studies of fossils found in subsurface rocks near Buffalo, New York, scientists have inferred that the climate of this area during the Ordovician Period was much warmer than the present climate. Which statement best explains this change in climate?
  (1) The sun emitted less sunlight during the Ordovician Period.
  (2) Earth was farther from the sun during the Ordovician Period.
  (3) The North American continent was nearer to the equator during the Ordovician Period.
  (4) Many huge volcanic eruptions occurred during the Ordovician Period.

Part B

Base your answers to questions 16 through 19 on the following diagrams. Columns A and B represent two widely separated areas of exposed bedrock. The symbols show the rock types and the locations of fossils found in the rock layers. The rock layers have not been overturned.

16 State one method of correlating rock layers found in the exposed bedrock represented by Column A with rock layers found in the exposed bedrock represented by Column B. [1]

17 An unconformity (buried erosion surface) exists between two layers in the exposed bedrock represented by Column A. Identify the location of the unconformity by drawing a thick wavy line ∼∼∼ at the correct position on column A.

18 State the evidence that limestone is the most resistant layer in these areas of exposed bedrock. [1]

19 State the oldest possible age, in millions of years, for the fossils in the siltstone layer. [1]

---

20 In what era and period of geologic time were much of the present-day coal deposits formed? [1]

21 What produced most of the oxygen presently found in Earth's atmosphere? [1]

22 How can divergence of lithospheric plates affect the evolution of life on a continent? [1]

23 Why do large masses of the evaporite sedimentary rocks—rock salt and rock gypsum—exist in Silurian rocks of western New York State but are not forming there today? [1]

24 What are two events associated with the impact of a comet or an asteroid with Earth that would cause a major extinction of life? [2]

25 Why did most of the iron that existed near Earth's surface around 4.5 billion years ago end up in Earth's core? [1]

26 Compare the age of Earth and our solar system to the age of the most distant galaxies. [1]

27 While exploring a stream a student found a rock containing a trilobite fossil. Name the most likely type of rock this student found. [1]

28 If a rock contains a trilobite fossil in what geologic era did the rock most likely form? [1]

Part C

Base your answers to questions 29 through 32 on the geologic cross section below. Radioactive dating indicates that the granite intrusion is 279 million years old and the vesicular basalt is 260 million years old. The rock layers have not been overturned.

29 List the six rock units in the order from the oldest to the youngest. [1]

30 During which geologic time period did the shale layer form? [1]

31 The granite intrusion caused part of the limestone layer to undergo metamorphism. What metamorphic rock would most likely be found in this zone of contact metamorphism? [1]

32 Between which two rock layers in the diagram is there most likely an unconformity? [1]

33 Why can life, as we presently know it, exist on Earth and not on other planets in our solar system? [1]

34 In natural exposed bedrock, how is it possible that a meter-wide piece of sandstone can be found within an igneous rock such as granite? [1]

Read the following article about radon. Use your knowledge of earth science and the information in the following article to answer questions 35–38.

Radon (gas) gained public attention in 1984 when a worker in a Pennsylvania nuclear power plant set off radiation alarms—not when he left work, but as he entered. His clothing and hair were contaminated with radon decay products. Investigation revealed that his basement at home had a radon level 2800 times the average level in indoor air. The home was located along a geological formation known as the Reading Prong—a mass of uranium-bearing rock that runs from near Reading, Pennsylvania, to near Trenton, New Jersey.

Radon is continually generated by the gradual decay of uranium. Because uranium has a half-life of about 4.5 billion years, radon will be with us forever. Radon itself decays, having a half-life of only about four days. Its decay products (except lead 206) are all radioactive solids that adhere to dust particles, many of which we inhale. Steadily accumulating evidence indicates radon may be a significant cause of lung cancer, second only to smoking.

From *Earth: An Introduction to Physical Geology* by Edward J. Tarbuck and Frederick K. Lutgens. © 1999 by Prentice-Hall, Inc. Used by permission.

35 If the half-life of radon is only about four days, why does the Reading Prong, which is many million years old, still produce radon gas? [1]

36 Radon is often most concentrated in basements. What does this suggest about the density of radon gas compared to that of air? [1]

37 Would radon be a suitable radioactive element to use in radioactive dating? Explain. [2]

38 If you were a homeowner on the Reading Prong, what might you do to ensure the lowest possible concentration of radon gas in your home? [1]

Base your answers to questions 39 through 41 on the passage below.

Fossils and the History of Earth's Rotation

Data from coral fossils support the hypothesis that Earth's rotation rate has been slowing down by about 2.5 seconds per 100,000 years. Scientists believe this is due to the frictional effects of ocean tides. This slowing rotation rate decreases the number of days in the year.

Scientists have discovered that corals produce a thin layer of shell every day, resulting in growth rings. These daily layers are separated by yearly ridges.

The Devonian coral fossil, *Pleurodictyum*, has approximately 400 growth rings between each yearly ridge, which suggests that there were about 400 days in a year during the Devonian Period.

Supporting this hypothesis, scientists have found coral from the Pennsylvanian Period that have about 390 growth rings per year, while present-day corals have about 365 growth rings per year.

39 Approximately how many fewer Earth days per year are there today than there were during the Devonian Period?
(1) 10   (3) 35
(2) 25   (4) 40

40 What inference can be made about the number of growth rings per year for a coral from the Permian Period and Ordovician Period compared to the number of growth rings per year for the Devonian coral, *Pleurodictyum*?
(1) Ordovician coral would have fewer, but Permian coral would have more.
(2) Ordovician coral would have more, but Permian coral would have fewer.
(3) Both Ordovician and Permian coral would have fewer.
(4) Both Ordovician and Permian coral would have more.

41 The evidence of the fossil *Pleurodictyum* found in surface bedrock in the Finger Lakes region of New York State suggests that this region was once
(1) covered by a glacial ice sheet
(2) covered by a warm, shallow sea
(3) located in a desert area
(4) located in a tropical rain forest

Base your answers to questions 42 through 44 on the paragraph below, which provides background information regarding recent fossil discoveries in Canada.

Scientific evidence indicates that the earliest mammals may have evolved approximately 225 million years ago from an ancient reptile group called the therapsids. For millions of years afterward, early mammals and therapsids coexisted until the therapsids apparently became extinct 165 million years ago. However, geologists have recently found a fossil they believe to be a therapsid that is only 60 million years old. They found the fossil, which they have named *Chronoperates paradoxus* (paradoxical time-wanderer), near Calgary in Canada. This find suggests that for 105 million years after the apparent extinction of the therapsids, a few of the reptiles continued to live in a narrow geographic range in Canada.

42 According to fossil evidence, during which geologic period did the earliest mammals appear on Earth? [1]

43 Explain briefly why *Chronoperates paradoxus* would not be a good index fossil. [1]

44 State one method geologists could have used to determine that *Chronoperates paradoxus* lived 60 million years ago. [1]

Base your answers to questions 45 and 46 on the cross sections below, which show widely separated outcrops at locations W, X, Y, and Z. The rock layers have not been overturned. Line AB in the cross section at location W represents an unconformity. Fossils are shown in some of the layers.

(Not drawn to scale)

45 Determine the relative geologic age of the four fossils by correlating the rock layers between these outcrops. Number the fossils from 1 to 4 in order of relative age, with 1 as the oldest and 4 as the youngest. [1]

46 Identify *two* of the processes involved in the formation of the unconformity represented by line *AB* in the cross section at location *W*. [1]

Base your answers to questions 47 through 49 on the cross section below and on your knowledge of Earth science. The cross section shows a portion of Earth's crust. The age, in millions of years, of each boundary between the different sedimentary rock layers is shown. The age of boundary X between the sedimentary rock and the metamorphic rock is not shown. Assume no overturning has occurred.

47 Identify the geologic feature represented by boundary *X*. [1]

48 Describe how the rock type below boundary *X* was formed. [1]

49 Identify by name one index fossil that existed when the limestone rock shown in the cross section was being formed. [1]

Base your answers to questions 50 through 53 on the cross section below which shows a portion of Earth's crust. Letters A through J represent rock units or geologic structures. The rock units have not been overturned.

50 On the cross section, draw a circle around the letter of the oldest rock unit shown. [1]

51 On the same cross section, place an **X** to indicate a location where the rock, marble, was formed. [1]

52 Describe *one* piece of evidence shown in the cross section that suggests rock unit *D* is younger than rock unit *F*. [1]

53 Explain why rock unit *H* is *not* one continuous layer. [1]

Landscape Development and Environmental Change

How Scientists Study Erosion in Arid Regions

? *What do you think causes the most natural erosion in deserts?* **?**

Believe it or not, running water is the dominant natural agent of erosion in deserts. The lack of vegetation to hold sediments in place makes it easy for running water to pick up and move sediments in arid regions. When it does rain, thunderstorms can potentially cause flash floods, which can cause a great deal of erosion in a short amount of time.

Read the section on "Effects of Climate on Landscape Development" in this topic to find out more.

Landscape Development and Environmental Change

Vocabulary

escarpment	mountain	ridges
landscape	plain	stream drainage pattern
landscape region	plateau	uplifting forces

Memory Jogger

Recall that the lithosphere is the layer of rock that forms Earth's solid outer shell. The hydrosphere is the layer of liquid water that rests on the lithosphere. The atmosphere is a mixture of gases that surrounds the rest of Earth.

Topic Overview

Landscapes, or topography, are the features of Earth's surface at the interfaces between the atmosphere, or hydrosphere, and the top of the lithosphere. Landscapes also exist on all other solid celestial bodies. Some of the characteristics of landscapes are the slope of the land, shape of the landscape features, stream drainage patterns, stream slope, soil properties, and evidences of human occupation such as cities and mines. A **stream drainage pattern** is the shape of the stream courses in an area as viewed from the sky. (See Figure 14-8.) Landscape features range in size from a raindrop impression in mud to a continent.

Measuring Landscape Characteristics

The shape and slope of the land, the stream drainage patterns, and some soil features can be measured by using actual observations or models such as contour maps, aerial photographs, satellite images, and the types of landscape maps and drawings shown in this topic. The use of these tools has shown that landscape features such as mountains, valleys, and steam drainage patterns have distinctive shapes by which they can be identified. These models can also be interpreted to show the changes in landscapes through time, for example, shoreline erosion, deforestation, retreat of glaciers, and the advance of deserts.

Gradient and Profile One measurable characteristic of land and streams is the gradient, or slope. Profiles show the elevation, shape, and slope of landscape features. (See Figure 14-1.)

Mountains, Plateaus, and Plains On the basis of gradient, elevation, and rock structure, landscapes are divided into three major types— mountains, plateaus, and plains. (See Figure 14-1.)

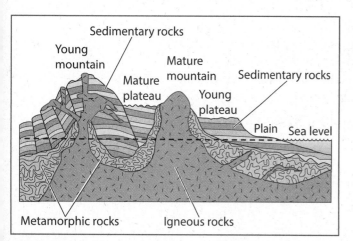

Figure 14-1. Profiles and structures of the three major types of landscapes—mountains, plateaus, and plains

A **mountain** is an area of high elevation, compared to the surrounding area or sea level, that usually has regions of steep gradient and many changes in slope. Its peak is usually thousands of feet higher than its base. Internally, mountains are characterized by distorted rock structures such as faults, folds, or volcanic rocks. Mountains are usually composed of much <u>igneous rock</u> and <u>metamorphic rock.</u>

There are many types of mountains, and it is their origin that determines their type. Some examples include faulted mountains, folded mountains, and volcanic mountains. (See Figure 14-7.)

A **plateau** is also an area of high elevation, but it has undistorted horizontal rock structure and often a more level slope or gradient than mountains have. A plateau may have steep slopes because of valleys cut by streams and/or glaciers. Examples include the Grand Canyon in the Colorado Plateau or the many valleys of the Catskill Plateau of New York. Plateaus are composed of horizontal strata of sedimentary rocks or layers of extrusive igneous lava flows.

A **plain,** usually composed of sedimentary rocks, has a low elevation and generally level surface with little change in slope. One example is the Atlantic Coastal Plain of Long Island, New York. Some earth scientists consider old mountain areas that have been eroded to low elevations a type of plain. Composed of distorted metamorphic rocks, parts of the Manhattan Prong landscape region around New York City are an example of this type of eroded mountain or plain.

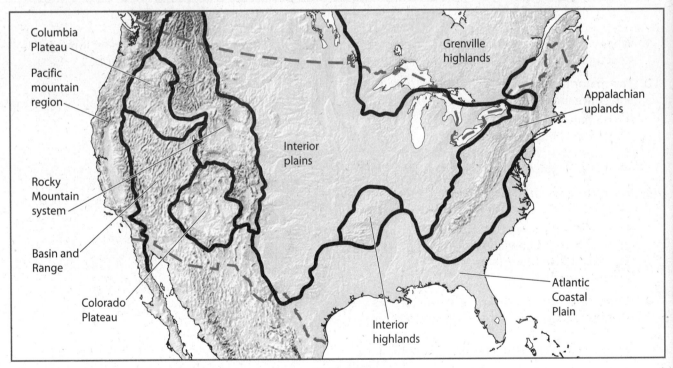

Figure 14-2. Major landscape regions of the contiguous United States

Figure 14-3. Generalized landscape regions of New York State (Also see Appendix 3)

Landscape Regions

Landscape characteristics—elevation, bedrock structure, stream drainage patterns, soil characteristics, and amount of slope—occur in combinations that form identifiable areas called **landscape regions.**

Continental Landscape Regions Any continental land mass has several landscape regions that can be identified by the surface characteristics. The landscape regions of the contiguous United States are shown in Figure 14-2. The landscape regions for New York State are shown in Figure 14-3 and in the Appendix. You should also carefully study the New York State landscape regions in the *Earth Science Reference Tables*.

®

Landscape Boundaries The boundaries between landscape regions are usually well defined, as shown in Figures 14-2 and 14-3 for the United States and New York State. Landscape boundaries usually consist of characteristics of the landscape that have been brought about by changes in the structure of rocks. Such characteristics include mountain edges, fault zones, ridges, cliffs, changes in the amount of slope, or river courses that follow the direction of the structural change.

Review Questions

1. Why would you expect to find distorted rock structures in mountain landscapes?

2. The major landscape regions of the United States are identified chiefly on the basis of

   (1) similar surface characteristics
   (2) similar climatic conditions
   (3) nearness to major mountain regions
   (4) nearness to continental boundaries

3. In which New York State landscape region is 44° N latitude and 74°30′ W longitude found?

   (1) Hudson-Mohawk Lowlands
   (2) St. Lawrence Lowlands
   (3) Adirondack Mountains
   (4) the Catskills

4. Which New York State landscape region has the lowest elevation, the most level land surface, and is composed primarily of Cretaceous through Pleistocene unconsolidated sediments?

   (1) the Hudson-Mohawk Lowlands
   (2) the Atlantic Coastal Plain
   (3) the Champlain Lowlands
   (4) the Erie-Ontario Lowlands

5. Boundaries between landscape regions in New York State are best described as being

   (1) straight lines running north and south
   (2) invisible on the surface
   (3) usually well defined
   (4) generally unchanging

6. The boundaries between landscape regions are usually indicated by sharp changes in

   (1) bedrock structure and elevation
   (2) weathering rate and method of deposition
   (3) soil associations and geologic age
   (4) stream discharge rate and direction of flow

Factors of Landscape Development

Two groups of forces form and change current landscapes—uplifting forces and leveling or destructional forces. Uplifting forces are also called tectonic forces because they are the results of Earth's plate movements. The impact of asteroids, comets, and meteorites is a third force of landscape development.

Uplifting and Leveling Forces

Uplifting forces originate beneath or within Earth's lithosphere. They displace and form new rock material to raise the land, build mountains, and cause the growth of continental regions. These uplifting forces include volcanic action, earthquakes, and the many other movements associated with plate interactions. These forces obtain their energy from Earth's interior as the result of decay of radioactive materials and from the residual heat from Earth's formation. It is inferred that most of the heat is distributed to the lithosphere by convection currents within the mantle.

Recall that a <u>convection current</u> transfers heat energy by circular movements caused by differences in density.

Most <u>leveling forces</u> operate at or near Earth's solid surface. These forces lower and level out Earth's surface by breaking down the rocks of landmasses, transporting sediments along Earth's surface, and depositing sediments. The leveling forces include <u>weathering, erosion, deposition,</u> and <u>sinking</u>. The source of energy for the leveling forces is energy from the sun—<u>insolation</u>—and gravity.

Leveling forces, such as erosion and weathering, are always at work at all areas of Earth's solid surface, but the uplifting forces may or may not be operating at the same time. When both groups of forces are present, the landscape will be uplifted or lowered, depending on which forces are dominant (operating at a faster rate).

If the uplifting forces are dominant, level land of low elevation may be changed into mountains with steep hillslopes and high elevations. With higher elevations, streams will gain more energy to erode, glaciers may form, and higher lands will alter wind patterns. These uplifting forces are most dominant at plate boundaries and hot spots where earthquakes, volcanic actions, and the growth of young mountains are going on.

In areas where the leveling forces are acting alone or are dominant, elevation is decreasing, and the land eventually becomes flatter or smoother in slope. Weathering and erosion are destroying the rocks faster than uplift (if any) is occurring. Deposition by running water, wind, gravity, glaciers, and shoreline processes contributes to the leveling and forms the many depositional landscape features.

Sinking of Earth's surface may be due to the compaction of sediments under the influence of gravity. The withdrawal of fluids such as water and petroleum can also contribute to the lowering of the land.

Impact Craters

The impact (collision) of meteorites, asteroids, and comets has been a major contributor to the landscapes of Earth, especially in the first two billion years of Earth's history. During that time more stray objects moved around

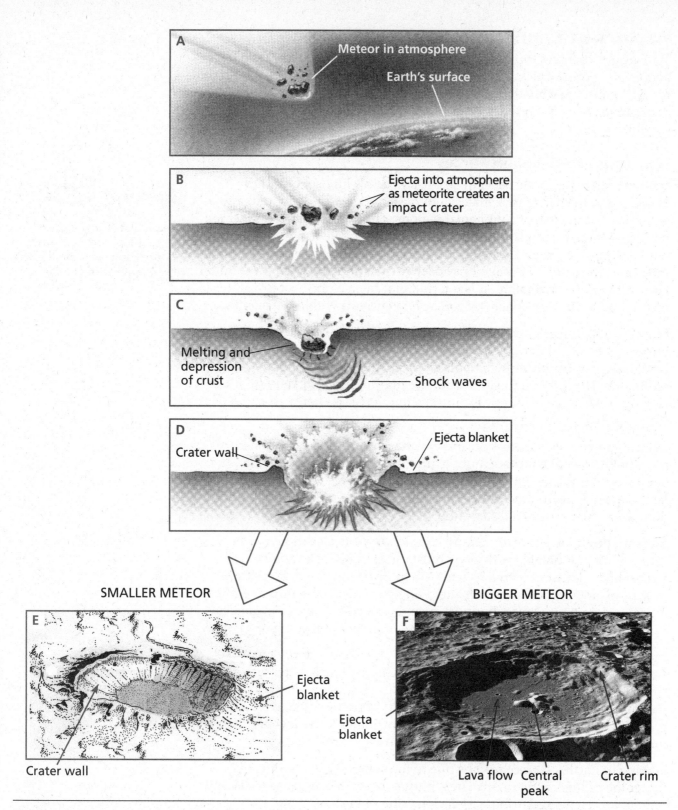

Figure 14-4. Impact Craters: (A) Meteor (from a meteoroid, asteroid, or comet in space) passing through Earth's atmosphere. (B) As the meteor hits Earth's surface (or any other solid body in the solar system) parts of the meteor/meteorite and surface material are shot or ejected into the atmosphere. (C) Friction results in melting much of the meteorite and parts of the crust around the newly forming impact crater. Shock waves cause the crust to depress and result in seismic waves. (D) Ejecta blanket surrounds the crater and may have rays like on our Moon. (E) In smaller meteor impacts, a crater like the one shown, forms. (F) With larger meteor impacts, a larger crater is created with a central peak and the crater floor is covered with a hardened lava flow. The rebounding of the crust in the depression created by the shock waves and expanding gases causes the formation of the central peak or mountain.

the solar system, and thus more collisions with Earth occurred. The major landscape feature caused by the impacting bodies from outer space is an impact crater. (See Figure 14-4.) About 185 impact craters have been located on Earth's surface with more being discovered each year. Another feature of meteorite collisions is impact lava flows, caused by the melting of the meteorite and Earth's crust. Additionally, deposits of meteorite ejecta shoot into the atmosphere and then are deposited, often as part of the crater rim.

Many other solid surface objects in the Solar System, such as the Moon, other moons, the planets Mercury and Mars, and asteroids, have a greater density of impact craters when compared to Earth. Earth's lower density and smaller total number of craters is due to destruction by weathering and erosion, melting during subduction, and coverage by deposition of sediments and rocks. Also, smaller meteorites burn up in Earth's atmosphere and those that hit the ocean are slowed down or broken into smaller pieces.

Time and Landscape Stages

The features of a landscape at any one time are partly the result of the length of time the uplifting and leveling processes have acted on the rocks and loose materials of Earth's surface. An area often experiences a time when the uplifting forces are dominant, followed by a long time when the leveling forces are dominant. When this happens, an area's landscape goes through stages of development, with each stage having characteristic conditions.

Figure 14-5 is a model of the stages of landscape development in a mountainous region of a humid climate. In stage A—youth—the uplifting gives the leveling forces such as gravity, running water, and glaciers a large amount of potential energy, and the rate of leveling becomes great. As the uplifting forces decrease in intensity, the leveling forces carve away the land, creating a rugged landscape of lower elevation characteristic of stage B—maturity. If the leveling forces continue to be dominant for millions of years, the landscape will become progressively smoother in slope and lower in elevation. When the former mountain region is smooth enough to resemble a plain, it is considered to be in stage C—old age.

Although landscape development is a continuous process leading to a gradual change in the landscape, at any one time the landscape condition reflects a state of balance among many environmental factors. This is a condition of <u>dynamic equilibrium</u>. If a change occurs in any of the factors, a change in the landscape features will occur until a new equilibrium is established.

Stage A: Youth Uplifting forces are dominant, causing folding and faulting, and the formation of mountains with high elevations and steep slopes.

Stage B: Maturity Leveling forces are dominant, creating a rugged landscape with lower elevations.

Stage C: Old Age Leveling forces are still dominant but less effective because low elevations and gentle slopes provide little potential energy.

Figure 14-5. Stages of landscape development

Effects of Climate on Landscape Development

The rate of development and the characteristics of the landscape in an area are greatly influenced by temperature and moisture conditions, which in turn affect the type and amount of vegetation. Any change in an area's climate will alter the rate of development and the conditions of the landscape. On the other hand, changes in landscape sometimes cause changes in climate. For example, the growth of a new mountain range will block air mass movement and change the precipitation and temperature patterns. In turn, more landscape changes will occur in response to the climate change. One example of this effect is that increased elevations may result in alpine glaciers that will carve rugged, sharp landscapes.

Hillslopes in Arid and Humid Climates The steepness of hillslopes is partly affected by the balance between production of sediments by weathering and the removal of these sediments by erosion. In <u>arid climates,</u> there is little vegetation to hold the sediments in place on steeper slopes or at the bases of slopes, so wind and running water can rapidly carry the sediments away. This rapid removal of sediments causes many arid regions to be characterized by steep slopes and sharp and angular landscape features common in the southwestern United States. Arid regions are also characterized by sand dunes and bedrock sandblasted and sculptured by wind-blown sand. (See Figure 14-6A.)

In humid climates, sediments on hillslopes and at the bases of hillslopes are better held in place by more abundant vegetation; therefore, areas with humid climates are characterized by the smoother and more rounded landscape features common in the eastern United States. The surfaces of the humid landscapes are more likely to be soil and thick vegetation, not the rough and irregular bedrock surfaces of an arid region. The greater rate of chemical weathering of bedrock in humid climates also contributes to their rounded landscapes. Figure 14-6B illustrates the smoother, more rounded landscapes of a humid climate, such as the Tug Hill and Catskill plateaus of New York State.

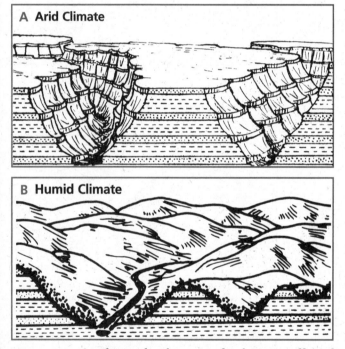

Figure 14-6. Landscape development of a plateau as affected by climate: The rock types and rock structure are assumed to be similar in both diagrams.

Glaciation and Landscapes In climates where glaciers exist or have existed in recent times the landscape will show much evidence of glacial erosion and deposition. Review the Pleistocene ice ages in the Geologic History of New York State in the *Earth Science Reference Tables.* Some of the landscape features of glaciation are:

- mountaintops and steep slopes without much soil
- transported soil covering large areas
- unsorted soil with a large range of particle size—clay to boulders—even at the surface
- wide valleys with U-shaped profiles—as compared to a stream's V-shaped profile

- many lakes, including finger lakes and kettle lakes
- disrupted—not well connected—stream drainage patterns
- many small hills composed of sediments such as drumlins and moraines
- bedrock surfaces with polish, parallel grooves, and scratches
- the features of the glaciers themselves

Stream and Climate Some characteristics of streams are controlled by climate. In arid regions, most streams, being temporary or intermittent, are without water for much of the time; many streams in humid regions are permanent, having discharge most or all of the time.

Internal drainage is common in arid regions and occurs when runoff is channeled into basins not connected by streams to the oceans. Examples of such basins include the Great Salt Lake region in Utah, Death Valley in California, and other basins in Nevada. Internal drainage exists in arid regions because the streams have not had time to carve interconnecting valleys for drainage to the oceans. Also characteristic of arid regions are land deltas located at the base of steep slopes where streams rapidly lose velocity and deposit sediment.

Soils and Climate One of the most important factors in determining soil characteristics—composition, porosity, permeability, and particle size—is climate. Soils in arid regions are often thin or nonexistent because there is little or no vegetation to help make the soil hold in place. The soil that does exist is often very sandy because smaller sediments have been blown away. Arid soils often contain many minerals not commonly found in the soil of humid regions, where <u>infiltration</u> and runoff would dissolve and carry minerals away. If the climate is hot and humid, like many areas near the equator, the soil will be infertile because chemical weathering and infiltration rapidly remove organic material and mineral nutrients, leaving the soil lacking these components.

Memory Jogger

Recall that <u>drumlins</u> are low, long, narrow streamlined hills that are formed at the bottom of glaciers. <u>Moraines</u> are mounds, small hills, or sheets of unsorted, unlayered sediment deposited directly from an edge or bottom of a glacier.

Review Questions

7. Landscape regions in which leveling forces are dominant over uplifting forces are often characterized by

(1) volcanoes
(2) mountain building
(3) low elevations and gentle slopes
(4) high elevations and steep slopes

8. The Adirondacks and the Catskills are both areas of high elevation. Why are the Adirondacks classified as a mountain landscape, whereas the Catskills are classified as a plateau landscape?

9. In a certain area, the processes of uplift and leveling are in dynamic equilibrium. If this condition continues, what will be the overall long-term effect on the elevation of the area?

10. Which New York State landscape region is best represented by the block diagram below?

(1) Allegheny Plateau
(2) Adirondack Mountains
(3) Atlantic Coastal Plain
(4) Erie-Ontario Lowlands

11. Which characteristics of a landscape region would provide the best information about the stage of development of the landscape?

  (1) the age and fossil content of the bedrock
  (2) the types of hillslopes and the stream patterns
  (3) the amount of precipitation and the potential evapotranspiration
  (4) the type of vegetation and the vegetation growth rate

12. The three diagrams below represent the same location at different times. What is the best explanation for the differences in appearance of this location?

  (1) This region was exposed to leveling forces for different lengths of time.
  (2) This region has different underlying bedrock structures.
  (3) This region developed in different climate regions.
  (4) This region has the same type of underlying rock layers.

13. Which factor is most important in determining the evolution of a landscape?

  (1) surface topography
  (2) development of drainage
  (3) plant cover
  (4) climate

14. Which change would occur in a landscape region where uplifting forces are dominant over leveling forces?

  (1) topographic features becoming smoother with time
  (2) no dynamic equilibrium over time
  (3) streams decreasing in velocity with time
  (4) hillslopes increasing in steepness with time

15. The diagrams below represent geologic cross sections from two widely separated regions.

The layers of rock appear similar, but the hillslopes and shapes are different. These differences are most likely the result of

  (1) volcanic eruptions
  (2) earthquake activity
  (3) age of bedrock
  (4) climate variations

16. List two landscape characteristics you would expect to find in an area which has undergone glacial erosion.

17. Contrast the cross-sectional profiles of a glacial valley and a stream valley.

18. Characteristics such as composition, porosity, permeability, and particle size are usually used to describe different types of

  (1) hillslopes
  (2) stream drainage patterns
  (3) soils
  (4) ridges

Bedrock

The composition and structural features of bedrock are major factors in the rate of development and the features of landscapes. Therefore, the primary reason New York State has several landscape regions is that various regions have different bedrock characteristics.

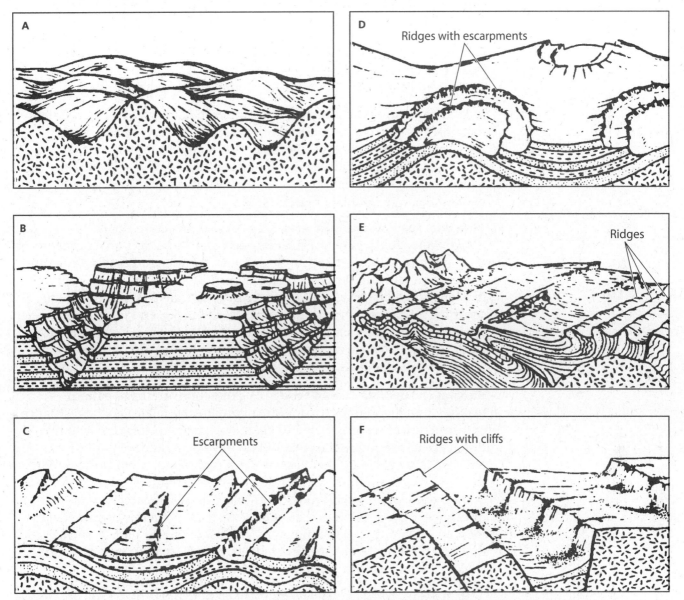

Figure 14-7. Effect of bedrock structure and rock types on landscape features: **(A)** No special structural features or rock resistance differences **(B)** Undistorted sedimentary rocks of a plateau **(C)** Gently folded sedimentary strata of varying resistance **(D)** Domed mountain structure of folded sedimentary rocks above intrusive igneous rocks **(E)** Complex bedrock structure **(F)** Fault block mountain in igneous rocks

Rock Types and Hillslopes

In any one climate, different rock types have varying degrees of resistance to weathering and erosion. If all the rocks in an area exposed to the surface have about the same resistance, the landscape will be controlled by structural features such as faults, folds, and joints and by uplifting and leveling forces. (See diagram E in Figure 14-7.) If there are no special structural features or rock resistance differences, the landscape features will be random in location and without rapid changes in hillslopes. (See diagram A in Figure 14-7.)

If the rocks exposed at the surface have different degrees of resistance, the rocks will weather and erode at varying rates. For example, sandstone layers will generally be more resistant than shale in areas of sedimentary rock and will weather and erode away more slowly. The result will be a marked difference in slope between layers of different resistance, often with steeper slopes called **escarpments**, or cliffs, along the edge of the more-resistant layers. (See the escarpments in diagram C and small cliffs in diagram B associated with the sandstone layers in Figure 14-7.)

In landscapes of folded, faulted, igneous, or metamorphic rocks, resistant rocks form long narrow uplands called ridges. Ridges form the more-resistant rocks of the higher portions of the southern part of the Hudson-Mohawk Lowlands landscape region of southeastern New York. This region is often called the ridge and valley landscape region. (See the ridges in diagrams D, E, and F of Figure 14-7.)

Structural Features and Hillslopes Types of rock structure—such as horizontality, folds, joints, and faults—have a major effect on landscapes. If an area's rocks have many faults or joints, then the forces of weathering and erosion will find it easier to break up and remove the rocks, resulting in a lower area like a valley. A study of the diagrams in Figure 14-7 will show the influence of horizontal rocks, folded rocks, and faulted rocks on the landscape appearance. Generally, the greater the variety of structural features found in an area, the more varied the changes in hillslopes and types of landscape features created, as shown in diagram E of Figure 14-7.

Streams and Bedrock Characteristics The direction, drainage pattern, features, and gradient of streams are often directly related to the resistance and structure of underlying bedrock. In horizontal rock layers with little difference in resistance, the streams will develop a random pattern and have few changes in gradient as shown in diagram A of Figure 14-8. When the rocks in an area have varying degrees of resistance or there are folded, domed, jointed, or faulted rocks, the stream drainage patterns and directions of the streams will be at least partly, if not totally, controlled by these rock features. See diagrams B, C, and D of Figure 14-8. In such cases, there are often sharp changes in gradient, as indicated by waterfalls and rapids flowing over ridges and escarpments.

Soils and Rock Composition The different compositions of the soil are due in part to differences in the underlying bedrock, or in the transported sediment from which the soil formed. A soil formed from a sedimentary rock such as sandstone, will be sandier than soil formed from an igneous rock such as basalt. Even though most of New York's soil has been transported by glaciers or streams, there is still a close correlation in soil properties and rock types, as shown on a geologic map such as the Ⓡ Generalized Bedrock Geology of New York State in the *Earth Science Reference Tables.*

A

B Ridges and escarpments

C

D

Streams

Contour lines

Streams

Contour lines

Contour lines

Streams

Contour lines

Streams

Random, or dendritic, drainage This pattern is characteristic of horizontal sedimentary rocks and lava flows with little difference in rock resistance.

Trellis, or block, drainage This pattern is observed in folded rocks with much difference in resistance, and also in faulted and jointed rock.

Radial drainage This pattern occurs in areas of domed structure (such as some volcanoes) with little difference in rock resistance.

Annular drainage This pattern of concentric circles is found in areas of domed structure with much difference in rock resistance.

Figure 14-8. Effect of bedrock structure and varying rock resistance on stream drainage patterns.

Review Questions

19. Which cross-sectional diagram below best represents a landscape region that resulted from faulting?

(1)

(3)

(2)

(4)

20. In the cross section of the hill shown below, which rock units are probably most resistant to weathering?

(1) I and II   (3) I and III
(2) II and III   (4) II and IV

21. The primary reason several landscape regions have formed in New York State is that the various regions have different

(1) climates
(2) latitudes
(3) soil characteristics
(4) bedrock characteristics

22. How was the valley shown in the diagram below most likely formed?

(1) by the deposition of sediments
(2) by the extrusion of igneous material
(3) by the faulting of rock layers
(4) by the folding of rock layers

23. Which of the following stream patterns is most characteristic of horizontal rock structure?

24. Which kind of stream pattern would most likely be found on the type of landscape shown in the diagram?

25. According to the surface landscape development indicated in the diagram, which rock type or types are most resistant to weathering and erosion in this environment?

(1) rock E
(2) rock H
(3) rocks C and F
(4) rocks D and G

People, Environmental Change, and Landscapes

How people live, work, play, and keep safe is in part determined by landscape factors that include environmental hazards. People also affect the environment both positively and negatively.

Effects of Landscape Conditions on People

Many people have settled near streams because of the ease of transportation, hydropower, water supply, and recreation. However, some areas on a flood plain could have dangerous flooding. People have made the choice to live in these flood-prone areas, but they risk losing their lives or possessions.

Ocean shores, such as much of Long Island, New York, are appealing for their moderated climate, attractive landscapes, and recreation opportunities. However, these same areas have the potential for flooding from high tides, hurricanes, winter mid-latitude cyclones, and the rise in sea level from global warming.

Regions with soils that have a high clay content can easily experience a type of slow gravity erosion or mass movement called soil creep. Also, clay soils can easily liquefy during moderate or strong earthquakes. Constructing roads and buildings on ridges and hillslopes having soil with a high clay content can result in mass movements such as landslides. Building on bedrock that is too steep or on rock that is highly fractured can also result in landslides. These mass movements can cause harm to people and to buildings.

Proper environmental planning, coupled with laws and zoning limitations, can reduce potential future damage to buildings as well as minimize human injury or death. If it is impractical to remove humans from an area of potential environmental hazard, planning escape procedures in advance can help avoid injury and loss of life.

Environmental Change of the Landscape by People

People have greatly affected the environment, including the landscape. They have cut down forests and plowed up the land, allowing the soil to be eroded. They have carved up or smoothed out the land for mining and construction of roads, buildings, and airports. They have polluted the land with their trash. They have added chemicals to the land, air, and water that aid weathering. They have even made "new" land by filling in lakes and parts of the ocean with their garbage in landfills.

Landscape Pollution and Population Landscape pollution is generally greatest in areas of high population density. Figure 14-9 is a graph showing that the human population has been increasing at a very rapid rate.

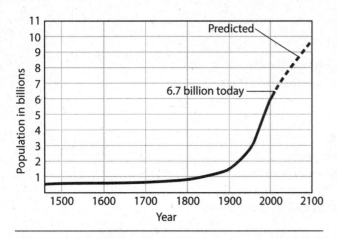

Figure 14-9. Estimated human population of the world (projected to the year 2100)

People also cause rapid changes in their environment because of technology—the application of scientific discoveries to methods of producing goods and services. Many changes caused by actions of people have resulted in the extinction of wildlife, loss of natural habitats, and destruction of landscapes that were used for farming and grazing.

Atmospheric Pollution and Landscape Change The addition of liquid and solid aerosols to the atmosphere can increase reflection and scattering of insolation. This may result in less energy at the surface of Earth for natural landscape-producing processes, such as weathering. Less energy at Earth's surface could also result in an ice age and an increase in glacial erosion. On the other hand, the addition of carbon dioxide, water vapor, and methane to the atmosphere can increase the greenhouse effect and thus cause an increase in energy at Earth's surface for landscape change. Such changes may include an increase in arid environments and a decrease in glacial environments. Many industrial and individual activities add substances to the atmosphere that cause greater amounts of cloud coverage than would naturally occur. Increased cloud coverage can increase the amount of precipitation, which in turn affects the amounts of stream erosion. The addition of sulfur and nitrogen compounds to the atmosphere, largely by burning fossil fuels and through mineral refining, has significantly increased the acid content of precipitation. This acid precipitation has increased chemical weathering of rocks, including many stone buildings, and has caused the destruction of animal species and large areas of forest. One prime example of air pollution and landscape change is the modern urban micro-environment, as shown in Figure 14-10.

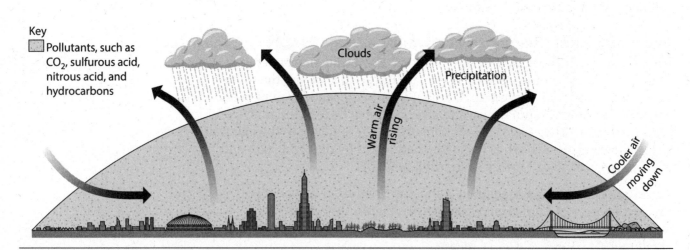

Figure 14-10. An urban microenvironment: A city or urban area is an example of how humans have altered, or polluted, the atmosphere and landscapes. The changes that have directly altered the environment include the addition of pollutants and the constructions of objects such as buildings and roads. The concentration of humans and buildings cause heat to be given off that increases the air temperature above the urban area. The result is an atmosphere that is hotter, more smoggy, less windy, more humid, cloudier, more foggy, and less transparent. Other results include more precipitation and a higher acid precipitation.

Environmental Conservation

Natural resources—such as soil for agriculture, land for home sites, and pure water for consumption, irrigation, manufacturing processes, and recreation—can be conserved by careful planning. Reclamation of polluted environments, reduction in production of environmental pollutants, and the choice to use alternative resources and recycle our waste products are some ways to conserve natural resources. This can result in preservation of natural resources and minimal environmental harm while still providing the resources needed for human use.

Review Questions

26. The diagram shows a New York State highway road cut.

The water well has probably gone dry because

(1) crustal uplift has altered the landscape
(2) human activities have altered the landscape
(3) the climate has become more humid
(4) the bedrock porosity has changed

27. Humans can cause rapid changes in the environment, sometimes producing catastrophic events. Which statement below is the best example of this concept?

(1) Mountainside highway construction causes a landslide.
(2) Lightning causes a forest fire.
(3) Shifting crustal plates cause an earthquake.
(4) Changing seasonal winds cause flooding in an area.

28. As population increases, the amount of alteration of the landscape by human activity will most likely

(1) decrease
(2) increase
(3) remain the same

29. The addition of pollutants to the atmosphere may change the rate of energy absorption and radiation. This could result in

(1) a renewal of volcanic activity
(2) the formation of a new fault zone
(3) a landscape-modifying climate change
(4) a change in the times of high and low tides

30. Which graph best represents human population growth?

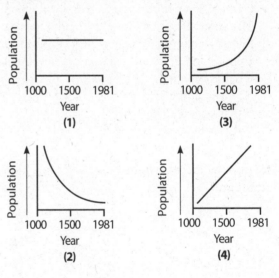

Directions

Review the Test-Taking Strategies section of this book. Then answer the following questions. Read each question carefully and answer with a correct choice or response.

Part A

1 Models of hillslopes and landform shapes can be made with the use of
   (1) isobars
   (2) contour lines
   (3) isotherms
   (4) parallels

2 If a landscape is in dynamic equilibrium and uplift occurs,
   (1) there can never again be dynamic equilibrium in the area
   (2) the dynamic equilibrium will remain the same
   (3) a new dynamic equilibrium will be established
   (4) a new landscape will form without dynamic equilibrium

3 If a new mountain range were to form where the Mississippi River is today, the landscape east of this new mountain range would become more angular and less rounded because the climate would become
   (1) drier and warmer
   (2) drier and cooler
   (3) moister and warmer
   (4) moister and cooler

Refer to the diagram below to answer questions 4 through 9.

4 The climate of this area is most likely
   (1) arid
   (2) humid
   (3) hot
   (4) cold

5 The cliffs or escarpments around location A are most directly the result of
   (1) igneous intrusion
   (2) resistant rock layers
   (3) the different ages of the rock
   (4) movement along faults

6 What can be said about rock layer B compared to rock layer F?
   (1) B is younger
   (2) B is more resistant
   (3) B is less resistant
   (4) B is lower because of its environment of deposition

7 How would you classify the geologic forces producing the landscapes at locations C and G?
   (1) At both places uplifting forces are dominant.
   (2) At both places leveling forces are dominant.
   (3) At C uplifting is dominant, and at G leveling is dominant.
   (4) At C leveling is dominant, and at G uplifting is dominant.

8 What immediate effects would increased rainfall have on the rate of leveling of this landscape?
   (1) increase
   (2) decrease
   (3) remain the same

9 The primary reason for the cliff at D is
   (1) volcanic action
   (2) resistant rock layers
   (3) movement along a fault
   (4) joints in the rock layers

10 What is the most practical way to control pollution?
(1) slowing the rate of technological growth
(2) decreasing the population
(3) careful planning of environmental usage
(4) more government control of industry

11 The most practical way individuals can help fight pollution is by
(1) becoming aware of the problems and thus changing their attitudes and actions
(2) recycling paper
(3) using fewer products produced by technology
(4) changing their lifestyles to conform to that of nineteenth-century rural America

12 Which New York State landscape region is mostly a direct result of the last ice age?
(1) Newark Lowlands
(2) Taconic Mountains
(3) Atlantic Coastal Plain
(4) Hudson-Mohawk Lowlands

13 A landscape region with only intermittent (not permanent) streams and no drainage connected to the ocean would most likely have what type of climate?
(1) arid
(2) humid
(3) hot and wet
(4) cool and wet

14 Which New York State landscape region is composed mostly of intensely metamorphosed surface bedrock?
(1) Hudson-Mohawk Lowlands
(2) Tug Hill Plateau
(3) Hudson Highlands
(4) Allegheny Plateau

15 If global warming continues to result in higher ocean levels, the increased ocean wave and current erosion will have the greatest effect on what New York State landscape region?
(1) Newark Lowlands
(2) Atlantic Coastal Plain
(3) Erie-Ontario Lowlands
(4) Hudson Highlands

Part B

Base your answers to questions 16 through 18 on the information below.

A mountain is a landform with steeply sloping sides whose peak is usually thousands of feet higher than its base. Mountains often contain a great deal of igneous and metamorphic rock and have distorted rock structures caused by faulting and folding of the crust.

A plateau is a broad, level area at a high elevation. It usually has an undistorted, horizontal rock structure. A plateau may have steep slopes as a result of erosion.

16 State why marine fossils are not usually found in the bedrock of the Adirondack Mountains. [1]

17 State the agent of erosion that is most likely responsible for shaping the Catskill Plateau so that it physically resembles a mountainous region. [1]

18 State the approximate age of the surface bedrock of the Catskills. [1]

19 Identify one source of pollution caused by human activity that contributes to the precipitation becoming more acidic. [1]

20 Part of which generalized New York State landscape region is drained by the Susquehanna river and its tributaries? [1]

Base your answers to questions 21 through 23 on the map below and your knowledge of earth science. The map shows houses, asphalt roads, drilled water wells and the amount of insecticide in parts per million (ppm) for each well except at house Q. The insecticide was spread on the lawn of one of the houses and seeped into the ground water.

21 Write the letter of the house that is the probable source of the insecticide. [1]

22 State a reasonable value for the concentration of insecticide in ppm at house Q. [1]

23 These houses were recently built on land that was originally forest. Indicate how the amount of runoff from precipitation compares today with that of the original forest. Then state a reason for this change in runoff. [2]

Part C

The following article, though fictitious, represents events that have happened in Washington State along the Pacific coast. Use your knowledge of earth science and the information in the following article to answer questions 24 through 27.

The death toll from a mudslide in the town of Coastal, Washington, rose to over 50 today, and local authorities began discussing whether to allow people to move back into this housing development, to only use the land for seaside recreation, or to declare the land off limits. Because the forecast is calling for another two weeks of heavy rain on top of what has already fallen in this area, local emergency management officials feel that there is a real threat of more devastating mudslides.

Many of the 70 or so homes that were destroyed or severely damaged had been built on or just behind a sea cliff that has been declared unstable by local and state authorities. Since the houses were built over ten years ago, the owners, under the pre-existing laws, were allowed to remain in their homes on the cliff.

Local geologists indicate that one of the major reasons for the danger of additional mudslides is the fact that the soil is partly composed of clay layers formed by ash from eruptions of the volcanoes in the Cascade Mountains to the east. Another factor is related to new home construction a few miles inland, which has resulted in both deforestation and disruption of the local stream drainage.

The emergency management and other government officials now have to make the tough decisions: Should people be evicted from their homes in nearby areas with similar landscape? Should people be allowed to rebuild in the mudslide area? Should the area be zoned just as park land? Should the area be declared unsafe for any human activity?

24 What landscape and weather conditions resulted in these mudslides at Coastal, Washington? [2]

25 What three landscape features would you expect geologists and government officials to investigate to determine future land use in this part of Coastal, Washington? [3]

26 What feature of the Tectonic Plate Map in the *Earth Science Reference Tables* might affect the use of land in this part of Washington State? [1]

27 Describe an actual experiment geologists could conduct at this landscape site to help determine future mudslide potential. [2]

Base your answers to questions 28 and 29 on the geologic cross section shown below and on your knowledge of Earth Science. The cross section shows the surface of a landscape region in the southwestern United States and indicates the age, type, and thickness of the bedrock.

28 State *one* characteristic, other than the horizontal bedrock structure, shown in the cross section that supports the idea that this region is correctly classified as a plateau landscape. [1]

29 Which New York State landscape region has surface bedrock of the same geologic age as the surface bedrock shown in this cross section? [1]

30 Describe the arrangement of sediment found in a glacial moraine. [1]

Appendix 1:
Earth Science Reference Tables

Appendix 1:
Earth Science Reference Tables

Using the Reference Tables

You should become thoroughly familiar with all details of these tables. Look for the (R) on the topic pages to see where the content is enhanced by the reference tables. Some of the ways for which these reference tables are used in Regents Examination questions include:

- to find a specific fact, such as the composition of the Earth's inner core

- to find the relationship between two facts on different parts of the reference tables, such as the latitude and longitude of the center of the Tug Hill Plateau

- using an equation on the reference tables to solve a problem, such as a rate of change of an event

- graphing or recognizing the correct graph of data on the reference tables, such as the percent by mass of the elements in the Earth's crust

- decoding a graphic symbol in a question, such as present weather or air mass type on a weather map

- performing a procedure using part of the reference tables, such as determining the distance of a location to an epicenter using the Earthquake P-wave and S-wave Travel Time graph

- interpretation of data on the reference tables, such as the temperature of white dwarf stars

Reference Tables for Physical Setting/EARTH SCIENCE

Radioactive Decay Data

RADIOACTIVE ISOTOPE	DISINTEGRATION	HALF-LIFE (years)
Carbon-14	$^{14}C \rightarrow {^{14}N}$	5.7×10^3
Potassium-40	$^{40}K \begin{smallmatrix} \nearrow {^{40}Ar} \\ \searrow {^{40}Ca} \end{smallmatrix}$	1.3×10^9
Uranium-238	$^{238}U \rightarrow {^{206}Pb}$	4.5×10^9
Rubidium-87	$^{87}Rb \rightarrow {^{87}Sr}$	4.9×10^{10}

Specific Heats of Common Materials

MATERIAL	SPECIFIC HEAT (Joules/gram • °C)
Liquid water	4.18
Solid water (ice)	2.11
Water vapor	2.00
Dry air	1.01
Basalt	0.84
Granite	0.79
Iron	0.45
Copper	0.38
Lead	0.13

Equations

$$\text{Eccentricity} = \frac{\text{distance between foci}}{\text{length of major axis}}$$

$$\text{Gradient} = \frac{\text{change in field value}}{\text{distance}}$$

$$\text{Rate of change} = \frac{\text{change in value}}{\text{time}}$$

$$\text{Density} = \frac{\text{mass}}{\text{volume}}$$

Properties of Water

Heat energy gained during melting . . . . 334 J/g

Heat energy released during freezing . . . . 334 J/g

Heat energy gained during vaporization . . . . . 2260 J/g

Heat energy released during condensation . . . 2260 J/g

Density at 3.98°C . . . . 1.0 g/mL

Average Chemical Composition of Earth's Crust, Hydrosphere, and Troposphere

ELEMENT (symbol)	CRUST		HYDROSPHERE	TROPOSPHERE
	Percent by mass	Percent by volume	Percent by volume	Percent by volume
Oxygen (O)	46.10	94.04	33.0	21.0
Silicon (Si)	28.20	0.88		
Aluminum (Al)	8.23	0.48		
Iron (Fe)	5.63	0.49		
Calcium (Ca)	4.15	1.18		
Sodium (Na)	2.36	1.11		
Magnesium (Mg)	2.33	0.33		
Potassium (K)	2.09	1.42		
Nitrogen (N)				78.0
Hydrogen (H)			66.0	
Other	0.91	0.07	1.0	1.0

2011 EDITION

This edition of the Earth Science Reference Tables should be used in the classroom beginning in the 2011–12 school year. The first examination for which these tables will be used is the January 2012 Regents Examination in Physical Setting/Earth Science.

Eurypterus remipes

New York State Fossil

Generalized Landscape Regions of New York State

Key

— Major geographic province boundary

········· Landscape region boundary

—··— State boundary

—···— International boundary

Generalized Bedrock Geology of New York State

modified from
GEOLOGICAL SURVEY
NEW YORK STATE MUSEUM
1989

GEOLOGIC PERIODS AND ERAS IN NEW YORK

CRETACEOUS and PLEISTOCENE (Epoch) weakly consolidated to unconsolidated gravels, sands, and clays

LATE TRIASSIC and EARLY JURASSIC conglomerates, red sandstones, red shales, basalt, and diabase (Palisades sill)

PENNSYLVANIAN and MISSISSIPPIAN conglomerates, sandstones, and shales

DEVONIAN limestones, shales, sandstones, and conglomerates

SILURIAN *also contains salt, gypsum, and hematite.*

ORDOVICIAN limestones, shales, sandstones, and dolostones

CAMBRIAN

CAMBRIAN and EARLY ORDOVICIAN sandstones and dolostones
moderately to intensely metamorphosed east of the Hudson River

CAMBRIAN and ORDOVICIAN (undifferentiated) quartzites, dolostones, marbles, and schists
intensely metamorphosed; includes portions of the Taconic Sequence and Cortland Complex

TACONIC SEQUENCE sandstones, shales, and slates
slightly to intensely metamorphosed rocks of CAMBRIAN through MIDDLE ORDOVICIAN ages

MIDDLE PROTEROZOIC gneisses, quartzites, and marbles
Lines are generalized structure trends.

MIDDLE PROTEROZOIC anorthositic rocks

Dominantly sedimentary origin

Dominantly metamorphosed rocks

Intensely metamorphosed rocks
(regional metamorphism about 1,000 m.y.a.)

Surface Ocean Currents

NOTE: Not all surface ocean currents are shown.

Key

→ Warm currents

⇒ Cool currents

Tectonic Plates

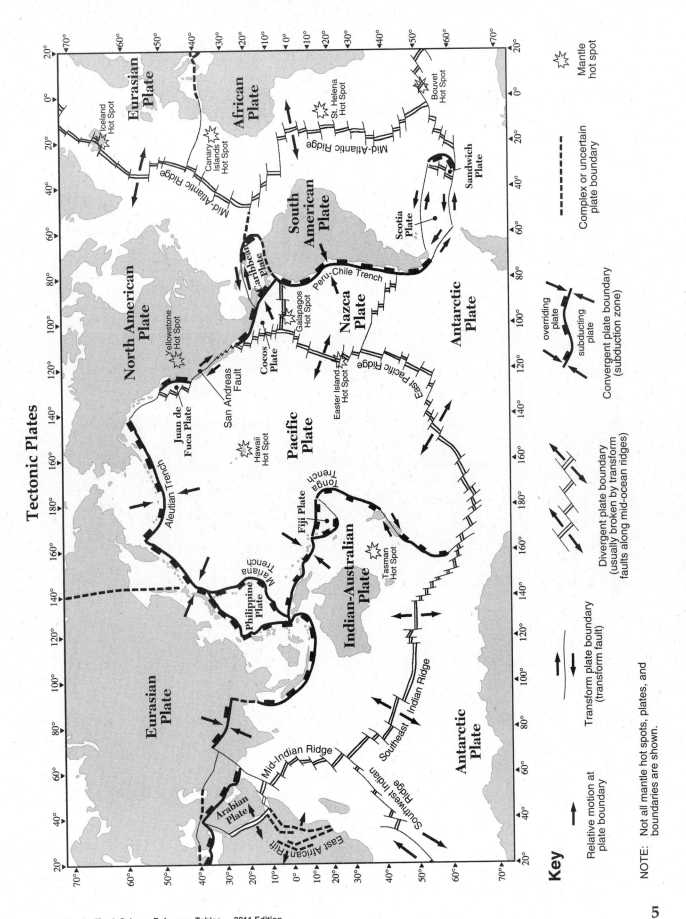

Key

Mantle hot spot

Complex or uncertain plate boundary

overriding plate / subducting plate
Convergent plate boundary (subduction zone)

Divergent plate boundary (usually broken by transform faults along mid-ocean ridges)

Transform plate boundary (transform fault)

Relative motion at plate boundary

NOTE: Not all mantle hot spots, plates, and boundaries are shown.

Rock Cycle in Earth's Crust

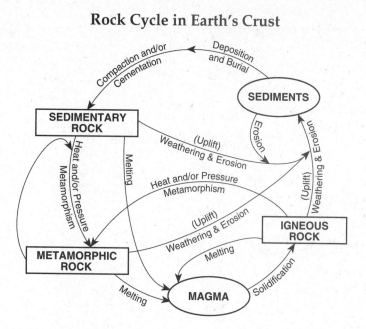

Relationship of Transported Particle Size to Water Velocity

This generalized graph shows the water velocity needed to maintain, but not start, movement. Variations occur due to differences in particle density and shape.

Scheme for Igneous Rock Identification

Scheme for Sedimentary Rock Identification

INORGANIC LAND-DERIVED SEDIMENTARY ROCKS					
TEXTURE	**GRAIN SIZE**	**COMPOSITION**	**COMMENTS**	**ROCK NAME**	**MAP SYMBOL**
Clastic (fragmental)	Pebbles, cobbles, and/or boulders embedded in sand, silt, and/or clay	Mostly quartz, feldspar, and clay minerals; may contain fragments of other rocks and minerals	Rounded fragments	Conglomerate	
			Angular fragments	Breccia	
	Sand (0.006 to 0.2 cm)		Fine to coarse	Sandstone	
	Silt (0.0004 to 0.006 cm)		Very fine grain	Siltstone	
	Clay (less than 0.0004 cm)		Compact; may split easily	Shale	

CHEMICALLY AND/OR ORGANICALLY FORMED SEDIMENTARY ROCKS					
TEXTURE	**GRAIN SIZE**	**COMPOSITION**	**COMMENTS**	**ROCK NAME**	**MAP SYMBOL**
Crystalline	Fine to coarse crystals	Halite	Crystals from chemical precipitates and evaporites	Rock salt	
		Gypsum		Rock gypsum	
		Dolomite		Dolostone	
Crystalline or bioclastic	Microscopic to very coarse	Calcite	Precipitates of biologic origin or cemented shell fragments	Limestone	
Bioclastic		Carbon	Compacted plant remains	Bituminous coal	

Scheme for Metamorphic Rock Identification

TEXTURE	GRAIN SIZE	COMPOSITION	TYPE OF METAMORPHISM	COMMENTS	ROCK NAME	MAP SYMBOL
FOLIATED — MINERAL ALIGNMENT	Fine	MICA QUARTZ FELDSPAR AMPHIBOLE GARNET PYROXENE	Regional (Heat and pressure increases)	Low-grade metamorphism of shale	Slate	
	Fine to medium			Foliation surfaces shiny from microscopic mica crystals	Phyllite	
				Platy mica crystals visible from metamorphism of clay or feldspars	Schist	
FOLIATED — BANDING	Medium to coarse			High-grade metamorphism; mineral types segregated into bands	Gneiss	
NONFOLIATED	Fine	Carbon	Regional	Metamorphism of bituminous coal	Anthracite coal	
	Fine	Various minerals	Contact (heat)	Various rocks changed by heat from nearby magma/lava	Hornfels	
	Fine to coarse	Quartz	Regional or contact	Metamorphism of quartz sandstone	Quartzite	
		Calcite and/or dolomite		Metamorphism of limestone or dolostone	Marble	
	Coarse	Various minerals		Pebbles may be distorted or stretched	Metaconglomerate	

GEOLOGIC HISTORY

Eon	Era	Period	Epoch	Life on Earth	NY Rock Record

NY Rock Record: ▨ Sediment ■ Bedrock

Million years ago (Eon scale): 0, 500, 1000, 2000, 3000, 4000, 4600

PHANEROZOIC

PROTEROZOIC — LATE, MIDDLE, EARLY
ARCHEAN — LATE, MIDDLE, EARLY
PRECAMBRIAN

Life on Earth — Million years ago:

Era	Period	Epoch	Life on Earth (Million years ago)
CENOZOIC	QUATERNARY	HOLOCENE — 0	
		PLEISTOCENE — 0.01 / 1.8	Humans, mastodonts, mammoths
	NEOGENE	PLIOCENE — 5.3	Large carnivorous mammals
		MIOCENE — 23.0	Abundant grazing mammals
	PALEOGENE	OLIGOCENE — 33.9	Earliest grasses
		EOCENE — 55.8	Many modern groups of mammals
		PALEOCENE — 65.5	Mass extinction of dinosaurs, ammonoids, and many land plants
MESOZOIC	CRETACEOUS	LATE	
		EARLY — 146	Earliest flowering plants / Diverse bony fishes
	JURASSIC	LATE	Earliest birds
		MIDDLE	Abundant dinosaurs and ammonoids
		EARLY — 200	
	TRIASSIC	LATE	Earliest mammals
		MIDDLE	Earliest dinosaurs
		EARLY — 251	Mass extinction of many land and marine organisms (including trilobites)
PALEOZOIC	PERMIAN	LATE	
		MIDDLE	Mammal-like reptiles
		EARLY	Abundant reptiles
	CARBONIFEROUS — PENNSYLVANIAN	LATE — 299	Extensive coal-forming forests
		EARLY — 318	Abundant amphibians
	CARBONIFEROUS — MISSISSIPPIAN	LATE	Large and numerous scale trees and seed ferns (vascular plants); earliest reptiles
		MIDDLE	
		EARLY — 359	
	DEVONIAN	LATE	Earliest amphibians and plant seeds / Extinction of many marine organisms
		MIDDLE	Earth's first forests / Earliest ammonoids and sharks
		EARLY — 416	Abundant fish
	SILURIAN	LATE	Earliest insects / Earliest land plants and animals
		EARLY — 444	Abundant eurypterids
	ORDOVICIAN	LATE	
		MIDDLE	Invertebrates dominant / Earth's first coral reefs
		EARLY — 488	
	CAMBRIAN	LATE	Burgess shale fauna (diverse soft-bodied organisms)
		MIDDLE	Earliest fishes / Extinction of many primitive marine organisms
		EARLY — 542	Earliest trilobites / Great diversity of life-forms with shelly parts
		— 580	Ediacaran fauna (first multicellular, soft-bodied marine organisms)
		— 1300	Abundant stromatolites

Precambrian annotations (left side):
- First sexually reproducing organisms
- Oceanic oxygen begins to enter the atmosphere
- Oceanic oxygen produced by cyanobacteria combines with iron, forming iron oxide layers on ocean floor
- Earliest stromatolites / Oldest microfossils
- Evidence of biological carbon
- Oldest known rocks
- Estimated time of origin of Earth and solar system

(Index fossils not drawn to scale)

A — Elliptocephala
B — Cryptolithus
C — Phacops
D — Valcouroceras / Hexameroceras
E — Centroceras
F — Manticoceras
G — (Manticoceras)
H — Eucalyptocrinus
I — Ctenocrinus
J — Tetragraptus
K — Dicellograptus
L — Coelophysis
M — Eurypterus
N — Stylonurus

OF NEW YORK STATE

Time Distribution of Fossils
(including important fossils of New York)

The center of each lettered circle indicates the approximate time of existence of a specific index fossil (e.g. Fossil Ⓐ lived at the end of the Early Cambrian).

NAUTILOIDS
DINOSAURS
MAMMALS
BIRDS
AMMONOIDS
CRINOIDS
VASCULAR PLANTS
CORALS
GASTROPODS
BRACHIOPODS
TRILOBITES
EURYPTERIDS
GRAPTOLITES
PLACODERM FISH

Ⓞ Ⓢ
Ⓛ
Ⓒ Ⓕ Ⓖ Ⓝ Ⓠ Ⓡ Ⓧ Ⓩ
Ⓘ Ⓥ
Ⓗ Ⓜ Ⓟ
Ⓔ Ⓤ Ⓨ
Ⓚ
Ⓑ Ⓓ Ⓣ Ⓦ
Ⓙ
Ⓐ

Important Geologic Events in New York

Advance and retreat of last continental ice

Sands and clays underlying Long Island and Staten Island deposited on margin of Atlantic Ocean

Dome-like uplift of Adirondack region begins

Initial opening of Atlantic Ocean
North America and Africa separate
⟨ Intrusion of Palisades sill ⟩
Pangaea begins to break up

Alleghenian orogeny caused by collision of North America and Africa along transform margin, forming Pangaea

Catskill delta forms
Erosion of Acadian Mountains
Acadian orogeny caused by collision of North America and Avalon and closing of remaining part of Iapetus Ocean

Salt and gypsum deposited in evaporite basins

Erosion of Taconic Mountains; Queenston delta forms
Taconian orogeny caused by closing of western part of Iapetus Ocean and collision between North America and volcanic island arc

Widespread deposition over most of New York along edge of Iapetus Ocean

Rifting and initial opening of Iapetus Ocean

Erosion of Grenville Mountains

Grenville orogeny: metamorphism of bedrock now exposed in the Adirondacks and Hudson Highlands

Inferred Positions of Earth's Landmasses

59 million years ago

119 million years ago

232 million years ago

359 million years ago

458 million years ago

Ⓞ Mastodont
Beluga Whale
Ⓟ Cooksonia
Aneurophyton
Ⓠ Naples Tree
Ⓡ Bothriolepis
Ⓢ Condor
Ⓣ Lichenaria
Ⓤ Cystiphyllum
Pleurodictyum
Ⓥ
Ⓦ Maclurites
Ⓧ Platyceras
Ⓨ Eospirifer
Ⓩ Mucrospirifer

ADU (2011)

Inferred Properties of Earth's Interior

Earthquake P-Wave and S-Wave Travel Time

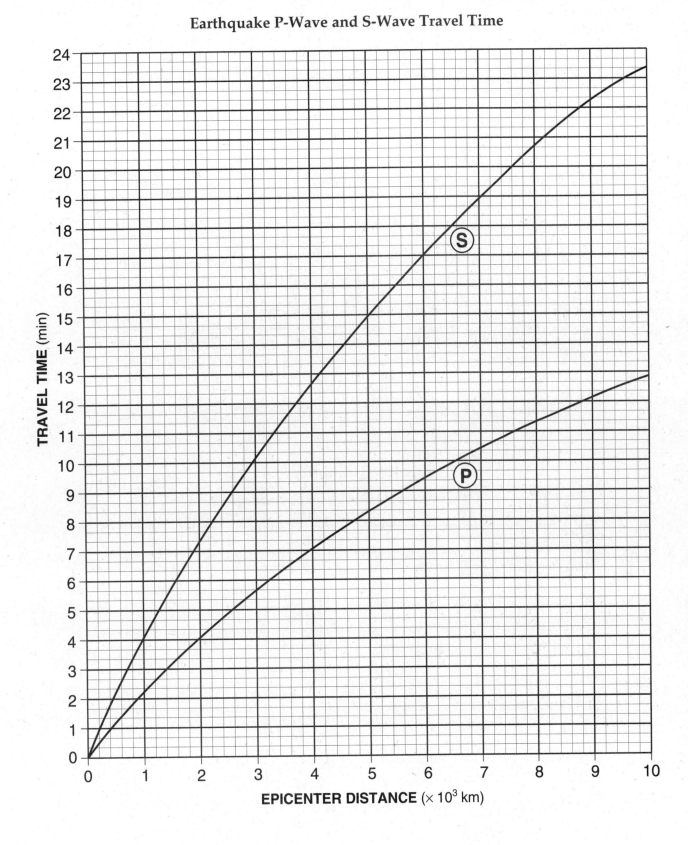

Dewpoint (°C)

Dry-Bulb Temperature (°C)	Difference Between Wet-Bulb and Dry-Bulb Temperatures (C°)															
	0	1	2	3	4	5	6	7	8	9	10	11	12	13	14	15
−20	−20	−33														
−18	−18	−28														
−16	−16	−24														
−14	−14	−21	−36													
−12	−12	−18	−28													
−10	−10	−14	−22													
−8	−8	−12	−18	−29												
−6	−6	−10	−14	−22												
−4	−4	−7	−12	−17	−29											
−2	−2	−5	−8	−13	−20											
0	0	−3	−6	−9	−15	−24										
2	2	−1	−3	−6	−11	−17										
4	4	1	−1	−4	−7	−11	−19									
6	6	4	1	−1	−4	−7	−13	−21								
8	8	6	3	1	−2	−5	−9	−14								
10	10	8	6	4	1	−2	−5	−9	−14	−28						
12	12	10	8	6	4	1	−2	−5	−9	−16						
14	14	12	11	9	6	4	1	−2	−5	−10	−17					
16	16	14	13	11	9	7	4	1	−1	−6	−10	−17				
18	18	16	15	13	11	9	7	4	2	−2	−5	−10	−19			
20	20	19	17	15	14	12	10	7	4	2	−2	−5	−10	−19		
22	22	21	19	17	16	14	12	10	8	5	3	−1	−5	−10	−19	
24	24	23	21	20	18	16	14	12	10	8	6	2	−1	−5	−10	−18
26	26	25	23	22	20	18	17	15	13	11	9	6	3	0	−4	−9
28	28	27	25	24	22	21	19	17	16	14	11	9	7	4	1	−3
30	30	29	27	26	24	23	21	19	18	16	14	12	10	8	5	1

Relative Humidity (%)

Dry-Bulb Temperature (°C)	Difference Between Wet-Bulb and Dry-Bulb Temperatures (C°)															
	0	1	2	3	4	5	6	7	8	9	10	11	12	13	14	15
−20	100	28														
−18	100	40														
−16	100	48														
−14	100	55	11													
−12	100	61	23													
−10	100	66	33													
−8	100	71	41	13												
−6	100	73	48	20												
−4	100	77	54	32	11											
−2	100	79	58	37	20	1										
0	100	81	63	45	28	11										
2	100	83	67	51	36	20	6									
4	100	85	70	56	42	27	14									
6	100	86	72	59	46	35	22	10								
8	100	87	74	62	51	39	28	17	6							
10	100	88	76	65	54	43	33	24	13	4						
12	100	88	78	67	57	48	38	28	19	10	2					
14	100	89	79	69	60	50	41	33	25	16	8	1				
16	100	90	80	71	62	54	45	37	29	21	14	7	1			
18	100	91	81	72	64	56	48	40	33	26	19	12	6			
20	100	91	82	74	66	58	51	44	36	30	23	17	11	5		
22	100	92	83	75	68	60	53	46	40	33	27	21	15	10	4	
24	100	92	84	76	69	62	55	49	42	36	30	25	20	14	9	4
26	100	92	85	77	70	64	57	51	45	39	34	28	23	18	13	9
28	100	93	86	78	71	65	59	53	47	42	36	31	26	21	17	12
30	100	93	86	79	72	66	61	55	49	44	39	34	29	25	20	16

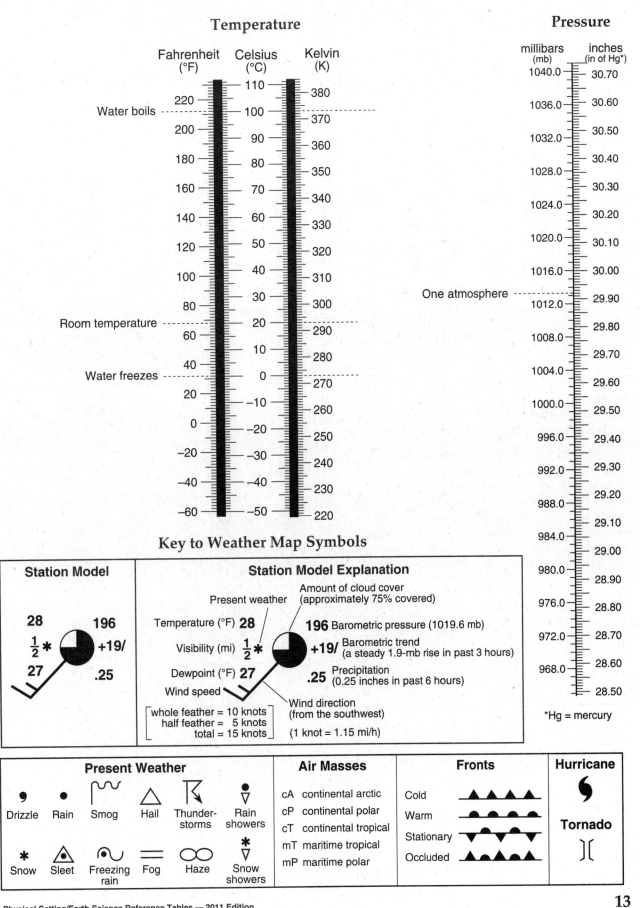

Temperature

Fahrenheit (°F) Celsius (°C) Kelvin (K)

Water boils

Room temperature

Water freezes

Pressure

millibars (mb)   inches (in of Hg*)

One atmosphere

*Hg = mercury

Key to Weather Map Symbols

Station Model	Station Model Explanation
28 196 ½ * +19/ 27 .25	Amount of cloud cover (approximately 75% covered) Present weather Temperature (°F) **28** **196** Barometric pressure (1019.6 mb) Visibility (mi) **½ *** **+19/** Barometric trend (a steady 1.9-mb rise in past 3 hours) Dewpoint (°F) **27** **.25** Precipitation (0.25 inches in past 6 hours) Wind speed Wind direction (from the southwest) [whole feather = 10 knots / half feather = 5 knots / total = 15 knots] (1 knot = 1.15 mi/h)

Present Weather						Air Masses	Fronts	Hurricane
Drizzle	Rain	Smog	Hail	Thunder-storms	Rain showers	cA continental arctic cP continental polar cT continental tropical mT maritime tropical mP maritime polar	Cold Warm Stationary Occluded	Tornado
Snow	Sleet	Freezing rain	Fog	Haze	Snow showers			

Selected Properties of Earth's Atmosphere

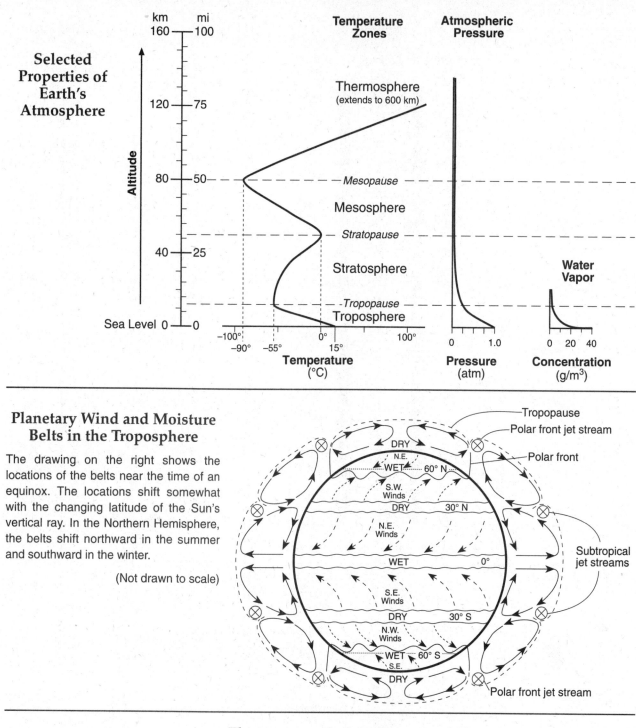

Temperature Zones

Thermosphere (extends to 600 km)

Mesopause

Mesosphere

Stratopause

Stratosphere

Tropopause

Troposphere

Atmospheric Pressure

Water Vapor

Altitude

km	mi
160	100
120	75
80	50
40	25
Sea Level 0	0

Temperature (°C)

−100° −90° −55° 0° 15° 100°

Pressure (atm)

0   1.0

Concentration (g/m³)

0   20   40

Planetary Wind and Moisture Belts in the Troposphere

The drawing on the right shows the locations of the belts near the time of an equinox. The locations shift somewhat with the changing latitude of the Sun's vertical ray. In the Northern Hemisphere, the belts shift northward in the summer and southward in the winter.

(Not drawn to scale)

Tropopause
Polar front jet stream
Polar front
Subtropical jet streams
Polar front jet stream

DRY
N.E.
WET — 60° N
S.W. Winds
DRY — 30° N
N.E. Winds
WET — 0°
S.E. Winds
DRY — 30° S
N.W. Winds
WET — 60° S
S.E.
DRY

Electromagnetic Spectrum

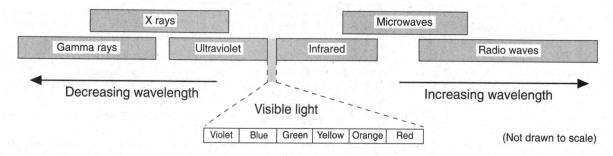

X rays

Microwaves

Gamma rays

Ultraviolet

Infrared

Radio waves

← Decreasing wavelength

Increasing wavelength →

Visible light

Violet	Blue	Green	Yellow	Orange	Red

(Not drawn to scale)

Characteristics of Stars

(Name in italics refers to star represented by a ⊕.)
(Stages indicate the general sequence of star development.)

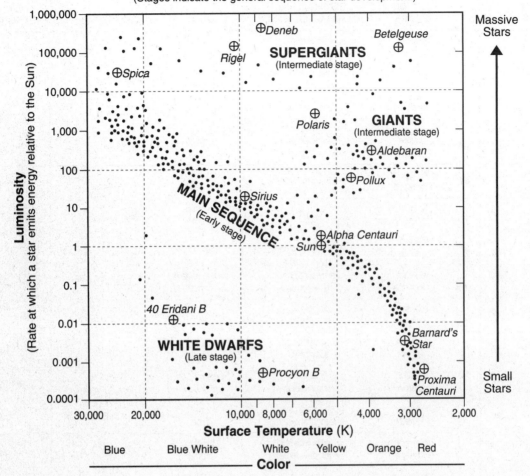

Solar System Data

Celestial Object	Mean Distance from Sun (million km)	Period of Revolution (d=days) (y=years)	Period of Rotation at Equator	Eccentricity of Orbit	Equatorial Diameter (km)	Mass (Earth = 1)	Density (g/cm³)
SUN	—	—	27 d	—	1,392,000	333,000.00	1.4
MERCURY	57.9	88 d	59 d	0.206	4,879	0.06	5.4
VENUS	108.2	224.7 d	243 d	0.007	12,104	0.82	5.2
EARTH	149.6	365.26 d	23 h 56 min 4 s	0.017	12,756	1.00	5.5
MARS	227.9	687 d	24 h 37 min 23 s	0.093	6,794	0.11	3.9
JUPITER	778.4	11.9 y	9 h 50 min 30 s	0.048	142,984	317.83	1.3
SATURN	1,426.7	29.5 y	10 h 14 min	0.054	120,536	95.16	0.7
URANUS	2,871.0	84.0 y	17 h 14 min	0.047	51,118	14.54	1.3
NEPTUNE	4,498.3	164.8 y	16 h	0.009	49,528	17.15	1.8
EARTH'S MOON	149.6 (0.386 from Earth)	27.3 d	27.3 d	0.055	3,476	0.01	3.3

Properties of Common Minerals

LUSTER	HARD-NESS	CLEAVAGE	FRACTURE	COMMON COLORS	DISTINGUISHING CHARACTERISTICS	USE(S)	COMPOSITION*	MINERAL NAME
Metallic luster	1–2	✔		silver to gray	black streak, greasy feel	pencil lead, lubricants	C	Graphite
Metallic luster	2.5	✔		metallic silver	gray-black streak, cubic cleavage, density = 7.6 g/cm³	ore of lead, batteries	PbS	Galena
Metallic luster	5.5–6.5		✔	black to silver	black streak, magnetic	ore of iron, steel	Fe_3O_4	Magnetite
Metallic luster	6.5		✔	brassy yellow	green-black streak, (fool's gold)	ore of sulfur	FeS_2	Pyrite
Either	5.5 – 6.5 or 1		✔	metallic silver or earthy red	red-brown streak	ore of iron, jewelry	Fe_2O_3	Hematite
Nonmetallic luster	1	✔		white to green	greasy feel	ceramics, paper	$Mg_3Si_4O_{10}(OH)_2$	Talc
Nonmetallic luster	2		✔	yellow to amber	white-yellow streak	sulfuric acid	S	Sulfur
Nonmetallic luster	2	✔		white to pink or gray	easily scratched by fingernail	plaster of paris, drywall	$CaSO_4 \cdot 2H_2O$	Selenite gypsum
Nonmetallic luster	2–2.5	✔		colorless to yellow	flexible in thin sheets	paint, roofing	$KAl_3Si_3O_{10}(OH)_2$	Muscovite mica
Nonmetallic luster	2.5	✔		colorless to white	cubic cleavage, salty taste	food additive, melts ice	NaCl	Halite
Nonmetallic luster	2.5–3	✔		black to dark brown	flexible in thin sheets	construction materials	$K(Mg,Fe)_3$ $AlSi_3O_{10}(OH)_2$	Biotite mica
Nonmetallic luster	3	✔		colorless or variable	bubbles with acid, rhombohedral cleavage	cement, lime	$CaCO_3$	Calcite
Nonmetallic luster	3.5	✔		colorless or variable	bubbles with acid when powdered	building stones	$CaMg(CO_3)_2$	Dolomite
Nonmetallic luster	4	✔		colorless or variable	cleaves in 4 directions	hydrofluoric acid	CaF_2	Fluorite
Nonmetallic luster	5–6	✔		black to dark green	cleaves in 2 directions at 90°	mineral collections, jewelry	$(Ca,Na)(Mg,Fe,Al)$ $(Si,Al)_2O_6$	Pyroxene (commonly augite)
Nonmetallic luster	5.5	✔		black to dark green	cleaves at 56° and 124°	mineral collections, jewelry	$CaNa(Mg,Fe)_4(Al,Fe,Ti)_3$ $Si_6O_{22}(O,OH)_2$	Amphibole (commonly hornblende)
Nonmetallic luster	6	✔		white to pink	cleaves in 2 directions at 90°	ceramics, glass	$KAlSi_3O_8$	Potassium feldspar (commonly orthoclase)
Nonmetallic luster	6	✔		white to gray	cleaves in 2 directions, striations visible	ceramics, glass	$(Na,Ca)AlSi_3O_8$	Plagioclase feldspar
Nonmetallic luster	6.5		✔	green to gray or brown	commonly light green and granular	furnace bricks, jewelry	$(Fe,Mg)_2SiO_4$	Olivine
Nonmetallic luster	7		✔	colorless or variable	glassy luster, may form hexagonal crystals	glass, jewelry, electronics	SiO_2	Quartz
Nonmetallic luster	6.5–7.5		✔	dark red to green	often seen as red glassy grains in NYS metamorphic rocks	jewelry (NYS gem), abrasives	$Fe_3Al_2Si_3O_{12}$	Garnet

*Chemical symbols:

Al = aluminum	Cl = chlorine	H = hydrogen	Na = sodium	S = sulfur
C = carbon	F = fluorine	K = potassium	O = oxygen	Si = silicon
Ca = calcium	Fe = iron	Mg = magnesium	Pb = lead	Ti = titanium

✔ = dominant form of breakage

Performance Test

As of this printing, the New York State Education Department has not announced any changes in the Earth Science Performance test from what was used in the last few years. For your convenience, this Appendix provides some information on the three stations included in these exam periods. Check with your teacher or administrator a few weeks before you take a Regents Examination in earth science to see if there have been any recent changes in the details of the performance test.

About 15% of the Earth Science Regents test grade is derived from a performance test designed to evaluate various laboratory and classroom procedures refined during the yearly course of study. The test is designed to measure some of the standards outlined in The Physical Setting: Earth Science Core Curriculum of the New York State Education Department. This performance test is normally given about two weeks before the rest of the Regents Examination.

Station 1: Mineral and Rock Identification

The section on Minerals, Rocks, and Mineral Resources in this book may be helpful to review for this station.

Materials

- One hand-sized mineral sample. Any mineral can be used, both familiar and unfamiliar, as long as the properties to be tested are clear and unmistakable.
- Three hand-sized rock samples to include one igneous rock, one sedimentary rock, and one metamorphic rock. The rock samples can only be rocks listed on the rock identification charts from the 2011 edition *Earth Science Reference Tables* and must have unambiguous and unmistakable diagnostic properties.
- Mineral identification kit containing a glass scratch plate, a streak plate, and a hand lens.

Station 2: Locating an Epicenter

The section on Earthquakes in this book may be helpful to review for this station.

Materials

- Safe drawing compass

Station 3: Constructing and Analyzing an Asteroid's Elliptical Orbit

The section on Planet Revolution in this book may be helpful to review for this station.

Materials

- Cotton string
- Triple-walled cardboard, foam board or other suitable material
- Two push pins
- Small container for push pins
- One 30-cm metric ruler
- One four-function calculator

Doing Well on the Performance Test

How well you perform on this test is determined by the accuracy and precision of your answers. Carefully read the directions given with the test and record your answers neatly and accurately. Answer the questions with the degree of accuracy asked for, not less, not more. As an example, if the directions asked for an answer to the nearest 0.1 (tenth) of a gram, don't give a whole number or extend your answer to the nearest 0.01 (hundredth). Another common problem is using the wrong units, such as using inches instead of centimeters or millimeters instead of centimeters.

Landscape Regions and Their Characteristics

New York has a greater number of different landscape regions than any other state. The chief reason for this variety of landscape regions is the great variation in age, structure, and resistance of the bedrock found within the state. The present climate of the state is uniformly humid and has not been a major factor in producing variations in landscape development.

Almost all of New York was affected by the Pleistocene glaciation that ended in New York about 10,000 years ago. As a result, glacial depositional features are observed throughout the state, superimposed on the other characteristics of the different landscape regions. One of the most important features left by the glaciers is the transported soils, which are young and have small and incomplete profiles.

The landscape regions that are shown on the facing map have the following distinguishing characteristics.

Atlantic Coastal Plain This region consists of all of Long Island and portions of Staten Island, New York. The bedrock consists of horizontal sedimentary rocks of late Mesozoic and Cenozoic age, with elevations near sea level, covered by thick glacial deposits reaching elevations of about 125 meters above sea level in some areas. The features of glacial deposition result in minor changes of slope on a generally smooth plain. Waves and ocean currents have created many typical shore features, such as bars, beaches, and lagoons.

Newark Lowlands This region is composed of weak sedimentary rocks of early Mesozoic age, which have been leveled to lower elevations than the surrounding landscape regions. The generally smooth landscape has moderate changes in slope caused by faults. A volcanic intrusion called the Palisades Sill borders the Hudson River. Because of its greater resistance, it forms a cliff that ranges up to more than 150 meters above sea level.

Hudson Highlands—Manhattan Prong These two regions are extensions of the New England Highlands to the east. These mountains in the mature and old-age stages are composed of highly distorted metamorphic rocks, mostly early Paleozoic and Precambrian in age and more resistant than the rocks of surrounding regions. There are also many Paleozoic igneous intrusions such as the Cortlandt Complex. In the northern parts of the Hudson Highlands there are elevations of up to 500 meters with steep slopes; in the southern parts of the Manhattan Prong, the rocks have been eroded to low elevations and little slope typical of the plainlike topography of mountains in old age.

Taconic Mountains These greatly eroded mountains were originally uplifted in the Paleozoic Era. They consist mostly of metamorphic rocks that are highly folded and faulted. Today they have moderate elevations (up to about 600 meters) and gradual changes in slope, so that the topography has the form of rolling hills.

Hudson-Mohawk Lowlands The rocks of this region are distorted sedimentary rocks of the Paleozoic age that have lower resistance than the surrounding rocks. They have therefore been leveled by weathering and the erosion of the Mohawk and Hudson Rivers to generally low elevations. Variations in slope are associated with escarpments that have been formed by resistant layers, and with the valleys carved by the rivers. South of Albany the Hudson River has an elevation of sea level and may be considered an inlet of the ocean—an estuary.

Allegheny Plateau This part of the Appalachian Plateau is composed of horizontal sedimentary rocks, mostly of Paleozoic age. Much erosion by streams and glaciers has resulted in steep slopes and many changes in elevation, so that some sections, such as the Catskills, resemble mountains. Elevations range from about 500 meters in the west to over 1250 meters in the Catskills. The region contains many lakes, such as the Finger Lakes, which are the result of glacial erosion and deposition.

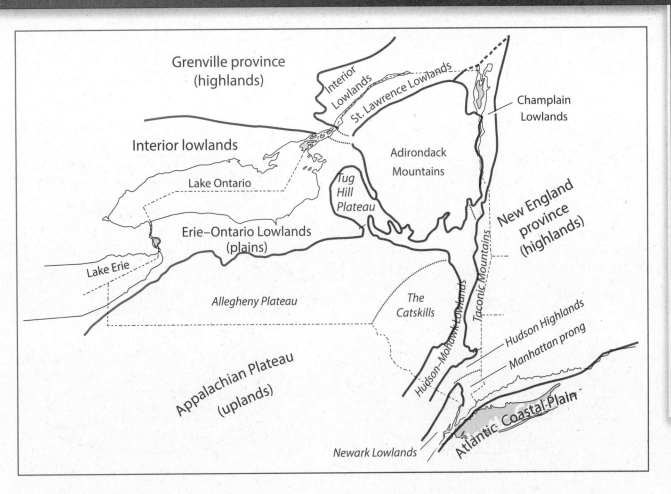

The map shows regions including: Grenville province (highlands), Interior lowlands, Lake Ontario, Erie–Ontario Lowlands (plains), Lake Erie, Allegheny Plateau, Appalachian Plateau (uplands), Tug Hill Plateau, Interior Lowlands, St. Lawrence Lowlands, Champlain Lowlands, Adirondack Mountains, New England province (highlands), Taconic Mountains, The Catskills, Hudson-Mohawk Lowlands, Hudson Highlands, Manhattan prong, Atlantic Coastal Plain, Newark Lowlands.

Erie-Ontario Lowlands This region is a plain of horizontal sedimentary rocks of Paleozoic age, covered by much glacial transported sediment. The northern section is especially smooth because of deposition of sediments from glacial lakes that were the ancestors of Lakes Erie and Ontario. In some places, resistant rocks have been eroded to escarpments of up to 500 meters in elevation, but elevations and slopes are generally small throughout the region.

Tug Hill Plateau This plateau of horizontal sedimentary rocks of Paleozoic age has a resistant surface layer that has resulted in fairly uniform elevations of about 600 to 700 meters. However, steep slopes occur where rivers have cut valleys, such as the Black River Valley that separates this region from the Adirondacks.

Adirondack Mountains These are mature mountains composed mostly of metamorphic rocks of Precambrian age. There are moderate elevations in the western section, but the highest elevations in the state (over 1600 meters at mountain peaks) occur in the eastern section. The landscape is rugged, with much change in elevation and steep slopes, and with valleys related to faults and rocks of lesser resistance. Stream drainage patterns are of radial and trellis types except where glacial deposition has blocked the former drainage paths, resulting in many swamps and lakes.

St. Lawrence-Champlain Lowlands This plain is composed generally of horizontal sedimentary rocks of lower resistance than rocks of surrounding regions, and therefore has lower elevations. The St. Lawrence section is mostly flat, with changes in elevation of usually no more than 30 meters. Some steep slopes exist in the Champlain section as the result of uplift and subsidence caused by faults. Lake Champlain is the site of a subsided block.

Appendix 4:
Paths of the Sun at Different Times and Latitudes

1. 90° N
6/21
Summer
Solstice

A= 23 ½°
D= 24h

2. 90° N
3/21 or 9/23
Equinoxes

A= 0°
D=12h

3. 90° N
12/21
Winter Solstice

A= None
D=0h

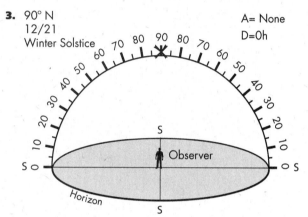

4. 66 ½° N
6/21
Summer
Solstice

A= 47°
D= 24h

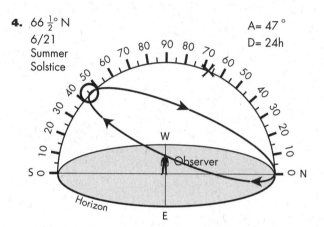

5. 66 ½° N
3/21 or 9/23
Equinoxes

A= 23 ½°
D=12h

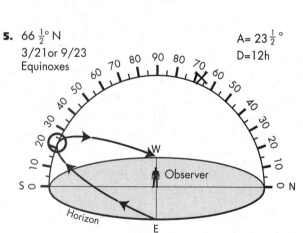

6. 66 ½° N
12/21
Winter Solstice

A= 0°
D= 0h

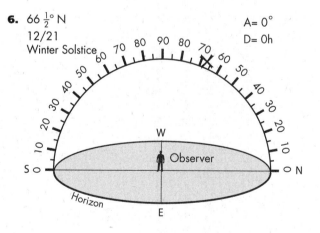

Key

S – South
N – North
E – East
W – West
A – altitude of sun at Solar Noon in degrees

D – duration of insolation in hours
> – direction of sun's movement in the sky
X – location of North Star (Polaris)
O – noon location of sun

7. $41\frac{1}{2}°$ N
6/21
Summer
Solstice

A= 72°
D= $15\frac{1}{2}$ h

8. $41\frac{1}{2}°$ N
3/21 or 9/23
Equinoxes

A= $48\frac{1}{2}°$
D= 12h

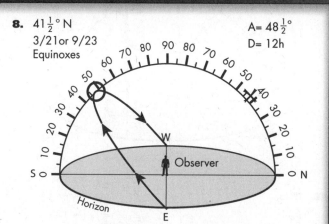

9. $41\frac{1}{2}°$ N
12/21
Winter Solstice

A= 25°
D= $8\frac{1}{2}$ h

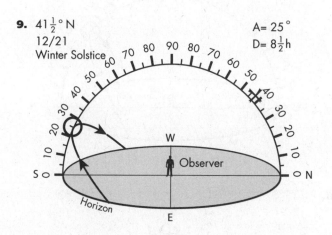

10. $23\frac{1}{2}°$ N
6/21
Summer
Solstice

A= 90°
D= $13\frac{1}{2}$ h

11. $23\frac{1}{2}°$ N
3/21 or 9/23
Equinoxes

A= $66\frac{1}{2}°$
D= 12h

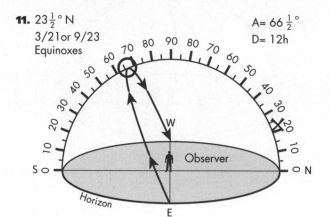

12. $23\frac{1}{2}°$ N
12/21
Winter Solstice

A= 43°
D= $10\frac{1}{2}$ h

Key
S – South
N – North
E – East
W – West
A – altitude of sun at Solar Noon in degrees

D – duration of insolation in hours
> – direction of sun's movement in the sky
X – location of North Star (Polaris)
O – noon location of sun

13. 0° lat.
6/21
Summer
Solstice

A= 66½°
D= 12h

14. 0° lat.
3/21 or 9/23
Equinoxes

A= 90°
D=12h

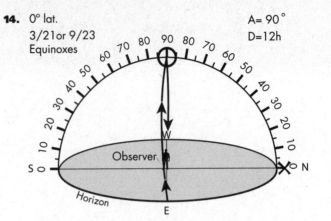

15. 0° lat.
6/21
Summer
Solstice

A= 66½°
D= 12h

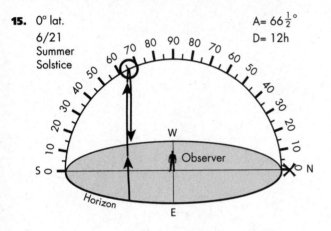

16. 23½°S
6/21
Summer
Solstice

A= 43°
D= 10½h

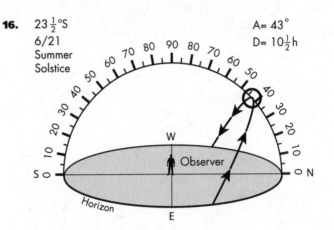

17. 23½°S
3/21 or 9/23
Equinoxes

A= 66½°
D= 12h

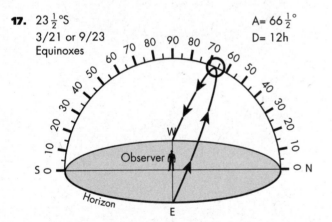

18. 23½°S
12/21
Winter
Solstice

A= 90°
D= 13½h

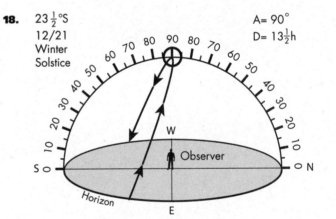

Key
S – South
N – North
E – East
W – West
A – altitude of sun at Solar Noon in degrees

D – duration of insolation in hours
> – direction of sun's movement in the sky
X – location of North Star (Polaris)
O – noon location of sun

19. $66\frac{1}{2}$°S
6/21
Summer
Solstice

A= 0°
D= 0 h

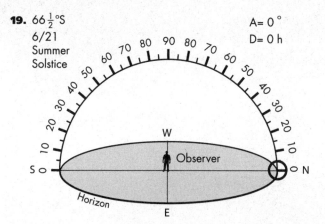

20. $66\frac{1}{2}$°S
3/21 or 9/23
Equinoxes

A= $23\frac{1}{2}$°
D= 12 h

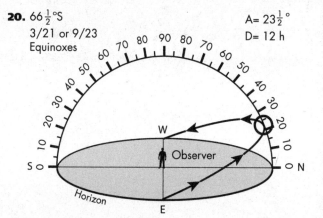

21. $66\frac{1}{2}$°S
12/21
Winter Solstice

A= 47°
D= 24h

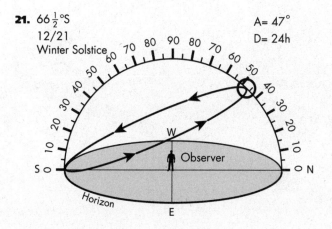

22. 90°S
6/21
Summer
Solstice

A= None
D= 0 h

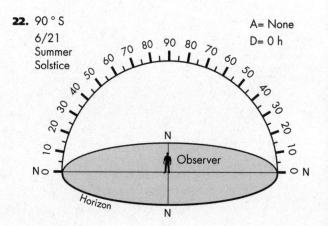

23. 90°S
3/21 or 9/23
Equinoxes

A= 0°
D= 12h

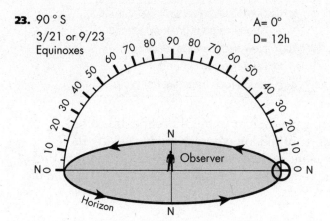

24. 90°S
12/21
Winter
Solstice

A= $23\frac{1}{2}$°
D= 24 h

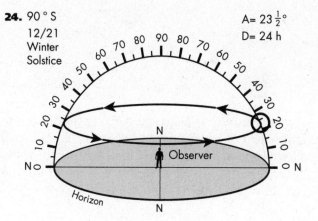

Key
S – South
N – North
E – East
W – West
A – altitude of sun at Solar Noon in degrees

D – duration of insolation in hours
> – direction of sun's movement in the sky
X – location of North Star (Polaris)
O – noon location of sun

Appendix 5:
Erosion and Deposition from Groin Construction

Key

— — —	Shoreline before groin construction
• • •	Shoreline after groin construction
▓▓▓	New sediment depositing
✗ ✗ ✗	Area recently eroded
⬡⬡⬡	Large rock fragments of groin

A **groin** or **jetty** is a structure built out into the water perpendicular to the shoreline. It is often composed of large stones or concrete. A groin will interrupt the longshore current, causing its slowdown. This results in the deposition of sediment (sand) and causes the growth of land into the ocean. On the side down current of the groin, the deficit of sediment results in erosion and retreat of the shoreline toward the land.

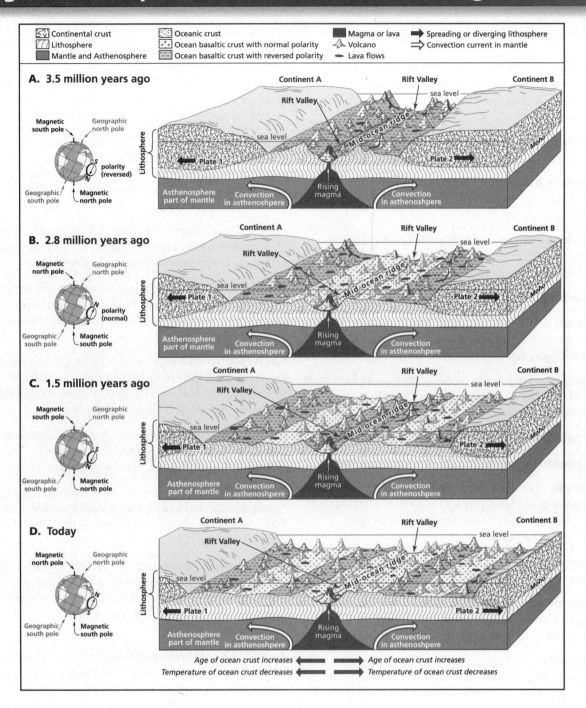

(A) Divergence has separated continental crust into two plates. At the center of the divergences, rising magma rises in a mid-ocean ridge and a central rift valley. The mid-ocean ridge is composed of basaltic rock of reversed polarity and contains many volcanoes and lava flows. (B) Plate divergence has continued at the mid-ocean ridge but now the Earth's magnetic poles have reversed to a time of normal polarity and a strip of normal polarity ocean crust is forming. The older reversed polarity ocean crust has divided into parts (stripes) as it moved away from the mid-ocean ridge. (C) Plate divergence continues at mid-ocean ridge and a magnetic reversal has resulted in a time of reversed polarity, resulting in a new stripe at the mid-ocean ridge of reversed polarity. The older stripes have now moved further away from the mid-ocean ridge, which continues to build more oceanic crust and lithosphere. (D) Plate divergence continues and the size of the ocean crust continues to expand. There has been another magnetic reversal and the stripe of rock forming at the mid-ocean ridge has normal polarity. All other stripes of basaltic crust have spread further away from the mid-ocean ridge forming parallel stripes on each side of the mid-ocean ridge.

Glossary

Glossary items with asterisks are Topic Vocabulary Terms.

*abrasion the physical action of scraping, rubbing, grinding, or wearing away of rock surfaces and sediments due to the movement of solid sediments in an erosional system such as a stream or wind

*absolute age the actual age, or date, in years when a geological event occurred or a rock was formed

absolute humidity the amount (mass) of water vapor in a unit volume of air, such as in grams/cubic meter

absolute zero theoretically, the lowest possible temperature; no heat energy can be extracted at this temperature

absorbed taken into a material

aerosol small solid or liquid particles suspended in a gas; suspended solid or liquid water are the aerosols that compose fog and clouds

*air mass a large body of air in the troposphere with similar characteristics of pressure, moisture, and temperature

*air pressure see **atmospheric pressure**

*air pressure gradient see **pressure gradient**

altitude (1) the vertical distance (elevation) between a point and sea level or Earth's surface (2) the angle of a celestial object above the horizon; usually expressed in degrees

*anemometer a weather instrument used to measure wind speed

*angle of incidence the angle at which the sun's rays hit Earth's surface; also called angle of insolation

anticyclone a high-pressure mass of air within the troposphere in which air moves out from the center; rotating clockwise in the Northern Hemisphere and counterclockwise in the Southern Hemisphere; also called a **high**

aphelion the point in a planet's orbit when it is farthest from the sun

apparent diameter the diameter a celestial object appears to have, depending on its distance from an observer; not the actual diameter

apparent motion a motion of an object that is not real but appears to be real, such as the daily motion of the stars in the sky caused by the real motion of Earth's rotation

apparent solar day a day of varying length determined by the time it takes for the sun to arrive at its highest point in the sky on two consecutive days at the same location, often measured by a sundial; see also **mean solar day**

arc a curved line that is part of a circle; the shape of the path of most celestial objects, such as the sun, in their daily motion paths through Earth's sky

arid climate a dry climate where the precipitation is less than the potential evapotranspiraton for a large part of the year, producing a deficit of moisture and a drought much of the time

*asteroid a solid, rocky and/or metallic body that independently orbits the sun; large, irregularly shaped, except for the few larger spherical ones; mostly located between the orbits of Mars and Jupiter

*asthenosphere the plastic, partly solid, partly liquid layer of Earth's mantle just below the lithosphere that allows plate movements

*atmosphere the layers of gases surrounding Earth or other celestial object; Earth's atmosphere is divided into layers according to differences in chemical and physical properties

*atmospheric pressure the weight of the overlying atmosphere pushing down on a given unit of area; affected by changes in temperature, water vapor, and altitude; also called air **pressure** or **barometric pressure**

*atmospheric transparency how transparent the atmosphere is to insolation; how easily insolation can pass through the air

atom the smallest part of matter or an element which can't be separated by most chemical or physical processes

atomic structure see **crystal structure**

*axis (of rotation) an imaginary line through Earth from the north to the south geographic poles, about which Earth rotates; all rotating celestial bodies have an axis

banding the layered arrangement of mineral crystals in some medium to coarse metamorphic rocks; a special type of foliation caused by layering and separation of minerals

*__barometer__ an instrument used to measure air pressure

*__barometric pressure__ see **atmospheric pressure**

*__barrier island__ a long narrow island, parallel to the shore, built of sand deposited by ocean waves, ocean currents, and wind; separated from the coast by a lagoon

beach the narrow portion of the shore or coastline between the low and high tide lines, usually covered with loose sediments

*__bedrock__ an area's mostly unweathered rock beneath vegetation, soil, other loose materials, and human-built structures; also called local rock

bench mark a permanent marker, usually metal, at a specific location on Earth's surface, that indicates an exact elevation or altitude at the time of installation

*__Big Bang theory__ states that the present universe started as a big explosion 10 to 17 billion years ago and has been expanding ever since

*__bioclastic sedimentary rock__ any rock made by living organisms or mostly composed of materials from life forms; also called **organic sedimentary rock**

blizzard a storm with winds of 35 miles an hour or greater with considerable falling or blowing snow causing low visibility

*__breaking waves__ the result of waves dragging on the ocean bottom causing the water in the waves to fall forward as the waves bunch together, rise up, and break against the shore

*__calorie__ a unit of heat energy defined as the amount of heat needed to raise the temperature of one gram of water one degree Celsius

calorimeter an instrument used in studies of heat

*__capillarity__ the process by which water is drawn into openings due to the attractive force between water molecules and the surrounding Earth materials

capillary migration the upward movement of water, against gravity, in part of the soil, loose materials, or bedrock due to capillarity; also called capillary action

capillary water the water held in soil, loose materials, and rocks in the zone of aeration as a result of the process of capillarity

carbon-14 a radioactive isotope of carbon with a short half-life (5,700 years); used to date recent (up to 70,000-year old) remains of organic material

*__carbon-14 dating__ the use of carbon-14 in dating rocks and organic remains of relatively recent origin

carbon dioxide a colorless, odorless gas, CO_2, an important greenhouse gas present in the atmosphere; given off when a fuel containing carbon is burned

*__celestial object__ any object in the universe outside of Earth's atmosphere, including moons, comets, planets, stars, and galaxies

cementation the process by which solid sediments or clasts are "glued" together by precipitated minerals, forming a sedimentary rock

change the alteration or modification of the characteristics of a part of the environment

change of state see **phase change**

channel (stream) see **stream channel shape**

*__chemical sedimentary rock__ a rock composed of interconnected crystals of just one mineral that form by evaporation and/or precipitation of dissolved minerals; include rock salt and rock gypsum; also called an **evaporite**

*__chemical weathering__ the processes by which chemicals, such as oxygen, acids, and water, break down rocks and other Earth materials, resulting in more stable new minerals (chemicals); example— rusting

*__classification__ the grouping together of similar observations and inferences to make the study of objects and events in the environment more meaningful or easier to understand

*__clastic sedimentary rock__ rock that is largely composed of solid sediments, such as the sand in sandstone

clasts the solid sediments, fragments, or grains in a clastic sedimentary rock such as the sand grains of sandstone

clay (1) a chemical group of minerals (2) very small solid sediments or clasts (less than 0.0004 cm in diameter) that often remain suspended in water for long periods of time

*cleavage the tendency of a mineral to break along the zones of weakness and form smooth to semi-smooth parallel surfaces

*climate the overall view of a region's weather conditions over long periods of time; includes not only averages, but extremes

cloud a visible mass of suspended liquid water droplets and/or ice crystals in the atmosphere

*cloud cover the fraction or percent of the total sky at a location that is covered by clouds; usually expressed in tenths

*cold front the boundary of an advancing cold air mass and a warmer air mass, where the underlying cold air pushes forward like a wedge; characterized by a steep slope, rapid changes in weather, thunderstorms, and sometimes hail and tornadoes

*comet a low density object composed of materials (ices) that easily vaporize and some other solids; independently orbits the sun or other stars; usually has highly eccentric orbit; partly vaporizes forming a visible tail when near the sun

compaction the reduction in volume of sediments in the formation of sedimentary rocks, usually caused by the weight of overlying sediments and water causing a reduction of pore space and liquid water

compound a substance made of two or more elements chemically combined in a specific proportion, such as most minerals

*condensation the change in state or phase from a gas to a liquid, such as when water vapor changes to liquid water droplets as clouds form

*conduction the transfer of heat energy from atom to atom or molecule to molecule, in any state of matter, when vibrating atoms or molecules collide

*constellation a group of stars that form a pattern and are used to help people locate celestial objects

contact metamorphic zone a type of interface or transition zone between rock types caused by the baking or altering of older bedrock by contact with molten rock (lava or magma); much of the older rock is changed into metamorphic rock

*contact metamorphism process in which older rocks come in contact with the magma of an intrusion or lava of an extrusion and the heat and mineral fluids of the liquid rock alter the older rock by recrystallization

continental climate the climate of inland areas not moderated by a large body of water; characterized by hot summers and cold winters, and thus having a wide annual temperature range

*continental crust the part of Earth's crust (upper lithosphere) that makes up the continents and larger islands; thicker and lower in density than the oceanic crust, and granitic rather than basaltic in composition

continental glacier very large glaciers (like those of Antarctica and Greenland), so thick that they cover all landscape features except the highest mountains; tend to create a smooth and low landscape by erosion and deposition; see **mountain glacier**

continental arctic air mass (cA) the coldest and driest air masses that only invade the contiguous United States from Arctic regions at the coldest times of the year

continental polar air mass (cP) cold and dry air masses that invade the contiguous United States from Canada

continental tropical air mass (cT) relatively rare hot dry air masses that form in the southwestern United States or northern Mexico, that may cause very hot and dry weather for the contiguous United States in the summer

contour interval the difference in elevation indicated by two consecutive contour lines (of different value) on contour or topographic maps

*contour line an isoline on a topographic, or contour, map that connects points of equal elevation on the surface of any solid celestial body, such as Earth

contour map see **topographic map**

*convection the transfer of heat energy by circulatory movements in a fluid (usually liquids or gases) that results from differences in density within the fluid

convection current a circulatory motion in a fluid due to convection; also called a convection cell

convergence (1) the coming together of air currents at Earth's surface and at the top of the troposphere (2) the direct collision of lithospheric plates in the **plate tectonic theory**

*convergent plate boundary the boundary between two colliding plates; often associated with mountain building, ocean trenches, and volcanic island arcs

*coordinate system a grid or a system of lines for determining location of a point on a surface, such as latitude and longitude of a point on Earth

core the center part of Earth below the mantle thought to be composed of iron and nickel; inner part is a solid and outer part a liquid

*Coriolis effect the deflection of all moving particles of matter (such as winds and surface ocean currents) at Earth's surface to the right in the Northern Hemisphere and to the left in the Southern Hemisphere, which provides evidence for Earth's rotation

*correlation in geology, the process of showing that rocks or geologic events from different places are the same or similar in age

crater see **impact crater**

*cross cutting relationships a principle of relative dating; when features such as igneous intrusions (sills and dikes), veins, faults, and joints cut across other rocks, these features are younger in age than the rocks they cut across

*crust the outermost portion of Earth's solid lithosphere; separated from the uppermost mantle and lower lithosphere by the thin **Moho** interface

crystal (1) the individual mineral grains of many rocks (2) a solid with a definite internal structure of atoms arranged in a characteristic, regular, repeating pattern

crystalline composed of intergrown or interconnected mineral crystals; having a specific arrangement of atoms

*crystallization a type of solidification in which molten rock (magma or lava) cools to form igneous rocks composed of mineral crystals; also see **solidification**

*crystal shape the outward 3-D shape or geometric shape of a mineral specimen that reflects the internal atomic structure; also called crystal form

*crystal structure the pattern or arrangement of atoms that characterizes each mineral; also called atomic structure

*cyclic change an orderly change in the environment in which an event repeats itself with reference to time and space; the opposite of random change

*cyclone a low-pressure portion of the troposphere that has air moving towards its center; usually rotates counterclockwise in the Northern Hemisphere and clockwise in the Southern Hemisphere; includes hurricanes, tornadoes, and mid-latitude cyclones, also called a **low**

*cyclonic storm a large type of low-pressure storm system formed in the mid–latitudes; also called mid-latitude cyclones

daily motion the apparent, usually east to west movement of celestial objects in the sky caused by Earth's west to east rotation; objects appear to move in circular or arc-shaped paths

day the amount of time it takes a planet or other celestial object to make one rotation

*deforestation the cutting down of trees and other plants of a forest

*delta the deposit of sediment at the mouth or end of a river or stream where it flows into a quiet or still body of water such as a lake or ocean

*density the concentration of matter in an object; the ratio of the mass of an object to its volume—the mass per each unit of volume

*deposition the process by which sediments are released, dropped, or settled from erosional systems; includes the precipitation of dissolved minerals in the formation of chemical sedimentary rocks; also called sedimentation

desert a region with an arid climate where the average yearly precipitation is much smaller than potential evapotranspiration

dew droplets of liquid water that form on Earth's solid surface by condensation; NOT a type of precipitation

*dew point the temperature at which the air becomes saturated with water vapor and the relative humidity is 100%; at temperatures below the dew point, condensation or sublimation of water vapor occurs

direct rays rays of sunlight (insolation) that strike Earth at an angle of 90°; also called vertical rays or perpendicular insolation

discharge the amount of water that passes a certain spot in a stream in a specific amount of time, such as liters per minute

distorted structure the curving and folding of the foliations (mineral layers) and grains or crystals in metamorphic rocks caused by heat and pressure

divergence (1) the spreading out of air from rising or falling currents of air in the troposphere (2) the type of plate movement in which Earth's plates spread or rift apart from each other, according to the **plate tectonic theory**

*divergent plate boundary the boundary between two plates that are spreading apart at a mid-ocean ridge or at a continental rift zone

*Doppler effect the apparent wavelength shifting of electromagnetic energy (such as visible light) caused by the relative motion between the energy source and the observer; also see **redshift**

down cutting the erosional process whereby a stream "digs" deeper into Earth's surface

down-warped ocean basin an ocean basin, at the margin of a continent, formed by the bending down of the ocean lithosphere by plate movements

drizzle liquid precipitation with drops smaller than raindrops

drought a time of abnormal dry weather with a large enough deficit of water to cause crops and local water supplies to fail

*drumlin a low, long, narrow, streamlined oval mound of unsorted sediment that is formed at the bottom of glaciers, usually continental ones

dry-bulb thermometer the thermometer of a sling psychrometer without a wick around its bulb, providing normal temperature values

dune see **sand dune**

duration of insolation the length of time sunlight is received at a location in a day, or the amount of time between sunrise and sunset

*dynamic equilibrium a condition of the balancing out of opposing forces or actions, such as evaporation and condensation or erosion and deposition

*earthquake a natural, rapid shaking of the lithosphere caused when rocks are displaced due to the release of energy stored in rocks; most caused by rapid movement along faults, but also associated with other events, such as volcanic eruptions

earthquake magnitude scale a numbering system that ranks earthquakes according to the total energy they emit

*Earth's interior the region extending from the rocky part of Earth's surface to Earth's center; also called the **geosphere**

Earth materials water, gases, soils, minerals, rocks, mineral resources, and other materials and energy sources that are of value to people

*eccentricity the degree of ovalness of an ellipse, or how far an ellipse is from being a circle; computed using the following formula

$$\text{eccentricity} = \frac{\text{distance between foci}}{\text{length of the major axis}}$$

*eclipse the complete or partial blocking of light when one celestial body moves into the shadow of another celestial body; see **lunar eclipse** and **solar eclipse**

eclipse of the moon see **lunar eclipse**

*electromagnetic energy energy that is radiated (given off) from all objects not at a temperature of absolute zero, in the form of transverse waves from vibrating matter into any part of the universe; examples—visible light, radio waves, infrared radiation, and ultraviolet radiation; often called light or radiant energy

*electromagnetic spectrum a model, such as a chart, that shows the full range of types of electromagnetic energy, usually in order of wavelengths

element any of the different types of atoms such as oxygen, iron, and mercury; 90 naturally occurring elements exist on Earth

*elevation the vertical distance or height above or below sea level

*ellipse a closed curve around two fixed points, called foci, in which the sum of the distances between any point of the curve and the foci is a constant; example—the shape of all planetary orbits

*El Niño a series of weather changes on Earth caused by a change from cold surface ocean water to warm surface ocean water in the eastern Pacific Ocean off western South America; occurs every two to ten years

emergency preparedness the steps or plans society, government agencies, organizations, and individuals can do to get ready to cope with disasters; planning an escape route in case of a hurricane or flooding, or storing food at home for a blizzard

*energy the ability to do work

environmental equilibrium the balance that exists among the natural parts of the environment even though all parts of the environment are constantly changing

eon the largest division of geologic time, which is divided into eras

*epicenter the place on Earth's surface lying directly above the focus, or the origin of an earthquake

epoch one of the small divisions of geologic time that are combined into periods

*equator the parallel on Earth midway between the geographic North and South poles with a latitude of 0°

equinox a time when the sun is directly overhead at noon at the equator, and there are 12 hours of daylight and 12 hours of darkness over all of Earth

era the second longest division of geologic time; combined into eons and divided into periods

*erosion the carrying away of sediment by wind, water, ice, and other agents; the process by which sediments are obtained and transported; the wearing away and lowering of Earth's land surface features

erosional-depositional system the various agents such as streams, glaciers, wind, ocean currents that pick up, transport, and deposit sediments at or near Earth's (or similar celestial object's) surface

error the amount of deviation or incorrectness in a measurement; see also **percent error**

*escarpment a steep slope or cliff in layered rocks; often formed from certain rock layers that are resistant to weathering and erosion

evaporation the change in state from liquid to a gas, such as liquid water into water vapor; also called vaporization

evapotranspiration the combination of the processes of **evaporation** and **transpiration**

evaporite see **chemical sedimentary rock**

event the name used to describe the occurrence of a change in the environment

evolution see **organic evolution**

*extrusion a mass of igneous rock formed by the cooling and solidification of molten rock (lava) on Earth's surface; examples—a lava flow and a volcanic mountain

*extrusive igneous rock a rock formed by solidification of lava at or above Earth's surface; also called volcanic igneous rock

fault a crack in a mass of rock or soil along which there has been displacement, shifting, or movement of the rock or soil on each side of the crack

*faulted (rock) rock layers that are offset or displaced along a type of crack called a fault

faulting rapid movements along faults

*field any part of the universe that has some measurable value of a given quantity at every point, such as Earth's magnetic or Sun's gravitational fields

*finger lake a body of water that forms in a long, narrow U-shaped glacial valley, often partly dammed at one end by a mound of glacial moraine sediment; example—the Finger Lakes of central New York

flood condition in which so much water flows into a stream that the water pours over the stream's confining banks onto areas not normally covered with water; other types of floods occur on shores when coastal storms invade or there are very high tides and when lowlands become saturated during long rainy periods or spring snow melting.

*flood plain a nearly level plain that borders a stream that is subject to flooding unless protected artificially; usually composed of layers of river-deposited sediment

*focus (plural foci) (1) in an ellipse, either of two fixed points located so that the sum of their distances to any point on the ellipse is constant; example—the sun at one of the two foci of the orbit of each solar system planet (2) the place where an earthquake originates

fog a cloud that is on, or just above, Earth's surface

*folded (rock) the bends in layered rock due to movement in the lithosphere; a type of deformed rock

*foliation texture of metamorphic rocks caused by the layering of mineral crystals

*fossil any physical evidence of former life, either direct or indirect

fossil fuel the organic fuels found within Earth's crust; includes oil (petroleum), natural gas, and coal

*Foucault pendulum a freely swinging pendulum whose path appears to change in a predictable way, thus providing evidence for Earth's rotation

*fracture the way in which a mineral breaks producing an uneven breaking surface; types of fracture—earthy, splintery, and curved (conchoidal)

freezing the change in state of a liquid to a solid by the removal of heat; also see **solidification**

freezing rain rain that freezes as it hits Earth's surface

*front the interface, or boundary, between two air masses of different characteristics

fusion the change of state from a solid to a liquid; also called **melting**; also see **nuclear fusion**

*galaxy the large groupings of millions or billions of stars and other forms of mass held together by gravitation; our galaxy is called the Milky Way

*geocentric model an early concept of celestial objects and their motions in which all celestial objects revolved around Earth, which was stationary and was the center of the universe

geographic poles the North and South poles of Earth, with a latitude of 90°; located at opposite ends of Earth's axis of rotation

*geologic time scale a chronological model of the geologic history of Earth using the divisions of **eons, eras, periods,** and **epochs;** see History of New York State in the *Earth Science Reference Tables*

geosphere see **Earth's interior**

*glacial groove a long narrow channel or furrow on bedrock formed by the gouging and sanding actions of rocks and sediments frozen to the bottom of a glacier; show the direction of former glacial movement

*glacial parallel scratches parallel cuts in bedrock formed by abrasion (gouging and sanding) of rocks and sediments frozen to the bottom of a glacier; show the direction of former glacial movement

*glacier a large mass of naturally formed ice on land that moves downhill due to gravity; also see **continental glacier** and **mountain glacier**

*global warming a recent trend towards a warming of Earth's surface and lower atmosphere (troposphere) possibly caused by human pollution

graded bedding a layering of sediment or sedimentary rock that shows a gradual change in particle size, with the largest particles on the bottom and the smallest ones on top

*gradient the rate of change from place to place within a field; also called slope

$$\text{gradient} = \frac{\text{amount of change in field}}{\text{distance through which change occurs}}$$

*gravitation the attractive force that exists between any two objects in the universe; proportional to the product of the masses of the objects and inversely proportional to the square of the distance between their centers; also called gravitational force

$$\text{force} \propto \frac{\text{mass}_1 \times \text{mass}_2}{(\text{distance between their centers})^2}$$

gravity the force that pulls objects toward the center of Earth

*greenhouse gases gases such as carbon dioxide, water vapor, and methane, present in the atmosphere, which absorb long-wave infrared radiation

greenhouse effect the process by which the atmosphere transmits short-wave radiation from insolation and absorbs long-wave radiation emitted by Earth's surface; warms the atmosphere and reduces heat loss by radiation from Earth's surface

*groundwater the subsurface water found beneath the water table in the zone of saturation; sometimes used to mean all **subsurface water**

hail a round solid form of precipitation composed of concentric layers of ice and snow; only forms from cumulonimbus (thunderhead) clouds

*half-life the time required for half of the atoms in a given mass of a radioactive isotope to decay, or change, to a different isotope

*hardness the resistance a mineral offers to being scratched or dented; usually measured by comparison to the Mohs hardness scale of minerals

hazard an object, process, or situation that holds the possibility of injury or death to humans or damage to property

haze a condition of the atmosphere in which the aerosol content is so high that distant images are blurred, and a cloudless sky does not appear blue

*heat budget the result of the balance between the total amount of energy an object receives and the total energy it emits, or loses; measured as the average temperature of an object

*heat energy energy that is transferred from one body to another as a result of a difference in temperature or thermal energy of two bodies; also called heat; also see **thermal energy**

*heliocentric model the modern concept of celestial objects and their motions, in which a rotating Earth and other planets revolve around the sun

high see **anticyclone**

high tide the bulge of ocean water directly under the moon's position and on the opposite side of Earth

*hot spot major regions of volcanic activity that are usually in the interior of plates away from plate boundaries; may also be at plate boundaries like Iceland; likely cause of chains of volcanic activity such as the Hawaiian Islands

humid climate a moist or wet climate where the precipitation is greater than potential evapotranspiration on a yearly average

*humidity the amount of water vapor (gaseous water) in the atmosphere; also see **relative humidity** and **absolute humidity**

hurricane a large, strong cyclonic storm that forms over tropical ocean waters with sustained winds of 74 miles per hour or greater

*hydrologic cycle see **water cycle**

*hydrosphere the liquid water (mostly the oceans) that rests on much of the Earth's solid or rocky surface; included by some scientists—the subsurface water, water in the atmosphere, sea ice, glaciers, and water in life forms

*ice ages times of widespread glaciation outside of polar areas (see the Pleistocene epoch in Geologic History Of New York State At A Glance in the *Earth Science Reference Tables*)

*igneous rock a rock formed when natural, molten rock-forming material (magma or lava) cools and turns into a solid—above, below, or on Earth's surface

*impact crater an oval-shaped depression with a raised rim formed by a meteorite, asteroid, or comet colliding with Earth's, or any other solid celestial object's, solid surface

*impact event the colliding of comets, asteroids, and meteoroids or any other type of celestial body

*inclusion a body of older rock within an igneous rock formed when pieces of rock surrounding liquid rock fall into the magma or lava, but don't melt before the liquid rock solidifies

*index fossil a fossil used in correlation and relative dating of rocks; must have lived for a short time and have been distributed over a large geographic area

*inertia the concept that an object at rest will tend to remain at rest and that an object in motion will maintain the direction and speed of that motion unless an opposing force affects it

*inference an interpretation of an observation; a mental process that proposes causes, conclusions, or explanations for what has been observed

*infiltrate water entering or sinking into, under the influence of gravity, the upper parts of Earth's lithosphere where the water becomes subsurface water; also called seep

infrared a type of long-wave electromagnetic radiation

*inner core the innermost zone of Earth's core, which is thought to be composed of iron and nickel in a solid state

*inorganic not organic, thus not part of a life form or made by living or former life forms

*insolation (INcoming SOLar radiATION) the part of the sun's radiation that is received by Earth; also called solar energy

*instrument a device invented by people to extend the senses beyond their normal limits, thus enabling them to make observations that would otherwise be impossible or highly inaccurate

intensity of insolation the relative strength of the sun's radiation intersecting a specific area of Earth in a specific amount of time, such as calories per square meter per minute

*interface the boundary between regions with different properties; the usual place for energy exchange

interpretation see **inference**

*intrusion a mass of igneous rock formed when molten rock (magma) squeezes or melts into preexisting rocks and crystallizes; examples—sills and dykes

*intrusive igneous rock a rock that forms by the cooling and solidification of magma beneath Earth's solid surface; examples—granite or gabbro; also called plutonic igneous rock

*island arc a curved series of volcanoes and volcanic islands that stretch hundreds of miles; form at subduction zones where plates converge and magma rises to form volcanoes; also called a **volcanic island arc**

*isobar an isoline used on weather and climate maps that connects points of equal air pressure

*isoline a line used on a model of a field, such as a map, which connects points of equal value of a field quantity; examples—isotherms, isobars, and contour lines

isotherm an isoline used on weather and climatic maps to connect points of equal air temperature

*isotope one of the varieties of an element, which all have the same atomic number and chemical properties, but differ in their atomic masses and physical properties; examples—carbon isotopes carbon-12 and carbon-14

*jet stream a concentrated curving band of high speed, easterly moving winds usually at the top of Earth's troposphere

joint a crack in rocks along which there has been no relative movement or displacement, such as there is with a fault

*Jovian planets planets that are far from the sun, largely gaseous, and have relatively large diameters, many moons, rings, and low densities; Jupiter, Saturn, Uranus, and Neptune

*kettle lake a lake formed when a large block of ice buried in glacial sediments melts, leaving an oval depression which becomes filled with water; very common in New York State

kinetic energy the energy of movement of any object; the greater the speed and mass of an object, the greater the kinetic energy

knots nautical miles per hour; unit of wind speed

landform individual features of Earth's (or any other solid celestial object's) surface from mountain ranges to a mud crack in a puddle

*landscape the features of Earth's surface at the interfaces between the atmosphere or the hydrosphere and the top of the lithosphere; also on all other solid celestial bodies

*landscape region a portion of Earth's surface with landscape (topographic) characteristics that distinguish it from other areas; distinguishing characteristics—rock structure, elevation, degree of slope, and stream drainage pattern

*latitude the angular distance north or south of the equator; usually expressed in units of angular measurement such as degrees; minimum latitude 0° at the equator and maximum 90° N or 90° S at the geographic poles

latitudinal climatic pattern east-west belts, or zones, of climate types on Earth caused by latitudinal changes in climate factors, such as temperature, precipitation amount, wind, and ocean currents

lava (1) liquid rock material at or above Earth's surface (2) the extrusive or volcanic igneous rock that forms from solidification of liquid lava

leveling forces forces that operate at or near Earth's surface and break down rocks, transport material from higher to lower elevations, and tend to level off and lower the land; examples—weathering, erosion, deposition, and subsidence

light see **electromagnetic energy**

*lithosphere the whole crust and the uppermost portion of the mantle (layer of rock that forms the solid outer shell at the top of Earth's interior)

*lithospheric plate see **plate**

*local time time based on the rotation of Earth as reflected in motions of the sun in the sky

*longitude an angular distance east or west of the prime meridian; usually expressed in degrees; minimum longitude 0° at the prime meridian, which runs through Greenwich, England, and maximum longitude 180° E or 180° W

longshore currents ocean or lake currents that move parallel and close to shore due to the angled advance of waves from one direction; a major agent of erosion and deposition

long-wave electromagnetic energy electromagnetic energy with a wavelength longer than visible light, especially infrared energy

low see **cyclone**

low tide the level of low ocean water, occurring at right angles to the positions of high tide

*luminosity (of a star) measures how bright a star would be in relation to the sun if all stars were the same distance from the observer

lunar eclipse the darkening of the moon caused by Earth's shadow

*luster the way a mineral looks or shines in reflected light

*magma liquid rock material beneath Earth's solid surface

magnitude see **earthquake magnitude scale**

*mantle the mostly solid part of Earth between the crust and the outer core

marine ocean or sea-like

marine climate a coastal climate moderated by the effects of a large body of water (ocean, sea, or lake); having warmer winters and colder summers than areas of similar latitude not near a large body of water; have a smaller annual temperature range than inland areas

maritime polar air mass (mP) cool and humid air masses that invade the contiguous United States from the oceans to the northeast and northwest

maritime tropical air mass (mT) a very common warm and humid air mass that invades the contiguous United States from the oceans to the south, east, and west

*mass the amount of matter in an object; unlike weight, not affected by location

*mass movement any variety of erosion and deposition done directly by gravity; examples—soil creep, earthflows, mudslides, avalanches, slumping, and landslides; also called gravity erosion

mean solar day the 24-hour day established for convenience in time-keeping; derived by averaging the lengths of the apparent solar days in a year

mean solar time a type of local time divided into exactly 24 hours for the convenience of timekeeping

*meander a curve or bend in a stream or river

*measurement a means of expressing an observation with greater accuracy or precision; provides a numerical value for an aspect of the object or event being observed by comparison with a standard; example—measuring the length of this page with a ruler

*mechanical energy all the energy of an object or system not related to the individual motions of atoms and molecules; the total of the potential and kinetic energy of an object or system

melting the change in state or phase from a solid to a liquid; see also **fusion**

*meridian of longitude any north–south semicircle of constant longitude on maps and globes connecting the north and south geographic poles: also called a meridian

*metamorphic rock a rock that forms from changes in previously existing rocks (igneous, sedimentary, or other metamorphic rocks) due to heat, pressure, and/or chemical fluids (not by weathering or melting)

*metamorphism the process by which heat, pressure, and/or exposure to chemical fluids can change previously existing rock into metamorphic rock

*meteor path of light from a meteoroid burning as it passes through Earth's atmosphere; also called a shooting star

meteorite a meteoroid that has landed on Earth's surface

meteoroid solid particles smaller than asteroids and comets that orbit the sun

methane the organic compound CH_4, often called swamp gas, that is an important greenhouse gas; major part of the fossil fuel called natural gas

mid-latitude cyclone see **cyclonic storm**

*mid-ocean ridge a mountain range at the bottom of the ocean, composed mostly of volcanoes and lava flows; forms at zones of diverging plates

*Milky Way Galaxy the spiral-shaped galaxy that Earth and our solar system are part of

*mineral a naturally occurring, crystalline solid having a somewhat definite chemical composition and physical and chemical properties that vary within specified limits; has a unique crystal (atomic) structure

*mineral crystal an individual grain of a mineral

*mineral resources Earth materials that people need, including minerals, rocks, and fossils fuels

misconception an idea, notion, or concept believed to be correct, but which is NOT true or correct

*model any way of representing the properties of an object, event, or system; includes graphs, drawings, charts, mental pictures, numerical data, or scaled physical objects

*Moho the interface, or boundary zone, between Earth's crust and mantle; short for Mohorovicic discontinuity

Mohs hardness scale a scale used to measure the relative hardness of minerals; ranges from 1 to 10 with talc assigned a hardness of 1 and diamond a hardness of 10

moisture a somewhat vague term used to mean the liquid or gaseous water in the atmosphere or in the ground (soil, loose materials, or bedrock)

moisture capacity a measure of the total amount of water vapor the air can hold at a particular temperature; the maximum absolute humidity of a parcel of air at a particular temperature

*monsoons cyclic and extreme weather changes caused by the shifting wind and pressure belts; especially strong in southeast Asia where summer brings wet weather from the ocean and winter brings dry weather from the continental interior

*moon (1) the one natural satellite of Earth (2) a body that orbits a planet or an asteroid as those objects orbit the sun

*moraine a mound, ridge, or sheet of unsorted, unlayered sediment deposited directly from an edge or bottom of a glacier; types—lateral, medial, and ground

*mountain usually an area of high elevation, compared to the surrounding area or sea level, that usually has regions of steep gradient and many changes in slope; internally, mountains are characterized by distorted rock structures

mountain glacier a long narrow glacier confined to valleys in mountains; results in sharp angular landscape features; see **continental glacier**

*natural hazard a non-human-related object, process, or situation that has the possibility of causing loss of life, personal injury, or loss of property; includes volcanic eruptions, earthquakes, landslides, floods, storms, and asteroid impacts; also called a natural disaster

*natural resources the materials and energy sources found in the environment that humans use in their daily lives

North Pole the location on Earth's surface at the north end of the axis of rotation with a 90° N latitude; also called the geographic north pole

North Star see **Polaris**

*nuclear decay see **radioactive decay**

*nuclear fusion the combining of the nuclei of smaller elements to form the nuclei of larger elements with some mass being converted into energy; example—the sun produces energy in this way

*observation the perception of some aspect of the environment by one or more human senses, with or without the aid of instruments

*occluded front the boundary of opposing wedges of cold air masses formed when a cold front overtakes a warm front, lifting the warm air mass off Earth's surface, forming mid-latitude cyclones (lows)

ocean the continuous salty water body that covers 70% of Earth's surface or any one of its major parts such as the Atlantic Ocean; the major part of the **hydrosphere**

ocean currents see **surface ocean currents**

ocean floor spreading see **sea floor spreading**

*oceanic crust the portion of Earth's crust that is usually below the oceans and not associated with continental areas; thinner and higher in density than continental crust and basaltic rather than granitic in composition

*ocean trench the long, steep, and narrow depression produced by the bending down of subducting plates, which warps the crust

orbit the path of an object revolving around another object, such as the path of Earth around the sun

orbital speed the speed of an orbiting body along its orbit at any given time similar to orbital velocity

ore a rock or mineral deposit that can supply a mineral resource that is worthwhile to mine or drill

*organic an Earth material that is composed of and/or was formed by life forms

*organic evolution (theory of) the theory stating that life forms change through time; new species of organisms arise by gradual transitional changes from existing species

organic sedimentary rocks see **bioclastic sedimentary rocks**

*original horizontality a concept that states that sedimentary rocks and some extrusive igneous rocks, such as lava flows, form in horizontal layers parallel to Earth's surface

orogeny (1) the process of mountain building (2) a portion of geologic time when there is much uplift and mountain building such as the Grenville Orogeny in Geologic History Of New York State in the *Earth Science Reference Tables*; caused by plate convergence or collision

outcrop location at Earth's surface where bedrock is exposed without a cover of soil or other materials

*outer core the zone of Earth between the mantle and the inner core; thought to be a liquid because earthquake S-waves do not go through it; believed to be composed of iron and nickel

*outgassing the seeping out of gases from Earth's interior through cracks and volcanic eruptions to Earth's surface

*outwash plain the landform feature composed of sorted and layered sediments deposited in front of a glacier by running water from the melting ice; example—southern Long Island

oxidation a process where oxygen is added to other elements in chemical weathering; such as in the rusting of the black mineral magnetite to the red mineral hematite

*ozone a three-atom molecule of oxygen (compared to the more common two-atom molecule of oxygen) that is a pollutant in the troposphere, but is important in the stratosphere where it absorbs much of the ultraviolet insolation from the sun

parallels of latitude east-west circles on maps or globes that are equidistant from the equator at all points; and thus maintain the same value of latitude; also called parallels

Ⓡ

passive margin basin a broad and long depression of the crust at the border of a continent that is not the site of a plate boundary; usually the site of much deposition of sediments

*pauses (of atmosphere) the interfaces, or boundaries, of the layers of Earth's atmosphere

*percent deviation, or **percent error** the numerical amount, expressed as a percent, by which a measurement differs from a given standard or accepted value

$$\text{deviation (\%)} = \frac{\text{difference from accepted value}}{\text{accepted value}} \times 100\%$$

perihelion the point in a planet's orbit when it is closest to the sun; occurs for Earth about January 3, when Earth is about 147,000,000 kilometers from the sun

period (1) the amount of time it takes a planet to make one orbit, or revolution, around the sun; called a year for that planet (2) in geology, a part of the geologic time scale smaller than an era but larger than an epoch

*permeability the degree to which a porous material (such as rock or soil) will allow fluids, such as water and oil, to pass through it; commonly measured in centimeters per hour

permeability rate the speed at which a certain amount of fluid, such as water or oil, can pass through a porous material; the speed at which water moves from above to below Earth's surface, becoming subsurface water—a special permeability rate called infiltration rate; commonly measured in liters per minute

perpendicular insolation see **direct rays**

*phase (1) one of the three main forms of matter—liquid, solid, or gas; also called state of matter (2) the varying portion of the lighted part of the moon, Venus, or Mercury visible from Earth

phase change the change of a substance from one phase or state to another, such as liquid water to gaseous water

*physical weathering the mechanical or physical breakdown of rock and other Earth materials at or near Earth's surface into smaller pieces (sediments) without a change in the mineral or chemical composition; example—frost action splitting rock

*plain a landscape of low elevation and generally level surface with little change in slope; usually characterized by horizontal rock structure

planet largest of non-star celestial objects that independently revolve around a star; Earth and seven other planets revolve around our sun

*planetary wind belts east-west zones on Earth where the wind blows from one direction much of the time; also see **prevailing winds;** example—the prevailing southwest winds that blow over the contiguous United States

*plate section of the lithosphere that moves around Earth's solid surface; also called a **lithospheric plate** or **tectonic plate**

*plateau a landscape of relatively high elevation composed of undistorted horizontal rock structure and often a more level slope or gradient than that of most mountains

*plate tectonic theory states that Earth's lithosphere is divided into sections called plates that can move up and down or sideways on the plastic part of the upper mantle—diverging, converging, and sliding past each other, which results in many of Earth's major physical features and events, including continent and mountain formation, volcanoes, and earthquakes

plutonic igneous rocks see **intrusive igneous rocks**

*polar front an ever-changing boundary between the colder air masses toward the poles and the warmer air masses toward the middle latitudes; storm systems (cyclones) of the mid-latitudes are formed at the polar front

Polaris the star that is presently almost directly over the geographic North Pole of Earth; also called the North Star

pollutants substances or forms of energy that pollute the environment; they include solids, liquids, gases, life forms, and forms of energy such as heat, visible light, and sound

*pollution the occurrence in the environment of a substance or form of energy in concentrations large enough to have an adverse effect on people, their property, or plant or animal life

*porosity percentage of open space (pores and cracks) in a material compared to its total volume

potential energy the energy possessed by an object as a result of its position or location, chemical conditions, or phase (state) of matter

potential evapotranspiration the amount of water that would be lost from a portion of Earth's surface through evaporation and transpiration over a given time IF the water were available

*precipitation (1) falling liquid or solid water from clouds toward Earth's surface; (2) a type of sediment deposition in which dissolved minerals come out of solution to form solids, as in the formation of chemical sedimentary rocks such as rock salt

precipitation gauge any instrument used to measure the amount of atmospheric precipitation, such as a rain gauge

*prediction a type of inference about the conditions and behavior of the environment in the future

present is the key to the past concept that the physical, chemical, biological, and geological events today are similar to those in the past; thus we can interpret the past by understanding the present

present weather the conditions or state of the atmosphere for a short period of time at a location determined by comparison with a standard list produced by the United States Weather Service; partial abbreviated list is found on the sample station model in Weather Map Information in the *Earth Science Reference Tables*

pressure gradient the amount of difference in air pressure over a specific distance; the greater the pressure gradient, the greater the speed of the wind; also called air pressure gradient

*prevailing winds winds that blow from a certain compass direction for a large part of a year; usually associated with the **planetary wind belts**

primary waves see **P-waves**

*prime meridian the meridian of 0° longitude; also called the Meridian of Greenwich

*principle of superposition see **superposition**

*probability the chance of some environmental event, such as rain or an earthquake, taking place

*profile a model, usually drawn from a topographic map, that uses upward and downward changes of a line to show changes in elevation and slope; a side view of an area's topography, or landscape

*psychrometer an instrument that is used to indirectly measure the amount of water vapor in air, such as a sling psychrometer; with the use of data tables, temperature readings from a psychrometer can be used to determine relative humidity and dew point

*P-waves the waves in earthquakes that travel through Earth's interior and cause particles through which they travel to vibrate in the direction the waves are moving; the fastest-moving of all earthquake waves; also called primary waves

*radar (RAdio Detection And Ranging instrument) an instrument that uses radio/microwave electromagnetic radiation to observe many weather features such as precipitation, tornadoes, and hurricanes; wind speeds calculated using Doppler radar have greatly aided tornado predictions

*radiation (1) the emission or giving off of energy in the form of electromagnetic energy; (2) the method by which electromagnetic energy moves from place to place by way of transverse waves

*radioactive dating the use of radioactive isotopes to determine the absolute age of rocks and geologic events

*radioactive decay the natural spontaneous breakdown of the nucleus of unstable atoms into more stable atoms of the same or different elements; releasing energy and/or small subatomic particles, also called **nuclear decay**

radioactive material any rock or mineral that contains radioactive atoms

rain liquid precipitation larger than drizzle or 0.5 mm

rain gauge a type of precipitation gauge that measures liquid precipitation

rain shower brief, rapidly forming, and rapidly ending liquid precipitation; often heavy rain associated with thunderstorm-type clouds

*rate of change how much a measurable aspect of the environment, called a field, is altered over a given time—years, hours, or seconds

$$\text{rate of change} = \frac{\text{change in field value}}{\text{change in time}}$$

recrystallization a process in the formation of metamorphic rocks by which mineral crystals grow in size at the expense of older crystals or sediments without true melting

*red shift the type of Doppler effect caused by an increase in distance between the observer and the source of the electromagnetic radiation; a displacement towards longer wavelengths of electromagnetic energy; used as evidence for the Big Bang theory of the origin of the universe

reflected turned back electromagnetic energy or other type of waves; waves bounced off a material

reflection a change in direction of waves when the waves strike the surface of a material, in which the waves leave the surface at the same angle at which they arrived

refracted waves bent during passage through materials of varying density so that the direction is changed; example—light waves refracted by water

refraction a change in direction and velocity of waves when they pass from one type of material into another with a different density

*regional metamorphism process of formation of metamorphic rock over large areas due to an increase in temperature and pressure, usually as the result of mountain building associated with plate collision or convergence

relative dating the determination of the age of a rock or event in relation to the age of other rocks or events

*relative humidity the ratio of the amount of water vapor in the air to the maximum amount it can hold; often expressed as a percent; can be calculated by obtaining temperature readings from a psychrometer and using tables such as Relative Humidity (%) in the *Earth Science Reference Tables*

resources anything that may be useful to humans in the future; see **natural resources**

reversal of Earth's magnetic polarity the fact that Earth's magnetic field and magnetic poles switch polarity (north for south and south for north) in intervals of thousands of years in no known cycle

*revolution a planet's movement around the sun in a path called an orbit; the movement of one body around another body in a path called an orbit

*ridge a long, narrow, high, steep-sloped part of the landscape that is usually part of a mountain range

rift a long narrow valley in a continental area bounded by faults caused by rifting or splitting of the lithosphere; usually the site of plate divergence such as the East African Rift or Grand Canyon Rift; also used to mean the valley in the middle of mid-ocean ridges

rock any naturally formed solid that is part of Earth or any other celestial body; usually composed of one or more minerals, except for a few rocks, such as coal, obsidian, and coral, which don't have any minerals

*rock cycle a model of the interrelationships of the different rock types (sedimentary, igneous, and metamorphic), the materials they form from and the processes that produce the rocks

rock-forming mineral any one of a small number of minerals (20-30) that are commonly found in rocks; mostly silicates

rock structure the features of rock that can be observed in an outcrop; including folds, faults, joints, tilting, and thickness of strata

*rotation the spinning of an object, such as a planet, moon, or star, on an imaginary axis—like a top

running water any erosional-depositional agent caused by the flowing of liquid water on land including rain splashing, sheet wash, and stream or river flow; called a stream or river when confined to a channel

*runoff all the natural liquid water flowing at Earth's solid surface, including stream flow

*sandbar a pile or low ridge of sand, often just above or just below water level, deposited by waves and currents; found near ocean shores or within streams and rivers

*sandblasting an erosional process by which blowing sand impacts and abrades rock surfaces resulting in shaped landscape features and new sediments

*sand dune a pile, hill, or mound of sand deposited by wind on a land surface

satellite any celestial object, either natural or human-made, that revolves around another celestial object

saturation the condition of being filled to capacity; example—at saturation, the relative humidity of the atmosphere is 100%

scattered waves that are refracted and/or reflected in various directions

sea-floor spreading the principle that the oceanic lithosphere spreads outward (plate divergence or rifting) at mid-ocean ridges; also called ocean-floor spreading

seasons the divisions of the year with characteristic weather conditions

secondary waves see **S-waves**

*sediment particles or materials formed by the weathering and erosion of rocks or organic materials; material transported by erosional systems

*sedimentary rock rock that forms directly from sediments deposited near Earth's surface by the processes of cementation, precipitation of minerals, loss of water, and compaction

*seep see **infiltrate**

*seismic waves the energy waves given off by an earthquake; also called earthquake waves

seismogram the chart or record of earthquake movement (wiggles) recorded by a seismograph

seismograph an instrument used to detect and record seismic or earthquake waves

senses the five human abilities or faculties—sight, touch, hearing, taste, and smell—by which one observes

shore, or shoreline the interface between land and a water body such as a lake or ocean; the narrow strip of land at the coast between high and low tide

shower see **rain shower** or **snow shower**

sink in an energy system, a region that has a lower energy concentration than its surroundings

sleet precipitation composed of transparent ice pellets, less than 5 mm in size; forms by freezing of falling rain

slope see **gradient**

smog a haze or fog, usually brownish, which is highly polluted

snow precipitation that is composed of one or more solid six-sided ice crystals that form in the clouds directly by sublimation of water vapor to ice

snow shower a brief, heavy snowfall

soil the part of the ground that will support rooted plants; the product of weathering of rock and the actions of living organisms

solar eclipse an eclipse caused by Earth's moon blocking out part or all of the sun from view, and the moon's shadow passing over part of the daytime side of Earth

solar energy see **insolation**

solar day the time it takes for Earth to rotate from solar noon to solar noon on two successive days at any fixed location on Earth

solar noon the time at which the sun reaches its highest point in the sky at any fixed location

*solar system (1) the sun and all objects that orbit the sun under its gravitational influence (in this book) (2) any star or a small group of orbiting stars and all the other objects that revolve around the star (s)

solar time the local time based on the actual motions of the sun in the sky; sundial time

*solidification the processes by which a liquid changes to a solid, such as when molten rock (lava and magma) changes into igneous rock; also see **crystallization**

solstices the two times of the year when the vertical rays of the sun fall the farthest from the equator; see **summer solstice** and **winter solstice**

*sorted a condition in which all the particles in a material are the same or similar in size, density, or shape

*sorted sediments a deposit of sediments that are similar in size (or shape, or density); the greater the similarity of particles the more sorted the sediments

source in an energy system, a region that has a higher energy concentration than its surroundings; energy flows from the source

source region the area of Earth's surface over which an air mass forms and acquires its characteristics

space the portion of the universe above Earth's atmosphere; also called outer space

*species a group of organisms which are similar enough to be able to interbreed and produce fertile young

*specific heat the quantity of heat, in calories, needed to raise the temperature of one gram of a substance one degree Celsius; the degree of difficulty a material offers to heating up or cooling off

speed how much distance is covered in a specific amount of time, such as kilometers per second

standard time a worldwide system of 24 north–south zones, that are 15 degrees of longitude wide, which keep the same local time

stages of landscape development stages (including youth, maturity, and old age) in the evolution of a landscape feature or region; stages characterized by certain features, including types of dominant forces, the amount of slope, elevation, and the amount of change in slope

*star usually a large ball of gas held together by gravity that produces tremendous amounts of energy and shines; also called a sun

state of matter see **phase**

*stationary front a weather condition in which the boundary between two air masses remains in the same position

*station model cities and other weather station sites on weather maps represented by circles, with symbols in and around each circle that indicate the many weather variables

storm a violent disturbance in the atmosphere that usually creates dangerous, destructive, and/or unpleasant conditions at Earth's surface

strata the layers or beds of sedimentary rock and extrusive igneous rock

*streak the color of the powder of a mineral which is usually more consistent than normal mineral color

*stream water flowing through a channel on land; examples—a large river or a narrow creek

*stream abrasion the rounding, smoothing, and size reduction of sediments resulting from the rolling, sliding, or bouncing of solid sediments along a stream bottom; also the erosion (lowering) of the stream bed by impact of solid sediments

stream bed the bottom or floor of a stream

*stream channel shape the shape of the body of rock or loose materials that confine the stream

*stream discharge see **discharge**

*stream drainage pattern the shape of the stream courses in an area as viewed from the sky

structure see **rock structure**

*subduction the plate tectonic process in which one of the plates at a convergent boundary sinks under the other plate and eventually melts into the asthenosphere

subduction zone the portion of a plate that sinks down into Earth's interior (asthenosphere) where converging plates cause subduction to take place

sublimation the change of state from a solid directly to a gas or from a gas to a solid with no intermediate liquid state; example—the forming of frost by sublimation of water vapor into ice; also called **deposition**

subsidence the sinking or depression of part of Earth's surface

subsurface water all liquid water found in soil, sediment, and bedrock beneath Earth's surface; see also **groundwater**

summer solstice on about June 21, the vertical rays of the sun fall on 23 1–2° N latitude and the duration and angle of incidence are greatest for most of the Northern Hemisphere and least in the Southern Hemisphere; see **winter solstice**

sun (1) star at the center of our solar system (2) another name for any star

sundial an ancient time-keeping device that uses the position of the sun to determine apparent solar, local, or sundial time

*sunspot a darker region of the sun's visible surface; increased numbers of sunspots are associated with increased electromagnetic energy emitted from the sun

sun's vertical rays see **direct waves**

superposition a principle applied in the relative dating of layered sedimentary and some extrusive igneous lava flow rocks stating that the youngest rock layer is found on top and that rock age increases with depth; exceptions—in deformed rocks, and where there are igneous intrusions; also called **principle of superposition**

surface ocean currents a continuous horizontal flow of water at or near the ocean's surface driven by the prevailing winds; also called **ocean currents**

synoptic method a method of weather prediction that uses a synopsis or summary of the total weather picture (often using a weather map) to predict future weather

*S-waves earthquake waves that move through Earth's interior and cause the particles through which they travel to vibrate at right angles to the direction of the wave motion; will only travel through solids, not through liquids or gases; also called **secondary waves**

technology the use of scientific information to serve human needs; the means by which a society provides objects required for human subsistence, comfort, and pleasure

tectonic forces the forces that create the large- scale structural features of Earth's lithosphere, such as mountains and continents, caused by lithospheric movements; energy comes from Earth's interior

*tectonic plate see **plate**

*temperature a measure of the average kinetic energy of the particles in a body of matter; a measure of how hot or cold a substance is

*terrestrial planets the planets (Mercury, Venus, Earth, and Mars) that are Earth-like in being relatively close to the sun, mostly solid, and having relatively small diameters and high densities

terrestrial radiation the infrared electromagnetic energy emitted by the Earth's surface towards the atmosphere

*texture (1) the roughness or smoothness of a surface; (2) the size, shape and arrangement of the mineral crystals, sediments, clasts, and glass that make up a rock

thermal energy the energy of motion of atoms and molecules; see **heat energy**

thermometer an instrument used to measure temperature that usually consists of a confined fluid (alcohol or mercury) that expands and contracts with temperature changes

thunderstorm a local, short-lived storm from cumulonimbus (thunderhead) clouds that always has lightning and thunder; often associated with heavy rain, high winds, hail, and less commonly, tornadoes and flooding

*tides the cyclic rise and fall of ocean water on Earth caused by the gravitational attraction of the moon and to a lesser degree the sun

tilted strata a type of deformed rock in which the strata, or layers, have been forced out of a horizontal position by tectonic movement

time the sense of things happening one after another or the duration of an event

time zone One of the 24 north-south trending zones, that are 15 degrees of longitude wide, which keep the same standard time as the central meridian of the zone. An example is the Eastern Standard Time Zone of the United States which generally extends between 82° and 67° west longitude with the central meridian at 75° west longitude

*topographic map a model of the elevation field of a solid celestial object, such as Earth, using contour lines and other symbols; also called a contour map

topography see **landscape**

tornado a narrow cyclonic storm with very high wind speeds characterized by a very low air pressure and a twisting funnel that touches the ground; formation often associated with cumulonimbus (thunderhead) clouds and can result in much damage and loss of life; commonly called a twister

track the path of movement of an air mass, front, or storm; weather tracks are often predictable, which helps in forecasting

trade-off an outcome that results when choices are made; example—the choice to build a dam for a local water supply as compared to using the land that will be flooded by building the dam for farming and homes

*transform plate boundary a boundary at which plates slide by each other, such as the San Andreas fault that separates the North American and Pacific Plates; also called a lateral fault plate boundary

*transpiration the process by which plants release water vapor into the atmosphere as part of their life functions

transported sediment weathered or eroded rock and organic materials that have been moved by an erosional system from their place of origin

transported soil soil that has been moved from its place of original formation; examples—glacial soils common in the northern United States and the river-deposited soils found in flood plains and deltas

transverse wave a wave that vibrates at right angles to its direction of motion; examples—electromagnetic energy and earthquake S–waves

*tributary small stream or river that flow into a larger stream or river

*troposphere the part of the atmosphere immediately above Earth's surface; where most weather changes occur

*tsunami very fast large wavelength ocean wave or waves produced by impact events and disturbances of the ocean floor caused by earthquakes, volcanic eruptions, or landslides; tsunamis can become very high and cause much wave damage near ocean shores

ultraviolet radiation a form of electromagnetic radiation of shorter wavelength than visible light; mostly absorbed by gases of the atmosphere, especially ozone in the stratosphere, before reaching Earth's surface

*unconformity a buried eroded surface causing a break, or gap, in the rock record

*universe the totality of all things that exist—all matter, time, energy, and space

*unsorted a condition in which the particles in a material are of mixed sizes (or shape, or density)

*unsorted sediments a deposit of sediments that are mixed in size (or shape, or density); the greater the difference in the size of the particles the more unsorted the sediments

*uplifted raised up; as in mountain building

*uplifting forces forces that originate beneath or within Earth's lithosphere that raise the land, build mountains, and cause continental growth; examples—volcanic action, earthquakes, and plate movements

*uranium-238 a radioactive isotope of uranium with an atomic mass of 238 units and a half-life of 4.5 billion years; decays to lead-206

*urbanization the growth of a city environment (an area of high human-population density)

*U-shaped valley the characteristic shape of a valley after it has been eroded by glaciers, especially mountain glaciers, as compared to the V-shaped valley eroded by streams

*vaporization see **evaporation**

vein a sheetlike shaped mineral deposit formed from a solution by precipitation of dissolved minerals that has filled a crack or permeable zone in previously formed rocks; younger than the rocks into which it intrudes

vertical rays see **direct rays**

*visibility the farthest distance at which one can see a prominent object at Earth's surface with the naked eye; decreased by fog, air pollution, and precipitation

*volcanic ash small pieces of extrusive igneous rock that are shot into the air during a volcanic eruption

*volcanic eruption the giving off of gases, lava, and/or lava rock onto Earth's surface or into the atmosphere through the opening or vent of a volcano

volcanic igneous rock see **extrusive igneous rock**

volcanic island arc see **island arc**

*volcano a mound or mountain composed of extrusive (volcanic) igneous rock

*volume the amount of space that an object occupies

*V-shaped valley the characteristic shape of a valley eroded by a stream or river, as compared to a U-shaped glacial valley

*warm front the boundary of an advancing warm air mass and a retreating wedge of a cooler air mass; characterized by a gentle slope, long periods of precipitation, and strato (layered) clouds

*water cycle a model, often a diagram, used to illustrate the movement and changes of state (phase) of water at and near Earth's surface; also called the hydrologic cycle

*water retention storing or retaining of precipitation on Earth's land surfaces as ice or snow, or as liquid water on trees and other plants

*watershed the area of land drained by any one stream; also called a drainage area

*water table the interface between the zone of saturation and the zone of aeration

*water vapor gaseous water in the atmosphere; also called moisture or steam

wave the up and down motion of water in an ocean or lake; usually caused by wind

wave action the erosion and deposition of landforms near coastlines caused by ocean or lake waves

*wavelength the distance between a point on a wave and the corresponding point on the next wave, such as the distance between two successive crests in an electromagnetic wave or an ocean wave

weather the condition of the atmospheric variables, such as temperature, air pressure, wind, and water vapor, at a particular location for a relatively short period of time

*weathering the chemical and physical alterations of rock and other Earth materials at or near Earth's surface, through the action of temperature changes, water, chemical agents, atmospheric gases, and organic materials

*weather variable condition of the atmosphere such as temperature, air pressure, wind, moisture conditions, cloud cover, precipitation, and storms

weight the effect of gravity on mass; unlike mass, weight varies with location

wet-bulb thermometer the thermometer of a psychrometer with a wick soaked in water around its bulb

wind the horizontal movement (compared with Earth's surface) of air in the atmosphere

wind direction the compass direction wind is blowing from; often indicated by a wind vane

wind erosion an erosional and depositional agent that is most common in desert and shoreline areas which lack much vegetation

wind speed how fast the wind is; see **wind velocity**

wind vane an instrument that spins in the wind and points to the direction the wind is blowing from, which is the wind direction name

wind velocity wind speed with a directional aspect

winter solstice on about December 21 the vertical rays of the sun fall on $23\frac{1}{2}°$ S latitude and the duration, insolation, and angle of incidence are greatest for most of the Southern Hemisphere and least in the Northern Hemisphere; see **summer solstice**

year the time it takes for a planet to make one revolution around the sun; also see **period**

*young mountains mountains that are presently rising because they are at the location of converging plates or at the site of a hot spot

zone of aeration the soil, loose materials, or bedrock from Earth's surface down to the water table, where the pores are only partly filled with liquid water; air fills the rest of the pores

zone of saturation the portion of the soil, loose materials, or bedrock that is below the water table, where the pores are filled with groundwater

Index

Acknowledgments

Author Acknowledgments:

Many individuals have helped in the completion of this book. Most of these people are acknowledged on page ii. In addition, I would like to give special thanks for help in editing the manuscript to my wife Angie Callister, retired from the English Department of Newburgh Free Academy, Newburgh, New York. I would also like to thank Lee Cabe, Velma Garey, Barry Heil, Paul Hill, Alexandra Passas, and Alfred Romano, Jr—my former colleagues in the science department at Newburgh Free Academy, Newburgh, New York—for their research and guidance.

New York Regents Examinations

The New York Regents Examinations that follow are provided so that you can practice taking an actual Earth Science Regents Examination. All of the tests included in this book cover the key concepts of the Physical Setting: Earth Science Core Curriculum. You will find that the content of this book provides specifically what you need to review for the Physical Setting: Earth Science Regents Examination.

Using the Regents Examinations

The best way to use these examinations is to take the entire test after you have reviewed the course content. Use the tests to determine if you have reviewed enough to do well on the Regents Examination and to determine where further review will be most helpful.

Do not look up any information or answers while you take the examinations. Answer each question just as you would during a real test. As you take the examination, use the margin of the paper to note any question where you are just guessing. Leave the more difficult questions for last, but be sure to answer each question. Every point counts so do not skip over a long question that is only worth a point or two. A long question could be easier than it looks and may make the difference between an A or a B or between passing or failing.

When you finish, have your teacher score your Examination and help you determine the areas where you need the most work. Also review the "guesses" you noted in the margin to find out what you need to study to ensure that you will be able to answer similar questions on the next test. Once you have determined your weaknesses, you can focus your review on those topics in this book.

Reviewing the areas where you know the least will give you the best chance of improving your final score. Spending time on areas where you are doing quite well will not produce much improvement in your total score, but it is still important if time permits.

Answer Key All answers to these Regents Examinations are included in the Answer Key, which also includes Diagnostic Tests to help you assess what you know before starting to study a topic and Topic Quizzes to help you assess your progress topic-by-topic.

Part A

Answer all questions in this part.

Directions (1–35): For *each* statement or question, choose the word or expression that, of those given, best completes the statement or answers the question. Some questions may require the use of the *2011 Edition Reference Tables for Physical Setting/Earth Science*. Record your answers on your separate answer sheet.

1. The gravitational attraction between two objects in the solar system is greatest when their masses are

   (1) small, and the objects are close together
   (2) small, and the objects are far apart
   (3) large, and the objects are far apart
   (4) large, and the objects are close together

2. Cosmic background radiation detected from all directions in space provides evidence for the

   (1) greenhouse effect   (3) geocentric theory
   (2) Doppler effect   (4) Big Bang theory

3. Which characteristic is directly related to a planet's average distance from the Sun?

   (1) period of revolution
   (2) period of rotation
   (3) eccentricity of orbit
   (4) equatorial diameter

4. The frequency of Earth's cycle of ocean tides is primarily controlled by

   (1) Earth's rotation and the Moon's rotation
   (2) Earth's rotation and the Moon's revolution
   (3) Earth's revolution and the Moon's rotation
   (4) Earth's revolution and the Moon's revolution

5. What is the approximate altitude of *Polaris* when viewed from New York City?

   (1) 90°   (3) 49°
   (2) 74°   (4) 41°

6. The diagram below represents a large Foucault pendulum that has been in motion over an 8-hour period. The arrow labeled *X* represents the apparent change in the direction of swing over time.

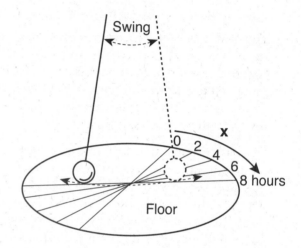

   This apparent change in the direction of swing is evidence that Earth

   (1) is tilted on its axis
   (2) rotates on its axis
   (3) revolves in an elliptical orbit
   (4) has magnetic poles that reverse over time

7. Which observation provides the best evidence that Earth orbits the Sun?

   (1) The Sun has a cyclic pattern of sunspot events.
   (2) The Sun appears to rise and set in a cyclic pattern.
   (3) The constellations that can be seen at night from Earth change with the seasons.
   (4) The constellations appear to move in a circular pattern around Earth.

[2]

8 The diagram below represents two columns, *A* and *B*, that were used to determine the infiltration rate and water retention of two different particle sizes by pouring equal amounts of water through each column.

Column A   **Column B**

(Not drawn to scale)

Compared to column *A*, column *B* had a

(1) lower rate of infiltration and retained less water
(2) lower rate of infiltration and retained more water
(3) higher rate of infiltration and retained less water
(4) higher rate of infiltration and retained more water

9 Which *two* factors will increase the rate of a stream's flow?

(1) decreased precipitation and decreased slope
(2) decreased precipitation and increased slope
(3) increased precipitation and decreased slope
(4) increased precipitation and increased slope

10 Which condition normally lowers the water table?

(1) irrigation of fields for several weeks, using well water
(2) several days of moderate rainfall
(3) streambanks overflowing during spring runoff
(4) several days of heavy snowfall, followed by rain

11 What is the dewpoint when the air temperature is 28°C and the relative humidity is 47%?

(1) 8°C   (3) 16°C
(2) 13°C   (4) 19°C

12 Clouds are formed when moist, rising air

(1) contracts and cools, and water vapor condenses
(2) contracts and warms, and water evaporates
(3) expands and cools, and water vapor condenses
(4) expands and warms, and water evaporates

13 Specific heat is used to explain why different substances

(1) sink or float in water
(2) change temperature at different rates
(3) vaporize or condense at different temperatures
(4) melt and freeze at the same temperature

14 What is the approximate percentage of Earth's history during which humans have existed, compared to the age of Earth?

(1) 0.04%   (3) 4.65%
(2) 1.79%   (4) 8.32%

15 Which two mantle hot spots are located at mid-ocean ridges?

(1) Iceland and Yellowstone
(2) Galapagos and Tasman
(3) St. Helena and Hawaii
(4) Easter Island and Bouvet

16 Approximately how many million years ago (mya) were all of Africa and South America inferred to be located south of the equator?

(1) 59 mya   (3) 232 mya
(2) 119 mya   (4) 359 mya

17 Which fossil has *not* been found in the New York State rock record?

(1) Silurian eurypterids
(2) Triassic dinosaur footprints
(3) Permian trilobites
(4) Pleistocene mastodont bones

[3]   [OVER]

Regents Examination A

18 What are the inferred pressure and interior temperature at the boundary between Earth's outer core and inner core?

(1) 3.1 million atmospheres pressure and an interior temperature of 6300°C

(2) 3.1 million atmospheres pressure and an interior temperature of 6700°C

(3) 3.6 million atmospheres pressure and an interior temperature of 6300°C

(4) 3.6 million atmospheres pressure and an interior temperature of 6700°C

19 The photograph below shows parallel scratches on the surface of limestone bedrock near Rochester, New York.

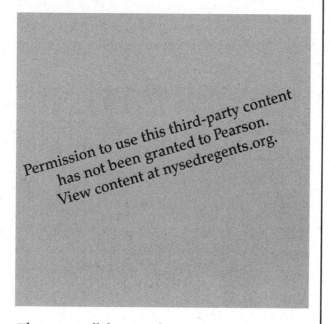

These parallel scratches were most likely caused by

(1) ocean waves
(2) running water
(3) movement of glacial ice
(4) sandblasting by wind

20 Landscapes with a faulted and folded surface bedrock structure, steep slopes, and high elevations are classified as

(1) mountains   (3) plains
(2) lowlands   (4) plateaus

21 The diagram below represents a volcano.

Which stream drainage pattern would most likely form on the entire surface of this volcano?

(1)

(3)

(2)

(4)

22 What is the largest particle size that a stream can transport at a velocity of 5 centimeters per second?

(1) cobble   (3) sand
(2) pebble   (4) silt

23 The diagram below represents a portion of a meandering stream. Letters *A*, *B*, *C*, and *D* represent locations on the bottom of the stream.

At which two locations would the stream most likely be the deepest?

(1) *A* and *B* (3) *C* and *D*
(2) *B* and *C* (4) *D* and *A*

24 The mineral anorthite is typically white to gray in color, has a hardness of 6.0, cleaves in two directions, and is used in making glass and ceramics. Which mineral has properties most similar to anorthite?

(1) quartz (3) pyroxene
(2) calcite (4) plagioclase feldspar

25 What is the texture of inorganic land-derived sedimentary rocks?

(1) bioclastic (3) clastic
(2) crystalline (4) vesicular

26 Which rock will weather at the fastest rate when exposed to acid rain?

(1) granite (3) gneiss
(2) limestone (4) quartzite

27 The photograph below shows the mineral muscovite mica.

Which physical property can be observed in this photograph?

(1) cleavage (3) magnetism
(2) hardness (4) streak

28 Which map symbol is used to represent rock that formed as a result of the evaporation of seawater?

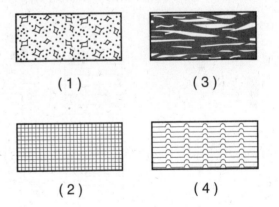

(1) (3)

(2) (4)

29 At which New York State location can intensely metamorphosed surface bedrock be found?

(1) Rochester (3) Slide Mountain
(2) Old Forge (4) Utica

Regents Examination A

30 The diagram below represents a model of the planet Saturn drawn to a scale of 1 centimeter = 40,000 kilometers.

Which diagram best represents Earth drawn to this same scale?

(1)   (2)   (3)   (4)

31 Columns *A*, *B*, *C*, and *D* below represent outcrops, of the same sequence of bedrock layers, found within 20 miles of each other. The rock layers have *not* been overturned.

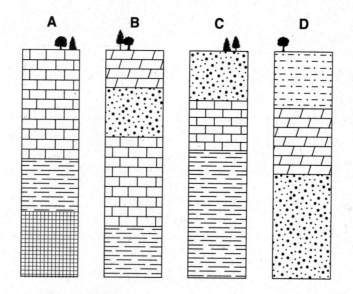

Which surface bedrock is youngest in age?

(1) siltstone
(2) dolostone

(3) limestone
(4) sandstone

[6]

32 The block diagrams below represent two large regions on Earth's surface.

White Sandy Region   **Vegetative Region**

Compared to the white sandy region, the vegetative region is
(1) less humid and absorbs less insolation   (3) more humid and absorbs less insolation
(2) less humid and absorbs more insolation   (4) more humid and absorbs more insolation

33 The graph below shows the change in the heights of tides for two days.

If this pattern continues, during the first six hours on Wednesday, tidal height will
(1) decrease, only   (3) increase, only
(2) decrease, then increase   (4) increase, then decrease

34 Which diagram best represents sediments with the greatest degree of sorting by size?

(1)

(3)

(2)

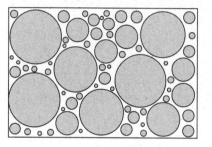

(4)

35 The photograph below shows a depositional feature located near the shore of Texas. Letter *X* represents a location on this feature.

Permission to use this third-party content has not been granted to Pearson. View content at nysedregents.org.

On which depositional feature is location *X* found?

(1) an island arc
(2) a barrier island

(3) a drumlin
(4) a floodplain

[OVER]

Regents Examination A

Part B–1

Answer all questions in this part.

Directions (36–50): For *each* statement or question, choose the word or expression that, of those given, best completes the statement or answers the question. Some questions may require the use of the *2011 Edition Reference Tables for Physical Setting/Earth Science*. Record your answers on your separate answer sheet.

Base your answers to questions 36 through 38 on the diagram below and on your knowledge of Earth science. The diagram represents Earth's orbit around the Sun. Positions A, B, C, and D represent Earth's location on the first day of each season. Letter N indicates the North Pole.

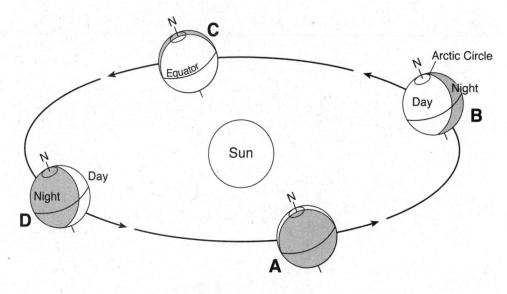

(Not drawn to scale)

36 At each position in Earth's orbit, the North Pole is pointing toward
  (1) *Pollux*   (3) *Polaris*
  (2) the Sun   (4) the Moon

37 Earth revolves around the Sun at the rate of approximately
  (1) 1° per day   (3) 15° per hour
  (2) 360° per day   (4) 23.5° per hour

38 Which graph best shows the hours of daylight that occur at the equator on all four Earth positions shown?

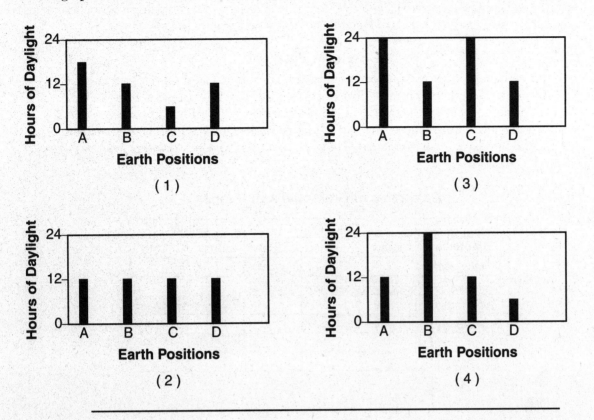

(1)

(3)

(2)

(4)

Base your answers to questions 39 through 41 on the passage, data table, and diagrams below and on your knowledge of Earth science. The age ranges shaded on the data table show the geologic periods and epochs when six different graptolite fossils existed on Earth. Diagrams of the six graptolites are shown.

Graptolite Fossils

Although graptolite fossils are found in bedrock from the Cambrian Period into the Pennsylvanian Period, their remains are most abundant in Ordovician and Silurian rock layers. During their existence on Earth, graptolites evolved quickly and spread widely due to ocean circulation. These tiny and fragile fossils are usually found in dark shales that formed in marine environments. They are rare in sandstones or other rocks that formed near shore.

Data Table of Graptolite Age Ranges

Fossil Graptolite	Ordovician			Silurian	
	Early	Middle	Late	Early	Late
Climacograptus		▓	▓		
Clonograptus	▓	▓			
Cyclograptus				▓	▓
Didymograptus	▓	▓			
Dimorphograptus				▓	
Goniograptus	▓				

Climacograptus   Clonograptus   Cyclograptus   Didymograptus   Dimorphograptus   Goniograptus

39 Which graptolite from the data table would best serve as an Early Ordovician index fossil?

(1) *Climacograptus*
(2) *Clonograptus*
(3) *Didymograptus*
(4) *Goniograptus*

40 A *Clonograptus* fossil was found in the surface bedrock at 43° N 73°30′ W. In which New York State landscape region was this fossil found?

(1) Adirondack Mountains
(2) Taconic Mountains
(3) Allegheny Plateau
(4) Champlain Lowlands

41 Which graptolite lived at the same time that large amounts of salt and gypsum were deposited in evaporite basins in New York State?

(1) *Clonograptus*
(2) *Cyclograptus*
(3) *Didymograptus*
(4) *Goniograptus*

Base your answers to questions 42 and 43 on the seismogram below and on your knowledge of Earth science.

42 Which statement best describes the arrival of *P*-waves and *S*-waves recorded at a station located closer to the epicenter of this same earthquake?

(1) The time difference between the arrival of the first *P*-wave and *S*-wave would be less than 4 minutes.

(2) The time difference between the arrival of the first *P*-wave and *S*-wave would be greater than 4 minutes.

(3) *P*-waves would be recorded, but no *S*-waves would arrive.

(4) *S*-waves would be recorded, but no *P*-waves would arrive.

43 The rock movement that caused the earthquake occurred 10 kilometers below Earth's surface. In which Earth layer did this earthquake originate?

(1) lithosphere   (3) stiffer mantle

(2) asthenosphere   (4) outer core

Regents Examination A

Base your answers to questions 44 through 46 on the weather map below and on your knowledge of Earth science. The weather map shows a low-pressure system over New York State on a July day. The **L** represents the center of the low, and two fronts extend from this center. Locations of some cities are indicated.

44 If the center of the low-pressure system follows a normal storm track, toward which city would the center of this low most likely move?

(1) Buffalo
(2) Elmira

(3) New York City
(4) Plattsburgh

45 Severe weather was occurring in Elmira, New York. Which present weather symbol was most likely recorded on the station model for Elmira?

(1)   (2)   (3)   (4)

[14]

46 Which map shows the most probable areas of precipitation that would appear on a radar image taken at the time of these frontal positions?

Key
☐ Precipitation

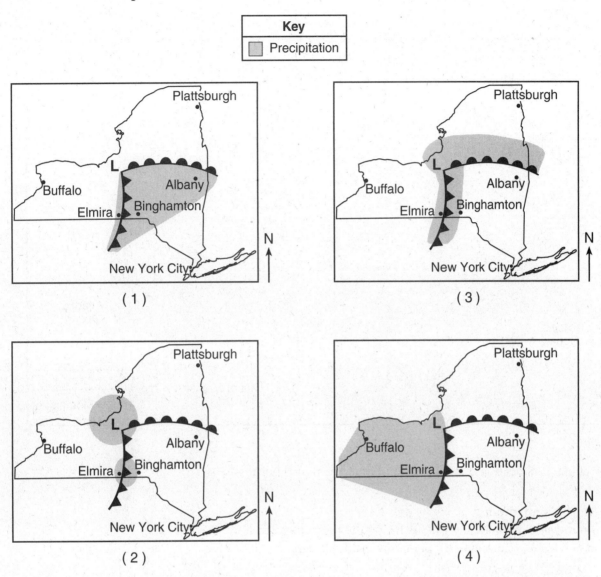

Regents Examination A

Base your answers to questions 47 through 50 on the map below and on your knowledge of Earth science. The map shows the continental United States and parts of Mexico and Canada. Letters *A* through *F* represent surface locations.

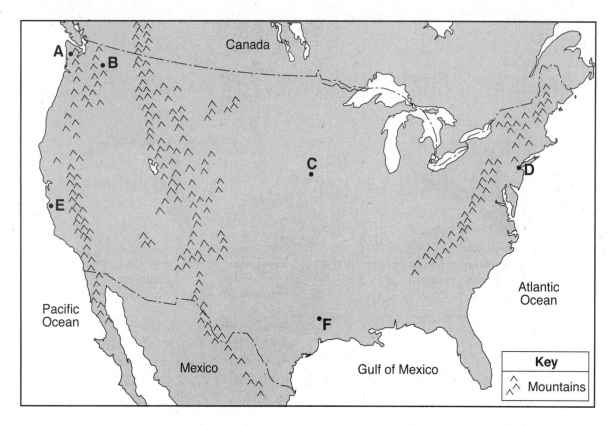

47 The climate of location *A* is more humid than location *B* because *A* is

(1) at a lower elevation
(2) at a higher latitude
(3) on the side of a mountain range facing the prevailing wind
(4) receiving a greater amount of energy from the Sun

48 Compared to the annual range in temperatures at location *C*, the annual range in temperatures at location *D* will be

(1) less, because *D* is located near a large body of water
(2) less, because *D* is located at a greater longitude
(3) greater, because *D* is located near a large body of water
(4) greater, because *D* is located at a greater longitude

49 The table below compares the average annual temperature for locations C and F.

Location	Average Annual Temperature
C	55°F
F	68°F

The best explanation for this temperature difference is that location C

(1) is in the polar NE wind belt

(2) is farther from the equator

(3) has less cloud cover

(4) has more frequent tornadoes

50 What is the relative temperature and name of the surface ocean current that affects the climate of location E?

(1) warm Alaska Current

(2) warm Gulf Stream Current

(3) cool Peru Current

(4) cool California Current

Regents Examination A

Answer all questions in this part.

Directions (51–65): Record your answers in the spaces provided in your answer booklet. Some questions may require the use of the *2011 Edition Reference Tables for Physical Setting/Earth Science.*

Base your answers to questions 51 and 52 on the map and photograph below and on your knowledge of Earth science. The map shows a path across northeastern North America, where a total solar eclipse will be visible on April 8, 2024. The photograph shows an example of a total solar eclipse.

Total Solar Eclipse

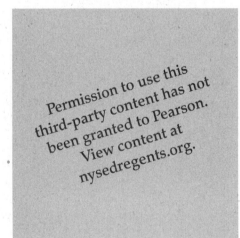

Permission to use this third-party content has not been granted to Pearson. View content at nysedregents.org.

51 On the chart *in your answer booklet*, place a check mark (✔) in the box next to each New York State location where a total solar eclipse will be visible with clear skies on April 8, 2024.   [1]

52 On the diagram *in your answer booklet*, place an **X** on the Moon's orbit to indicate the Moon's position during the solar eclipse on April 8, 2024.   [1]

Base your answers to questions 53 through 56 on the passage, cross section, and map below and on your knowledge of Earth science. The cross section represents the relative movement of two tectonic plates, labeled *A* and *B*, at the Mariana Trench. Arrows in the plates indicate the direction of this movement.

Challenger Deep

Challenger Deep is the deepest known point in Earth's oceans. This relatively narrow depression, only 7 miles long and 1 mile wide, is located in the bottom of the southern end of the Mariana Trench near the Mariana Islands, which includes the island of Guam. Challenger Deep is 6.83 miles deep, compared to Mount Everest, which is 5.49 miles above sea level.

53 Identify the names of tectonic plate *A* and tectonic plate *B*.   [1]

54 Identify the type of tectonic plate boundary shown in the cross section.   [1]

55 Identify *one* other geologic surface feature, other than a trench, found at the region represented in the cross section.   [1]

56 The diagram *in your answer booklet* represents the depth of Challenger Deep. For comparison, on the Height of Mount Everest scale to the right, draw a horizontal line across the scale to indicate the height above sea level of Mount Everest.   [1]

Base your answers to questions 57 through 59 on the diagram and photograph below and on your knowledge of Earth science. The diagram represents the constellation Ursa Major. One star, *Phecda*, has been labeled. Letter *X* represents the location of the Messier 81 galaxy (M81), which can be observed near Ursa Major. The photograph shows the Messier 81 galaxy as viewed through a telescope.

Ursa Major

Messier 81 Galaxy

57 *Phecda* has a surface temperature of approximately 9500 K and a luminosity of 63. Identify the name of the star found on the Characteristics of Stars chart in the *2011 Edition Reference Tables for Physical Setting/ Earth Science* that has a surface temperature and luminosity closest to *Phecda*. [1]

58 State the name of the nuclear process occurring in *Phecda* that produces this star's energy by combining lighter elements into heavier elements. [1]

59 The study of spectral lines from the Messier 81 galaxy suggests that it is moving toward Earth. Identify the color toward which these spectral lines shift when visible light from the Messier 81 galaxy is observed on Earth. [1]

_____

Base your answers to questions 60 through 62 on the diagram in your answer booklet and on your knowledge of Earth science. The diagram represents a model of the radioactive decay of carbon-14. The white boxes represent radioactive carbon-14 remaining, and the black boxes represent the disintegration product after the first half-life.

60 On the diagram *in your answer booklet*, shade in the correct number of carbon-14 boxes to represent the additional disintegration product after the second half-life. [1]

61 State the name of the disintegration product of carbon-14. [1]

62 Explain why carbon-14 would *not* be used to find the age of a *Coelophysis* fossil. [1]

_____

Regents Examination A

Base your answers to questions 63 through 65 on the topographic map below and on your knowledge of Earth science. Points *X*, *Y*, and *Z* indicate surface locations. Elevations are shown in meters.

Contour interval = 50 meters

0   1   2   3 km

N

63 State *one* possible elevation of point *X*. [1]

64 Calculate the gradient of Otter Creek, in meters per kilometer, between points *Y* and *Z*. [1]

65 Identify the compass direction toward which Canary Creek is flowing. [1]

Regents Examination A

Part C

Answer all questions in this part.

Directions (66–85): Record your answers in the spaces provided in your answer booklet. Some questions may require the use of the *2011 Edition Reference Tables for Physical Setting/Earth Science.*

Base your answers to questions 66 through 70 on the air pressure field map in your answer booklet and on your knowledge of Earth science. The map shows air pressures recorded in millibars (mb) at locations in eastern North America. Four isobars are shown. Points W, X, Y, and Z represent locations on Earth's surface. Letter **L** represents the center of a low-pressure system.

66 On the map *in your answer booklet*, draw the 1000 mb and 996 mb isobars. [1]

67 Which location on the map, W, X, Y, or Z, most likely has the greatest wind speed? Describe *one* piece of evidence on the map indicating that this location has the greatest wind speed. [1]

68 Identify the weather instrument used to measure air pressure. [1]

69 Describe the *two* characteristics of the general surface wind circulation pattern associated with this low-pressure system. [1]

70 One air mass associated with this pressure system originally formed over the Gulf of Mexico. Write the two-letter weather map symbol for this type of air mass. [1]

Base your answers to questions 71 through 74 on the passage and photographs below and on your knowledge of Earth science. The photographs show "dark streaks" of water that form and become longer over the summer months on Mars.

Water on Mars

NASA scientists have found evidence of flowing water on Mars. Mysterious "dark streaks" have been viewed forming on the slopes of Martian craters and mountain valleys during the summer months on Mars. These streaks were first thought to be landslides. Additional study caused scientists to infer that these streaks are salt compounds with water chemically attached to them. This salty-water compound is inferred to rise up from underground storage areas after thawing in the summer, or is formed when salts on the surface of Mars absorb water from the atmosphere until there is enough liquid water to run downhill. These salty-water flows are promising sites to find life on Mars. Future human missions to Mars may obtain and process water from this natural source.

Flowing Water On Mars

Before Martian Summer:
No "dark streaks"
are visible.

Early Martian Summer:
"Dark streaks"
first become visible.

Late Martian Summer:
"Dark streaks" become longer
and more numerous.

Dark Streaks

71 Identify the force that causes the type of mass movement first inferred to have formed the "dark streaks." [1]

72 Identify *one* event that could have formed the Martian craters. [1]

73 Determine the number of days from the first day of summer on Mars to the next first day of summer on Mars. [1]

74 Indicate whether Mars is classified as a terrestrial planet or Jovian planet by circling the correct term *in your answer booklet*. Explain why Mars is classified as this type of planet. [1]

[24]

Base your answers to questions 75 through 79 on the data table below and on your knowledge of Earth science. The data table shows how the destruction of the ozone layer in Earth's atmosphere has affected the amount of ultraviolet radiation reaching Earth's surface beneath the areas of ozone destruction.

Ozone Loss and Ultraviolet Radiation

Ozone Destruction (%)	Average Increase in Ultraviolet Radiation Reaching Earth's Surface (%)
0	0
5	5
10	12
15	20
20	28
25	36
30	47
35	60
40	76

75 On the grid *in your answer booklet*, construct a line graph by plotting the data for the average increase in ultraviolet radiation reaching Earth's surface for each percentage of ozone destruction shown on the data table. Connect *all nine* plots with a line. [1]

76 Ozone destruction was estimated to be 22% in the atmosphere above a Lake Ontario beach. Based on the pattern shown in the data table, predict the average increase in ultraviolet radiation reaching that beach. [1]

77 The ozone layer is mostly concentrated between 20 and 25 kilometers above Earth's surface. State the name of the atmospheric temperature zone layer where this ozone concentration can be found. [1]

78 On the table *in your answer booklet*, place one check mark in each row to compare the relative wavelengths of other types of electromagnetic radiation to ultraviolet (UV) radiation. [1]

79 Ozone closer to Earth's surface has been identified as a greenhouse gas. Identify *two* other gases in Earth's atmosphere that are considered major greenhouse gases. [1]

Base your answers to questions 80 through 82 on the diagram in your answer booklet and on your knowledge of Earth science. The diagram represents the apparent paths of the Sun observed in solar time (time based on the Sun's position in the sky) at Albany, New York, on June 21 and December 21. A portion of the Sun's path on June 21 is shaded. A protractor has been included in the diagram.

80 On the diagram *in your answer booklet*, draw an **X** to indicate the position of sunrise on March 21.   [1]

81 Determine the altitude of the Sun at solar noon on December 21 and June 21.   [1]

82 The shaded portion on the June 21 path represents 45 degrees of the Sun's apparent motion. Determine the number of hours that this shaded portion represents.   [1]

Base your answers to questions 83 through 85 on the geologic cross section below and on your knowledge of Earth science. The cross section represents sedimentary rock units labeled *A* through *D*, a layer of volcanic ash deposits, and a basalt extrusion. An unconformity is present between rock units *B* and *C*. Line *XY* represents a fault. The rock layers have *not* been overturned.

Key

Basalt	
Volcanic ash	
Contact metamorphism	

83 State the name of *one* metamorphic rock that most likely formed in the zone of contact metamorphism between rock unit *A* and the basalt. [1]

84 Fossils of the first multicellular, soft-bodied marine organisms were found in rock unit *D*. Identify the eon that indicates the geologic age of this rock unit. [1]

85 Determine the relative age sequence of the following geologic features, in order from oldest to youngest: [1]

> • Basalt
> • Fault *XY*
> • Volcanic ash

[27]

Regents Examination A

PHYSICAL SETTING
EARTH SCIENCE

ANSWER BOOKLET

Student . . . .

Teacher . . . .

School . . . . Grade . . . .

Record your answers for Part B–2 and Part C in this booklet.

Part B–2

51

New York State Location	Total Solar Eclipse Visible
Kingston	
Massena	
Niagara Falls	
Riverhead	
Oswego	

52

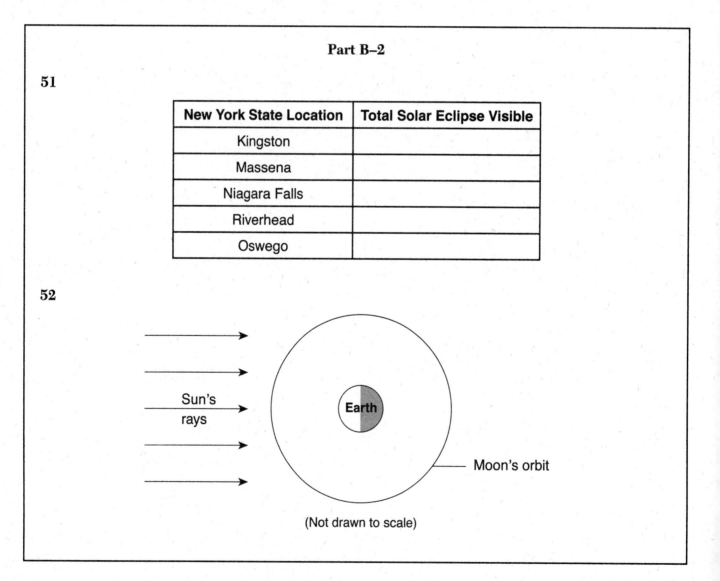

Sun's rays

Earth

Moon's orbit

(Not drawn to scale)

53 Plate _A_:_____ **Plate**

Plate _B_:_____ **Plate**

54 _____

55 _____

56

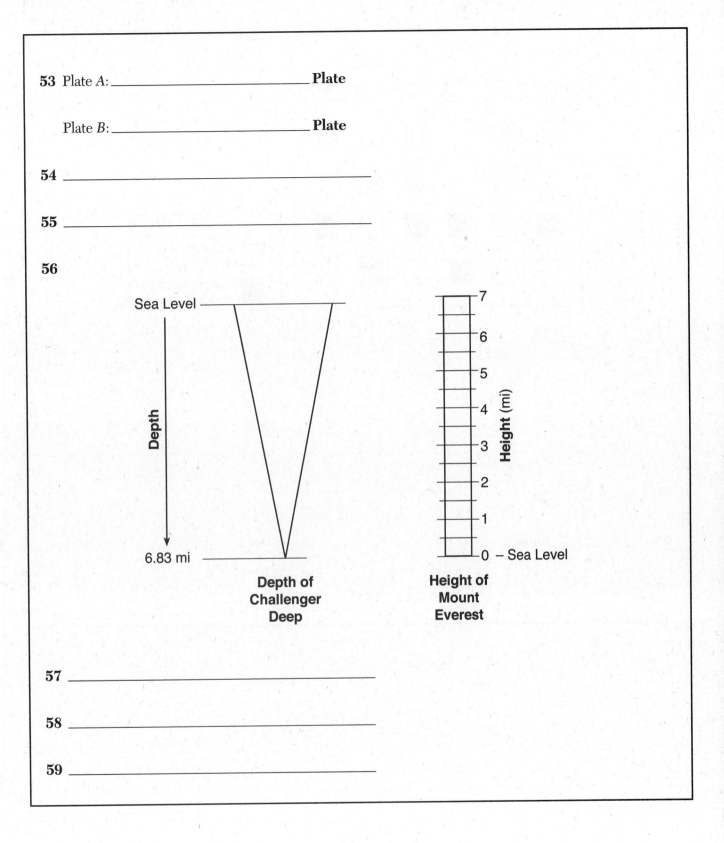

Depth

Sea Level

6.83 mi

Depth of Challenger Deep

Height (mi)

7
6
5
4
3
2
1
0 – Sea Level

Height of Mount Everest

57 _____

58 _____

59 _____

60

Model of Carbon-14 Radioactive Decay

Key	
☐	Radioactive carbon-14
■	Disintegration product

61 _____

62 _____

_____

63 _____ m

64 _____ m/km

65 _____

66

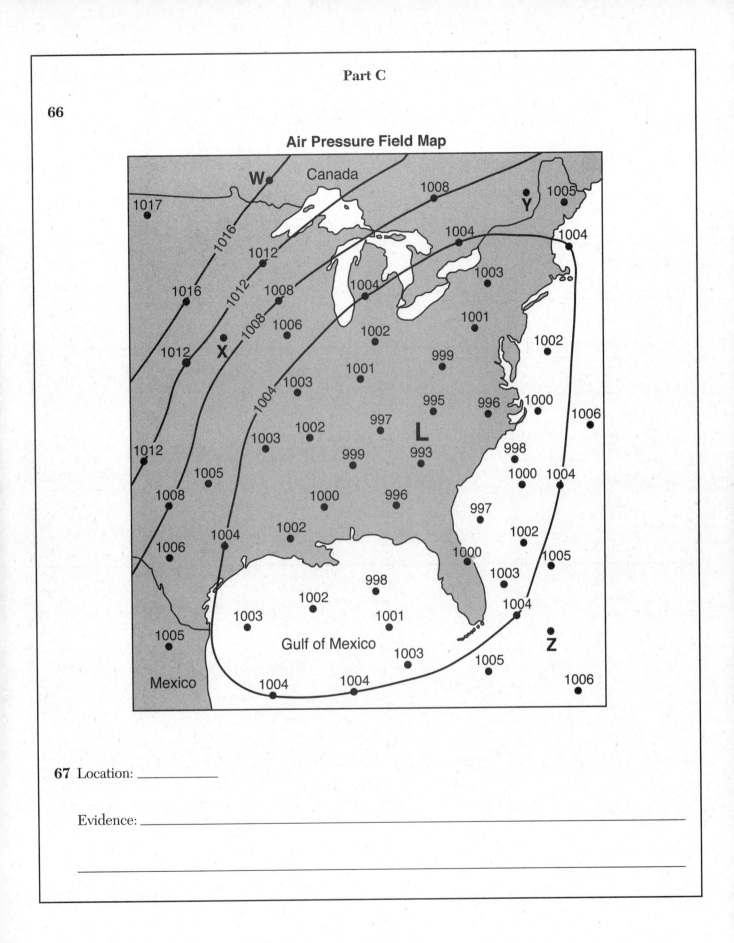

Air Pressure Field Map

67 Location: _____

Evidence: _____

_____

68 _____

69 Characteristic 1: _____

Characteristic 2: _____

70 _____

71 _____

72 _____

73 _____ **d**

74 Circle one: **Terrestial Planet**   **Jovian Planet**

Explanation: _____

_____

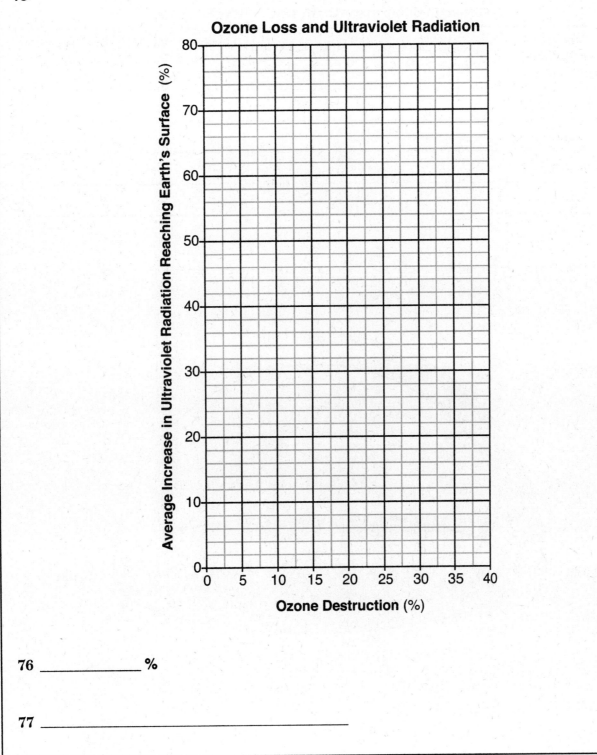

Ozone Loss and Ultraviolet Radiation

Average Increase in Ultraviolet Radiation Reaching Earth's Surface (%)

Ozone Destruction (%)

76 _____ %

77 _____

Regents Examination A

78

Wavelength Comparison to Ultraviolet (UV) Radiation

Type of Electromagnetic Radiation	All Wavelengths Shorter Than UV	All Wavelengths Longer Than UV	Some Wavelengths Shorter and Some Wavelengths the Same as UV
Gamma Rays			
Microwaves			
Visible light			
X rays			

79 _____ and _____

80

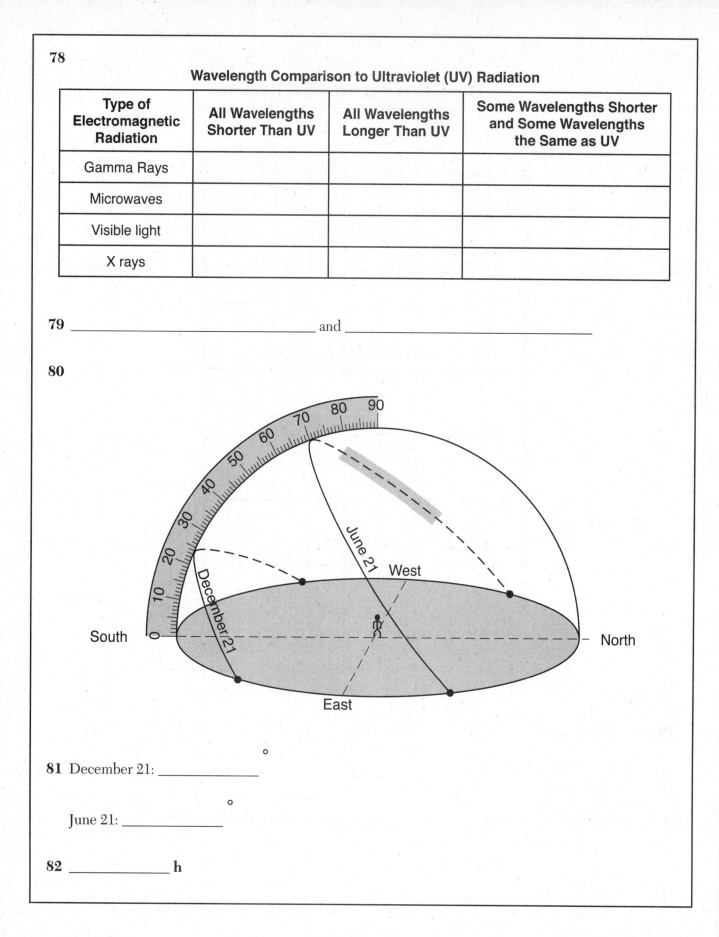

81 December 21: _____ °

June 21: _____ °

82 _____ h

[OVER]

Regents Examination A

83 _____

84 _____ **Eon**

85 _____ → _____ → _____
           Oldest   Youngest

Part A

Answer all questions in this part.

Directions (1–35): For *each* statement or question, choose the word or expression that, of those given, best completes the statement or answers the question. Some questions may require the use of the *2011 Edition Reference Tables for Physical Setting/Earth Science*. Record your answers on your separate answer sheet.

1 The diagram below represents a sundial positioned in New York State. During daylight, the shadow cast by the gnomon (pointer) moves across the disc, with the tip of the shadow pointing to the time of day.

Gnomon

This motion of the gnomon's shadow on the sundial is mainly due to

(1) Earth's rotation
(2) Earth's revolution
(3) the Sun's rotation
(4) the Sun's revolution

2 The formation of the planet Uranus is estimated to have occurred approximately

(1) 100,000 million years ago
(2) 2.0 billion years ago
(3) 4.6 billion years ago
(4) 13.7 billion years ago

3 Compared to the Jovian planets in our solar system, the terrestrial planets have

(1) less mass and are less dense
(2) less mass and are more dense
(3) more mass and are less dense
(4) more mass and are more dense

4 The diagram below represents the constellation Leo that can be seen by an observer in New York State at midnight during March.

Leo

Leo is *not* visible to this observer at midnight during September because

(1) Leo has rotated on its axis
(2) Leo has revolved in its orbit around the Sun
(3) Earth has rotated on its axis
(4) Earth has revolved in its orbit around the Sun

5 An observer in New York City measured the angle of insolation at solar noon each day. During which month did this observer see the noontime angle of insolation increase each day?

(1) April   (3) September
(2) July   (4) December

6 The Coriolis effect occurs as a result of Earth's

(1) rotation   (3) tilted axis
(2) revolution   (4) magnetic field

[2]

7 During the process of condensation, water vapor

   (1) releases 334 J/g of heat energy
   (2) releases 2260 J/g of heat energy
   (3) gains 334 J/g of heat energy
   (4) gains 2260 J/g of heat energy

8 Infiltration is generally greater than runoff where the land has a

   (1) gentle slope and permeable soil
   (2) gentle slope and impermeable bedrock
   (3) steep slope and permeable soil
   (4) steep slope and impermeable bedrock

9 Nearly 90% of the water vapor that enters Earth's atmosphere comes from the evaporation of Earth's surface waters. Most of the remaining 10% is water vapor that enters the atmosphere through

   (1) precipitation from clouds
   (2) transpiration from plants
   (3) condensation within the troposphere
   (4) melting of polar ice caps

10 What is the relative humidity if the dry-bulb temperature is 26°C and the wet-bulb temperature is 18°C?

   (1) 13%   (3) 45%
   (2) 33%   (4) 51%

11 Most of the long-wave energy radiated from Earth and lost to space on a cloudless night is

   (1) ultraviolet   (3) visible light
   (2) infrared   (4) gamma rays

12 In addition to carbon dioxide, two other major greenhouse gases in Earth's atmosphere are

   (1) oxygen and nitrogen
   (2) oxygen and methane
   (3) water vapor and nitrogen
   (4) water vapor and methane

13 The arrows in the diagram below represent the movement of air over a mountain.

Clouds are forming on the windward side of this mountain because the air is

   (1) expanding and cooling to the dewpoint
   (2) expanding and warming to the dewpoint
   (3) compressing and cooling to the dewpoint
   (4) compressing and warming to the dewpoint

14 The graph below shows the average monthly amount of insolation received throughout a year at four locations (A, B, C, and D) on Earth.

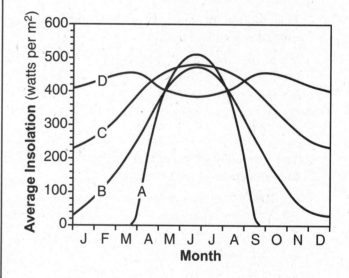

Which line on the graph best represents the average monthly insolation received at the equator?

   (1) A   (3) C
   (2) B   (4) D

15 Earth's polar regions have cold, dry climates because the Sun's rays are at a

(1) low angle, and upper atmospheric air is sinking
(2) low angle, and upper atmospheric air is rising
(3) high angle, and lower atmospheric air is sinking
(4) high angle, and lower atmospheric air is rising

16 Atmospheric transparency will increase when

(1) volcanic eruptions occur
(2) fog is produced
(3) insolation is reflected by clouds
(4) precipitation removes dust particles from the air

17 The existence of which group of organisms spans the shortest geologic time?

(1) birds   (3) dinosaurs
(2) humans   (4) placoderm fish

18 Which New York State geologic event occurred most recently?

(1) Taconian orogeny
(2) Grenville orogeny
(3) formation of the Catskill delta
(4) dome-like uplift of the Adirondack region

19 The only dinosaur fossils found in New York State are footprints found on 210-million-year-old bedrock. In which New York State landscape region were these dinosaur fossils found?

(1) Tug Hill Plateau
(2) Newark Lowlands
(3) Allegheny Plateau
(4) Adirondack Mountains

20 The first *P*-wave of an earthquake travels 5600 kilometers from the epicenter and arrives at a seismic station at 10:05 a.m. At what time did this earthquake occur?

(1) 9:49 a.m.   (3) 10:02 a.m.
(2) 9:56 a.m.   (4) 10:14 a.m.

21 The photograph below shows a New York State index fossil.

What is the best classification of this fossil, and during which geologic time period did the organism that produced this fossil exist?

(1) Classification: Coral
    Geologic time period: Permian
(2) Classification: Coral
    Geologic time period: Ordovician
(3) Classification: Trilobite
    Geologic time period: Permian
(4) Classification: Trilobite
    Geologic time period: Ordovician

22 As a quartz pebble is transported by a stream, the pebble will become more rounded as a result of

(1) dissolving as water is running over the rock
(2) abrasion by colliding with other rocks
(3) deposition in well-sorted layers
(4) resistance to weathering and erosion

23 Which three minerals are most likely used in the construction of a house?

(1) graphite, pyrite, and halite
(2) garnet, galena, and sulfur
(3) talc, amphibole, and fluorite
(4) selenite gypsum, dolomite, and muscovite mica

[4]

24 The topographic map below shows a portion of a volcanic island in the Pacific Ocean. Elevations are shown in feet. Letters *A* and *B* represent locations on Earth's surface. Locations *A* and *B* are 2.5 miles apart.

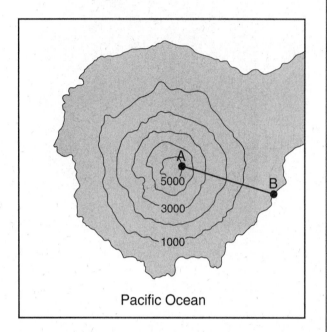

Pacific Ocean

What is the approximate gradient from point *A* to point *B* on the island?

(1) 1000 ft/mi   (3) 2000 ft/mi
(2) 1250 ft/mi   (4) 2500 ft/mi

25 Which two rocks usually consist of only one mineral, but may contain additional minerals?

(1) hornfels and diorite
(2) quartzite and dunite
(3) rock salt and basalt
(4) gabbro and bituminous coal

26 Which rock has never melted, but was produced by great heat and pressure, which distorted and rearranged its minerals?

(1) siltstone   (3) pegmatite
(2) breccia   (4) metaconglomerate

27 The map below shows a portion of the North Carolina coastline, including some of the Outer Banks. The Outer Banks is a string of narrow barrier islands consisting of well-sorted sand along the Atlantic Ocean coast.

Which agent of erosion is primarily responsible for the formation of these barrier islands?

(1) wave action   (3) streams
(2) landslides   (4) glacial ice

28 The photograph below shows a magnified view of a portion of a rock that can float if placed in water.

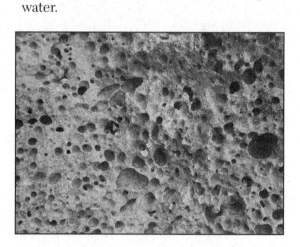

Which terms best describe this rock?

(1) non-crystalline and vesicular
(2) coarse and non-vesicular
(3) clastic and fragmental
(4) foliated and banded

Regents Examination B

29 The map below shows three locations, labeled *A*, *X*, and *B*, on Earth's surface.

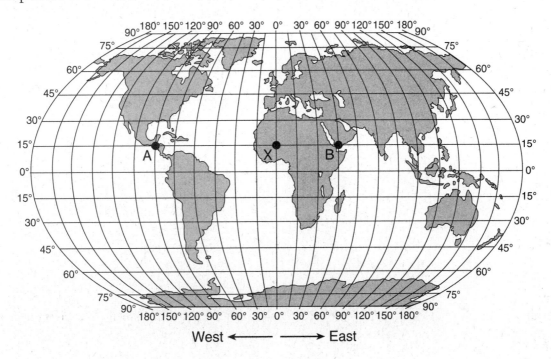

West ◄———— ————► East

Which table correctly indicates the solar times at locations *A* and *B* when it is 12 noon at location *X*?

Location	Solar Time
A	6 a.m.
B	9 a.m.

(1)

Location	Solar Time
A	6 p.m.
B	9 a.m.

(3)

Location	Solar Time
A	6 a.m.
B	3 p.m.

(2)

Location	Solar Time
A	6 p.m.
B	3 p.m.

(4)

30 Which equation is used to determine the approximate rate of Earth's revolution?

(1) Approximate rate of Earth's revolution $= \dfrac{365°}{360 \text{ days}}$

(2) Approximate rate of Earth's revolution $= \dfrac{360°}{24 \text{ hours}}$

(3) Approximate rate of Earth's revolution $= \dfrac{360°}{365 \text{ days}}$

(4) Approximate rate of Earth's revolution $= \dfrac{24°}{360 \text{ hours}}$

[6]

31 Which cross section best represents a cold front?

32 The isolines on the map below show snowfall totals from a lake-effect storm that affected a portion of New York State.

The surface winds that produced this storm came from which direction?

(1) northwest

(2) northeast

(3) southeast

(4) southwest

33 The photograph below shows Mount Rainier, a volcano in the state of Washington.

Which map best shows the complete stream drainage pattern for this mountain?

    (1)   (2)   (3)   (4)

34 Which table best represents the characteristics of the continental crust and the oceanic crust?

Type of Crust	Density (g/cm³)	Composition	Relative Thickness
Continental	3.0	basaltic	thicker
Oceanic	2.7	granitic	thinner

(1)

Type of Crust	Density (g/cm³)	Composition	Relative Thickness
Continental	2.7	granitic	thinner
Oceanic	3.0	basaltic	thicker

(3)

Type of Crust	Density (g/cm³)	Composition	Relative Thickness
Continental	3.0	granitic	thicker
Oceanic	2.7	basaltic	thinner

(2)

Type of Crust	Density (g/cm³)	Composition	Relative Thickness
Continental	2.7	granitic	thicker
Oceanic	3.0	basaltic	thinner

(4)

Regents Examination B

35 The map below shows the locations of some oil and gas fields in New York State.

Source: New York State Museum, State Geological Survey

Which type of bedrock contains these oil and gas deposits?

(1) extrusive igneous rock

(2) intrusive igneous rock

(3) metamorphic rock

(4) sedimentary rock

Regents Examination B

Part B–1

Answer all questions in this part.

Directions (36–50): For *each* statement or question, choose the word or expression that, of those given, best completes the statement or answers the question. Some questions may require the use of the *2011 Edition Reference Tables for Physical Setting/Earth Science*. Record your answers on your separate answer sheet.

Base your answers to questions 36 through 38 on the map below and on your knowledge of Earth science. The map shows typical weather systems over North America. Letters *X*, *Y*, and *Z* represent locations on the map. The isobars on the map are measured in millibars (mb).

36 Which map information indicates that the wind velocity is greater at location *Z* than at location *X*?

(1) Location *Z* is closer to the ocean.

(2) The isobars are closer together at *Z*.

(3) The latitude of location *X* is greater.

(4) Location *X* is closer to the front.

37 Which type of front extends northwest from location *Y*?

(1) warm front

(2) cold front

(3) occluded front

(4) stationary front

38 Which map best shows the locations for the centers of high pressure (**H**) and low pressure (**L**)?

(1)

(3)

(2)

(4)

[OVER]

Regents Examination B

Base your answers to questions 39 through 41 on the passage below and on your knowledge of Earth Science.

Supermoon Eclipse

On September 27, 2015, a rare total lunar eclipse of a supermoon occurred. A supermoon occurs when the entire lighted half of the Moon faces Earth (full Moon phase) and the Moon is at its closest point to Earth in its orbit. At this time, the Moon will appear 14% larger and 30% brighter than normal. Supermoon events are rare, but a total lunar eclipse during a supermoon is even more rare. There have been only six total supermoon lunar eclipses since 1900. The next one will not happen until 2033.

39 Supermoon total lunar eclipses are celestial events that

    (1) are random occurrences   (3) will never happen again after 2033

    (2) are predictable   (4) will happen every full Moon

40 The diagram below represents the Moon in four positions, *A* through *D*, in its orbit around Earth.

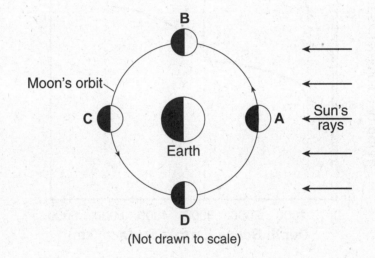

(Not drawn to scale)

At which position in its orbit was the Moon located during the 2015 supermoon total lunar eclipse?

    (1) *A*   (3) *C*

    (2) *B*   (4) *D*

41 The time it took for the Moon to go from this supermoon to the next full moon phase was

    (1) 15 days   (3) 29.5 days

    (2) 27.3 days   (4) 365 days

Base your answers to questions 42 through 44 on the diagram and graph below and on your knowledge of Earth science. The diagram represents a portion of Earth's interior. Letters A, B, and C represent interior layers. The graph shows the velocity of P-waves and S-waves at various depths in Earth's interior.

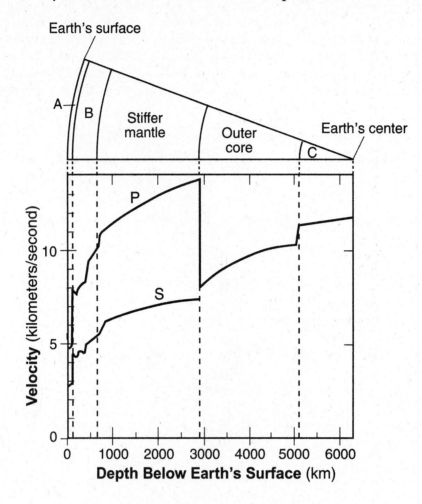

42 Which layers of Earth's interior are represented by letters A and B?

(1) A is the crust and B is the rigid mantle.
(2) A is the lithosphere and B is the asthenosphere.
(3) A is the asthenosphere and B is the crust.
(4) A is the rigid mantle and B is the lithosphere.

43 What is the approximate velocity in kilometers/second of the P-waves at a depth of 1000 kilometers?

(1) 6.2 km/s   (3) 11.3 km/s
(2) 7.2 km/s   (4) 13.8 km/s

44 Some locations within layer C have an inferred density of

(1) 3.4 g/cm^3 (3) 11.5 g/cm^3
(2) 5.6 g/cm^3 (4) 12.9 g/cm^3

Base your answers to questions 45 through 47 on the graph below and on your knowledge of Earth science. The graph shows the changes in a single star's luminosity and relative temperature from its formation (point 1) to its late stage (point 4) relative to the Sun.

Characteristics of Stars

45 Which is a possible surface temperature of this star at point 2?

(1) 3000 K   (3) 7000 K
(2) 5000 K   (4) 10,000 K

46 Between points 1 and 3, this star is visible to observers on Earth because it emits light energy. This energy is released by the process of nuclear fusion when

(1) dust collides with the star
(2) dust is broken apart by radiation
(3) lighter elements combine to form heavier elements
(4) heavier elements are broken down to form lighter elements

47 Which table correctly classifies this star at points 3 and 4?

Point	Classification
3	Giant
4	White Dwarf

(1)

Point	Classification
3	Supergiant
4	Main Sequence

(3)

Point	Classification
3	White Dwarf
4	Supergiant

(2)

Point	Classification
3	Giant
4	Main Sequence

(4)

GO ON TO THE NEXT PAGE ⇨

[OVER]

Regents Examination B

Base your answers to questions 48 through 50 on the photograph below and on your knowledge of Earth science. The photograph shows a meandering stream in a wooded area. Points *A* and *B* represent locations on the streambanks. Letter *X* represents a flat area near the stream.

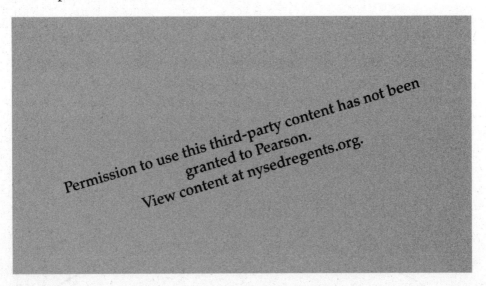

48 The streambank at location *B* is steeper than the streambank at location *A* because the water near location *B* is moving

(1) slower than the water near location *A*, causing more erosion
(2) slower than the water near location *A*, causing more deposition
(3) faster than the water near location *A*, causing more erosion
(4) faster than the water near location *A*, causing more deposition

49 The area labeled letter *X* represents a portion of a

(1) delta
(2) sand dune
(3) finger lake
(4) floodplain

50 Most of the particles deposited where the stream velocity *decreases* from 50 centimeters per second to 5 centimeters per second are

(1) small cobbles and large pebbles
(2) small pebbles and large sand
(3) small sand and large silt
(4) small silt and large clay

[16]

Part B–2

Answer all questions in this part.

Directions (51–65): Record your answers in the spaces provided in your answer booklet. Some questions may require the use of the *2011 Edition Reference Tables for Physical Setting/Earth Science*.

Base your answers to questions 51 through 54 on the diagram below and on your knowledge of Earth science. In the diagram, letters *A, B, C,* and *D* represent Earth's location on the first day of the four seasons as it orbits the Sun. Aphelion (Earth's farthest distance from the Sun) and perihelion (Earth's closest distance to the Sun) are labeled to show the approximate positions where they occur in Earth's orbit. The dashed lines represent Earth's axis, and the North Pole is labeled N.

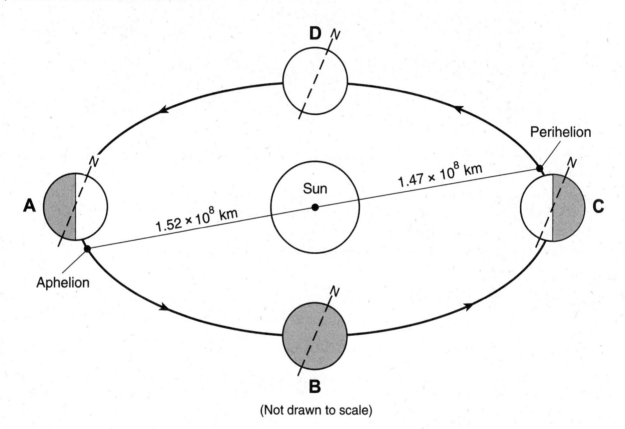

(Not drawn to scale)

51 State the number of degrees that Earth's axis is tilted from a line perpendicular to the plane of its orbit at each lettered location. [1]

52 Identify the season in New York State during which Earth is at perihelion. [1]

53 State the number of hours of daylight that an observer in New York State will experience when Earth is at position *D*. [1]

54 Identify the name of the star that is aligned with Earth's axis above the North Pole. [1]

Regents Examination B

Base your answers to questions 55 through 58 on the passage, chart of definitions and photograph below, and on your knowledge of Earth science. The passage is an excerpt from the 1994 novel *Inca Gold*, by Clive Cussler, which describes the formation of a sinkhole in the Andes Mountains of South America. The chart of definitions helps the reader understand some concepts in the passage. The photograph shows a sinkhole that formed in a South American village.

Excerpt from *Inca Gold*

…The sinkhole's early history began in the Cambrian era when the region was part of an ancient sea. Through the following geological eras, thousands of generations of shellfish and coral lived and died, their skeletal carcasses forming an enormous mass of lime and sand that compressed into a limestone and dolomite layer two kilometers thick. Then, beginning sixty-five million years ago, an intense earth uplifting occurred that raised the Andes Mountains to their present height. As the rain ran down from the mountains it formed a great underground water table that slowly began dissolving the limestone. Where it collected and pooled, the water ate upward until the land surface collapsed and created the sinkhole.…

Chart of Definitions

Sinkhole	A natural depression or hole in the ground surface caused by some form of collapse of the bedrock beneath. Most are caused when slightly acidic groundwater chemically breaks down the carbonate rocks or the carbonate cement holding the rock particles together. The removal of the carbonates by groundwater gradually forms a hollow space or cavern under the surface layer. As the roof of the cavern weakens, it sometimes collapses, forming a sinkhole.
Lime	A general term for material containing the element calcium that combined with oxygen.

Photograph of a Sinkhole

55 In the first line of the passage, referring to Cambrian as an "era" is scientifically incorrect. State the unit of geologic time that should be substituted for the word "era." [1]

56 Identify *one* group of animals that became extinct at the time the passage states that intense uplifting of the Andes Mountains began. [1]

57 Using chemical symbols, state the chemical composition of the mineral found in limestone. [1]

58 Describe the chemical weathering that contributes to the formation of sinkholes. [1]

_____

Base your answers to questions 59 through 61 on the geologic cross section below and on your knowledge of Earth science. The cross section represents rock units, labeled *A* through *K*, that have *not* been overturned. Two unconformities and a volcanic ash layer are indicated.

59 List the letters *E, H,* and *K* to indicate the correct order of rock unit formation, from oldest to youngest, that formed this portion of Earth's crust. [1]

60 Identify *two* processes that most likely caused the formation of both unconformities. [1]

61 Identify *one* metamorphic rock that most likely formed within rock unit *G* at the boundary of rock unit *K*. [1]

_____

Base your answers to questions 62 through 65 on the field map in your answer booklet and on your knowledge of Earth science. The map shows the depth of Cuba Lake, located in New York State at latitude 42°14' N, longitude 78°18' W. Isoline values indicate water depth, in feet. Points A and B represent locations on the shoreline of Cuba Lake. Points W, X, Y, and Z represent locations on the bottom of the lake. The 30-foot isoline has been partially drawn.

62 On the map *in your answer booklet*, complete the 30-foot water depth isoline from point W to point X. [1]

63 On the grid *in your answer booklet*, construct a profile of the bottom of Cuba Lake from point A to point B. Plot each point where an isoline showing depth is crossed by line AB. Connect the plots with a line, starting at A and ending at B, to complete the profile. [1]

64 State the compass direction and distance in feet (ft) from point Y to point Z. [1]

65 Identify the New York State landscape region where Cuba Lake is located. [1]

Part C

Answer all questions in this part.

Directions (66–85): Record your answers in the spaces provided in your answer booklet. Some questions may require the use of the *2011 Edition Reference Tables for Physical Setting/Earth Science.*

Base your answers to questions 66 through 68 on the table below and on your knowledge of Earth science. The data table lists some information about the dwarf planet Pluto, which revolves around our Sun, and the five known moons that orbit Pluto.

Data for Dwarf Planet Pluto and Its Five Moons

Object Name	Classification	Period of Revolution in Earth Days (d)	Eccentricity of Orbit	Diameter (km)
Pluto	Dwarf Planet	90,511.4 (247.8 years)	0.2488	2370
Charon	Moon	6.4	0.0022	1208
Styx	Moon	20.2	0.0058	10 to 15 *
Nix	Moon	24.9	0.0020	40
Kerberos	Moon	32.2	0.0033	13 to 34 *
Hydra	Moon	38.2	0.0059	33 to 43 *

* There is a range in diameters for these moons due to their irregular shapes.

66 Identify the name of Pluto's moon that most likely has an orbit farthest from Pluto. Explain how the data indicate that this moon's orbit has the greatest distance from Pluto. [1]

67 Describe the shape of the orbit of Pluto and the orbits of its five moons. [1]

68 Explain why Pluto and its five moons are considered to be part of our solar system. [1]

Base your answers to questions 69 through 73 on the passage and map below and on your knowledge of Earth science. The map shows a satellite image of a nor'easter that influenced the weather of the northeastern United States. The white areas represent clouds associated with this storm system. The locations of North Carolina and Albany, New York, are labeled on the map. The storm's low-pressure center is represented by letter **L**. Letters cP and mT represent two air masses.

Nor'easters

A nor'easter is a large, low-pressure storm system that moves along the east coast of the United States. The wind over the land blows generally from the northeast as the center of the low passes by a location, hence the name nor'easter. Due to the circulation of winds around the center of the low-pressure system, large amounts of precipitation occur as moist air is carried from the ocean to the land. These storms usually intensify off of the North Carolina coast as they track toward the northeast.

69 Describe *two* characteristics of the circulation pattern of the surface winds around the center of the low-pressure area represented on the map. [1]

70 Circle the terms that best describe the relative moisture and relative temperature characteristics of the mT air mass compared to the cP air mass shown on the map. [1]

71 The map below shows some of the principal storm tracks across the United States and the names of these storm tracks.

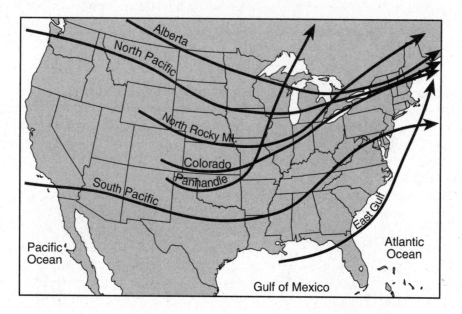

Identify the name of the storm track that this nor'easter most closely followed. [1]

72 The table below shows weather conditions recorded in Albany, New York, at the time that the satellite image was taken.

Weather Conditions

Dewpoint	22°F
Barometric Pressure	988.0 mb
Cloud Cover	100%
Present Weather	Snow

On the station model *in your answer booklet,* use the correct symbols and proper format to indicate the four conditions in the table. [1]

73 Identify *one* weather instrument that was most likely used to determine the dewpoint at Albany, New York. [1]

Base your answers to questions 74 through 76 on the data table below and on your knowledge of Earth science. The data table shows the mass of a sample of radioactive carbon-14 remaining after each half-life.

Data Table

Number of Half-lives	Mass of Carbon-14 (g)
0	64
1	32
2	16
3	8
4	4
5	2
6	1

74 On the grid *in your answer booklet*, construct a line graph by plotting the data for the mass of carbon-14 in the sample for *each* half-life shown on the data table. Connect the plots with a line. [1]

75 Identify the stable disintegration product of the radioactive isotope carbon-14. [1]

76 Determine the number of grams of carbon-14 remaining in this sample at 17,100 years. [1]

Base your answers to questions 77 through 79 on the data tables below and on your knowledge of Earth science. Data table 1 shows the average maximum and average minimum water temperatures at different depths in Lake Michigan. Data table 2 shows the average maximum and average minimum land temperatures at different depths in soil at St. Paul Minnesota (MN).

Table 1

Water in Lake Michigan, 45° N		
Water Depth Range (m)	Average Temperature (°C)	
	Maximum (Occurs in Summer)	Minimum (Occurs in Winter)
0 – 10	24.0	4.0
10 – 20	19.5	4.0
20 – 30	12.5	4.0
30 – 40	7.5	4.0
40 – 60	5.5	4.0
60 – 110	4.5	4.0
110 – 150	4.0	4.0

Table 2

Land in St. Paul, MN, 45° N		
Soil Depth Range (m)	Average Temperature (°C)	
	Maximum (Occurs in Summer)	Minimum (Occurs in Winter)
0 – 0.1	25.5	−6.0
0.1 – 1	23.0	−1.5
1 – 2	19.5	2.0
2 – 3	16.0	4.5
3 – 4	13.5	7.0
4 – 5	12.5	8.5
5 – 6	11.0	10.0

77 Identify the water depth range and the soil depth range, in meters, that have the same average maximum temperature of 12.5°C. [1]

78 Describe the general relationship between depth and average temperature for both water and soil in the summer. [1]

79 Explain why the winter water surface is warmer than the winter land surface. [1]

Base your answers to questions 80 through 82 on the map below and on your knowledge of Earth science. The map shows an enlargement of a portion of the *Tectonic Plates* map from the *Physical Setting/Earth Science Reference Tables*. Arrows showing plate motion have been omitted. Points Y and Z represent locations on plate boundaries.

80 Identify the type of tectonic plate boundary found at location Z. [1]

81 State the names of the tectonic plates on *each* side of the Bouvet Hot Spot. [1]

82 The cross section *in your answer booklet* represents a portion of Earth's interior beneath point Y. On this cross section, draw an arrowhead on *each* of the *four* bold lines, to represent the direction of the convection currents in the asthenosphere. [1]

Base your answers to questions 83 through 85 on the passage below and on your knowledge of Earth science.

Glacier Movement

Glaciers are thick sheets of ice in motion. Mountain glaciers tend to move down the slopes of mountains from higher elevations to lower elevations, while continental ice sheets move over large areas of continents. The bottom of a glacier is under great pressure due to the weight of the thick sheet of ice. This pressure causes the bottom of the glacier to partially melt, allowing the glacier to move. As the glacier thickens, more pressure is created and the glacier moves faster. Different parts of a glacier can move at different rates, depending on the amount of pressure and friction between the glacier and the underlying bedrock.

83 Describe the relationship between the thickness of a glacier and its rate of movement downhill. [1]

84 Describe the most likely shape of the cross section of a valley formed as a result of erosion by a mountain glacier. [1]

85 Compared to sediments deposited by meltwater from a glacier, describe the difference in the arrangement of the sediment deposited directly by a glacier. [1]

Regents Examination B

The University of the State of New York

REGENTS HIGH SCHOOL EXAMINATION

PHYSICAL SETTING EARTH SCIENCE

ANSWER BOOKLET

Student . . . .

Teacher . . . .

School . . . . Grade . . . .

Record your answers for Part B–2 and Part C in this booklet.

Part B–2

51 _____ °

52 _____

53 _____ h

54 _____

55 _____

56 _____

57 _____

58 _____

_____

59 Letters: _____, _____, _____

Oldest ————————→ Youngest

---

60 (1) _____

   (2) _____

61 _____

62

Cuba Lake

Regents Examination B

63

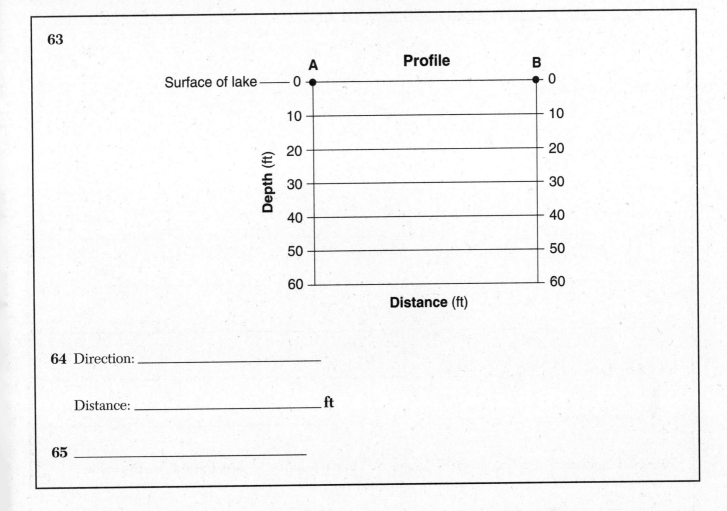

Profile

Surface of lake —— 0 **A** _____ **B** 0

Depth (ft)

10	10
20	20
30	30
40	40
50	50
60	60

Distance (ft)

64 Direction: _____

Distance: _____ **ft**

65 _____

Part C

66 Moon of Pluto: _____

Explanation: _____

_____

67 _____

68 _____

_____

69 Characteristic 1: _____

Characteristic 2: _____

70 Relative moisture of mT air mass (circle one):   **more humid**   **less humid**   **the same**

Relative temperature of mT air mass (circle one):   **cooler**   **warmer**   **the same**

71 _____

72

73 _____

[4]

74

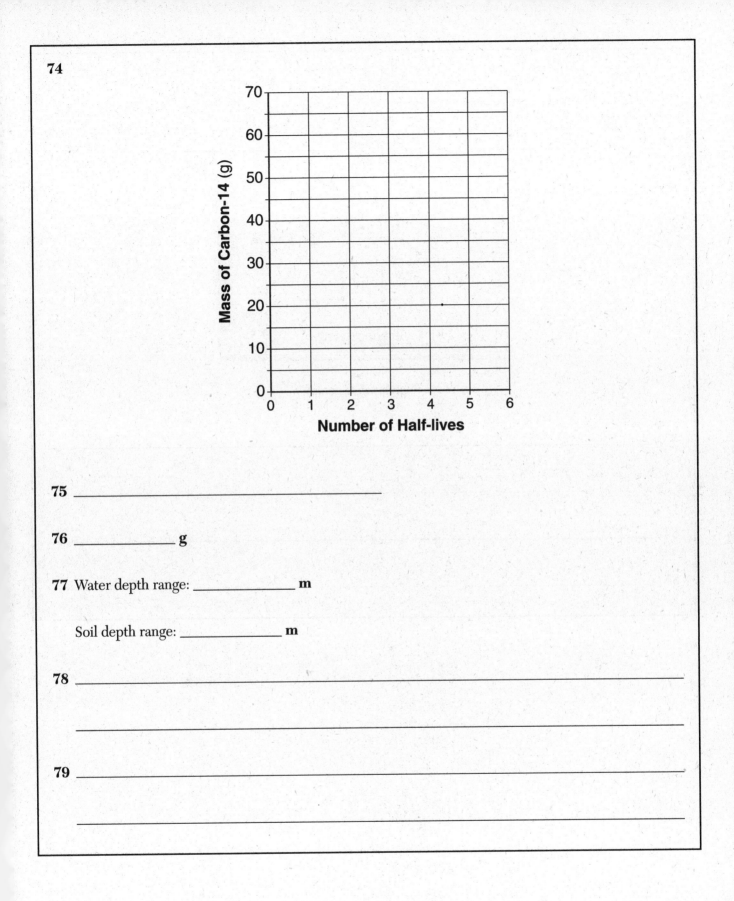

Mass of Carbon-14 (g) (y-axis, values 0, 10, 20, 30, 40, 50, 60, 70)

Number of Half-lives (x-axis, values 0, 1, 2, 3, 4, 5, 6)

75 _____

76 _____ **g**

77 Water depth range: _____ **m**

Soil depth range: _____ **m**

78 _____

_____

79 _____

_____

80 _____

81 _____ **Plate** and _____ **Plate**

82

(Not drawn to scale)

83 _____

_____

84 _____

85 _____

Part A

Answer all questions in this part.

Directions (1–35): For *each* statement or question, choose the word or expression that, of those given, best completes the statement or answers the question. Some questions may require the use of the *2011 Edition Reference Tables for Physical Setting/Earth Science*. Record your answers on your separate answer sheet.

1 The photographs below show two types of solar eclipses. Letters *A* and *B* represent two celestial objects.

Total Solar Eclipse   Partial Solar Eclipse

Which two celestial objects are represented by letters *A* and *B*?

(1) *A*-Moon; *B*-Sun   (3) *A*-Sun; *B*-Moon
(2) *A*-Moon; *B*-Earth   (4) *A*-Sun; *B*-Earth

2 Compared to the terrestrial planets, the Jovian planets
(1) are less massive
(2) are more dense
(3) have greater orbital velocities
(4) have shorter periods of rotation

3 Which event occurred more than 10 billion years ago?
(1) Big Bang
(2) origin of life on Earth
(3) Pangaea begins to break up
(4) origin of Earth and its Moon

4 In 1851, French physicist Léon Foucault used a swinging pendulum to demonstrate that Earth
(1) is rotating
(2) is revolving
(3) has a curved surface
(4) has a gravitational pull

5 Approximately how many degrees does Earth travel in its orbit in one month?
(1) 1°   (3) 30°
(2) 15°   (4) 360°

6 What is the relative humidity when the dry-bulb temperature is 16°C and the wet-bulb temperature is 10°C?
(1) 6%   (3) 33%
(2) 14%   (4) 45%

7 Boarding up windows would be one emergency action most likely taken to prepare for which natural disaster?
(1) earthquake   (3) flood
(2) hurricane   (4) tsunami

8 Which diagram best represents the general position and direction of flow of the polar front jet stream in the Northern Hemisphere during the winter months?

(1)

(3)

(2)

(4)

[2]

9 The diagram below represents four positions of the Moon, labeled *A* through *D*, as it orbits Earth.

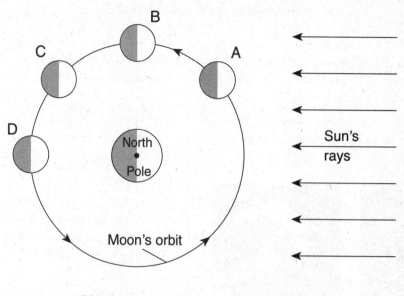

(Not drawn to scale)

Which diagram best represents the sequence of Moon phases, as seen by an observer in New York State, when the Moon travels from position *A* to position *D* in its orbit around Earth?

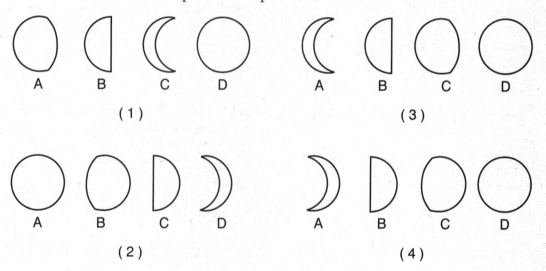

10 The diagrams below represent spectral lines of hydrogen gas observed in a laboratory and the spectral lines of hydrogen gas observed in the light from a distant star.

Compared to the spectral lines observed in the laboratory, the spectral lines observed in the light from the distant star have shifted toward the

(1) red end of the spectrum, indicating the star's movement toward Earth
(2) red end of the spectrum, indicating the star's movement away from Earth
(3) blue end of the spectrum, indicating the star's movement toward Earth
(4) blue end of the spectrum, indicating the star's movement away from Earth

11 The diagram below represents a cross-sectional view of the plane of Earth's orbit around the Sun. A line drawn perpendicular to the plane of Earth's orbit is shown on the diagram.

How many degrees is Earth's rotational axis tilted with respect to the perpendicular line shown in the diagram?

(1) 15°
(2) 23.5°
(3) 90°
(4) 180°

12 The larger white dots in the diagrams below represent stars in the constellations Scorpius and Orion. Information indicating when these constellations are visible from New York State is provided below the diagrams.

Scorpius

Visible in the New York State
nighttime sky during July;
not visible at all in January

Orion

Visible in the New York State
nighttime sky during January;
not visible at all in July

Which statement best explains why these two constellations are visible in the night sky in the months identified?

(1) Earth spins on its axis at a constant rate during a 24-hour period.
(2) Earth spins on its axis at a variable rate during the year.
(3) The nighttime side of Earth is facing different parts of our galaxy as Earth orbits the Sun.
(4) The nighttime side of Earth is facing different parts of our galaxy as the stars orbit Earth.

13 Which table correctly shows the interior temperature, melting point, and state (phase) of matter of the materials located 4000 kilometers below Earth's surface?

Interior Temperature (°C)	Melting Point (°C)	State of Matter
5700	5400	solid

(1)

Interior Temperature (°C)	Melting Point (°C)	State of Matter
5400	5700	solid

(3)

Interior Temperature (°C)	Melting Point (°C)	State of Matter
5700	5400	liquid

(2)

Interior Temperature (°C)	Melting Point (°C)	State of Matter
5400	5700	liquid

(4)

Regents Examination C

14 Which gas is a greenhouse gas that has increased in Earth's atmosphere partly as a result of deforestation over the last 100 years?

(1) ozone
(2) oxygen
(3) nitrogen
(4) carbon dioxide

15 Which ocean current brings warm water to the southeastern tip of Africa?

(1) Brazil Current
(2) Agulhas Current
(3) Guinea Current
(4) Benguela Current

16 Which pie graph is shaded to best represent the approximate percentage of time that humans have existed during Earth's entire history?

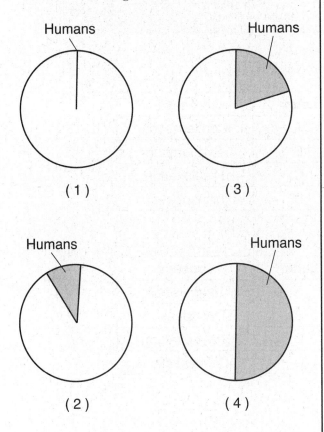

17 Volcanic ash can be used as a time marker to correlate rock layers because the ash

(1) is deposited rapidly over a large area
(2) represents a buried erosional surface
(3) forms intrusive igneous rock
(4) cuts across rock layers

18 The cross section below represents a mountain range. Points A and B represent locations on Earth's surface.

Compared to the climate of location A, the climate of location B is most likely

(1) cooler and wetter
(2) cooler and drier
(3) warmer and wetter
(4) warmer and drier

19 The photograph below shows conglomerate composed of pebbles cemented together with calcite.

Compared to the ages of the calcite cement and the conglomerate, the relative age of the pebbles is

(1) younger than both the calcite cement and the conglomerate
(2) younger than the calcite cement, but the same age as the conglomerate
(3) older than both the calcite cement and the conglomerate
(4) older than the calcite cement, but the same age as the conglomerate

20 The cross section below represents some parts of Earth's water cycle. Letters *A*, *B*, *C*, and *D* represent processes that occur during the cycle.

Which table correctly matches each letter with the process it represents?

Letter	Process
A	Condensation
B	Transpiration
C	Precipitation
D	Evaporation

(1)

Letter	Process
A	Condensation
B	Evaporation
C	Precipitation
D	Transpiration

(3)

Letter	Process
A	Evaporation
B	Precipitation
C	Transpiration
D	Condensation

(2)

Letter	Process
A	Evaporation
B	Transpiration
C	Precipitation
D	Condensation

(4)

21 Which table best shows the relationship between latitude and general climate conditions on Earth?

Latitude	Climate Conditions
90°N	Arid
60°N	Arid
30°N	Humid
0°	Humid
30°S	Humid
60°S	Arid
90°S	Arid

(1)

Latitude	Climate Conditions
90°N	Arid
60°N	Humid
30°N	Arid
0°	Humid
30°S	Arid
60°S	Humid
90°S	Arid

(2)

Latitude	Climate Conditions
90°N	Humid
60°N	Arid
30°N	Humid
0°	Humid
30°S	Humid
60°S	Arid
90°S	Humid

(3)

Latitude	Climate Conditions
90°N	Humid
60°N	Arid
30°N	Humid
0°	Arid
30°S	Humid
60°S	Arid
90°S	Humid

(4)

22 The photograph below shows different-sized rounded sediment.

Which table shows the most likely process and agent of erosion responsible for this rounded sediment?

Process	Agent of Erosion
sandblasting	running water

(1)

Process	Agent of Erosion
land slide	mass movement

(3)

Process	Agent of Erosion
abrasion	wave action

(2)

Process	Agent of Erosion
deposition	wind

(4)

[8]

23 The photograph below shows an outcrop with two basaltic intrusions, labeled *A* and *B*, in a rock unit, labeled *C*.

Permission to use this third-party content has not been granted to Pearson. View content at nysedregents.org.

What is the relative age of these three rock units from oldest to youngest?

(1) $B \rightarrow A \rightarrow C$

(2) $B \rightarrow C \rightarrow A$

(3) $C \rightarrow A \rightarrow B$

(4) $C \rightarrow B \rightarrow A$

24 The world map below shows Earth's major tectonic plate boundaries. Letters *A* through *D* represent four surface locations.

Which location is on a major rift valley?

(1) *A*

(2) *B*

(3) *C*

(4) *D*

[9]

[OVER]

25 The first *P*-wave of an earthquake took 11 minutes to travel to a seismic station from the epicenter of the earthquake. What is the seismic station's distance to the epicenter of the earthquake and how long did it take for the first *S*-wave to travel that distance?

(1) Distance to epicenter: 3350 km
   S-wave travel time: 4 min 50 sec
(2) Distance to epicenter: 3350 km
   S-wave travel time: 6 min 10 sec
(3) Distance to epicenter: 7600 km
   S-wave travel time: 9 min
(4) Distance to epicenter: 7600 km
   S-wave travel time: 20 min

26 The Catskills are commonly called mountains, but are actually part of the Allegheny Plateau. The Catskills are classified as a plateau because of their

(1) low elevation
(2) bedrock structure
(3) bedrock age
(4) high degree of metamorphism

27 The minimum stream velocity necessary to transport a sediment particle that is 0.1 centimeter in diameter is closest to

(1) 0.1 cm/s   (3) 5.5 cm/s
(2) 0.002 cm/s   (4) 10.0 cm/s

28 Which rock is classified as an evaporite?

(1) clastic shale
(2) foliated phyllite
(3) nonfoliated marble
(4) crystalline rock salt

29 Which pair of elements makes up most of Earth's crust by volume?

(1) nitrogen and potassium
(2) oxygen and silicon
(3) hydrogen and oxygen
(4) potassium and oxygen

30 The cross section below represents zones of soil labeled *A*, *B*, and *C*. Letter *D* represents underlying bedrock.

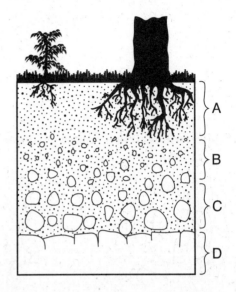

Which letter identifies the zone having the most organic and weathered material?

(1) *A*   (3) *C*
(2) *B*   (4) *D*

31 Which type of surface bedrock is most commonly found in the Utica, New York area?

(1) sedimentary, with limestone, shale, sandstone, and dolostone
(2) sedimentary, with limestone, shale, sandstone, and conglomerate
(3) metamorphic, with quartzite, dolostone, marble, and schist
(4) metamorphic, with gneiss, quartzite, marble, and slate

32 The diagram below represents a geologic landscape.

Which type of stream drainage pattern formed on this landscape?

(1)   (2)   (3)   (4)

33 The north polar view maps below show the average area covered by Arctic Sea ice in September of 1980, 2000, and 2011.

Arctic Sea Ice

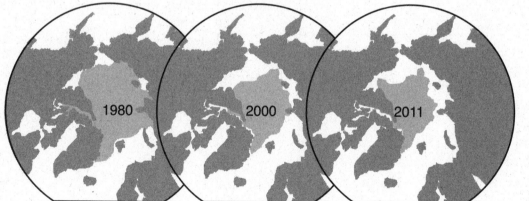

The maps best support the inference that Earth's climate is

(1) cooling, because the average area covered by Arctic Sea ice is decreasing
(2) cooling, because the average area covered by Arctic Sea ice is increasing
(3) warming, because the average area covered by Arctic Sea ice is decreasing
(4) warming, because the average area covered by Arctic Sea ice is increasing

34 The photographs below shows two depositional features labeled *A* and *B*.

Which terms correctly identify depositional features *A* and *B*?

(1) *A*-delta; *B*-barrier island

(2) *A*-sand bar; *B*-island arc

(3) *A*-barrier island; *B*-delta

(4) *A*-island arc; *B*-sand bar

35 Diagrams *A* and *B* represent magnified views of the arrangement of mineral crystals in a rock before and after being subjected to geologic processes.

Which geologic processes are most likely responsible for the banding and alignment of mineral crystals represented in diagram *B*?

(1) melting and solidification

(2) heating and increasing pressure

(3) compaction and cementation

(4) weathering and erosion

Part B–1

Answer all questions in this part.

Directions (36–50): For *each* statement or question, choose the word or expression that, of those given, best completes the statement or answers the question. Some questions may require the use of the *2011 Edition Reference Tables for Physical Setting/Earth Science*. Record your answers on your separate answer sheet.

Base your answers to questions 36 through 39 on the graph below and on your knowledge of Earth science. The graph shows the observed water levels, in feet (ft), for a tide gauge located at Montauk, New York, on the easternmost end of Long Island, from January 24, 2008 to noon on January 25, 2008.

Water Levels at Montauk, New York

36 What was the height of the water above average low tide level at noon on January 24?

(1) 1.2 ft

(3) 2.2 ft

(2) 1.6 ft

(4) 2.6 ft

37 These changing water levels at Montauk can best be described as

(1) cyclic and predictable

(3) noncyclic and predictable

(2) cyclic and not predictable

(4) noncyclic and not predictable

38 What causes the water-level variation pattern shown by the graph?

(1) changes in wind velocity produced by coastal storms

(2) changes in magnetic orientation of the North American Plate

(3) Earth's revolution and the distance from the equator

(4) Earth's rotation and the gravitational pull of the Moon

39 What is the approximate latitude and longitude of the tide gauge?

(1) 40°30' N 72°00' W

(3) 41°00' N 72°00' W

(2) 40°30' N 74°00' W

(4) 41°00' N 74°00' W

[13]

[OVER]

Regents Examination C

Base your answers to questions 40 through 42 on the diagram below and on your knowledge of Earth science. The diagram represents some of the inferred stages in the life cycle of stars according to their original mass.

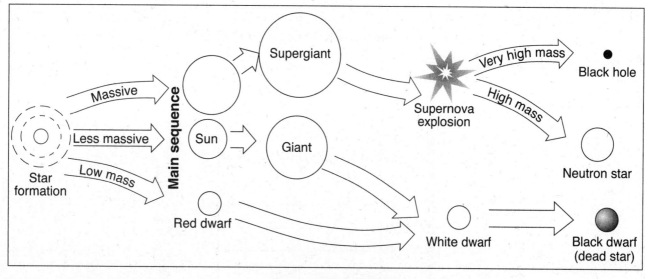

(Not drawn to scale)

40 The final stage in the life cycle of the most massive stars is a

(1) black hole
(2) black dwarf
(3) supergiant
(4) white dwarf

41 Which star may once have been similar to our Sun in mass and luminosity?

(1) *Deneb*
(2) *Spica*
(3) *Procyon B*
(4) *Proxima Centauri*

42 Energy is produced in the cores of main sequence stars when

(1) lighter elements undergo fusion into heavier elements
(2) heavier elements undergo fusion into lighter elements
(3) cosmic background radiation is absorbed
(4) cosmic background radiation is released

Base your answers to questions 43 and 44 on the graph below and on your knowledge of Earth science. The graph shows the number of radioactive Isotope X atoms present as a sample of the isotope undergoes radioactive decay.

Radioactive Decay of Isotope X

43 Based on the graph, the half-life of this radioactive isotope is
   (1) 6 h
   (2) 9 h
   (3) 3 h
   (4) 12 h

44 Based on the graph, what is the approximate number of radioactive atoms of Isotope X that are present when 8 hours of decay has occured?
   (1) 90
   (2) 115
   (3) 155
   (4) 200

Regents Examination C

Base your answers to questions 45 through 47 on the diagram below and on your knowledge of Earth science. The arrows in the diagram show air movement in a thunderstorm cloud. Point *A* represents a location in the atmosphere.

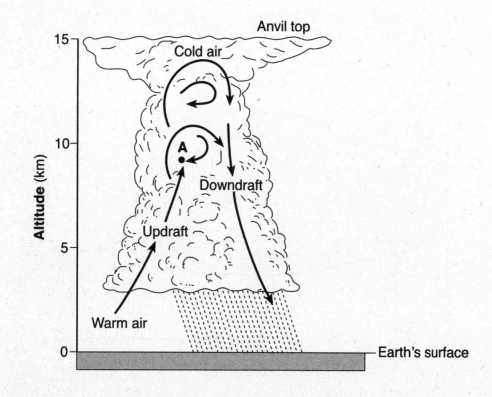

45 In which temperature zone of the atmosphere is point *A* located?

(1) thermosphere   (3) stratosphere

(2) mesosphere   (4) troposphere

46 The updrafts and downdrafts represented within this cloud are primarily caused by differences in

(1) altitude above sea level   (3) relative humidity

(2) air density   (4) specific heat

47 Which weather symbol would be placed on a station model to represent this weather event?

(1)   (2)   (3)   (4)

Base your answers to questions 48 through 50 on the topographic map below and on your knowledge of Earth science. On the map, points A, B, C, and D represent surface locations. The dashed line between points C and D represents a hiking trail. Elevations are in feet (ft).

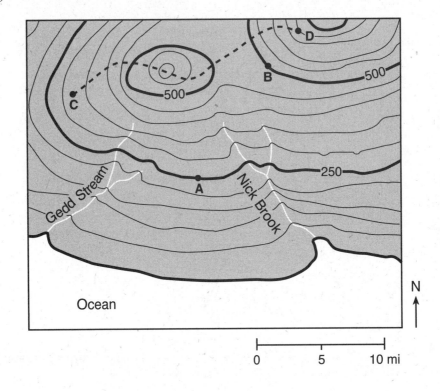

48 What is the contour interval on this map?

(1) 25 ft

(2) 50 ft

(3) 150 ft

(4) 250 ft

49 The gradient between location A and location B is approximately

(1) 0.04 ft/mi

(2) 25 ft/mi

(3) 40 ft/mi

(4) 50 ft/mi

50 A person walks along the trail from location C to location D. The person will be walking

(1) downhill then uphill, only

(2) downhill, then uphill, then downhill again

(3) uphill then downhill, only

(4) uphill, then downhill, then uphill again

Part B–2

Answer all questions in this part.

Directions (51–65): Record your answers in the spaces provided in your answer booklet. Some questions may require the use of the *2011 Edition Reference Tables for Physical Setting/Earth Science.*

Base your answers to questions 51 through 54 on the passage below and on your knowledge of Earth science.

The Mica Family

The familiar term "mica" is not the name of a specific mineral, but rather the name for a family of more than 30 minerals that share the same properties. All members of the mica family have high melting points and are similar in density, luster, hardness, streak, type of breakage, and crystal shape. As a result, telling the micas apart can be difficult. However, some common members of the family can be identified by color. For example, biotite is black to dark brown while muscovite can be light shades of several colors, or even colorless. When less common members of the mica family have any of these colors, or have similar colors, chemical tests are needed to tell them apart.

51 Identify the *two* chemical elements present in biotite mica that are *not* present in muscovite mica. [1]

52 Identify the luster, hardness, and dominant form of breakage for members of the mica family. [1]

53 State the name of the igneous rock in which crystals of biotite mica are larger than 10 millimeters in diameter. [1]

54 Large crystals of mica, sometimes weighing several hundred tons, have been found in igneous rock in Canada. Identify the environment of formation and the relative rate of cooling of the magma that formed the igneous rock containing these large crystals. [1]

Base your answers to questions 55 through 58 on the diagram in your answer booklet and on your knowledge of Earth science. The diagram represents the Sun's apparent daily path for the first day of three seasons at 43° North latitude. The solid lines represent daytime paths as seen by an observer at this latitude. The dashed lines represent the nighttime paths that can *not* be seen by the observer.

55 On the diagram *in your answer booklet*, draw an **X** to represent the solar noon position of the Sun as seen by the observer on April 21. [1]

56 Identify the rate of the Sun's apparent movement, in degrees per hour, along its path on December 21. [1]

57 Identify the compass direction toward which the observer's shadow would point at solar noon on March 21. [1]

58 List the three dates shown on the diagram from the least number of nighttime hours to the greatest number of nighttime hours. [1]

_____

Base your answers to questions 59 through 62 on the information below, on the map in your answer booklet, and on your knowledge of Earth science. The map shows a portion of the tectonic plates map from the *2011 Edition Reference Tables for Physical Setting/Earth Science*. Letters A and B represent locations on the ocean floor.

> The area between North America and South America is a tectonically active region of Earth. This region contains all of the types of tectonic plate boundaries, and it has frequent earthquake and volcanic activity. The tectonic plates on either side of the East Pacific Ridge move at an average rate of 7.5 cm/year.

59 On the map *in your answer booklet*, draw *one* arrow in each of the two boxes to show the relative motion of the Caribbean Plate and the North American Plate. [1]

60 On the set of axes *in your answer booklet*, draw a line to represent the relative age of the ocean floor bedrock from location *A* to location *B*. [1]

61 Identify the name of the hot spot shown on the map, and identify the name of the tectonic plate under which the center of this hot spot is located. [1]

62 Identify the type of mafic igneous bedrock that is most likely to make up the oceanic crust at location *A*, and state the average density of this oceanic crust. [1]

_____

Base your answers to questions 63 through 65 on the diagram and data table below and on your knowledge of Earth science. The diagram represents laboratory materials used for an investigation of the effects of particle diameter on permeability and porosity (percentage of pore space). Four separate plastic tubes were filled to the same level with different particles.

(Not drawn to scale)

Particle Type	Particle Diameter (cm)	Time for Water to Infiltrate (s)	Porosity (%)
Sand	0.1	7	42.0
Clay	0.0003	322	40.0
Mixture	from 0.0003 to 0.8	15	34.0
Plastic beads	0.4	4	44.0

63 Explain why the particle sizes fit together more closely in the mixture, resulting in the lowest porosity of all these particle types. [1]

64 The height of the column of sand is 28 centimeters. Calculate the rate of infiltration, in centimeters per second, for the water that flowed through the column of sand. [1]

65 Based on the particle diameter of the plastic beads, identify the type of sediment represented by these beads. [1]

_____

Regents Examination C

Part C

Answer all questions in this part.

Directions (66–85): Record your answers in the spaces provided in your answer booklet. Some questions may require the use of the *2011 Edition Reference Tables for Physical Setting/Earth Science.*

Base your answers to questions 66 through 68 on the weather map below and on your knowledge of Earth science. The map shows the location of a wintertime low-pressure system over Lake Ontario with two fronts extending into New York State. Isobar values are recorded in millibars. Partial weather station data are shown for several locations.

66 Describe the evidence shown on the map that indicates that the highest wind speeds occurred near Watertown, New York. [1]

67 Complete the table *in your answer booklet* by recording the weather data shown on the station model for Albany, New York. [1]

68 State the compass direction toward which the center of this low-pressure system moved over the next two days if the low followed a normal storm track. [1]

Regents Examination C

Base your answers to questions 69 through 72 on the information and data table below and on your knowledge of Earth science. The data table shows the average body volume, including the shell, of a brachiopod at certain times in geologic history. The geologic ages are shown in million years ago (mya). The average body volumes including the shell are shown in milliliters (mL).

Cope's Rule

Cope's Rule states that the average size of animals preserved in the fossil record tends to increase as each group evolves from a previous group. This rule was first proposed in the 1800s by Edward Drinker Cope, a famous fossil hunter of that time. Recent research, involving well over 10,000 fossil groups spanning the time since the start of the Cambrian Period until today, has shown that Cope's Rule is accurate for most animal groups. Brachiopod data support Cope's Rule.

Brachiopod Data Table

Geologic Age (mya)	Average Body Volume Including the Shell (mL)
480	0.1
460	0.2
430	0.6
410	1.0
380	1.1

69 On the grid *in your answer booklet*, plot the average brachiopod body volume for each of the geologic ages listed in the data table. Connect *all five* plots with a line. [1]

70 Identify, by name, *two* geologic periods when the brachiopods represented in the data table were living. [1]

71 State the names of the *two* brachiopod index fossils found in New York State bedrock. [1]

72 The earliest horses appeared in the Eocene epoch and were about the size of a large dog of today. Explain how the evolution of horses supports Cope's Rule. [1]

Base your answers to questions 73 through 75 on the snowfall map in your answer booklet and on your knowledge of Earth science. The snowfall map shows some average yearly snowfall values, measured in inches, recorded for a portion of New York State. Some average yearly snowfall isolines have been drawn. Line *XY* is a reference line on the map. The cities of Watertown and Oswego are shown on the map.

73 On the map *in your answer booklet*, draw the 240-inch average yearly snowfall isoline. [1]

74 On the grid *in your answer booklet*, construct a profile of the average annual snowfall along line *XY* by plotting the value of each isoline that crosses line *XY*. Connect *all six* plots with a line to complete the profile. [1]

75 The diagram *in your answer booklet* represents an observer standing next to the side of a building. Using the scale shown, draw an **X** on the side of the building to represent the height of the greatest amount of average yearly snowfall that is indicated on the map. [1]

Base your answers to questions 76 through 78 on the diagram below and on your knowledge of Earth science. The diagram represents a cutaway view of a flat-plate solar collector used to heat water at a New York State location.

Solar Collector

76 Identify the energy transfer process by which light travels through space from the Sun to the solar collector. [1]

77 Explain why the flow tubes and collector plate inside the solar collector are black in color. [1]

78 The glass cover on this solar collector allows visible light to enter the collector. Identify the type of electromagnetic energy emitted by the flow tubes and collector plate that is trapped inside the collector by the glass cover. Also, circle the relative wavelength of this trapped electromagnetic energy compared to wavelengths of visible light. [1]

Base your answers to questions 79 through 82 on the passage and diagram below, on the data table on the next page, and on your knowledge of Earth science. The diagram compares the inner planets of our solar system to the planetary system surrounding the star *Kepler-62*, which is located in our galaxy. The data table shows some data for the planets in the *Kepler-62* system.

Kepler-62 Planetary System

Five planets orbit a seven-billion-year-old star, *Kepler-62*, which has a surface temperature of approximately 4900 Kelvin. Two of these planets are located within the habitable zone, which is the region around a star where life may exist due to the possible presence of water in the liquid phase. The shaded areas in the orbital diagrams below indicate the habitable zone of each system.

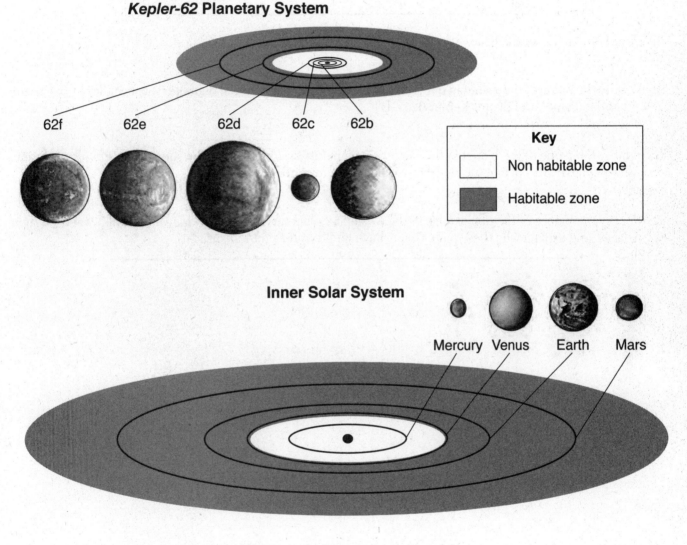

Kepler-62 Planetary System

62f 62e 62d 62c 62b

Key

☐ Non habitable zone

■ Habitable zone

Inner Solar System

Mercury Venus Earth Mars

(Planets and orbits are drawn to scale)

Regents Examination C

Data Table

Name of Planet	Distance from *Kepler-62* (million kilometers)	Equatorial Diameter (compared to Earth's diameter)
62b	8.23	1.31
62c	13.76	0.54
62d	17.95	1.95
62e	63.88	1.6
62f	107.41	1.4

79 Identify the name of the galaxy where the *Kepler-62* planetary system is located. [1]

80 Identify the name of the planet in our solar system that has an equatorial diameter most similar in size to the equatorial diameter of planet Kepler-62c. [1]

81 Identify the name of the planet in the *Kepler-62* planetary system that has the shortest period of revolution, and explain why this planet has the shortest period of revolution. [1]

82 Identify the names of the *two* planets in the *Kepler-62* planetary system that may have liquid water on their surfaces, and explain why these planets may have liquid water on their surfaces. [1]

[OVER]

Regents Examination C

Base your answers to questions 83 through 85 on the block diagram below and on your knowledge of Earth science. The diagram represents glacial features formed by a continental glacier and its melt water.

83 Describe the arrangement of the sediments found within the terminal moraine, which marks the farthest advance of the glacier. [1]

84 The cross sections below, labeled *A*, *B*, *C*, and *D*, represent four stages in the development of a kettle lake. The stages are *not* shown in the correct order.

Stages in Kettle Lake Formation

In your answer booklet, place the letters in the correct order to indicate the sequence of development of a kettle lake from earliest stage to latest stage. [1]

85 Terminal moraines found on Long Island were deposited during the advance and retreat of glacial ice during the last ice age. Identify, by name, the geologic epoch during which these moraines were deposited. [1]

Regents Examination C

PHYSICAL SETTING
EARTH SCIENCE

ANSWER BOOKLET

Student . . . .

Teacher . . . .

School . . . . Grade . . . .

Record your answers for Part B–2 and Part C in this booklet.

Part B–2

51 _____ and _____

52 Luster: _____

Hardness: _____

Dominant form of breakage: _____

53 _____

54 Environment of formation: _____

Relative rate of cooling: _____

Regents Examination C

55

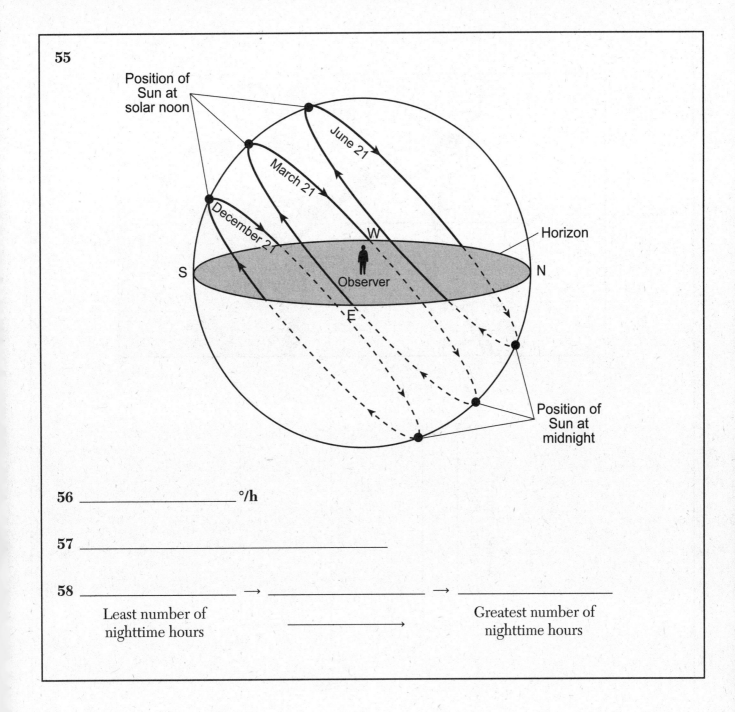

Position of
Sun at
solar noon

June 21

March 21

December 21

Horizon

W

S

Observer

N

E

Position of
Sun at
midnight

56 _____ °/h

57 _____

58 _____ → _____ → _____

Least number of
nighttime hours

Greatest number of
nighttime hours

59

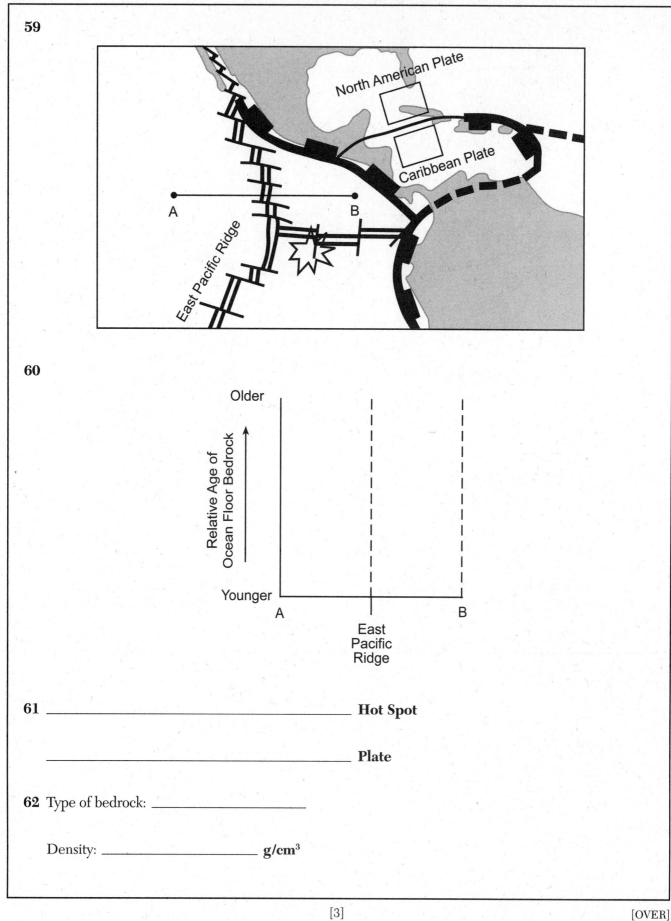

60

Older

Relative Age of Ocean Floor Bedrock →

Younger

A

East Pacific Ridge

B

61 _____ **Hot Spot**

_____ **Plate**

62 Type of bedrock: _____

Density: _____ **g/cm³**

63 _____

_____

64 _____ **cm/s**

65 _____

Part C

66 _____

_____

67

Albany, New York

Weather Variable	Weather Data
Dewpoint	°F
Cloud cover	%
Actual barometric pressure	mb

68 _____

69

Change in Brachiopod Size

70 _____ **Period** and _____ **Period**

71 _____ and _____

72 _____

_____

_____

Regents Examination C

Average Yearly Snowfall Map

74

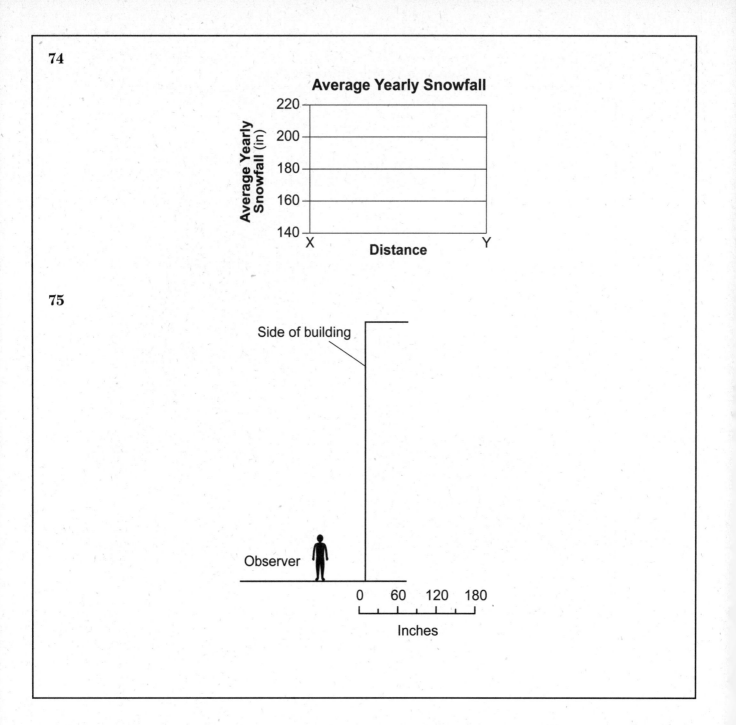

Average Yearly Snowfall

Average Yearly Snowfall (in)

220

200

180

160

140

X   Distance   Y

75

Side of building

Observer

0   60   120   180

Inches

Regents Examination C

76 _____

77 _____

_____

78 Emitted electromagnetic energy: _____

Relative wavelength (circle one):   shorter   longer   the same

79 _____

80 _____

81 Name of planet: _____

Explanation: _____

_____

82 _____ and _____

Explanation: _____

_____

83 _____

_____

84 _____ → _____ → _____ → _____

　　　Earliest stage　　　　　　 ————————————————→ 　　　Latest stage

85 _____ **epoch**

Part A

Answer all questions in this part.

Directions (1–35): For *each* statement or question, choose the word or expression that, of those given, best completes the statement or answers the question. Some questions may require the use of the *2011 Edition Reference Tables for Physical Setting/Earth Science.* Record your answers on your separate answer sheet.

1 The deflection of Earth's planetary winds is an example of

  (1) the Coriolis effect
  (2) the Doppler effect
  (3) convection
  (4) gravitational pull

2 The universe is approximately 13.8 billion years old. Compared to the age of the solar system, the age of the universe is approximately

  (1) the same age as the solar system
  (2) two times older than the solar system
  (3) three times older than the solar system
  (4) four times older than the solar system

3 Planets that are closest to the Sun are identified as

  (1) low-density Jovian
  (2) low-density terrestrial
  (3) high-density Jovian
  (4) high-density terrestrial

4 Which process of the water cycle occurs when water absorbs 2260 Joules of heat energy per gram?

  (1) melting of ice
  (2) condensation of water vapor
  (3) evaporation of water
  (4) freezing of water

5 In which temperature zone of Earth's atmosphere is the polar jet stream located?

  (1) lower thermosphere
  (2) lower mesosphere
  (3) upper stratosphere
  (4) upper troposphere

6 Arrows in the diagram below show three methods of energy transfer labeled *A*, *B*, and *C*.

Which list correctly identifies the energy transfer processes *A*, *B*, and *C*?

  (1) *A*–conduction   (3) *A*–convection
      B–convection   *B*–radiation
      C–radiation   *C*–conduction

  (2) *A*–convection   (4) *A*–conduction
      B–conduction   *B*–radiation
      C–radiation   *C*–convection

7 What is the relative humidity of the air when the dry-bulb temperature is 4°C and the dewpoint is −4°C?

  (1) 42%   (3) 51%
  (2) 46%   (4) 56%

[2]

8 The diagram below represents the light spectra given off by the same element as observed under two different conditions. Spectrum *A* was observed when that element was heated in a laboratory. Spectrum *B* shows the same element as seen in the light from a distant star.

Spectrum A: (laboratory)

Violet   Red

Spectrum B: (distant star)

Violet   Red

The light spectrum observed from this distant star shows a

(1) red shift, which indicates that the star is moving away from Earth
(2) red shift, which indicates that the star is moving toward Earth
(3) blue shift, which indicates that the star is moving away from Earth
(4) blue shift, which indicates that the star is moving toward Earth

9 The diagrams below represent the constellations seen by an observer in New York State while looking toward the southern horizon at midnight on July 9 and January 8.

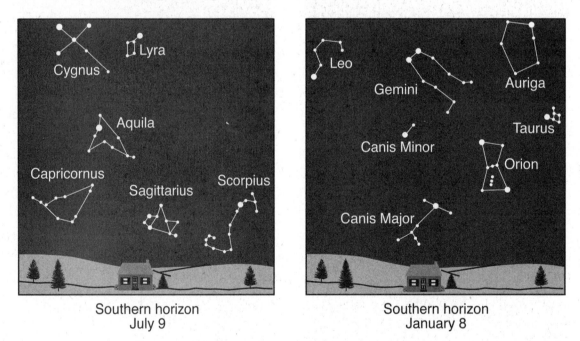

Southern horizon
July 9

Southern horizon
January 8

Which motion is mainly responsible for the difference in the constellations visible at midnight on these two dates?

(1) The Sun orbits Earth.
(2) Earth orbits the Sun.
(3) The stars in the constellations orbit Earth.
(4) Earth orbits the stars in the constellations.

[3]   [OVER]

10 Which graph best shows the general relationship between air pressure and altitude?

       (1)   (3)

       (2)   (4)

11 Most clouds form in the atmosphere when moist air

(1) rises, expands, and cools to the dewpoint
(2) rises, expands, and warms to the dewpoint
(3) sinks, compresses, and cools to the dewpoint
(4) sinks, compresses, and warms to the dewpoint

12 Equal areas of which surface would absorb the greatest amount of insolation on a sunny day?

(1) light-colored, smooth surface
(2) light-colored, rough surface
(3) dark-colored, smooth surface
(4) dark-colored, rough surface

13 Which natural event periodically weakens western surface ocean currents in the equatorial Pacific Ocean, resulting in a change in air temperature and precipitation patterns in the United States?

(1) El Niño   (3) ocean tides
(2) transpiration   (4) volcanic eruptions

14 Ocean gyres in the Northern Hemisphere consist of a number of surface ocean currents that, together, generally flow clockwise in a roughly circular pattern. Which list contains three warm surface ocean currents that make up most of the North Atlantic Ocean gyre?

(1) Kuroshio Current, North Pacific Current, and California Current
(2) Canary Current, North Equatorial Current, and Equatorial Countercurrent
(3) Labrador Current, North Atlantic Current, and East Greenland Current
(4) North Equatorial Current, Gulf Stream Current, and North Atlantic Current

15 Most of the oceanic oxygen that began to enter Earth's atmosphere in the early Proterozoic Era was probably produced by

(1) formation of silicate rocks
(2) photosynthesis by cyanobacteria
(3) impact events on Earth's surface
(4) outgassing from volcanoes

16 During which geologic period did plants and animals first appear in land environments?

(1) Cambrian   (3) Silurian
(2) Ordovician   (4) Devonian

17 Sedimentary rock layers that were deposited between 488 million and 444 million years ago are found on the surface at which two New York State locations?

(1) Ithaca and Jamestown
(2) Utica and Syracuse
(3) Oswego and Old Forge
(4) Albany and Massena

18 A volcanic ash layer is a good geologic time marker for correlating rock layers because the ash layer was deposited over a

(1) limited geographic area over a short time
(2) limited geographic area over a long time
(3) wide geographic area over a short time
(4) wide geographic area over a long time

19 The photograph below shows the results of a landslide.

This landslide is an example of

(1) wind abrasion

(2) glacial deposition

(3) wave action

(4) mass movement

20 Which cross section correctly represents a cold front and the air-mass movements associated with this front?

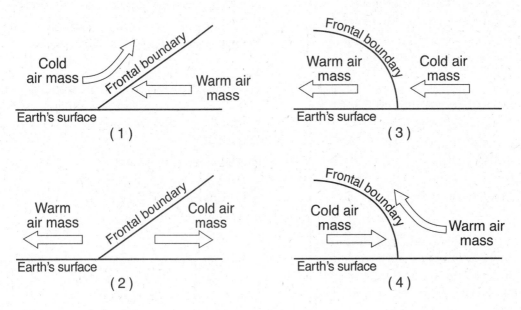

[OVER]

Regents Examination D

21 Earth's interior at a depth of 3500 kilometers is believed to be

(1) liquid at a temperature of approximately 4900°C
(2) solid at a temperature of approximately 4900°C
(3) liquid at a temperature of approximately 5400°C
(4) solid at a temperature of approximately 5400°C

22 Compared to the density and composition of the oceanic crust, the continental crust is

(1) less dense and more mafic
(2) less dense and more felsic
(3) more dense and less mafic
(4) more dense and less felsic

23 An earthquake occurs at 10:05 a.m. At 10:09 a.m., the first *P*-wave from this earthquake is detected at a seismic station. Approximately how many kilometers (km) from the epicenter is this seismic station located?

(1) 1000 km   (3) 2600 km
(2) 2000 km   (4) 5600 km

24 The aerial photograph below shows two streams that have been displaced by tectonic movement along the San Andreas fault. The arrows show the relative direction of movement along the fault.

This movement occurred along which type of plate boundary?

(1) convergent   (3) transform
(2) divergent   (4) complex

25 The magnitude of an earthquake is a number that represents the

(1) arrival time of the first *P*-wave
(2) difference in arrival times between *P*- and *S*-waves
(3) distance to the epicenter
(4) energy released by an earthquake

26 The Genesee River flows across both the Allegheny Plateau and the Erie-Ontario Lowlands in New York State. This river flows

(1) northward, in the same general direction as the Hudson River
(2) northward, in the same general direction as the Niagara River
(3) southward, in the same general direction as the Hudson River
(4) southward, in the same general direction as the Niagara River

27 What is the name of the largest sediment that can be transported by a stream moving at a velocity of 100 centimeters per second (cm/s)?

(1) silt   (3) pebbles
(2) sand   (4) cobbles

28 Which mineral is commonly used as an abrasive?

(1) garnet   (3) sulfur
(2) halite   (4) graphite

29 If a metamorphic rock bubbles when a drop of acid is placed on its surface, the rock is most likely

(1) schist   (3) marble
(2) slate   (4) quartzite

30 The map below shows a portion of the coast of Texas. Letter *X* indicates features formed by wave action.

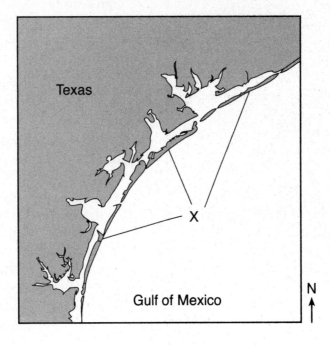

What is the name of the features indicated by letter *X*?

(1) barrier islands   (3) deltas

(2) island arc   (4) moraines

31 The diagrams below represent the crystal shape and type of cleavage of two different minerals.

Crystal shape: cubic
Cleavage: three directions
– all at right angles

Crystal shape: rhombohedral
Cleavage: three directions
– *not* at right angles

The crystal shape and type of cleavage of these two minerals are determined mainly by the minerals'

(1) color and type of luster   (3) composition and atomic arrangement

(2) streak and hardness   (4) density and magnetism

Regents Examination D

32 The block diagram below represents a meandering stream.

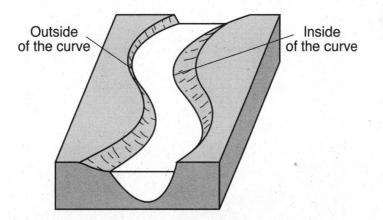

Outside of the curve

Inside of the curve

Which table indicates where the greatest stream velocity and the greatest rate of stream erosion occur?

Greatest Stream Velocity	Greatest Stream Erosion
outside of the curve	outside of the curve

(1)

Greatest Stream Velocity	Greatest Stream Erosion
inside of the curve	inside of the curve

(3)

Greatest Stream Velocity	Greatest Stream Erosion
outside of the curve	inside of the curve

(2)

Greatest Stream Velocity	Greatest Stream Erosion
inside of the curve	outside of the curve

(4)

33 The diagram below represents the size and shape of a pebble. This pebble and 20 other pebbles having a similar size and shape were placed in a rock tumbler with water and allowed to abrade for five days.

 Pebble

Which diagram best represents the size and shape of this pebble after the five-day period?

(1)

(2)

(3)

(4)

[8]

34 The photograph below shows bedrock composed of sediments that have been deposited by wind.

This bedrock is most likely

(1) sandstone

(2) limestone

(3) hornfels

(4) granite

35 Which diagram below best represents both the relative wavelength of visible light entering a house through a window and the relative wavelength of infrared rays being given off by a table within the house?

Part B–1

Answer all questions in this part.

Directions (36–50): For *each* statement or question, choose the word or expression that, of those given, best completes the statement or answers the question. Some questions may require the use of the *2011 Edition Reference Tables for Physical Setting/Earth Science*. Record your answers on your separate answer sheet.

Base your answers to questions 36 and 37 on the maps below and on your knowledge of Earth science. The maps show a portion of India and Southeast Asia, bordering on the Indian Ocean, during the winter and summer monsoon seasons. Large areas of high and low air pressure are shown during each season.

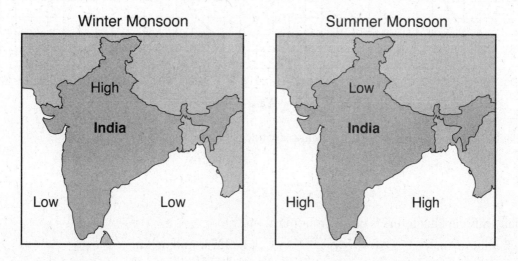

36 Which two-letter symbol represents the most likely air mass formed over portions of the Indian Ocean shown on the maps?

(1) mP   (3) cP

(2) mT   (4) cT

37 The heavy monsoon rains affecting India and Southeast Asia occur during

(1) winter, when winds blow from the land

(2) winter, when winds blow toward the high pressure

(3) summer, when winds blow from the ocean

(4) summer, when winds blow toward the high pressure

[10]

Base your answers to questions 38 through 40 on the graph below and on your knowledge of Earth science. The graph shows the closest distance between Earth and Mars during each year from 2001 to 2035. Distances are measured in astronomical units (AU). One AU equals the average distance from Earth to the Sun.

Closest Distance Each Year Between Earth and Mars

38 Mars reaches its closest distance to Earth approximately every

(1) 16 years   (3) 3 years
(2) 8 years   (4) 0.36 years

39 How many million kilometers is one astronomical unit?

(1) 108.2 million km   (3) 227.9 million km
(2) 149.6 million km   (4) 377.5 million km

40 The diagram below represents the positions of Earth and Mars in their orbits around the Sun when they were closest in the year 2003.

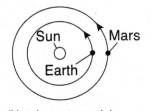

(Not drawn to scale)

Which diagram represents the positions of Earth and Mars approximately one-half of an Earth year (183 days) later?

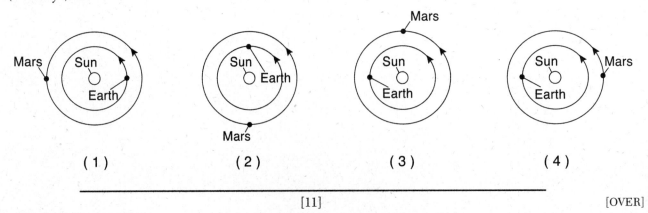

(1)   (2)   (3)   (4)

Regents Examination D

Base your answers to questions 41 through 44 on the three Sun's path diagrams below and on your knowledge of Earth science. The diagrams represent the position of the noon Sun along its apparent daily path as seen by an observer on the first day of three consecutive months (X, Y, and Z). The observer was located in Utica, New York.

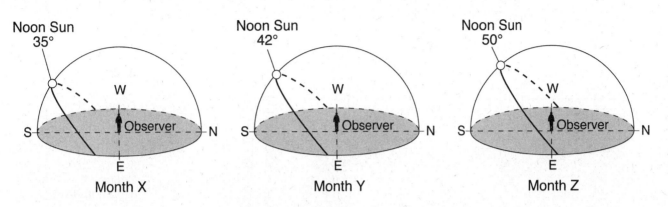

41 Which dates are represented by months X, Y, and Z?

(1) X-February 1, Y-March 1, Z-April 1
(2) X-May 1, Y-June 1, Z-July 1
(3) X-August 1, Y-September 1, Z-October 1
(4) X-November 1, Y-December 1, Z-January 1

42 Which characteristic of the Sun's apparent daily path stays constant from month X to month Z?

(1) locations of sunrise and sunset
(2) altitude of the noon Sun
(3) length of time that the Sun moves along its apparent path
(4) rate of the Sun's movement along its apparent path

43 For an observer in the Southern Hemisphere at 43° S latitude, the highest altitude of the noon Sun occurs when the Sun is above the

(1) eastern horizon
(2) western horizon
(3) northern horizon
(4) southern horizon

44 Position A represents the position of the Sun at another time of day during month Z. What is the time of day when the Sun is at position A?

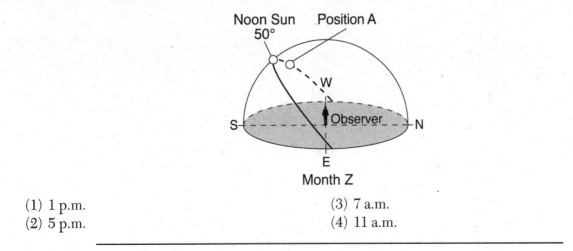

(1) 1 p.m.
(2) 5 p.m.
(3) 7 a.m.
(4) 11 a.m.

Base your answers to questions 45 through 47 on the geologic cross section of a portion of Earth's crust shown below and on your knowledge of Earth science. None of the rock units has been overturned.

45 The youngest rock unit shown in the cross section is

(1) breccia

(2) conglomerate

(3) sandstone

(4) shale

46 Which process most probably produced the irregularly shaped boundary between the limestone and the shale?

(1) folding

(2) faulting

(3) contact metamorphism

(4) erosion

47 Which sequence shows the relative ages of the gabbro, granite, and schist from oldest to youngest?

(1) gabbro → granite → schist

(2) gabbro → schist → granite

(3) schist → granite → gabbro

(4) schist → gabbro → granite

Regents Examination D

Base your answers to questions 48 through 50 on the cross section below and on your knowledge of Earth science. The cross section represents the landscape features and rock units of the Grand Canyon region in the southwestern United States. The names and ages of some rock formations are shown.

48 Which agent of erosion is mainly responsible for the formation of the Grand Canyon?

(1) running water
(2) glacial ice
(3) wind
(4) wave action

49 Approximately how many million years ago (mya) was the Coconino sandstone deposited as sediment?

(1) 180 mya
(2) 275 mya
(3) 330 mya
(4) 495 mya

50 If the climate of the Grand Canyon region became more humid, the rate of weathering and erosion would most likely

(1) decrease, and the landscape features would become more rounded
(2) decrease, and the landscape features would become more angular
(3) increase, and the landscape features would become more rounded
(4) increase, and the landscape features would become more angular

Answer all questions in this part.

Directions (51–65): Record your answers in the spaces provided in your answer booklet. Some questions may require the use of the *2011 Edition Reference Tables for Physical Setting/Earth Science.*

Base your answers to questions 51 and 52 on the diagram and data table below, and on your knowledge of Earth science. The diagram represents the laboratory materials used for an investigation of the effects of particle size on water retention. Five separate columns were filled to the same level with particles. The particle type is indicated for each column. The particles within each column are of uniform shape. A volume of 50 milliliters (mL) of water was poured through each column, and the amount of water retained was determined. The data table shows the results of this experiment.

(Not drawn to scale)

Water Retention

Particle Type (size)	Water Retained (mL)
Coarse pebbles	7
Fine pebbles	15
Coarse sand	32
Fine sand	38
Silt	46

51 Describe the general relationship between particle size and the amount of water retained. [1]

52 Name the particle type used in the investigation that most likely had the greatest permeability when the 50 milliliters of water were poured through these columns. [1]

Base your answers to questions 53 through 55 on the passage and the Characteristics of Stars graph below, and your knowledge of Earth science. Letters *A*, *B*, and *C* represent main sequence stars on the graph. The giant star *Aldebaran* is also shown.

Globular Star Clusters

Globular star clusters appear as small, hazy spots among the other stars. These clusters are groups of hundreds of thousands of stars held together by gravity. Individual stars within a cluster can be seen by using powerful telescopes, allowing scientists to determine their luminosities and temperatures.

All of the stars in a given cluster formed at the same time. In young clusters, most of the stars are classified as main sequence stars. As the stars in a cluster age, they eventually use up their core hydrogen and expand, changing from main sequence stars to giants. The most massive main sequence stars become supergiants. The less massive a star is in the cluster, the longer it remains a main sequence star. Over time, the number of main sequence stars in a cluster decreases.

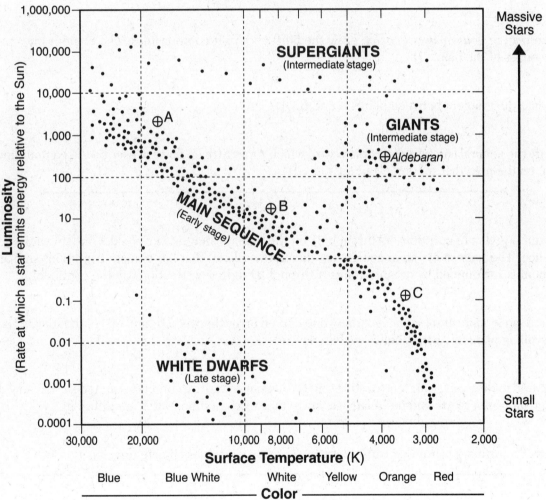

Characteristics of Stars

53 Compared to the relative amount of time that star *A* remains in the main sequence, state how the relative amount of time that star *C* remains in the main sequence is different. Explain why this amount of time is different. [1]

54 The globular star cluster containing stars *A*, *B*, and *C* is located in the same galaxy as our Sun. Identify the name of this galaxy. [1]

55 Identify the nuclear process that uses up a star's core hydrogen and produces the energy released by stars in a globular cluster. [1]

_____

Base your answers to questions 56 through 58 on the topographic map in your answer booklet and on your knowledge of Earth science. Points *A* and *B* represent locations on Earth's surface. Elevations are shown in feet. The 50-ft and 55-ft contour lines are *not* shown on the map.

56 On the map *in your answer booklet*, draw the 50-ft and 55-ft contour lines. The contour lines must extend to the edges of the map. [1]

57 Calculate the gradient between points *A* and *B*. [1]

58 Identify the general compass direction toward which Ames Stream flows. Describe the contour line evidence shown on the map that supports your answer. [1]

_____

Base your answers to questions 59 through 61 on the map in your answer booklet and on your knowledge of Earth science. The map shows an imaginary continent on a planet that has climate conditions similar to Earth. The continent is surrounded by oceans. Points *A* through *D* represent locations on the continent.

59 On the map *in your answer booklet*, draw one curved arrow between 0° and 30° N to indicate the direction of prevailing planetary winds between these latitudes. [1]

60 Compared to the average air temperature and the average moisture conditions at *A*, describe how the relative average air temperature and the relative average moisture conditions at *B* are different. [1]

61 Identify the primary factor that causes location *C* to have a colder climate than location *D*. [1]

_____

[17]   [OVER]

Base your answers to questions 62 through 65 on the map below and on your knowledge of Earth science. The map shows areas of daylight and darkness in New York State on March 21. Six locations are labeled on the map.

62 Identify the Earth motion that causes the daytime-nighttime boundary to appear to move. [1]

63 State the number of hours of nighttime that people in Syracuse will experience on March 21. [1]

64 State the name of the location labeled on this map where sunset will next be observed after Syracuse. [1]

65 State the altitude of *Polaris* as seen by an observer on Slide Mountain. [1]

Part C

Answer all questions in this part.

Directions (66–85): Record your answers in the spaces provided in your answer booklet. Some questions may require the use of the *2011 Edition Reference Tables for Physical Setting/Earth Science*.

Base your answers to questions 66 through 68 on the map and passage below and on your knowledge of Earth science. The map shows isolines that represent the thickness of a portion of the Greenland Ice Sheet in meters (m). Letters *A* and *B* represent points on the ice sheet's surface.

Thickness of Greenland Ice Sheet

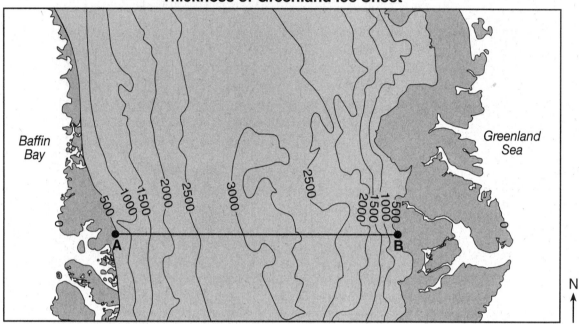

Greenland Ice Sheet

The Greenland Ice Sheet is a vast body of ice covering roughly 80 percent of the surface of Greenland. The ice sheet is almost 2400 kilometers long in a north-south direction. The ice sheet, consisting of layers of snow compressed over more than 100,000 years, contains a valuable record about Earth's past climates. The ice sheet glaciers continue to flow seaward and deposit sediment, but global warming has affected them. Warmer air temperatures have caused increased melting, resulting in a thinning of the ice sheet and faster glacial movement at the ice sheet edges.

66 On the grid *in your answer booklet*, construct a profile along line *AB* by plotting the thickness of the ice sheet where each isoline crosses line *AB*. Thicknesses of the ice sheet at *A* and *B* have been plotted on the grid. Connect *all twelve* plots with a line from *A* to *B* to complete the profile. [1]

67 Describe *one* glacial feature that could be found on the exposed surface bedrock of Greenland that would indicate the direction that the ice moved. [1]

68 Identify *two* major greenhouse gases that are inferred to contribute to global warming and increased temperatures in Greenland. [1]

Regents Examination D

Base your answers to questions 69 through 71 on the data table below, on the graph in your answer booklet, and on your knowledge of Earth science. The data table shows the percentage of the stable disintegration product produced over time by the radioactive decay of isotope X after each half-life. The graph shows the percentage of radioactive isotope X remaining over time during the radioactive decay of isotope X.

Disintegration Product of Isotope X

Percentage of Stable Disintegration Product (%)	Time (years)	Number of Half-Lives
0	0	0
50	5700	1
75	11,400	2
87.5	17,100	3
93.75	22,800	4

69 On the graph *in your answer booklet*, plot the percentage of stable disintegration product for each of the times shown on the data table and connect *all five* plots with a line. [1]

70 Determine the number of years (y) it takes for only 25% of radioactive isotope X to remain in a sample. [1]

71 Identify radioactive isotope X and its stable disintegration product. [1]

Base your answers to questions 72 through 75 on the diagram in your answer booklet and on your knowledge of Earth science. The diagram represents two positions of the Moon as it orbits Earth. Positions 1 and 2 are on opposite sides of Earth. Point C represents the location of a crater on the Moon's surface when the Moon is at position 1.

72 On the diagram *in your answer booklet*, draw a dot (•) on the Moon at position 2 to indicate the location of crater C when the Moon is at position 2. [1]

73 On the diagram *in your answer booklet*, place an **X** on the Moon's orbit to indicate the position of the Moon when a lunar eclipse could be viewed from Earth. [1]

74 Determine the number of days needed for the Moon to move from position 1 to position 2, completing one-half of its orbit. [1]

75 On the diagram *in your answer booklet*, shade the portion of the Moon that is in darkness as viewed from New York State when the Moon is at position 1. [1]

---

[20]

Base your answers to questions 76 through 78 on the weather map below and on your knowledge of Earth science. On the weather map, the location of the center of a high-pressure system (**H**) and a front are shown. Isobar values are labeled in millibars (mb). Weather station models represent the weather conditions at Atlanta, Georgia, and Tampa, Florida.

76 Complete the table *in your answer booklet* with the actual weather conditions represented by the weather station model at Atlanta, Georgia. [1]

77 Identify the type of front shown on the map. [1]

78 Describe *one* piece of evidence shown on the map that indicates that Tampa, Florida, has a high probability of precipitation. [1]

[OVER]

Regents Examination D

Base your answers to questions 79 through 81 on the map below and on your knowledge of Earth science. The map shows the surface location of a tectonic plate boundary along the western coast of South America. The Mid-Atlantic Ridge is also shown. Points *A* through *D* represent locations on Earth's surface.

79 Identify the names of the tectonic plates at locations *A* and *B*. [1]

80 Compared to the relative age of the surface oceanic bedrock at location *C*, state the relative age of the surface oceanic bedrock at location *D*. Explain why this difference in relative age occurs. [1]

81 Identify the term for the large ocean wave produced by offshore earthquakes that is hazardous to humans living along the west coast of South America. Describe *one* emergency action that should be taken to avoid loss of life when a warning for an approaching large wave has been given. [1]

Base your answers to questions 82 through 85 on the flowchart below and on your knowledge of Earth science. Letters A through D represent information that is missing in the chart.

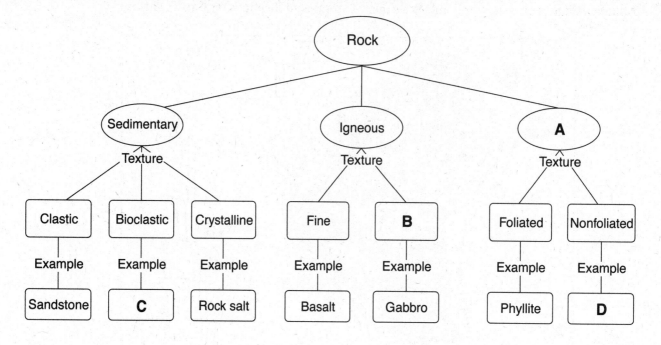

82 Complete the table *in your answer booklet* by writing the missing information represented by letters A through D. [1]

83 Identify the *two* elements that make up the chemical composition of the mineral in rock salt. [1]

84 The pie graph below shows the percentages of four minerals that compose the igneous rock gabbro. Letter X represents one of the minerals.

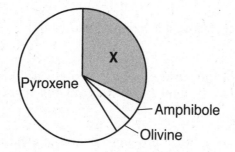

Identify the mineral represented by letter X in the graph. [1]

85 Identify the name of *one* foliated rock formed when phyllite undergoes increased heat and pressure. [1]

_____

Regents Examination D

The University of the State of New York

REGENTS HIGH SCHOOL EXAMINATION

PHYSICAL SETTING
EARTH SCIENCE

—————

ANSWER BOOKLET

Student . . . .

Teacher . . . .

School . . . . Grade . . . .

Record your answers for Part B–2 and Part C in this booklet.

Part B–2

51 _____

_____

52 _____

53 Relative time for star C: _____

Explanation: _____

_____

54 _____

55 _____

56

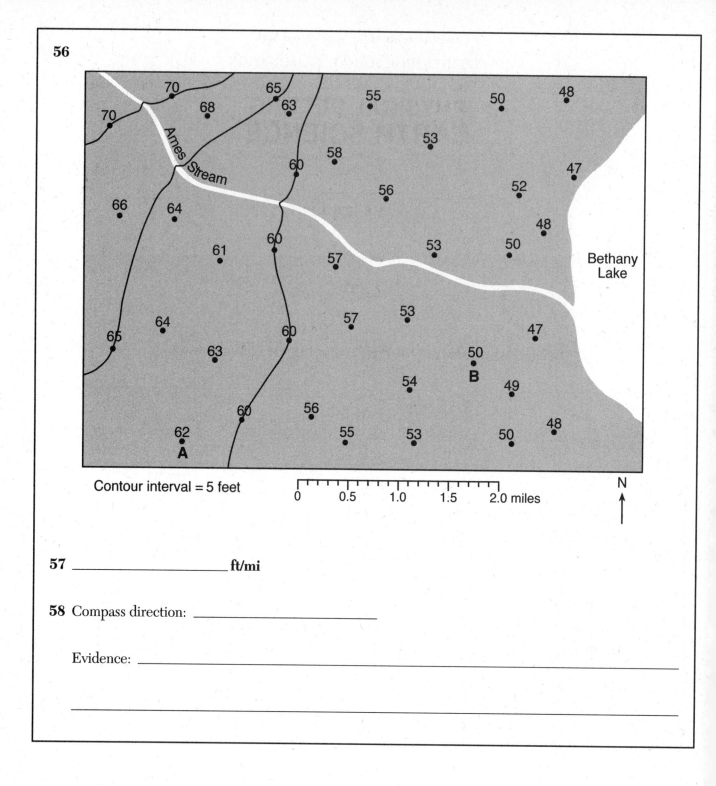

Contour interval = 5 feet

0   0.5   1.0   1.5   2.0 miles

N

57 _____ ft/mi

58 Compass direction: _____

Evidence: _____

_____

Regents Examination D

59

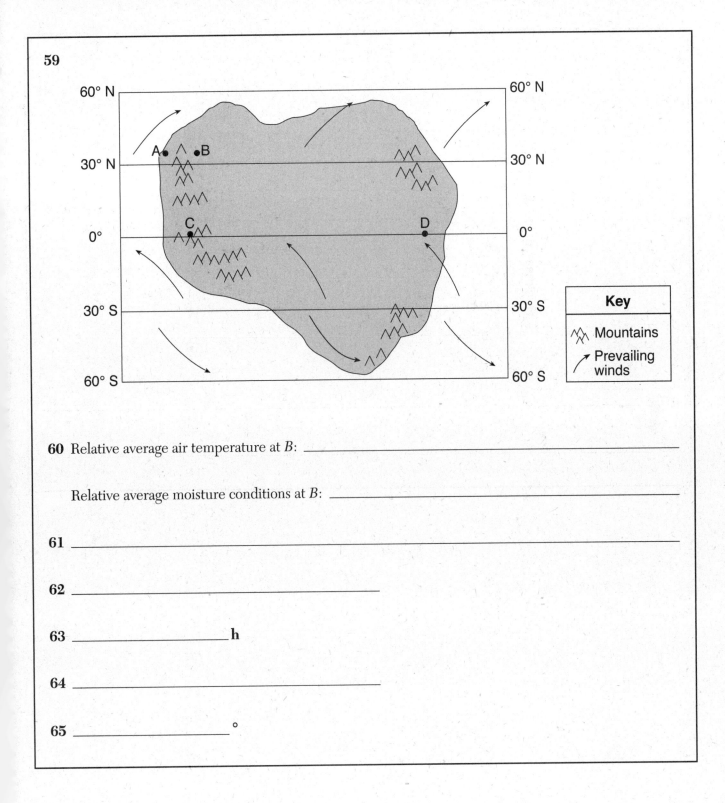

60 Relative average air temperature at *B*: _____

Relative average moisture conditions at *B*: _____

61 _____

62 _____

63 _____ **h**

64 _____

65 _____ °

Part C

66

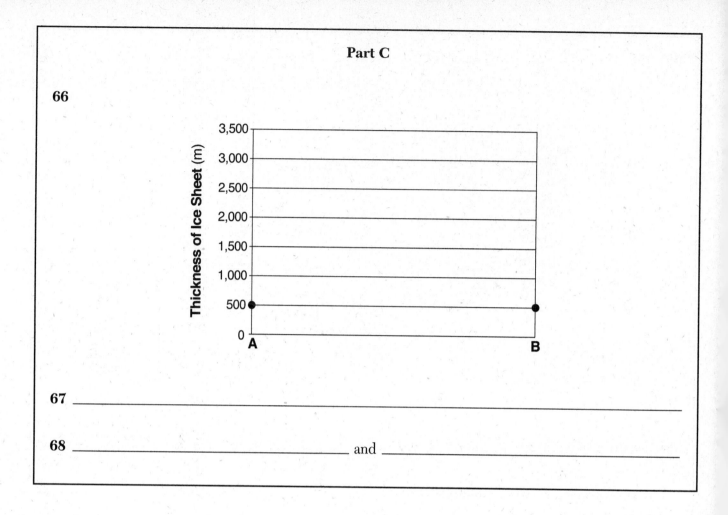

67 _____

68 _____ and _____

69

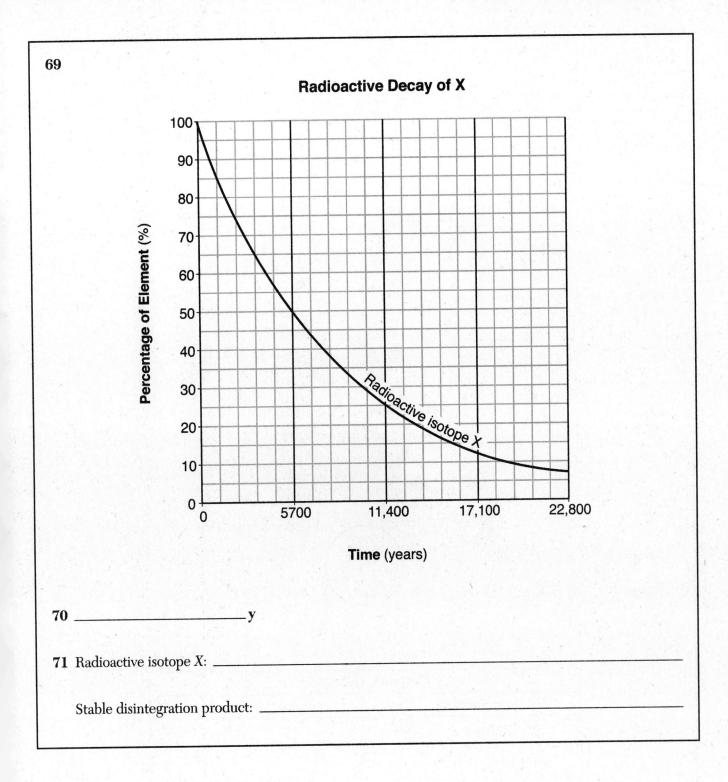

Radioactive Decay of X

(y-axis) Percentage of Element (%)

(x-axis) Time (years)

Radioactive isotope X

70 _____ y

71 Radioactive isotope X: _____

Stable disintegration product: _____

[OVER]

Regents Examination D

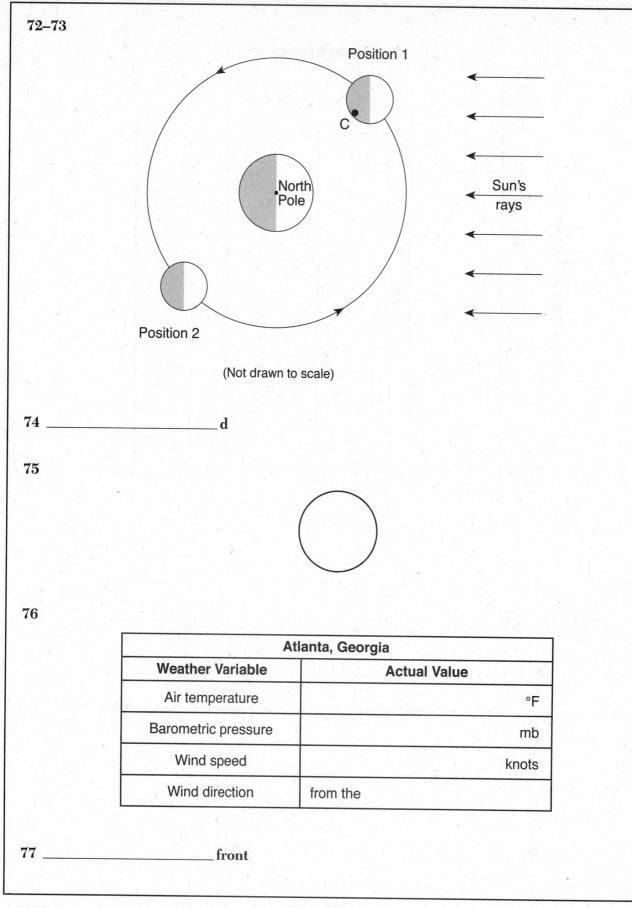

Position 1

C

North
Pole

Sun's
rays

Position 2

(Not drawn to scale)

74 _____ d

75

76

Atlanta, Georgia	
Weather Variable	**Actual Value**
Air temperature	°F
Barometric pressure	mb
Wind speed	knots
Wind direction	from the

77 _____ **front**

Regents Examination D

78 _____

_____

79 Location *A*: _____ **Plate**

Location *B*: _____ **Plate**

80 Relative age at location *D*: _____

Explanation: _____

_____

81 Term for large ocean wave: _____

Emergency action: _____

_____

82

Letter	Missing Information
A	
B	
C	
D	

83 _____ and _____

84 _____

85 _____

Part A

Answer all questions in this part.

Directions (1–35): For *each* statement or question, choose the word or expression that, of those given, best completes the statement or answers the question. Some questions may require the use of the *2011 Edition Reference Tables for Physical Setting/Earth Science*. Record your answers on your separate answer sheet.

1 In which sequence are the celestial objects correctly listed in order from the smallest mass to the largest mass?

(1) Saturn, solar system, Milky Way, universe
(2) Saturn, universe, Milky Way, solar system
(3) Milky Way, Saturn, solar system, universe
(4) Milky Way, universe, solar system, Saturn

2 The red shift of light from distant galaxies provides evidence that these galaxies are

(1) decreasing in size
(2) increasing in size
(3) decreasing in distance from Earth
(4) increasing in distance from Earth

3 The best evidence of Earth's rotation is provided by the

(1) Foucault pendulum and global warming
(2) Foucault pendulum and Coriolis effect
(3) Moon phases and global warming
(4) Moon phases and Coriolis effect

4 Which sphere of Earth covers approximately 70% of Earth's surface?

(1) atmosphere   (3) hydrosphere
(2) lithosphere   (4) asthenosphere

5 Some of the constellations that are visible to New York State observers at midnight in December are different from the constellations that are visible at midnight in June because

(1) constellations rotate on an axis
(2) constellations revolve around Earth
(3) Earth rotates on its axis
(4) Earth revolves around the Sun

6 The diagram below represents Earth and the Moon as viewed from above the North Pole. Points *A*, *B*, *C*, and *D* are locations on Earth's surface.

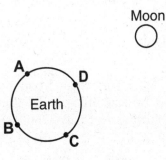

(Not drawn to scale)

According to the diagram, where will high ocean tides and low ocean tides most likely be located?

(1) high tides at *A* and *B*; low tides at *C* and *D*
(2) high tides at *B* and *D*; low tides at *A* and *C*
(3) high tides at *A* and *C*; low tides at *B* and *D*
(4) high tides at *C* and *D*; low tides at *A* and *B*

7 Urbanization affects the amount of vegetation and runoff in an area by

(1) decreasing vegetation and decreasing runoff
(2) decreasing vegetation and increasing runoff
(3) increasing vegetation and decreasing runoff
(4) increasing vegetation and increasing runoff

8 A severe thunderstorm warning was issued on a warm summer afternoon. Which present weather symbol represents the dangerous solid form of precipitation that is commonly associated with some of these severe thunderstorms?

(1)   (2)   (3)   (4)

[2]

9 The station model below represents the weather conditions for a location in New York State.

28   002

2   +02/

25

The barometric trend for the past three hours at this location indicates a steady increase of

(1) 0.2 mb   (3) 0.002 mb

(2) 2.0 mb   (4) 0.02 mb

10 Which New York State location is most often affected by lake-effect snow storms caused by winds blowing over Lake Ontario?

(1) Jamestown   (3) Oswego

(2) Plattsburgh   (4) Riverhead

11 Which type of air mass would most likely form over the Pacific Ocean north of the Aleutian Trench?

(1) mP   (3) cP

(2) mT   (4) cT

12 Mount Kilimanjaro is located in eastern Africa at 3° S. Which climate factor best explains the presence of permanent snow on its peak?

(1) latitude   (3) prevailing winds

(2) elevation   (4) ocean currents

13 In which portion of the electromagnetic spectrum is the maximum intensity of Earth's outgoing radiation?

(1) visible light   (3) infrared

(2) gamma rays   (4) ultraviolet

14 A solar water heater contains fluid-filled tubing that absorbs sunlight energy on its outside surface. Which tubing exterior will best absorb insolation?

(1) dark-colored and rough

(2) dark-colored and smooth

(3) light-colored and rough

(4) light-colored and smooth

15 Equal masses of granite, iron, copper, and lead are placed in sunlight. Based on specific heat, which material will warm up the fastest?

(1) granite   (3) copper

(2) iron   (4) lead

16 During explosive volcanic eruptions, large amounts of ash entering Earth's atmosphere often rise to an altitude of 20 kilometers. What is the most likely effect of this ash cloud?

(1) a decrease in the insolation reaching Earth's surface

(2) a decrease in the thickness of Earth's stratosphere layer

(3) an increase in the insolation reaching Earth's surface

(4) an increase in the thickness of Earth's stratosphere layer

17 The map below shows some tectonic plate boundaries near South America and Africa. Letters A, B, C, and D represent locations on Earth's surface.

Which location most likely has the youngest bedrock?

(1) A   (3) C

(2) B   (4) D

18 Compared to the average density and composition of oceanic crust, continental crust is

(1) less dense and more felsic
(2) less dense and more mafic
(3) more dense and more felsic
(4) more dense and more mafic

19 The Hawaiian Islands were formed as a result of

(1) lava flowing over Earth's surface where two tectonic plates move apart
(2) an oceanic plate moving over a mantle hot spot
(3) two oceanic plates colliding to form an island arc
(4) tectonic plates sliding past each other

20 The block diagram below represents the underlying bedrock structure of a landscape region.

Which diagram represents the most likely stream drainage pattern on the surface of this landscape?

(1)

(3)

(2)

(4)

21 Which characteristics identify mountain landscape regions?

(1) steep slopes with deformed bedrock
(2) steep slopes with horizontal bedrock
(3) gentle slopes with deformed bedrock
(4) gentle slopes with horizontal bedrock

22 Which agent of erosion causes the sandblasting of bedrock?

(1) glaciers   (3) running water
(2) wind   (4) wave action

23 The photograph below shows wire netting installed over a steep rock outcrop.

This wire netting has been installed to prevent loss of property or life resulting from

(1) crosscutting and downwarping
(2) folding and faulting
(3) weathering and erosion
(4) high winds and flooding

24 Which two minerals are commercial sources of iron?

(1) galena and graphite
(2) muscovite mica and biotite mica
(3) garnet and fluorite
(4) hematite and magnetite

25 Which mineral can be found in the rocks phyllite, sandstone, and granite?

(1) quartz   (3) gypsum
(2) pyroxene   (4) calcite

26 Which diagram best represents Earth's axis position relative to Earth's orbital plane?

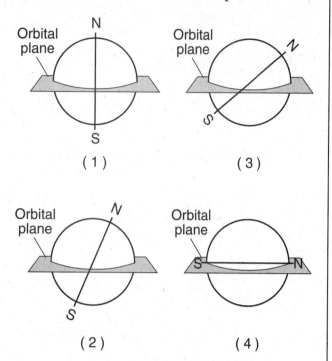

(1)

(3)

(2)

(4)

27 In which cross section do the arrows represent the most probable direction of air movement over land and water surfaces at an ocean coast on a hot, sunny, summer afternoon?

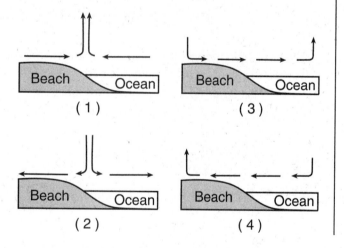

(1)

(3)

(2)

(4)

28 The table below shows the average diameter and falling velocity of five types of precipitation. The data for moderate rain have been left blank.

Type of Precipitation	Average Diameter (millimeters)	Falling Velocity (meters/second)
drizzle	0.96	4.1
light rain	1.24	4.8
moderate rain		
heavy rain	2.05	6.7
excessive rain	2.40	7.3

What are the probable values for the average diameter and falling velocity of the raindrops found in moderate rain?

(1) average diameter = 1.20 mm
falling velocity = 4.6 m/sec

(2) average diameter = 1.20 mm
falling velocity = 5.7 m/sec

(3) average diameter = 1.60 mm
falling velocity = 4.6 m/sec

(4) average diameter = 1.60 mm
falling velocity = 5.7 m/sec

29 Which New York State index fossil is classified as a coral?

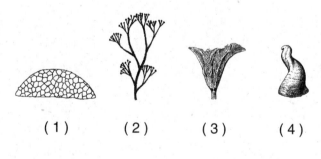

(1)   (2)   (3)   (4)

30 The map below shows the weak trade winds and strong equatorial countercurrent in the Pacific Ocean during El Niño conditions. This causes warm surface ocean water to migrate eastward, lowering the atmospheric pressure above this warm water.

El Niño Conditions

What are the most likely changes to atmospheric temperature and precipitation along the west coast of South America during El Niño conditions?

(1) lower temperatures and lower amounts of precipitation
(2) lower temperatures and higher amounts of precipitation
(3) higher temperatures and lower amounts of precipitation
(4) higher temperatures and higher amounts of precipitation

31 The cross sections below represent two bedrock outcrops 15 kilometers apart. Numbers 1 through 9 indicate rock layers. Some layers contain index fossils. No overturning of rock layers has occurred.

Which layers most likely formed during the same geologic time period?

(1) 1 and 8   (3) 3 and 7
(2) 2 and 9   (4) 4 and 5

[6]

32 Labeled lines on the map below show the inferred location of Earth's equator during the middle of several geologic periods.

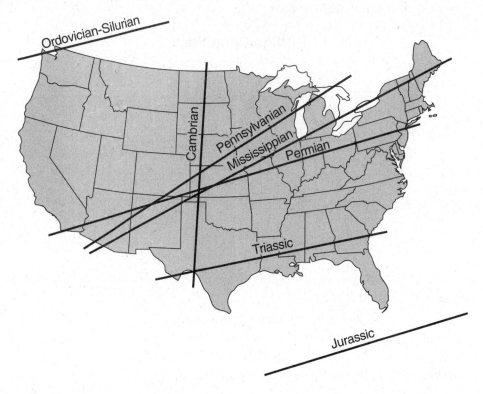

Approximately how many million years ago (mya) was the region around current-day Watertown, New York, located the nearest to the equator?

(1) 270 mya

(3) 340 mya

(2) 300 mya

(4) 450 mya

33 Which table correctly matches rock textures with a sedimentary rock that exhibits each texture?

Rock Texture	Sedimentary Rock
clastic	sandstone
crystalline	breccia
bioclastic	rock gypsum

(1)

Rock Texture	Sedimentary Rock
clastic	shale
crystalline	dolostone
bioclastic	sandstone

(3)

Rock Texture	Sedimentary Rock
clastic	dolostone
crystalline	limestone
bioclastic	siltstone

(2)

Rock Texture	Sedimentary Rock
clastic	conglomerate
crystalline	rock salt
bioclastic	limestone

(4)

[7]

[OVER]

Regents Examination E

34 The data table below shows the dry-bulb and wet-bulb temperatures measured with a psychrometer on four different days at the same location.

Temperatures Measured with a Psychrometer

Day	1	2	3	4
Dry-bulb temperature (°C)	0	5	10	15
Wet-bulb temperature (°C)	−5	0	5	10

According to the data shown in the table, which day had the highest relative humidity?

(1) 1

(2) 2

(3) 3

(4) 4

35 The cross section below represents a lithospheric plate boundary.

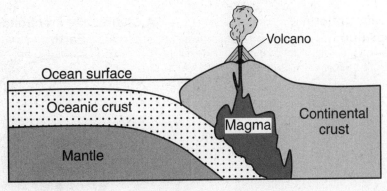

(Not drawn to scale)

In which diagram do the arrows show the relative directions of plate movement at this type of plate boundary?

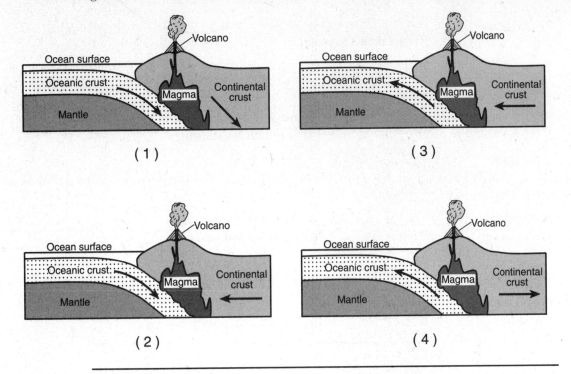

[8]

Part B–1

Answer all questions in this part.

Directions (36–50): For *each* statement or question, choose the word or expression that, of those given, best completes the statement or answers the question. Some questions may require the use of the *2011 Edition Reference Tables for Physical Setting/Earth Science*. Record your answers on your separate answer sheet.

Base your answers to questions 36 through 38 on the information and diagram below and on your knowledge of Earth science. The diagram represents a simplified model of the early formation of Earth's interior.

Early in its formation, Earth was a molten mass of evenly mixed composition. During the next few million years, the heavier and more dense elements sank to the center, while lighter and less dense elements rose toward the surface. This is called chemical fractionation.

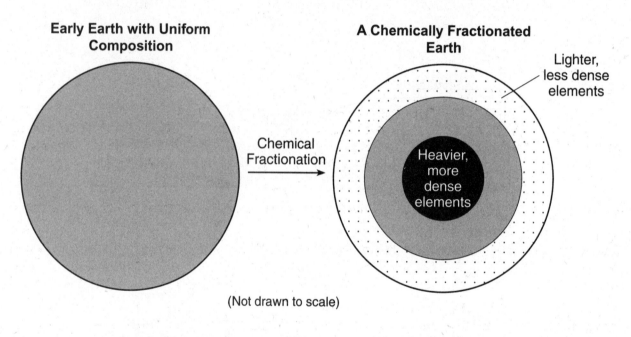

Early Earth with Uniform Composition

A Chemically Fractionated Earth

Lighter, less dense elements

Chemical Fractionation

Heavier, more dense elements

(Not drawn to scale)

36 Chemical fractionation is most likely caused by

  (1) solidification

  (2) gravity

  (3) magnetic force

  (4) chemical weathering

37 Approximately how many years ago did Earth and other planets in our solar system begin the process of chemical fractionation?

  (1) 8.2 billion years ago

  (2) 13.8 billion years ago

  (3) 542 million years ago

  (4) 4600 million years ago

38 Which pair of elements sank to Earth's center during chemical fractionation?

  (1) aluminum and silicon

  (2) carbon and sulfur

  (3) iron and nickel

  (4) oxygen and potassium

Regents Examination E

Base your answers to questions 39 through 41 on the diagram below and on your knowledge of Earth science. The diagram represents the apparent path of the Sun through the sky as viewed by an observer in the Northern Hemisphere. Points A, B, C, and D represent four positions of the Sun.

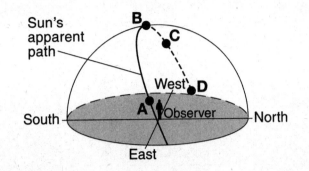

39 This apparent path of the Sun through the sky is caused by
(1) Earth's revolution around the Sun
(2) Earth's rotation on its axis
(3) the Sun's revolution around Earth
(4) the Sun's rotation on its axis

40 The observer has the longest shadow when the Sun is at position
(1) A
(2) B
(3) C
(4) D

41 What is the approximate time of day when the Sun is at position C?
(1) 6 a.m.
(2) 9 a.m.
(3) 3 p.m.
(4) 6 p.m.

[10]

Base your answers to questions 42 and 43 on the diagram below and on your knowledge of Earth science. The diagram represents three tubes, A, B, and C, each containing an equal volume of uniform-sized spherical beads. The bottom of each tube is covered with a wire screen. XY is a reference line.

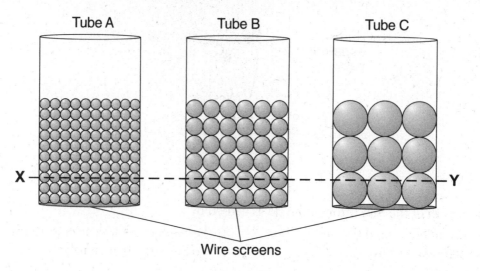

42 Which bar graph would best represent the rate of water infiltration through tubes A, B, and C?

43 These tubes are placed in water up to the level of line XY to demonstrate capillarity. After one hour, the height of the water above line XY will be

(1) highest in tube A
(2) highest in tube B

(3) highest in tube C
(4) the same height in all three tubes

Regents Examination E

Base your answers to questions 44 through 46 on the block diagram below and on your knowledge of Earth science. The block diagram represents a river drainage system. A portion of the river, seen in box *A*, has been enlarged. Points *X* and *Y* are on opposite sides of the river. Letter *B* indicates the location where the river enters the ocean.

44 The area of land drained by this river and its tributaries is best described as the river's

(1) topography

(2) watershed

(3) water table

(4) floodplain

45 Which cross section best represents the profile of the bottom of the river between points *X* and *Y* at location *A*?

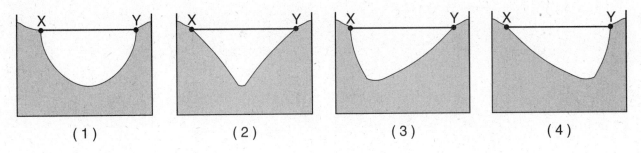

(1)   (2)   (3)   (4)

46 Which cross section represents the most likely pattern of sediments deposited where the river enters the ocean at location *B*?

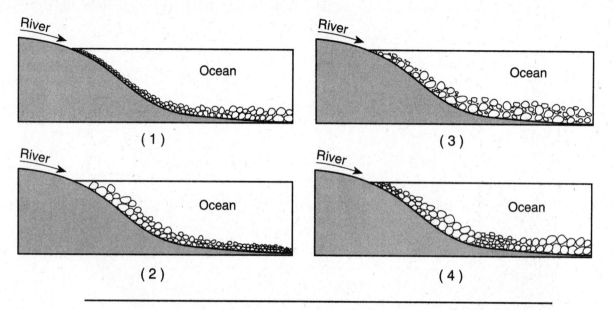

(1)

(2)

(3)

(4)

Base your answers to questions 47 through 50 on the graph below and on your knowledge of Earth science. The graph shows the percentages of the radioactive isotope carbon-14 (^{14}C) and its disintegration product produced during four half-lives of radioactive decay.

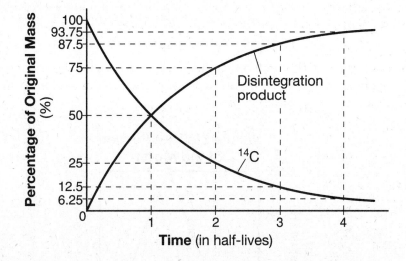

47 Radioactive carbon-14 is often useful in determining the absolute age of geologic samples because radioactive isotopes

(1) decay at a regular rate   (3) remain unchanged over time

(2) become less stable during decay   (4) stabilize after four half-lives

48 Which disintegration product is represented on the graph?

(1) ^{206}Pb (3) ^{40}Ar

(2) ^{87}Sr (4) ^{14}N

49 How many half-lives have passed if a sample contains 25% of its original carbon-14?

(1) 1 half-life   (3) 3 half-lives

(2) 2 half-lives   (4) 4 half-lives

50 The age of which index fossil could be determined by using carbon-14?

(1)   (2)   (3)   (4)

[14]

Part B–2

Answer all questions in this part.

Directions (51–65): Record your answers in the spaces provided in your answer booklet. Some questions may require the use of the *2011 Edition Reference Tables for Physical Setting/Earth Science.*

Base your answers to questions 51 through 53 on the graph below and on your knowledge of Earth science. The graph shows the percentage of the lighted portion of the Moon that is visible to an observer in New York State through eight consecutive Moon phases.

Visible Lighted Portion of the Moon

51 The phases of the Moon are said to be waxing when the lighted portion of the Moon gradually increases over time. Identify the numbered phase of the Moon when waxing begins and the numbered phase when waxing ends. [1]

52 On the diagram *in your answer booklet*, place an **X** on the Moon's orbit to represent the Moon's position at phase 5. [1]

53 The diagram below represents the appearance of the Moon at phase 3 as seen by an observer in New York State.

In the circle *in your answer booklet*, shade the part of the Moon that appears dark to an observer in New York State when the Moon is at phase 7. [1]

[15] [OVER]

Base your answers to questions 54 through 57 on the flowchart below and on your knowledge of Earth science. The flowchart represents possible pathways in the evolution of stars.

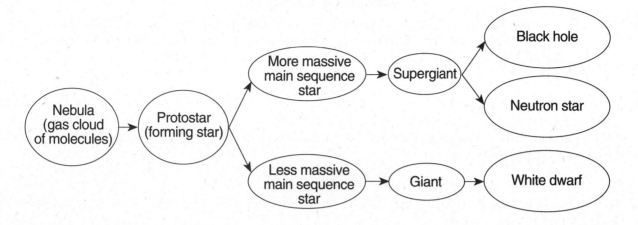

54 Based on this flowchart, identify the characteristic of a main sequence star that determines whether the star becomes a giant or a supergiant. [1]

55 State the name of *one* star labeled on the *Characteristics of Stars* graph in the *Earth Science Reference Tables* that may become either a black hole or neutron star. [1]

56 Identify the nuclear process that occurs when lighter elements in a star combine to form heavier elements, producing the star's radiant energy. [1]

57 *In your answer booklet*, circle the relative surface temperature and relative luminosity of the main sequence star *Sirius* compared with the surface temperature and luminosity of the Sun. [1]

_____

Base your answers to questions 58 through 61 on the topographic map in your answer booklet and on your knowledge of Earth science. Points A, B, C, and D represent locations on Earth's surface. Elevations are measured in meters.

58 On the map *in your answer booklet*, draw the 200-meter contour line in the southern portion of the map. Extend the contour line to the edges of the map. [1]

59 On the grid *in your answer booklet*, construct a topographic profile along line AB by plotting the elevation of *each* contour line that crosses line AB. The elevations of points A and B have been plotted on the grid. Connect *all ten* plots with a line from A to B to complete the profile. [1]

60 Calculate the gradient between points C and D. Label your answer with the correct units. [1]

61 Identify the compass direction toward which Kim Brook flows. Describe the evidence shown on the map that indicates the water flows downhill in that compass direction. [1]

_____

Base your answers to questions 62 through 65 on the information below and on your knowledge of Earth science.

Adirondack Earthquake

On October 7, 1983, a magnitude 5.3 earthquake occurred in New York State's Adirondack region. The earthquake's epicenter was at Blue Mountain Lake, which is located approximately 32 miles (50 kilometers) southwest of Mt. Marcy.

62 *In your answer booklet*, circle the New York State location (Old Forge *or* New York City) that recorded the greater amount of time between the arrival of the first *P*-wave and the arrival of the first *S*-wave from the Blue Mountain Lake earthquake. Explain why this location had the greater difference between the *P*-wave and *S*-wave arrival times. [1]

63 Determine how long it took the first *P*-wave to travel from Blue Mountain Lake to a seismic station 1200 kilometers away. [1]

64 Identify *one* type of metamorphic surface bedrock where this earthquake epicenter was located. [1]

65 Perth, Australia, is located almost directly on the opposite side of Earth from the epicenter of this earthquake. A seismograph in Perth received *P*-waves but *not* *S*-waves from this earthquake. Identify the interior layer of Earth and the characteristic of this layer that prevented the *S*-waves from arriving at Perth. [1]

Answer all questions in this part.

Directions (66–85): Record your answers in the spaces provided in your answer booklet. Some questions may require the use of the *2011 Edition Reference Tables for Physical Setting/Earth Science.*

Base your answers to questions 66 through 68 on the diagram below and on your knowledge of Earth science. The diagram represents Earth on the first day of a season. The equator, several lines of longitude, and the North and South Poles have been labeled. Letters *A* through *D* represent locations on Earth's surface.

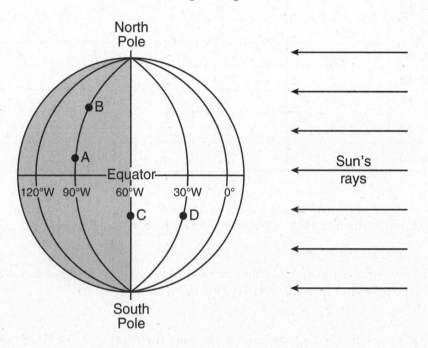

66 Identify *one* possible date that is represented by the position of Earth in this diagram. [1]

67 State whether the relative altitude of *Polaris* at location *A* is lower or higher than at location *B*. Explain why this difference is observed. [1]

68 State the solar time at location *D* if the solar time at location *C* is 6:00 a.m. Indicate a.m. or p.m. in your answer. [1]

Base your answers to questions 69 through 72 on the data table below, on the map in your answer booklet, and on your knowledge of Earth science. The data table shows latitude and longitude locations of the center of Hurricane Odile recorded at the same time each day from September 12 to September 18, 2014. The data table also shows the hurricane's barometric pressure in millibars (mb) and wind speed in knots (kt). The location of La Paz, Mexico, is indicated on the map.

Hurricane Odile

Date	Location		Barometric Pressure (mb)	Wind Speed (kt)
	Latitude (° N)	Longitude (° W)		
September 12	15	105	993	50
September 13	16	106	983	65
September 14	19	107	918	120
September 15	23	110	941	110
September 16	27	113	987	55
September 17	30	114	995	40
September 18	31	112	1003	25

69 On the map *in your answer booklet*, plot the seven locations of Hurricane Odile indicated by the latitudes and longitudes shown in the data table. Connect *all seven* plots with a line. [1]

70 Using the set of axes *in your answer booklet*, draw a line to represent the general relationship between barometric pressure and wind speed associated with Hurricane Odile. [1]

71 Identify *one* weather instrument that was used to measure the wind speed of Hurricane Odile. [1]

72 Describe *two* actions that a person living in La Paz, Mexico, could take to prepare for an approaching hurricane. [1]

_____

Base your answers to questions 73 through 75 on the cross section below and on your knowledge of Earth science. On the cross section, letters A through F represent rock units. Line XX' indicates an unconformity and line YY' indicates a fault. No overturning of rock layers has occurred.

Key

Igneous Rocks

Diorite   Basalt   Contact metamorphism

73 Identify the name of the rock formed in the zone of contact metamorphism between rock units A and F. [1]

74 List *two* processes that produced unconformity XX'. [1]

75 *In your answer booklet*, list the letters of rock units D, E, F, and fault YY' in the correct sequence from oldest to youngest. [1]

Base your answers to questions 76 through 79 on the passage and cross section below, and on your knowledge of Earth science. The cross section represents the elevation and depth of each Finger Lake in New York State. The gray shading in each lake represents the sediment fill at the bottom of each lake.

Formation of the Finger Lakes

The Finger Lakes originated as a series of south-flowing rivers that existed in what is now central New York State. Around 1.7 to 1.8 million years ago, a continental glacier advanced southward, beginning an ice age that consisted of many advances and retreats of glaciers. The Finger Lakes were carved by several of these advances, which gouged the valleys of the rivers into deep troughs, some of which extend below present-day sea level. As the glaciers advanced, they pushed a great amount of soil and rock ahead of them. During the time when the ice sheets were melting and retreating, glacial moraines were left behind. These deposits dammed the glacial valleys at their southern ends, and the valleys then flooded to form the Finger Lakes.

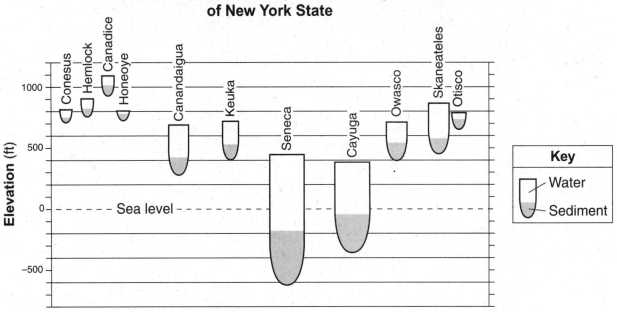

Elevation and Maximum Depth of the Finger Lakes of New York State

76 Identify *one* Finger Lake that has a maximum water depth of approximately 175 feet. [1]

77 Identify the geologic time period and epoch when these continental glaciers formed the Finger Lakes of New York State. [1]

78 Describe *one* way that the arrangement of sediments in the glacial moraines is different from the arrangement of sediments deposited in the earlier river channels. [1]

79 Describe the cross-sectional shape of the original river valleys before they were gouged by the advancing glaciers. [1]

Regents Examination E

Base your answers to questions 80 and 81 on the map below and on your knowledge of Earth science. The map shows the locations of the Coast Range and Cascade Range in the Pacific Northwest of the United States and two cities in this region.

Permission to use this third-party content has not been granted to Pearson. View content at nysedregents.org.

80 Identify the name of the cool surface ocean current that influences the climate of this region. [1]

81 Explain why the difference between average winter and summer temperatures is smaller in Long Beach than in Richland. [1]

Base your answers to questions 82 through 85 on the diagram below and on your knowledge of Earth science. The diagram represents a portion of the scheme for igneous rock identification. Line *AB* represents the percentages of the minerals in igneous rock 1 and line *CD* represents the percentages of the minerals in igneous rock 2.

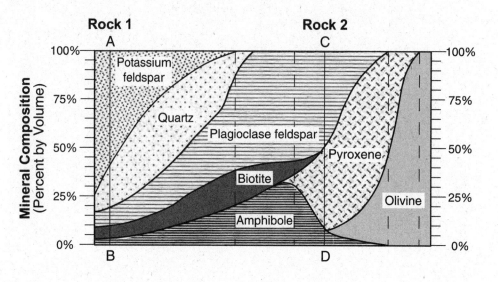

82 Rock 1 is a glassy, vesicular igneous rock. Identify the name of rock 1. [1]

83 Compared to the color and density of igneous rock 1, describe how the relative color and density of igneous rock 2 are different. [1]

84 Explain why andesite and diorite can both have the same percentage of mineral composition by volume, and yet be two different igneous rocks. [1]

85 The table *in your answer booklet* shows the composition of three minerals commonly found in igneous rocks. Complete the table by placing *one* **X** in each row to indicate if that mineral is found in both rock 1 and rock 2, neither rock 1 nor rock 2, rock 1 only, or rock 2 only. [1]

The University of the State of New York

REGENTS HIGH SCHOOL EXAMINATION

PHYSICAL SETTING
EARTH SCIENCE

ANSWER BOOKLET

Student . . . .

Teacher . . . .

School . . . . Grade . . . .

Record your answers for Part B–2 and Part C in this booklet.

Part B–2

51 Waxing begins: Phase _____

Waxing ends: Phase _____

52

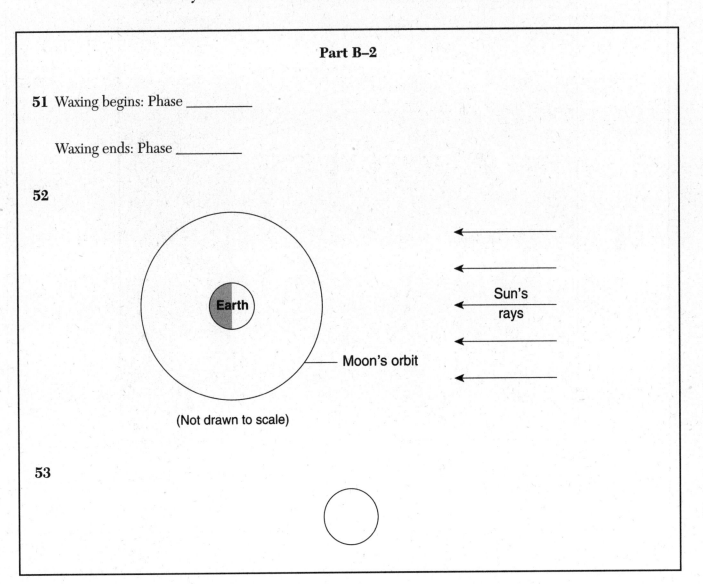

(Not drawn to scale)

53

---

54 _____

55 _____

56 _____

57 Relative surface temperature of *Sirius* (circle one):   **lower**   **higher**   **the same**

Relative luminosity of *Sirius* (circle one):   **less**   **greater**   **the same**

58

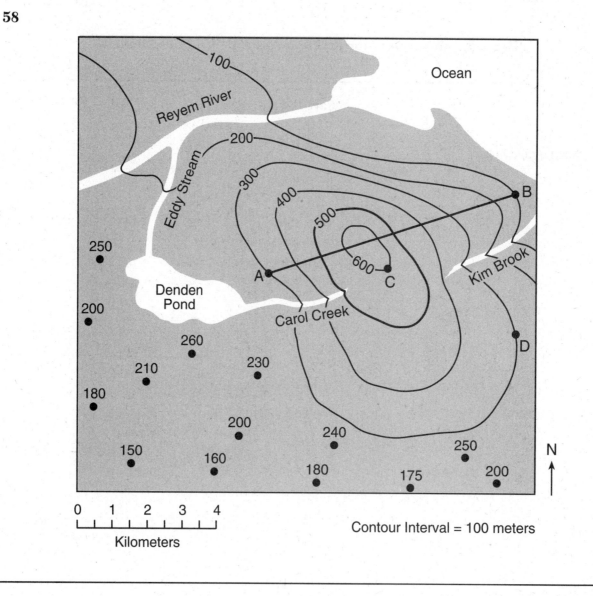

Regents Examination E

59

Profile

60 _____

61 Compass direction: _____

Evidence: _____

_____

62 Circle one: **Old Forge**   **New York City**

Explanation: _____

_____

63 _____ **min** _____ **s**

64 _____

65 Earth's interior layer: _____

Characteristic of this layer: _____

Part C

66 _____

67 Relative altitude of *Polaris* at location *A*: _____

Explanation: _____

_____

68 _____

69

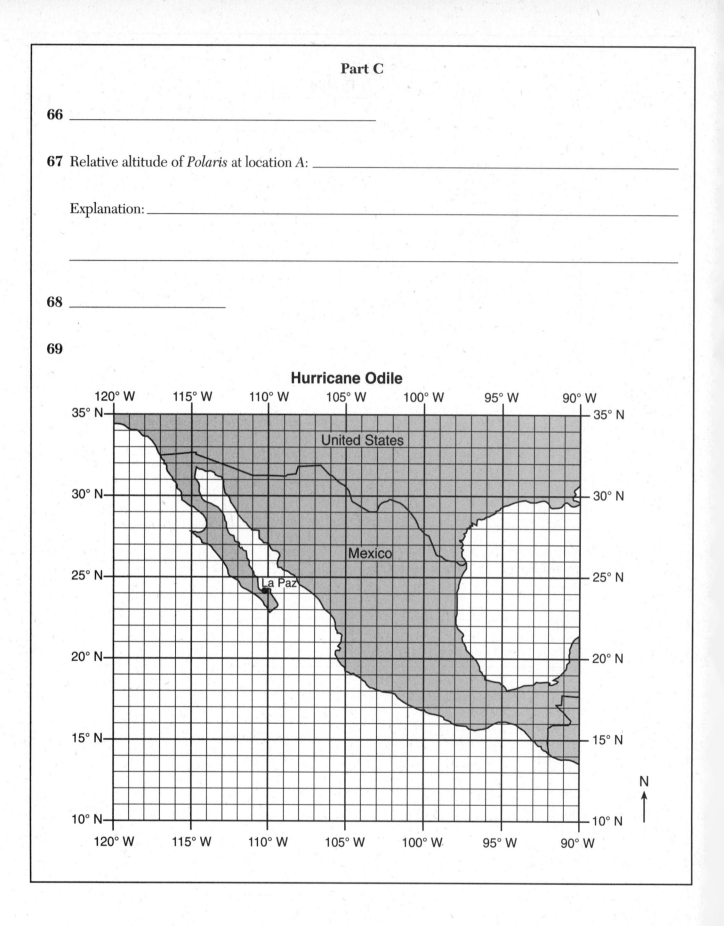

70

Wind Speed ↑

Barometric Pressure →

71 _____

72 Action 1: _____

Action 2: _____

73 _____

74 Process 1: _____

Process 2: _____

75 _____ → _____ → _____ → _____
Oldest ————————————→ Youngest

76 _____ Lake

77 _____ Period

_____ Epoch

78 _____

_____

79 _____

80 _____ Current

81 _____

_____

82 _____

83 Relative color of rock 2: _____

Relative density of rock 2: _____

84 _____

_____

85

Mineral Composition	Found in both rock 1 and rock 2	Found in neither rock 1 nor rock 2	Found in rock 1, only	Found in rock 2, only
$(Na,Ca)AlSi_3O_8$				
$KAlSi_3O_8$				
$(Fe,Mg)_2SiO_4$				

Part A

Answer all questions in this part.

Directions (1–35): For *each* statement or question, choose the word or expression that, of those given, best completes the statement or answers the question. Some questions may require the use of the *2011 Edition Reference Tables for Physical Setting/Earth Science*. Record your answers on your separate answer sheet.

1 Evidence that the universe is expanding is best supported by the observation that the wavelengths of light from distant galaxies are shifted toward the
   (1) red end of the spectrum because they are shortened
   (2) red end of the spectrum because they are lengthened
   (3) blue end of the spectrum because they are shortened
   (4) blue end of the spectrum because they are lengthened

2 Scientists infer that the Big Bang occurred approximately
   (1) 4.6 billion years ago
   (2) 7 billion years ago
   (3) 9 billion years ago
   (4) 13.8 billion years ago

3 Which process produces the largest amount of energy given off by stars?
   (1) nuclear fusion of lighter elements into heavier elements
   (2) nuclear fusion of heavier elements into lighter elements
   (3) radioactive decay of lighter elements into heavier elements
   (4) radioactive decay of heavier elements into lighter elements

4 Which two factors caused the interior layering of Earth and other planets in our solar system during their formation?
   (1) cosmic background radiation and density differences
   (2) cosmic background radiation and specific heat
   (3) gravity and density differences
   (4) gravity and specific heat

5 The map below shows the location of the Chicxulub impact crater, which was formed in the Gulf of Mexico approximately 65.5 million years ago. With an estimated 108-mile diameter, this crater, which is now buried beneath surface crustal rocks, is one of the largest craters on Earth.

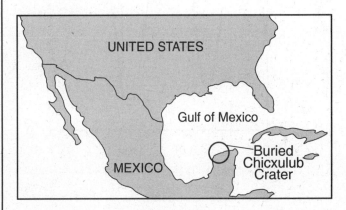

The asteroid impact that formed this large crater is theorized to have caused
   (1) a drop in sea level from the sea water draining into the large crater
   (2) warmer than normal worldwide ocean temperatures from the hot asteroid
   (3) mass extinctions of many species on Earth from extreme climate changes
   (4) an increase in worldwide greenhouse gases from vaporizing crustal rocks

6 The altitude of *Polaris* measured by an observer at the Tropic of Cancer is
   (1) 15°   (3) 66.5°
   (2) 23.5°   (4) 90°

7 During which month does the Sun rise north of due east in New York State?
   (1) February   (3) October
   (2) July   (4) December

[2]

8 The graph below shows the change in tide heights of the Hudson River at Newburgh, New York.

Tide Heights

According to the graph, the time difference between high tide and the next low tide is approximately

(1) 2 hours   (3) 6 hours
(2) 3 hours   (4) 12 hours

9 During a rainstorm, water is flowing down the side of a hill composed of solid bedrock. What will be the effect on the relative amounts of runoff and infiltration when the water reaches an area of unsaturated soil with a gentler slope?

(1) Runoff will decrease as infiltration decreases.
(2) Runoff will decrease as infiltration increases.
(3) Runoff will increase as infiltration decreases.
(4) Runoff will increase as infiltration increases.

10 What is the dewpoint when the dry bulb temperature is 20°C and the relative humidity is 17%?

(1) –5°C   (3) 11°C
(2) –2°C   (4) 15°C

11 The diagram below represents the apparent changes in the direction of swing of a Foucault pendulum.

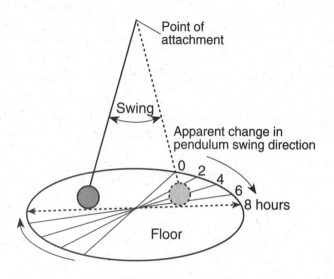

This apparent change in direction of swing provides evidence that Earth

(1) has a spherical shape
(2) is tilted on its axis
(3) orbits around the Sun
(4) turns on its axis

12 Which change in the heat energy content of water occurs when water changes phase from a liquid to a solid?

(1) gain of 334 Joules of heat energy per gram
(2) release of 334 Joules of heat energy per gram
(3) gain of 2260 Joules of heat energy per gram
(4) release of 2260 Joules of heat energy per gram

13 What is the primary source of energy for Earth's weather systems?

(1) incoming solar radiation
(2) subtropical jet streams
(3) precipitation from clouds
(4) heat from Earth's interior

[3]   [OVER]

Regents Examination F

14 The diagram below represents a view of Earth from above the North Pole. Points *A* and *B* represent locations on Earth's surface.

Locations *A* and *B* have the same

(1) latitude and local time
(2) latitude and elevation
(3) longitude and local time
(4) longitude and elevation

15 The diagram below shows an instrument used in weather forecasting.

This instrument measures atmospheric

(1) wind speed   (3) pressure
(2) wind direction   (4) temperature

16 The map of North America below shows the position of the polar front jet stream on January 7, 2014, and the location of Atlanta, Georgia.

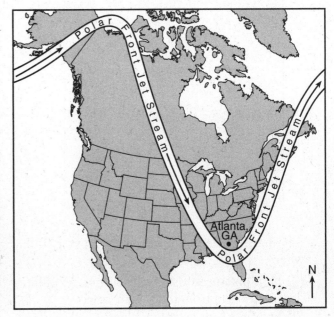

Which type of air mass was most likely located over Atlanta, Georgia?

(1) mT   (3) cT
(2) mP   (4) cP

17 As altitude increases in the troposphere and stratosphere, the air temperature

(1) decreases in the troposphere and increases in the stratosphere
(2) decreases in both the troposphere and stratosphere
(3) increases in the troposphere and decreases in the stratosphere
(4) increases in both the troposphere and stratosphere

18 Which factor causes the surface of Lake Ontario to cool at a slower rate than the surface of the land along the shore of the lake?

(1) Evaporating water releases more heat into the lake than into the land.
(2) Lake water has a higher specific heat than land.
(3) Water vapor cools the lake as it condenses.
(4) Sunlight passes through the top layers of the lake water.

[4]

19 The map below shows location X in northern India.

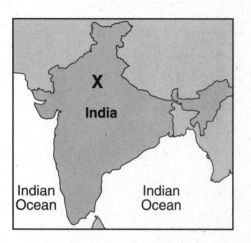

Summer monsoon rains normally occur in India when

(1) high pressure exists near location X, pulling moisture in from the Indian Ocean
(2) high pressure exists near location X, pushing moisture out to the Indian Ocean
(3) low pressure exists near location X, pulling moisture in from the Indian Ocean
(4) low pressure exists near location X, pushing moisture out to the Indian Ocean

20 Which gas absorbs some of the harmful insolation in Earth's upper atmosphere before that insolation reaches Earth's surface?

(1) nitrogen   (3) oxygen
(2) ozone   (4) hydrogen

21 Which ocean current brings warm water to the southeastern coast of Africa?

(1) Agulhas Current
(2) Benguela Current
(3) West Australian Current
(4) Equatorial Countercurrent

22 The intensity of insolation at solar noon from November 1 to February 1 in New York State will

(1) decrease, only
(2) increase, only
(3) decrease, then increase
(4) increase, then decrease

23 Most scientists infer that a major factor in the increased rate of melting of Earth's glaciers is

(1) a decrease in the output of energy from the Sun
(2) a decrease in Earth's atmospheric transparency
(3) an increase in Earth's orbital distance from the Sun
(4) an increase in carbon dioxide in Earth's atmosphere

24 What is the approximate percentage of geologic time that humans have existed on Earth since its origin?

(1) less than 1%   (3) 11.8%
(2) 1.8%   (4) more than 25%

25 The photograph below shows the East African Rift Valley in Africa. Which tectonic movement of Earth's crust is most likely responsible for this feature?

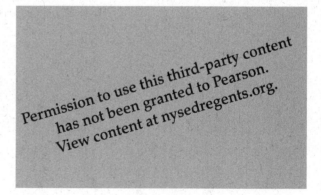

Permission to use this third-party content has not been granted to Pearson. View content at nysedregents.org.

(1) convergence of continental crust
(2) convergence of oceanic crust
(3) divergence of continental crust
(4) divergence of oceanic crust

26 Radioactive dating of fossils and rocks is possible because radioactive isotopes

(1) are found in all fossils and rocks
(2) are easily collected and measured
(3) disintegrate into organic substances
(4) disintegrate at a predictable rate

27 The photograph below shows the bedrock structure of a limestone outcrop.

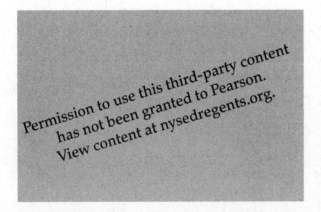

Permission to use this third-party content has not been granted to Pearson. View content at nysedregents.org.

Which process is responsible for the deformation of this bedrock?

(1) folding   (3) mass movement
(2) weathering   (4) volcanic activity

28 Which particles will be transported by a stream moving at a velocity of 5 cm/s?

(1) pebbles, sand, silt, and clay, only
(2) sand, silt, and clay, only
(3) silt and clay, only
(4) clay, only

29 The surface bedrock of New York State that is most likely to contain the mineral garnet can be found in an area 30 miles

(1) north of Binghamton
(2) south of Mt. Marcy
(3) east of Oswego
(4) west of Utica

30 The geologic cross section below represents surface landscape features that developed in an arid climate.

A change in climate to one that is more humid would cause the

(1) shape of the hills to become more rounded
(2) elevation of the area to become higher
(3) porosity of the bedrock to increase
(4) rate of chemical weathering to decrease

31 The cross section below represents an outcrop of sedimentary rock layers exposed on Earth's surface. Rock layers *A*, *B*, *C*, and *D* are labeled.

Which rock layer shows the greatest resistance to weathering and erosion?

(1) *A*   (3) *C*
(2) *B*   (4) *D*

[6]

32 The diagrams below represent the compass direction and altitude of the Sun's rays at noon for a location on Earth on four different dates.

Sun's rays

66.5°

S————————N

December 21

Sun's rays

90°

S————————N

March 21

Sun's rays

66.5°

S————————N

June 21

Sun's rays

90°

S————————N

September 23

What is the latitude of this location?

(1) 0°

(2) 23.5° N

(3) 23.5° S

(4) 90° N

33 The map below shows the present-day positions of the continents. Points A through D represent locations on Earth's surface. The location of New York State on the North American continent is indicated.

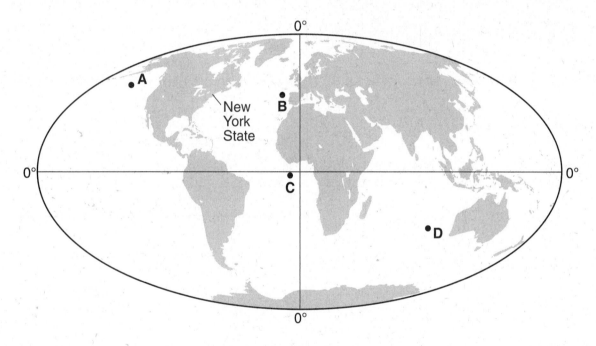

Which letter best represents the inferred position of the New York State region on Earth at the end of the Devonian Period?

(1) A

(2) B

(3) C

(4) D

[7]

[OVER]

34 The image below shows a spear point embedded in part of a mastodon's rib bone, found near Seattle, Washington.

Scientists infer that early North American humans hunted the mastodon. Carbon-14 dating of the rib bone indicates that 2.4 half-lives have passed since the mastodon was killed. Approximately how many years ago did the mastodon die?

(1) 5700

(2) 11,400

(3) 13,700

(4) 17,100

35 The cross section below represents two types of sorted-sand depositional features found at a coastal location.

Cross Section of a Coastal Location

Which table correctly pairs these depositional features with the agents of erosion that formed them?

Depositional Feature	Agent of Erosion
sand dune	mass movement
sand bar	wind

(1)

Depositional Feature	Agent of Erosion
sand dune	mass movement
sand bar	glaciers

(3)

Depositional Feature	Agent of Erosion
sand dune	glaciers
sand bar	waves

(2)

Depositional Feature	Agent of Erosion
sand dune	wind
sand bar	waves

(4)

[8]

Part B–1

Answer all questions in this part.

Directions (36–50): For *each* statement or question, choose the word or expression that, of those given, best completes the statement or answers the question. Some questions may require the use of the *2011 Edition Reference Tables for Physical Setting/Earth Science*. Record your answers on your separate answer sheet.

Base your answers to questions 36 through 38 on the diagram below and on your knowledge of Earth science. The diagram represents Earth's position in its orbit on the first day of each of the four seasons, one of which is labeled *A*. The North Pole is labeled *N*. Earth's closest distance to the Sun and Earth's farthest distance from the Sun are labeled in kilometers.

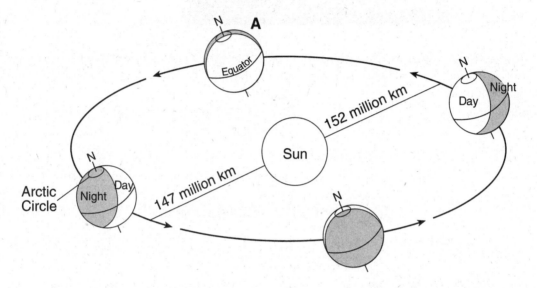

(Not drawn to scale)

36 How many hours (h) of daylight are received at the Arctic Circle when Earth is at position *A*?
- (1) 0 h
- (2) 12 h
- (3) 18 h
- (4) 24 h

37 When Earth is closest to the Sun, which season is occurring in the Northern Hemisphere?
- (1) spring
- (2) summer
- (3) fall
- (4) winter

38 What would most likely happen to New York State's summer and winter temperatures if the tilt of Earth's axis increased from 23.5° to 30°?
- (1) Both the summers and winters would become cooler.
- (2) Both the summers and winters would become warmer.
- (3) The summers would become cooler and the winters would become warmer.
- (4) The summers would become warmer and the winters would become cooler.

Regents Examination F

Base your answers to questions 39 and 40 on the diagrams below and on your knowledge of Earth science. The diagrams represent four columns, labeled A, B, C, and D, that are partially filled with equal volumes of dry, sorted sediments. A fine wire mesh screen covers the bottom of each column to prevent the sediment from falling out. The lower part of each column has been placed in a beaker of water.

(Particles not drawn to scale)

39 Capillarity will cause water to rise highest in column

(1) A   (3) C
(2) B   (4) D

40 Equal volumes of sediments from all four columns are mixed and poured into a column of water. Which diagram best represents how the sediments will most likely settle?

[10]

Base your answers to questions 41 and 42 on the cross sections below and on your knowledge of Earth science. The cross sections represent two rock outcrops, labeled I and II, located 10 miles apart. Letters *A* through *E* and numbers 1 through 8 identify rock units. The rock units have *not* been overturned.

41 In outcrop I, which geologic principle is best represented by the rock units?

(1) crosscutting relationships   (3) original horizontality
(2) correlation   (4) inclusion

42 The rock record in outcrop II suggests that an unconformity probably exists in outcrop I between rock units

(1) *A* and *B*   (3) *C* and *D*
(2) *B* and *C*   (4) *D* and *E*

Base your answers to questions 43 and 44 on the map and table below and on your knowledge of Earth science. The map shows the zones of observed effects reported after a 1944 earthquake that occurred near Massena, New York. The isolines on the map are boundaries between zones of observed effects described in the Modified Mercalli Scale table. Four cities are labeled on the map.

Massena Earthquake, 1944

Modified Mercalli Scale

Intensity Value	Description of Observed Effects
I	Usually detected only by instruments
II	Felt by a few persons at rest, especially on upper floors
III	Hanging objects swing; vibration like passing of truck; noticeable indoors
IV	Felt indoors by many, outdoors by few; sensation like heavy truck striking building; parked automobiles sway
V	Felt by nearly everyone; sleepers awakened; liquids disturbed; unstable objects overturned; some dishes and windows broken
VI	Felt by all; many frightened and run outdoors; some heavy furniture moved; glassware broken; books off shelves; damage slight
VII	Difficult to stand; noticed in moving automobiles; damage to some masonry; weak chimneys broken at roofline
VIII	Partial collapse of masonry; chimneys, factory stacks, columns fall; heavy furniture overturned; frame houses moved on foundations

[12]

43 How long did it take for the first *P*-wave to travel from the epicenter of this earthquake to a seismic station in Trenton, New Jersey?

(1) 1 minute 10 seconds

(3) 3 minutes 20 seconds

(2) 2 minutes 10 seconds

(4) 4 minutes 20 seconds

44 Based on the Modified Mercalli Scale, the darker shading on which map shows the area where the Massena earthquake was felt by nearly everyone?

(1)

(3)

(2)

(4)

Regents Examination F

Base your answers to questions 45 through 48 on the passage and map below and on your knowledge of Earth science. The map shows glacial features found in Mendon Ponds Park.

Mendon Ponds Park

Mendon Ponds Park, in New York State, is listed in the National Registry of National Landmarks due to its outstanding glacial landscape features. Glacial ice that covered most of New York State retreated northward at the end of the last ice age. As this glacial ice melted, great amounts of sediments were deposited at the glacier's southern edge. Four glacial features dominate the park's landscape. Kettles are bowl-shaped depressions formed when buried blocks of glacial ice melt. If the depressions fill with water, they are called kettle lakes. The Mendon Park ponds are all kettle lakes. Eskers are ridges of sorted sediments deposited within streams flowing beneath the melting glacier. Kames are small hills of unsorted sediment deposited at the base of waterfalls formed by streams flowing over the edge of a melting glacier.

45 The last continental ice sheet retreated northward across New York State during which geologic epoch?

(1) Pleistocene   (3) Eocene

(2) Pliocene   (4) Paleocene

46 The cross sections below represent how a present-day glacial landscape feature was formed in Mendon Ponds Park and its appearance at present.

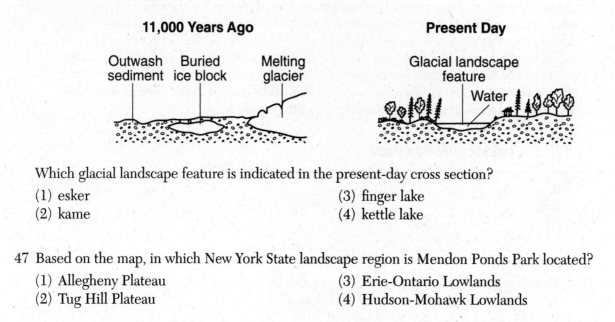

Which glacial landscape feature is indicated in the present-day cross section?

(1) esker   (3) finger lake

(2) kame   (4) kettle lake

47 Based on the map, in which New York State landscape region is Mendon Ponds Park located?

(1) Allegheny Plateau   (3) Erie-Ontario Lowlands

(2) Tug Hill Plateau   (4) Hudson-Mohawk Lowlands

48 Which landscape feature is also formed directly by glacial deposition?

(1) drumlin   (3) barrier island

(2) delta   (4) escarpment

Regents Examination F

Base your answers to questions 49 and 50 on the graph below and on your knowledge of Earth science. The graph shows the average global air temperature changes that have occurred since the late 1800s. Five volcanoes that experienced major eruptions during this time period are indicated.

Average Global Air Temperature Changes
(relative to the late 1800s)

49 In the years immediately after each volcanic eruption occurred, average global air temperatures

(1) decreased because volcanic gases and dust blocked insolation
(2) decreased because molten rock released heat
(3) increased because volcanic gases and dust blocked insolation
(4) increased because molten rock released heat

50 Which conclusion can be made from the data shown in the graph?

(1) Volcanic eruptions occur in a cyclic and predictable pattern.
(2) Volcanic eruptions have generally increased in strength since the late 1800s.
(3) Global air temperatures are warmer today than they were in the late 1800s.
(4) Global air temperatures have had fewer changes since 1950.

Part B–2

Answer all questions in this part.

Directions (51–65): Record your answers in the spaces provided in your answer booklet. Some questions may require the use of the *2011 Edition Reference Tables for Physical Setting/Earth Science.*

Base your answers to questions 51 through 53 on the diagram below and on your knowledge of Earth science. The diagram represents a planetary system, discovered in 2013, with seven exoplanets (planets that orbit a star other than our Sun) labeled *b* through *h* orbiting a star. The exoplanet orbits are represented with solid lines. For comparison, the orbits of three planets of our solar system are shown with dashed lines. The sizes of the star, exoplanets, and planets are not drawn to scale.

(Orbits are drawn to scale.)

51 Identify the name of the planet represented in the diagram that has the most eccentric orbit. [1]

52 *In your answer booklet*, circle the type of planet (terrestrial or Jovian) to indicate the classification of the three solar system planets shown in the diagram. Describe *one* characteristic of this type of planet that distinguishes it from the other type of planet. [1]

53 Identify the letter of the exoplanet with the shortest period of revolution and explain why that exoplanet has the shortest period of revolution. [1]

Base your answers to questions 54 through 56 on the star chart in your answer booklet and on your knowledge of Earth science. The star chart shows the approximate locations of the Big Dipper, Little Dipper, and Cassiopeia visible in the night sky from Syracuse, New York, at a particular time of night. The dots represent individual stars. During the night, these stars appear to move counterclockwise around the star in the center of the chart. Straight lines are at 15-degree intervals. The stars *Caph*, *Kochab*, and *Merak* are labeled.

54 On the star chart *in your answer booklet*, circle the dot that represents the star *Polaris*. [1]

55 On the star chart *in your answer booklet*, place an **X** to indicate the location of the star *Merak* after five hours have passed. [1]

56 Identify the Earth motion that causes the apparent counterclockwise movement of these stars. [1]

_____

Base your answers to questions 57 through 59 on the table below and on your knowledge of Earth science. The table shows how many million years each group of organisms existed on Earth before they became extinct.

Existence on Earth

Group of Organisms	Duration of Existence (million years)
Ammonoids	340
Eurypterids	200
Graptolites	195
Placoderm fish	70
Trilobites	270

57 Identify the group of organisms listed on the data table that was the first group to exist on Earth. [1]

58 Identify the name of *one* specific index fossil from the eurypterid group that is found in New York State bedrock. [1]

59 Identify the type of environment on Earth where all of these groups of organisms appear to have lived. [1]

_____

Base your answers to questions 60 through 62 on the cross sections below and on your knowledge of Earth science. The cross sections represent three different stages in the development of Denali (Mt. McKinley) and the growth of the North American Plate in Alaska near the boundary with the Pacific Plate. Arrows represent the direction of plate movement.

Formation of Denali (Mt. McKinley)

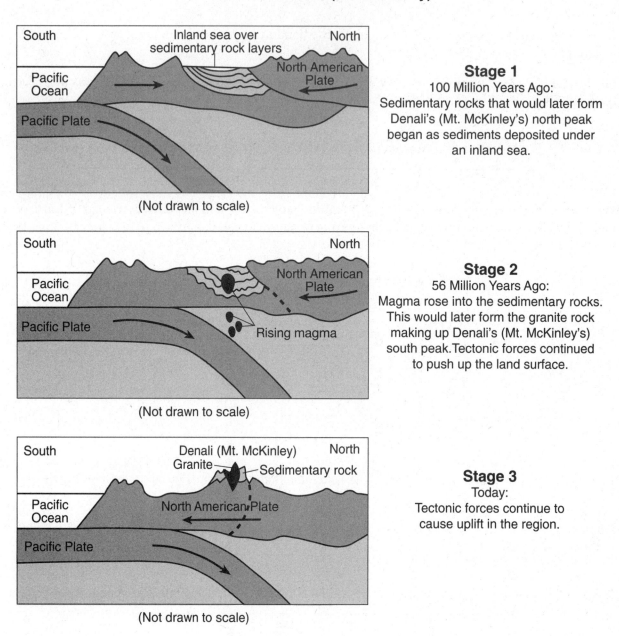

Stage 1
100 Million Years Ago:
Sedimentary rocks that would later form Denali's (Mt. McKinley's) north peak began as sediments deposited under an inland sea.

Stage 2
56 Million Years Ago:
Magma rose into the sedimentary rocks. This would later form the granite rock making up Denali's (Mt. McKinley's) south peak. Tectonic forces continued to push up the land surface.

Stage 3
Today:
Tectonic forces continue to cause uplift in the region.

60 Identify the type of plate boundary represented in the cross sections. [1]

61 *In your answer booklet*, circle either volcanic or plutonic to identify the environment of formation of the granite found on Denali (Mt. McKinley). Describe the cooling rate of the magma that produced this granite. [1]

62 State the average density of the continental crust of the North American Plate and the average density of the oceanic crust of the Pacific Plate. [1]

[19]   [OVER]

Regents Examination F

Base your answers to questions 63 through 65 on the map in your answer booklet and on your knowledge of Earth science. The map shows the total amount of snowfall, measured in inches, from a lake-effect snow storm that affected western New York from November 17 through November 21, 2014. The 20-inch and 40-inch snowfall isolines have been drawn. Niagara Falls and Cowlesville are labeled on the map.

63 On the map *in your answer booklet*, draw the 60-inch snowfall isoline. Extend the isoline to the edge of Lake Erie. [1]

64 Cowlesville, New York, received a total of 88 inches of snow in 85 hours. Calculate the average rate of snowfall in inches per hour (in/h) for Cowlesville. [1]

65 Describe *two* actions that people could take to prepare for a forecasted lake-effect snowstorm. [1]

_____

Regents Examination F

Part C

Answer all questions in this part.

Directions (66–85): Record your answers in the spaces provided in your answer booklet. Some questions may require the use of the *2011 Edition Reference Tables for Physical Setting/Earth Science.*

Base your answers to questions 66 through 68 on the diagram below and on your knowledge of Earth science. The diagram represents Earth as viewed from above the North Pole. The nighttime side of Earth and the Moon have been shaded. The Moon is represented in eight positions in its orbit around Earth.

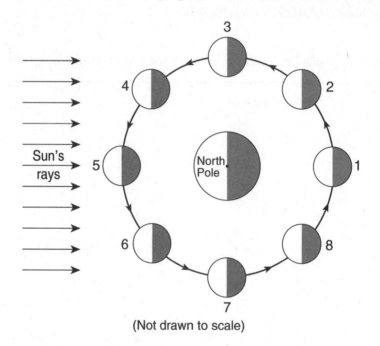

(Not drawn to scale)

66 Identify by number the Moon's position where a solar eclipse might be observed from Earth. [1]

67 The photographs *in your answer booklet* show the changing appearance of the Moon as viewed from New York State during three consecutive Moon phases. In the space below each photograph, identify the number of the Moon position that matches each of these phases. [1]

68 Explain how the Moon's rotation and revolution cause the same side of the Moon to always face Earth. [1]

Base your answers to questions 69 through 71 on the map in your answer booklet and on your knowledge of Earth science. The weather map shows isobars, recorded in millibars (mb).

69 On the map *in your answer booklet*, place an **L** to indicate the location of the center of a low-pressure system and place an **H** to indicate the location of the center of a high-pressure system. [1]

70 A weather station recorded the barometric pressure on a weather station model as shown below.

 026

On the map *in your answer booklet*, place an **X** to represent a possible location for this weather station. [1]

71 The table below lists some weather conditions for another location on this map.

Temperature (°F)	Dewpoint (°F)	Precipitation (inches in past 6 hours)	Present Weather
76	74	0.85	Rain showers

On the weather station model *in your answer booklet*, using the proper format, record the weather conditions listed in the table. [1]

Base your answers to questions 72 through 75 on the topographic map in your answer booklet and on your knowledge of Earth science. The map is centered on the peak of New York State's Slide Mountain at 42° North. Points *A*, *B*, and *X* represent locations on the map. Line *AB* is a reference line on the map. Elevations are shown in feet.

72 On the map *in your answer booklet*, draw a line showing the most likely path of a stream that begins at point *X* and flows to the edge of the map. [1]

73 Determine *one* possible elevation of point *X*. [1]

74 On the grid *in your answer booklet*, construct a topographic profile along line *AB* by plotting the elevation of each contour line that crosses line *AB*. Points *A* and *B* have already been plotted. Connect *all ten* plots with a line, starting at *A* and ending at *B*, to complete the profile. [1]

75 Describe *one* piece of evidence shown on the map that indicates that the northeastern side of Slide Mountain has the steepest slope. [1]

Regents Examination F

Base your answers to questions 76 through 79 on the passage and data table below, on the graph in your answer booklet, and on your knowledge of Earth science. The data table shows the average percentages of sodium and calcium, and the average densities of samples from each of the six varieties of plagioclase feldspar. The graph in your answer booklet shows the range of sodium and calcium percentages for each of the six varieties of plagioclase feldspar.

Plagioclase Feldspars

The plagioclase feldspars are a family of six silicate minerals that are difficult to tell apart. They have the same crystal structure, cleavage, and hardness, and can be similar in color; however, they do differ slightly in chemical composition and density. The general chemical composition for plagioclase is $(Na,Ca)AlSi_3O_8$. The percentages of sodium (Na) and calcium (Ca) vary relative to each other, causing the differences in density. The mineral albite is sodium-rich, with little or no calcium, while anorthite is calcium-rich, with little or no sodium. The plagioclase feldspars with higher sodium content are more likely to be found in felsic igneous rocks, while the plagioclase feldspars with higher calcium content are more likely to be found in mafic igneous rocks.

Data Table

Variety of Plagioclase Feldspar	Average Percentage of Sodium (%)	Average Percentage of Calcium (%)	Average Density (g/cm³)
albite	100	0	2.63
oligoclase	80	20	2.65
andesine	60	40	2.67
labradorite	40	60	2.69
bytownite	20	80	2.71
anorthite	0	100	2.73

76 Complete the line graph *in your answer booklet*, by plotting the average density for the average percentages of sodium and calcium of each sample shown on the data table. The data for albite and oligoclase have been plotted for you. Connect *all six* plots with a line. [1]

77 A sample of plagioclase feldspar was found to have a ratio of 35% sodium to 65% calcium. Based on the graph, state the name of this variety of plagioclase feldspar. [1]

78 A sample of plagioclase feldspar has a mass of 534 grams and a volume of 200 cubic centimeters. State the name of this variety of plagioclase feldspar. [1]

79 State the name of *one* variety of plagioclase feldspar that is more likely to be found in the igneous rock pegmatite. [1]

Base your answers to questions 80 through 83 on the passage and the map of South America below and on your knowledge of Earth science.

Two South American Deserts

South America is an excellent example of the influence that plate tectonic features have on climates. The Andes mountain range, formed by plate tectonics, is on the western edge of South America. When prevailing winds come from the southeast, which usually occurs between 0° and 30° S latitudes, rainfall is increased on the eastern side of the mountain range. The Atacama Desert lies in the rain shadow (dry area) to the west of the mountains. Farther south, the reverse pattern is found, due to different prevailing winds blowing between 30° S and 60° S latitudes. The Patagonian Desert lies on the eastern side of the Andes, between the Andes and the South Atlantic Ocean.

80 Name *one* tectonic plate that is interacting with the South American Plate to uplift the Andes Mountains. [1]

81 On the map *in your answer booklet*, draw *one* arrow in the box located on the Andes Mountains to indicate the surface planetary wind direction that helped produce the Atacama Desert. [1]

82 Glaciers are found on some of the mountains in the Andes near the equator. Identify *one* climate factor that causes the cold temperatures on these mountains. [1]

83 Andesite makes up much of the volcanic rock of the Andes Mountains. Name *three* minerals that are commonly found in a single andesite rock. [1]

_____

GO ON TO THE NEXT PAGE ⇨

Regents Examination F

Base your answers to questions 84 and 85 on the map and block diagrams below and on your knowledge of Earth science. The map shows a stream and its tributaries. Enlarged block diagrams, labeled *A*, *B*, and *C*, indicate the relative widths of floodplains in the rectangular areas along the stream. Points *W*, *X*, *Y*, and *Z* are locations on the stream banks.

Stream and Its Tributaries

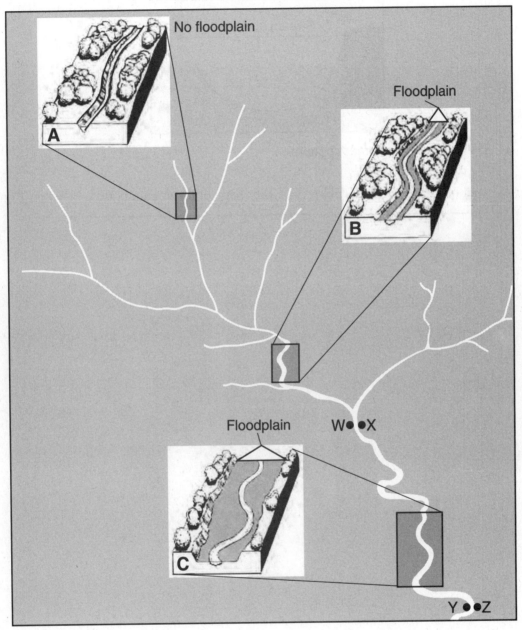

84 The slope of the stream in area *A* is steeper than the slope of the stream in area *C*. Describe *one* piece of evidence shown by the block diagrams that supports this statement. [1]

85 The cross section below represents the shape of the stream channel between *W* and *X*.

On the cross section *in your answer booklet*, draw the shape of the stream bottom between *Y* and *Z*. [1]

Regents Examination F

PHYSICAL SETTING
EARTH SCIENCE

ANSWER BOOKLET

☐ Male

Student . . . . Sex: ☐ Female

Teacher . . . .

School . . . . Grade . . . .

Record your answers for Part B–2 and Part C in this booklet.

Part B–2

51 _____

52 Circle one: terrestrial planet   Jovian planet

Characteristic of this type of planet: _____

53 Exoplanet: _____

Explanation: _____

_____

---

56 _____

57 _____

58 _____

59 _____

60 _____

61 Circle one: volcanic   plutonic

Cooling rate: _____

62 North American Plate continental crust: _____ **g/cm³**

Pacific Plate oceanic crust: _____ **g/cm³**

Regents Examination F

63

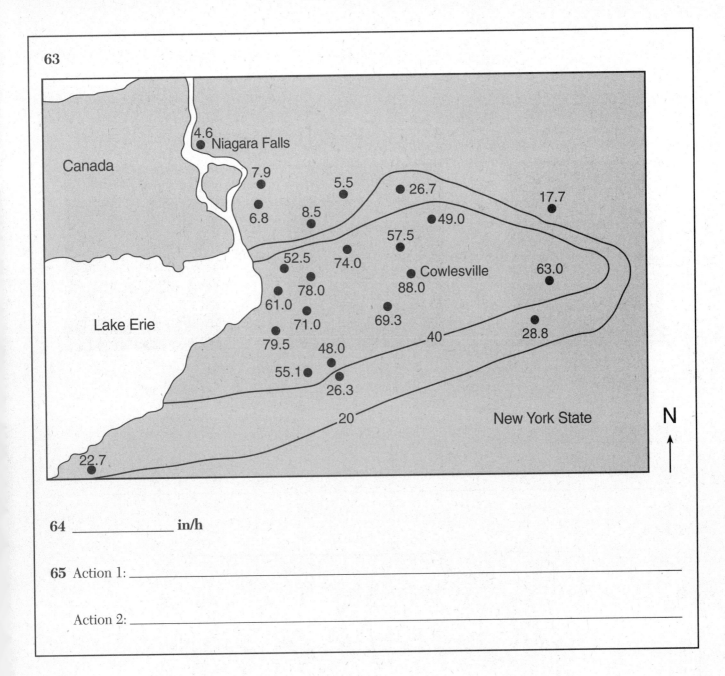

Canada

4.6
● Niagara Falls

7.9
●

6.8
●

8.5
●

5.5
●

26.7
●

17.7
●

49.0
●

57.5
●

52.5
●

74.0

Cowlesville
●

63.0
●

78.0

88.0
●

61.0
●

Lake Erie

71.0
●

69.3
●

28.8
●

79.5
●

48.0
●

40

55.1
●

26.3
●

20

New York State

N
↑

22.7
●

64 _____ in/h

65 Action 1: _____

Action 2: _____

66 Position: _____

67

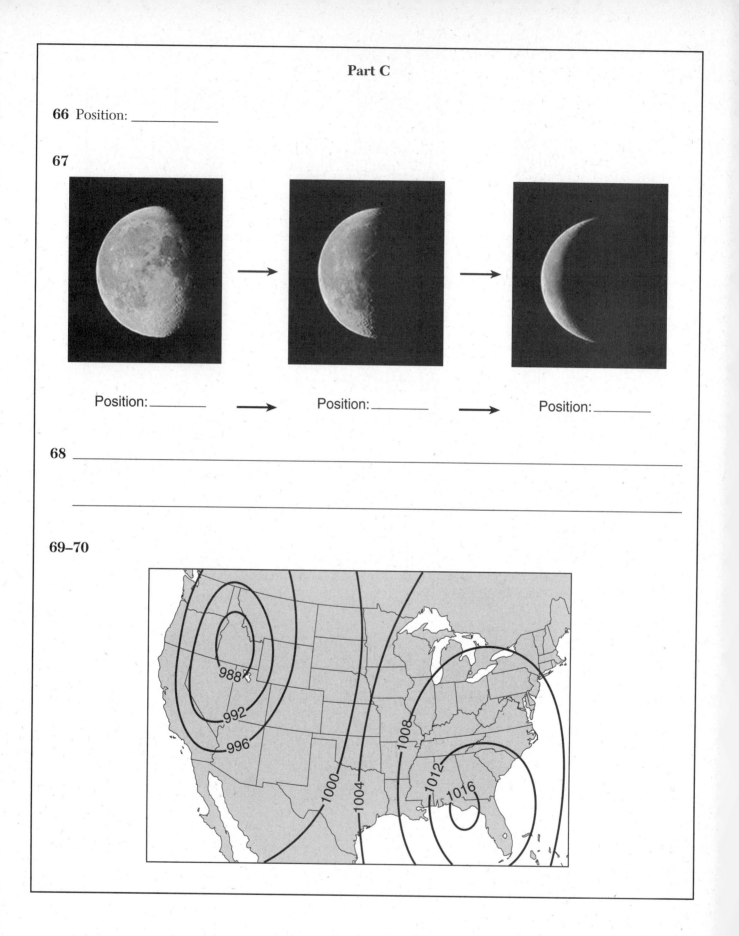

Position: _____ → Position: _____ → Position: _____

68 _____

_____

69–70

Regents Examination F

71

72

Slide Mountain

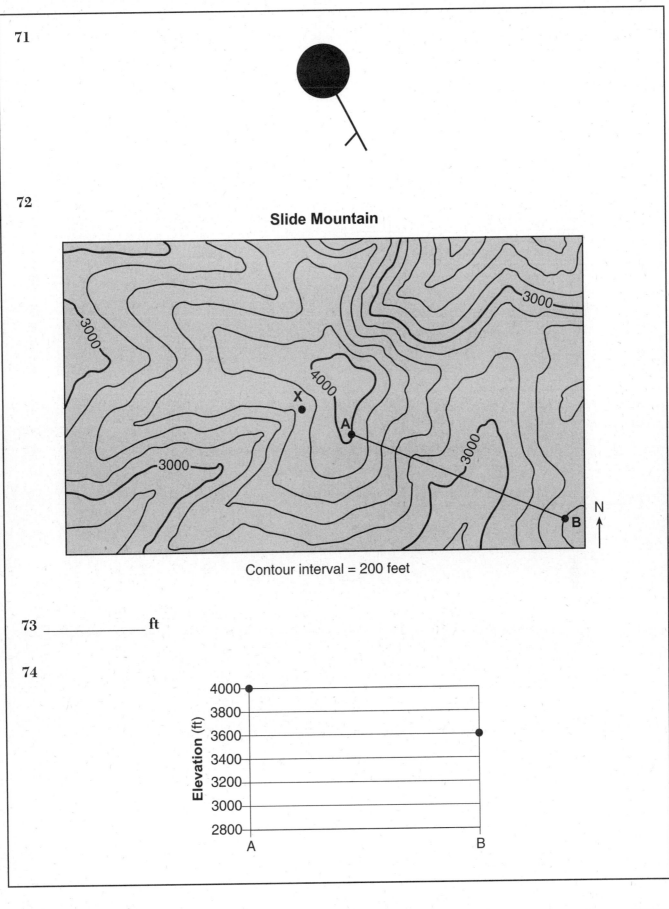

Contour interval = 200 feet

73 _____ ft

74

[OVER]

75 _____

_____

76

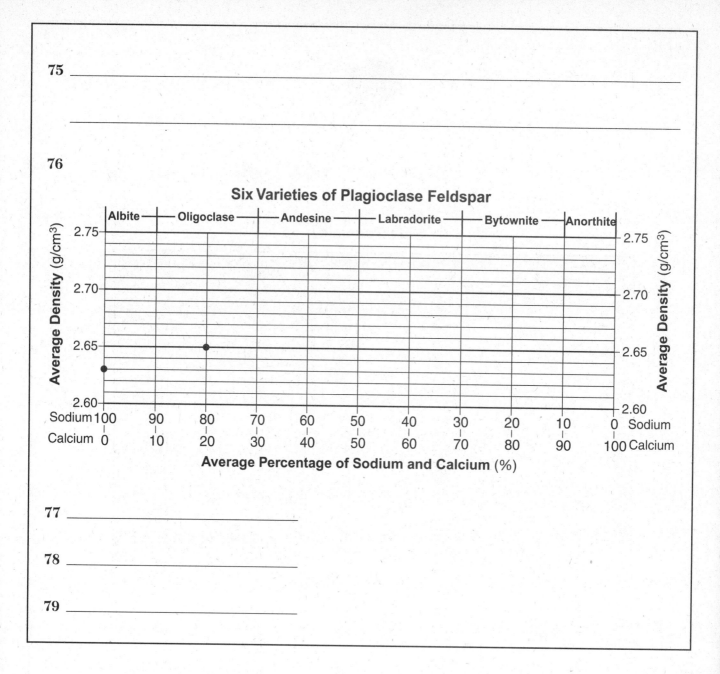

77 _____

78 _____

79 _____

80 _____ **Plate**

81

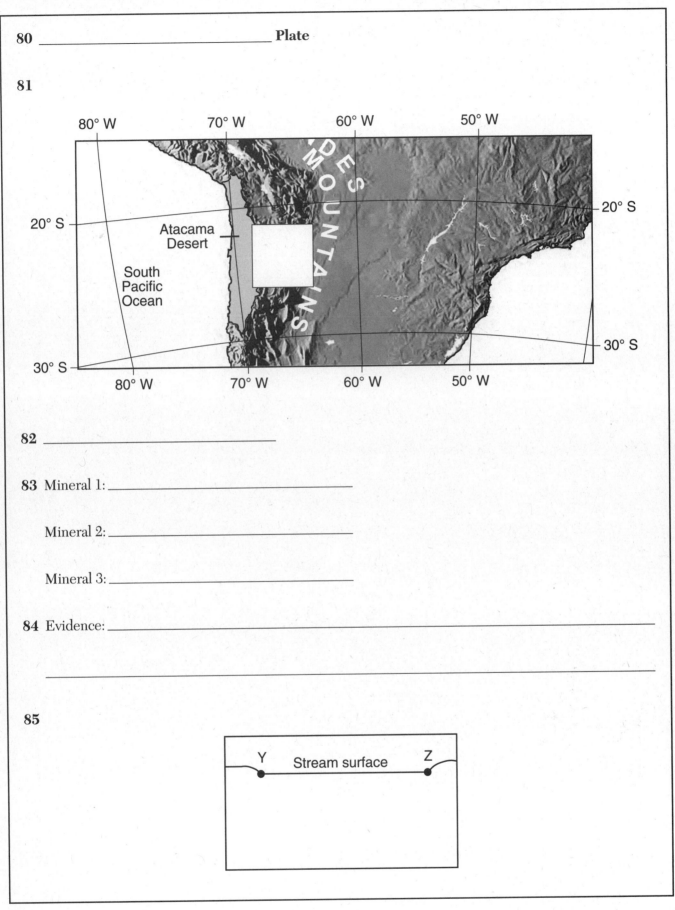

82 _____

83 Mineral 1: _____

Mineral 2: _____

Mineral 3: _____

84 Evidence: _____

_____

85

Regents Examination F